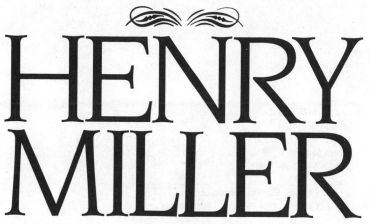

HENRY MILLER

STORIES, ESSAYS, TRAVEL SKETCHES

Edited by Antony Fine

MJF BOOKS

NEW YORK

Published by MJF Books
Fine Communications
POB 0930
Planetarium Station
New York, NY 10024-0540

Library of Congress Catalog Card Number 92-60773
ISBN 1-56731-009-5

10 9 8 7 6 5 4 3 2 1

Contents

v

BIG SUR AND AFTER
(1945–1980)

Introduction

Editing Henry Miller has not been easy; reading him has been a great pleasure. Miller's work has been difficult to edit for collection in part because of its sheer quantity, in part because of its diversity, but most of all because of my affection for so much of it, and for the vital, disorderly voice from which it bodied forth. Reading Miller I feel experience being communicated—not in a form that needs to be translated back from my head to my heart, but as if it were food and flowing straight to my gut.

For this collection, I did not generally excerpt from Miller's larger fictional works—the Tropic books, or the Rosy Crucifixion—for three reasons. The first is that it seems to me an unkind butchery to carve up works that Miller labored at some length to unify. Let the works stand complete. The second is that Miller produced a huge number of pieces other than his "sexy" ones that have never before been collected into one volume. Had this collection tried to gather gems from everything, including his novels, there is simply no way it could have been confined to one volume. I therefore chose to exclude what are in effect his best known works. Those works, like Miller, should be taken the way he preferred to take things—all or nothing. Finally, I decided that rather than showing sample specimens of his work in order to glimpse Henry Miller's style, I wanted to show aspects of the world as seen through his eyes, in order to reveal Henry Miller the man. Some repetition is therefore inevitable. The works included in this collection climb again and again to the same thematic peaks, but the ascent is always by a different route.

From the beginning, Miller was full of conflict. He grew up in rough surroundings, but he was intense and sensitive. He was intellectual but wanted to be anti-intellectual. He was a libertine and lascivious but longed for purity. He loved truth, but he was fascinated by corruption, which he saw in almost everything. Perhaps in these conflicts he was no different from anyone; what is different is that he fought his battles in public, on the page.

Most of all, he had a lifelong love/hate relationship with art. He wanted to be an artist—he was filled with the urge to shape his life, to articulate it. He wanted to squeeze all his intense experiences into words, something he apparently did often as a speaker. And yet he wanted to keep participating; he didn't want to let go of life long enough to chronicle it. He was enormously frustrated by the conventions of storytelling on the page: development, suspense, even simple chronology. These conventions did not fit his experience, and he ultimately discarded them.

However, he regarded the cerebral structures of the Modernists, such as Joyce, as too artificial. In "The Universe of Death" (1938), he writes: "As a naturalistic canvas *Ulysses* makes its appeal to the sense of smell only: it gives off a sublime mortuary odor. It is not the reality of nature here, still less the reality of the five senses. It is the sick reality of the mind . . . whether he is interested in history or not, Joyce *is* the history of our time, of this age which is sliding into darkness . . . Joyce is the lost soul of this soulless world; his interest is not in life, in men and deeds, not in history, not in God, but in the dead dust of books. He is the high priest of the lifeless literature of today."

Against this world "sliding into darkness" and its "lifeless literature," Miller affirmed his own soul. Miller had already searched and struggled and loved before starting to write; he had lived a life that in its early stages was dominated by intense desires. He experimented widely in his writing with a variety of styles, voices and standpoints, but not for form's sake; he was searching for his own true voice.

He therefore became a chronicler of his own rambunctious self, and a vitriolic critic of anything society required of him that might interfere with the desires of that self. This conception—of a fearless, joyful egotism—has precedents, but it is striking how doggedly he pursued this ideal, held it up as a model, and celebrated it when he thought he had found it in others.

Miller's first writings after he abandoned the conventional literary voice show the Miller style most starkly: it is a wild style, intimate, and revealing, disorderly, unstudied, but as full of color and momentum as the life he felt pulsating all around him just below the surface. Most of his work retains a rambling quality reminiscent of an old pal freely spouting off on whatever subject under the sun happens to catch his fancy in the moment. This is what makes his best writing so engaging and so effective—its warm personality, and by extension its humanity. Although I sometimes find myself disagreeing with him, I am almost always seduced by his tone. Miller was gifted with enormous charm, a charm that smoothes over many rough spots in his writing. His writing has the ring of plain talk, even at its most convoluted and most studded with outlandish words. For all his pronouncements, one never feels Miller taking himself too seriously. His fanciest pieces, full of passages that might seem pretentious coming from someone else, leave the impression of a gleeful, talented child playing with toys. It is a great tribute to Miller's natural talent that his passion remains so engaging.

Objections that Miller was sexist, racist, anti-Semitic, communist, and so on—I feel that these pale before the exuberance and profound honesty of his life's work. Perhaps Miller himself might have agreed to some of these accusations, but only in a spirit of good-natured conversation. He was equally gross to everyone. His chosen approach required mistakes and risks of him, and he stuck to it. He was not consistent; he was frank, about his prejudices as well as his preferences, which changed as he grew. In "Peace! It's Wonderful!" (1939), he writes: "I am a cosmological writer, and when I open my trap I broadcast to the whole world at once . . . Acting as I do I am apt to get it in the neck . . . But that's my temperament, and I'll stand or fall by it. Eventually I shan't even bother to be a cosmological writer, I shall just be a man. But first there's a lot of slaughtering to be done."

His inconsistency is ultimately one of his greatest strengths as a commentator. It contributes to his credibility that he was unafraid of change, and unafraid to contradict himself. Indeed, he revelled in his contradictions. Miller's writing has not fossilized and continues to live in part because it is full of conflict. It thus has the feel of life, and the ring of truth. He made no claims to knowledge; he only spoke of his own visions. To categorize him or hear his pronouncements as forming some ideological position is therefore to hobble him.

He hated the foolishly consistent America of the ideologue, the robotic "productive" citizen, the reformer, the capitalist plunderer. He saw them all using the same hypocritical, empty moralism. In his letter to Alfred Perlès we vividly see Miller's sour, amused view of this tintype America, the land of cardboard advertisement people. Yet in a way he needed this world, for by opposing himself to it he used it as a springboard to his own freedom and identity. Miller's search for artistic freedom became a search for moral freedom, for innocence. He combined the infantile egotism of a child stripping naked at a dinner party and crying, "look at me!" with the selflessness of a man trying to live an idea and enlighten the world. All around him in America he saw the opposite of the ideal of freedom its founding documents proclaimed—a society of automatons, ruled by the machine, hopelessly cut off from enjoyment, and numbed by stimulation fragmented from feeling. He had the fervent frustration of a drunken man bewildered at the good behavior of the crowd. He was a dissident, a believer in a life of dissidence—a quintessential American life, which he ironically fled to France in order to find.

As I absorbed Miller's work, I was astounded by the accuracy of his pitiless and perfectly expressed observations of America. Even when he misses his mark, he carries off a good piece of it. I was amazed that the America he described in the early 1940s was so recognizable today. This is a testament to his clear vision. He could often see through the surface distractions into the meat and muscle of things. His ability to maintain critical detachment and feel a deep passion simultaneously is especially striking in his commentaries written during World War II, when many of his opinions might have been seen as treasonous.

After he arrived at Big Sur, his output changed. Having opened up new territory with his radically frank style, he found many of his problems solved. He wrote less, and mellowed from a dynamo to a kind of guru. His inclination to wander also subsided, and with it the conflict within him between participant and chronicler. But most important was the change in emphasis within his evolving conception of the artist and the goal for his own life.

He still held on to his ideal of being an artist, but revised his conception of "the artist" into a kind of religious figure, far closer to a bodhisattva than to a superb craftsman. Now, this conception became one of a creative person loyal above all to a unique inner individual imperative, and yet paradoxically following a path of self-renunciation at the same time. This conception of the artist finally made central the ideal of personal authenticity—a simpler, more private authenticity than the exhibitionistic honesty that characterized his earlier years. His new authenticity was conscious, but quieter: an engaged abiding. This revised conception was consistent with his early goals. It was an ideal toward which he had always been moving, as shown by his life-long interest in mysticism and in the spiritual figures and traditions of the East. It was a successful solution to the initial conflicts of his life between mind and gut, artistic form and naturalistic truth, desire and morality.

Most of all, the ideal of the bodhisattva-artist transcended the supposed opposition between participant and chronicler. We thus see in his later writing the slow dawning of his discovery that searching, struggling, and even loving, in the sense he had thought of it, were all unnecessary. To live one's own life was sufficient—to live through the telling, and let the telling be part of the living. Miller's writing starts in these years to acquire a feeling of peace, a more solid (though still flexible) standpoint, a healed and healing quality. From this calmer standpoint, he looked back on the early emergence of his own authentic writing voice and reinterpreted it as a move towards a wider discovery of his authentic self. In the epilogue to *Big Sur and the Oranges of Hieronymus Bosch* (1957), Miller writes, "Whoever uses the spirit that is in him creatively is an artist. To make living itself an art, that is the goal."

This ideal of a synthesis between the creative and spiritual roles struck a responsive chord in the 1950s. No longer making pilgrimages, Miller became the object of pilgrimages. He became the wise old wild man of Big Sur, was transformed from a journeyman into a mentor, and died and was buried there in 1980. Many people still visit his grave site.

Henry Miller wrote on many topics, and at a first glance his favorite topic would seem to have been himself. But all his books are full of descriptions of other people—friends, artists, and various interesting characters he met along his way. His topic was not really himself alone, but the human character. He is always exploring personalities, his own or other people's, with the goal of revealing something deeper about human reality. When he does not find it, he adopts a sarcastic, disgusted tone, as in "Hollywood Soiree." When he discovers something curious, something that touches on larger moral or metaphysical issues, he dwells on the subject at length, as in "The Devil in Paradise." Even when he is describing scenery, his imagination peoples it with human figures from history or legend, as in *The Colossus of Maroussi*. Far from being vain or excessively self-absorbed, Miller was intensely involved in humanity, despite his passionate denials. The role he chose for himself in humanity's salvation was simply an artistic one, and the arena of conflict, his own soul. If he had wished to be placed in any literary tradition (it would have gone against his grain to admit it), it would have been that of Dostoevski and Lawrence.

By honestly revealing himself—all of himself, bad and good—Henry Miller held up a mirror to each of us and to our society, cutting through the muck of theory and the morass of detail to articulate the heart of the matter. He was unafraid of and unswayed by popular opinion; indeed, he was openly contemptuous of it. He steered by his own rudder. He belonged only to himself, and even then he bowed to a higher power he felt within. For all his apparent arrogance, he was humble. He is never trying to win you over. He is having a good time all by himself, and he only invites you to join him.

ANTONY FINE
New York City
May 1992

BROOKLYN, MANHATTAN, PARIS

•

(1891–1939)

Autobiographical Note

I was born in New York City December 26, 1891 of American parents. My grandfathers came to America to escape military service. All my ancestors are German and come from every part of Germany; the family is scattered all over the world, in the most remote and outlandish parts. The men were mostly seafarers, peasants, poets and musicians. Until I went to school I spoke nothing but German and the atmosphere in which I was raised, despite the fact that my parents were born in America, was German through and through. From five to ten were the most important years of my life; I lived in the street and acquired the typical American gangster spirit. The 14th Ward, Brooklyn, where I was raised, is particularly dear to me; it was an immigrant quarter and my companions were all of different nationality. The Spanish-American war, which broke out when I was seven, was a big event in my young life; I enjoyed the mob spirit which broke loose and which permitted me to understand at an early age the violence and lawlessness which is so characteristic of America.

My parents were relatively poor, hard-working, thrifty, unimaginative. (My father never read a book in his life.) I was well cared for and had a very happy, healthy time of it until I had to shift for myself. I had no desire to earn a living, no sense of economy, and no respect for my elders or for laws or institutions. I defied my parents and those about me almost from the time I was able to talk. I left City College a few months after I entered it, disgusted with the atmosphere of the place and the stupidity of the curriculum. Took a job in the financial district, with a cement company, and quickly regretted it. Two years later my father gave me the money to go to Cornell; I took the money and disappeared with my mistress, a woman old enough to be my mother. I returned home a year or so later and then left for good, to go West. Worked

3

in various parts of the country, mostly the southwest. Did all sorts of odd jobs, usually as a ranch hand. Was on my way to Juneau, Alaska, to work as a placer miner in the gold fields, when I was taken down with fever. Returned to New York and led a roving, shiftless, vagabond life, working at anything and everything, but never for very long. I was a good athlete and trained every day of my life for about five years—as though I were going to enter the Olympic games. I owe my excellent health to this early Spartan regime, the continuous poverty in which I have lived, and the fact that I never worry. I lived recklessly and rebelliously up to my thirtieth year, was the leader in everything, and suffered primarily because I was too honest, too sincere, too truthful, too generous.

Was forced to study the piano at an early age, showed some talent and later studied it seriously, hoping to become a concert pianist, but didn't. Gave it up entirely, my motto always being "all or nothing." Was obliged to enter my father's tailoring establishment, because he was unable to manage his affairs. Learned almost nothing about tailoring; instead, I began to write. Probably the first thing I ever wrote was in my father's shop—a long essay on Nietzsche's *Anti-Christ*. Usually I wrote letters to my friends, letters forty and fifty pages long, about everything under the sun: they were humorous letters, as well as pompously intellectual. (I still like writing letters best of all!) At any rate, I didn't think then that I would ever be a writer—I was almost afraid to think such a thing.

When America entered the war I went to Washington to work as a clerk in the War Department—sorting mail. In my spare time I did a little reporting for one of the Washington papers. I got out of the draft by using my head, came back to New York again and took over my father's business during his illness. I was always an out and out pacifist, and still am. I believe it is justifiable to kill a man in anger, but not in cold blood or on principle, as the laws and governments of the world advocate. During the war I married and became a father. Though jobs were plentiful at that time I was always out of work. I held innumerable positions, for a day or less often. Among them the following: dish-washer, bus boy, newsie, messenger boy, grave-digger, bill sticker, book salesman, bell hop, bartender, liquor salesman, typist, adding machine operator, librarian, statistician, charity worker, mechanic, insurance collector, garbage collector, usher, secretary to an evangelist, dock hand, street car conductor, gymnasium instructor, milk driver, ticket chopper, etc.

The most important encounter of my life was with Emma Goldman in San Diego, California. She opened up the whole world of

European culture for me and gave a new impetus to my life, as well as direction. I was violently interested in the I. W. W. movement at the time it was in swing, and remember with great reverence and affection such people as Jim Larkin, Elizabeth Gurley Flynn, Giovanitti and Carlo Tresca. I was never a member of any club, fraternity, social or political organization. As a youngster I had been led from one church to another—first Lutheran, then Presbyterian, then Methodist, then Episcopalian. I later followed with great interest the lectures at the Bahai Center and the Theosophists and New Thoughters and Seventh Day Adventists and so on. I was thoroughly eclectic and immune. The Quakers and the Mormons impressed me by their integrity and sincerity—and by their self-sufficiency. I think they make the best Americans.

In 1920, after serving as messenger and stool pigeon for the company, I became personnel director of the Western Union Telegraph Company, N. Y. City. I held the job almost five years and still consider it the richest period in my life. The scum and riff-raff of New York passed through my hands—well over a hundred thousand men, women and boys. During a three weeks' vacation, in 1923, I wrote my first book—a study of twelve eccentric messengers. It was a long book and probably a very bad one, but it gave me the itch to write. I quit the job without a word of notice, determined to be a writer. From then on the real misery began. From 1924 to 1928 I wrote a great many stories and articles, none of which were ever accepted. Finally I printed my own things and with the aid of my second wife I sold them from door to door, later in restaurants and night clubs. Eventually I was obliged to beg in the streets.

Through an unexpected piece of fortune I was able to come to Europe, in 1928, where I stayed the whole year, touring a good part of the continent. Remained in New York the year of 1929, again broke, miserable, unable to see a way out. Early in 1930 I raised the money to return to Europe, intending to go direct to Spain, but never getting any farther than Paris, where I have remained since.

In addition to the book on the messengers, which I wrote in three weeks, I completed two novels while in America, and I brought with me to Europe a third one, which was unfinished. On finishing it I offered it to a publisher in Paris who promptly lost it and then asked me one day if I were sure I had ever given it to him. I had no carbon copy of the book—three years' work gone up the flue. I began *Tropic of Cancer*, which is announced as my "first" book, about a year after landing in Paris. It was written from place to place on all sorts of paper, often on the backs of old manuscripts. I had little hope, when writing it, of ever seeing it published. It was an act of desperation. The publication of this book, by the Obelisk Press, Paris, opened the door to the world for me. It gave me innumerable friends and acquaintances, from all over the world. I still have no money and I still do not know how to earn a living, but I have plenty of friends and well-wishers, and I have lost my fear of starvation, which was becoming an obsession. I am now absolutely at one with my destiny and reconciled to anything which may happen. I haven't the slightest fear about the future, because I have learned how to live in the present.

As for influences . . . The real influence has been life itself, the life of the streets especially, of which I never tire. I am a city man through and through; I hate nature, just as I hate the "classics." I owe a lot to the dictionary and the encyclopaedia which, like Balzac, I read voraciously when I was a youngster. Until I was twenty-five I had scarcely read a novel, except for the Russians. I was interested almost exclusively in religion, philosophy, science, history, sociology, art, archaeology, primitive cultures, mythologies, etc. I scarcely ever looked at a newspaper—and I have never read a detective story in my life. On the other hand, I have read everything in the field of humor which I could lay hands on—there is precious little! I liked Eastern folk lore and fairy tales, especially Japanese tales, which are full of violence and malevolence. I liked writers like Herbert Spencer, Fabre, Havelock Ellis, Fraser, the older Huxley and such like. I was widely read in the European drama, thanks to Emma Goldman—knew the European dramatists before the English or the American. I read the Russians before the Anglo-Saxons, and the Germans before the French. My greatest influences were Dostoievski, Nietzsche and Elie Fauré. Proust and Spengler were tremendously fecundating. Of American writers the only real influences were Whitman and Emerson. I admit to Melville's genius, but find him boring. I dislike Henry James intensely, and absolutely detest Edgar Allen Poe. On the whole I dislike the trend of American literature; it is realistic, prosaic and "pedagogic"; it is written down, to please the lowest common denominator, and it is good, in my opinion, only in the realm of the short story. Men like Sherwood Anderson and Saroyan, who are poles apart, I consider masterful and the equals of, if not superior to, any European, in this realm. As for English literature, it leaves me cold, as do the English themselves: it is a sort of fish-world which is completely alien to me. I am thankful to have made a humble acquaintance with French literature which on the whole is feeble and limited, but which in comparison with Anglo-Saxon literature today is an unlimited world of the imagination. I owe much to the Dadaists and Surrealists. I prefer the French writers who are un-French. I think that France is the China of the Occident, though decidedly inferior in every way to the real China. I think France is the best place in the Occidental world to live and to work, but it is still far from being a healthy, vital world.

My aim, in writing, is to establish a greater REALITY. I am not a realist or naturalist; I am for life, which in literature, it seems to me, can only be attained by the use of dream and symbol. I am at bottom a metaphysical writer, and my use of drama and incident is only a device to posit something more profound. I am against pornography and for obscenity—and violence. Above all, for imagination, fantasy, for a liberty as yet undreamed of. I use destruction creatively, perhaps a little too much in the German style, but aiming always towards a real, inner harmony, an inner peace—and silence. I prefer music above all the arts, because it is so absolutely sufficient unto itself and because it tends towards silence. I believe that literature, to become truly communicable (which it is not at present), must make greater use of the symbol and the metaphor, of the mythological and the archaic. Most of our literature is like the text-book; everything takes place on an arid plateau of intellectuality. Ninety-nine percent of what is written—and this goes for all our art products—should be destroyed. I want to be read by less and less people; I have no interest in the life of the masses, nor in the intentions of the existing governments of the world. I hope and believe that the whole civilized world will be wiped out in the next hundred years or so. I believe that man can exist, and in an infinitely better, larger way, without "civilization."

HENRY MILLER.
(1938)

Letter to Alfred Perlès

(Excerpts)

I. In New York City

Dear Fred,

I will probably take the Champlain, the boat I arrived on, because it is French and because it leaves a day earlier than necessary. I will bring the stockings for Maggy—and anything else I can think of. Don't know yet about going to the Villa Seurat, but Hotel des Terrasses suits me down to the ground—because it's 13th Arrondissement and no eclogues. Make sure my bike is there. I am going to use it! And where is my phono? I am bringing back some of the famous jazz hits, the crooning, swooning lullabys sung by the guys without testicles. (The popular favorite is: "I Believe in Miracles." *Miracles!* How American! Well shit, I'll explain all this in detail when I see you, and have a fine bottle of wine handy, a mellow one, a costly one. Here nothing but California vintages, or dago red, which is vile stuff. One must "alkalize" every day . . . . I'll explain that too, later.)

So, Joey, what are we going to do for a living, hein? Search me! But I feel that we're going to live just the same. Anyway, I come. . . . The Jew who published my *Glittering Pie* in that revolutionary Dance Program got back at me by entitling it: "I came, I saw, I *fled.*" The expatriates are anathema to the Americans, particularly to the Communists. I have made myself heartily disliked everywhere, except among the dumb Gentiles who live in the suburbs and guzzle it over the weekends. With these blokes I sing, dance, whistle, make merry the whole night long. I have nothing in common with them aside from the desire to enjoy myself. To know how to enjoy oneself is something unknown here. Usually it consists in making a loud noise. At Manhasset one night Emil and

8

I did the cakewalk so strenuously that Emil dislocated one of his testicles. It was a marvellous night in which we drank ourselves sober. Towards the end I sat down and, striking every wrong note on the piano, I played as only Paderewski himself could play, *if he were drunk*. I broke a few keys and every nail on my fingers. Went to bed with a Mexican hat three feet broad. It lay on my stomach like a huge sunflower. In the morning I found myself in the child's bedroom and beside me a little typewriter made of hard rubber which I couldn't write on, drunk as I was. I also found a rosary and crucifix awarded by the Society of the Miraculous Medal, Germantown, Pa. It was *"indulgenced for a Happy Death and the Way of the Cross."*

I have had a lot of funny experiences, but few gay ones. When I get back to Paris I shall remember the evenings spent sitting on couches in studios with everybody talking pompously and callously about social-economic conditions—with cruel lapses of Proust and Cocteau. (To talk of Proust or Joyce today in America is to be quite up to the minute! Some one will ask you blandly— "what is all this crap about *Surréalisme? What is* it?" Whereupon I usually explain that *Surréalisme* is when you piss in your friend's beer and he drinks it by mistake.)

Met William Carlos Williams the other night and had a rousing time with him at Hiler's place. Holty arrived with two dopey brothers-in-law, one of whom played the piano. Everybody crocked, including Lisette. Just before all hands passed out someone yelled—"All art is local"—which precipitated a riot. After that nothing is clear. Hiler sits in his drawers, with legs crossed, and plays "Believe It Beloved," another hit of the season. The janitor comes and raises hell—he was an aviator for Mussolini. Then come the Dockstadter Sisters who write for the pulps. After that Monsieur Bruine who has been in America 39 years and looks exactly like a Frenchman. He is in love with a dizzy blonde from the Vanities. Unfortunately she got so drunk that she puked all over him while sitting on his lap. He's cured of her now.

I mention these little details because without them the American scene is not complete. Everywhere it is drunkenness and vomiting, or breaking of windows and smashing heads. Twice recently I narrowly missed being cracked over the head. People walk the streets at night lit up and looking for trouble. They come on you unexpectedly and invite you to fight—for the fun of it! It must be the climate—*and the machine*. The machines are driving them screwy. Nothing is done by hand anymore. Even the doors open magically: as you approach the door you step on a treadle and the door springs open for you. It's hallucinating. And then there are the patent medicines. Exlax for constipation—everybody has constipation!—and Alka-Seltzer for hangovers. Everybody wakes up with a headache. For breakfast it's a Bromo-Seltzer—with orange juice and toasted corn muffins, of course. To start the day right you must *alkalize*. It says so in all the subway trains. High-pressure talks, quick action, money down, mortgaged to the eyes, prosperity around the corner (it's always around the corner!), don't worry, keep smiling, believe it beloved, etc., etc. The songs are marvellous, especially as to words. They betray the incurable melancholy and optimism of the American race. I wish I were a foreigner and getting it from scratch. A good one just now is: "The Object of my Affection is to change my Complexion . . ." I'll bring this along too.

At the burlesk Sunday afternoon I heard Gypsy Rose Lee sing "Give Me a Lay!" She had a Hawaiian lei in her hand and she was telling how it felt to get a good lay, how even mother would be grateful for a lay once in a while. She said she'd take a lay on the piano, or on the floor. An old-fashioned lay, too, if needs be. The funny part of it is the house was almost empty. After the first half-hour every one gets up nonchalantly and moves down front to the good seats. The strippers talk to their customers as they do their stunt. The coup de grâce comes when, after having divested themselves of every stitch of clothing, there is left only a spangled girdle with a fig leaf dangling in front—sometimes a little monkey beard, which is quite ravishing. As they draw towards the wings they stick their bottoms out and slip the girdle off. Sometimes they darken the stage and give a belly dance in radium paint. It's good to see the belly button glowing like a glowworm, or like a bright half dollar. It's better still to see them holding their boobies, especially when said boobies are full of milk. Then there is the loudspeaker through which some idiotic jake roars: "Give the little ladies a hand please!" Or else—"Now, ladies and gentlemen, we are going to present to you that most charming personality fresh from Hollywood—Miss Chlorine Duval of the Casino de Paris." Said Chlorine Duval is generally streamlined, with the face of an angel and a thin squeaky voice that barely carries across the footlights. When she opens her trap you see that she is a half-wit; when she dances you see that she is a nymphomaniac; when you go to bed with her you see that she is syphilitic.

Last night I went to the Hollywood Restaurant, one of those colossal cabaret entertainments that cost a dollar and a half, *sans vin, sans pourboire*. Cold sober you watch a string of dazzling ponies, fifty or more, the finest wenches in the land and empty as a cracked peanut shell. The place is like a huge dance hall, thousands of people eating at once, guzzling it, socking it away. Most of them stone sober and their eyes jumping out of their sockets. Most of them middle-aged, bald, addlepated. They come to hear "torch songs" sung by middle-aged sirens. Sophie Tucker, the principal event of the evening, sings about a fairy whom she married by mistake. When she says "Nuts to you!" he answers— "Oh swish!" She is very fat now, Sophie, and has blue veins relieved by 36 carat rocks. She is advertised as "the last of the hot mommers." America isn't breeding any more of this variety. The new ones are perfect—tall, long-waisted, full-busted and rattle-headed. They all sing through the microphone, though one could hear just as well without it. There is a deafening roar which, without any wine under your belt, makes you sick and dizzy. They all know how to shout. They love it. They develop whiskey voices—hard, sour, brassy. It goes well with the baby face, the automatic gestures, the broken-hearted lullabys. A colossal show that must cost a fortune and leaves you absolutely unmoved— despite the fine busts I mentioned a while back. I do honestly believe that a poor, skinny, misshapen French woman with just an ounce of personality would stop the show. She would have what the Americans are always talking about but never achieve. She would have *it*. America is minus *it*. You think maybe I'm sour on my own country, but so help me God, that's what's the matter with America—IT. "They" and "it" go together—follow me?

And now, Joey, I'm going to tell you a little more about my lonely nights in New York, how I walk up and down Broadway, turning in and out of the side streets, looking into windows and doorways, wondering always when the miracle will happen, and if. And nothing ever happens. The other night I dropped into a lunch counter, a cheesy looking joint on West 45th Street, across the way from the Blue Grotto. A good setting for "The Killers." I met some pretty tough eggs, all dressed immaculately, all sallow complexioned and bushy eyebrowed. Faces like sunken craters. The eyes mad and piercing, eyes that pierce right through you and appraise you as so much horse meat. There were a few whores from Sixth Avenue together with some of the most astonishingly beautiful chorus girls I ever laid eyes on. One of these sat next to me. She was so beautiful, so lovely, so fresh, so virginal, so outrageously Palm Olive in every respect that I was ashamed to look her straight in the eye. I looked only at her gloves which were porous and made of fine silk. She had long hair, loose-flowing tresses which hung down almost to her waist. She sat on the high stool and ordered a tiny little sandwich and a container of coffee which she took to her room to nibble at with great delicacy. All the yegg men seemed to know her; they greeted her familiarly but respectfully. She could be "Miss America, 1935." She was a dream, I'm telling you. I looked at her furtively through the mirror. I couldn't imagine anyone laying her except he had a golden wand. I couldn't imagine her hoofing it either. I couldn't imagine her eating a big juicy steak with mushrooms and onions. I couldn't imagine her going to the bathroom, unless to clear her throat. I couldn't imagine her having a private life. I can only imagine her posing for a magazine cover, standing perpetually in her Palm Olive skin and never perspiring. I like the gangsters best. These boys go everywhere and by aeroplane and streamlined platinum, lighter than air, air-conditioned trains. They are the only ones in America who are enjoying life, while it lasts. I envy them. I like the shirts they wear, and the bright ties, and the flashy haircuts. They come fresh from the laundry and kill in their best clothes.

The opposite to this is the suburban life. Manhasset, for instance. The idea is—how to kill the weekend. Those who don't play bridge invent other forms of amusement, such as the peep show. Was taken to the cellar of a big advertising director and shown some dirty films. Not a consecutive film, but patches of this and that, *mostly ass.* You see a woman lying on a couch and a man running his hand up her leg; you see her stomach quiver and then another man is standing behind a woman, with his pants down, and he's socking it into her. Then you see a close-up of a cunt— just the cunt—and you watch it open like an oyster to swallow a long slimy penis belonging to a man with a derby. One thing after another, *sans suite.* Afterwards the men go upstairs and maul the women. They like to get undressed and dance over the weekends. To change wives. They don't know what to do with themselves after a hard week at the office. *Donc,* the car, the whiskey bottle, some strange cunt, an artist if possible. (I, for example, made a hit because "I was so unconventional." Sometimes, when you are regarded as being so unconventional, it is embarrassing to be obliged to refuse a choice piece of ass—your host's wife, let us say, size 59 and round as a tub. Larry's wife, for example, is a miniature hippopotamus who gets jealous if you dance with any of the good-looking wenches. She goes off and sulks.)

And now let me tell you what one brilliant man in the suburbs thought of last weekend to regale us. When we were all good and crocked he got out an old talking record of the Prince of Wales. We had to listen to that high and mighty potentate (then about nineteen years of age) tell us what the *idealllll* of the Englishman was. I don't have to tell you, Joey, that it was our old friend "fair

play." An Englishman never *twists* you. No sirree. It went on for
three records—it must have been a golden jubilee or something. In
the midst of it I got hysterical and began to laugh. I laughed and
laughed and laughed. Everybody began to laugh, even the host
who, I discovered later, was highly insulted. No sir, an Englishman
never *twists* you! He just falls asleep on you . . .

According to Mlle Bohy, who I agree is a horse's ass, there is
no demand here anymore for French literature. She says the
Americans are laying off the French. The truth is, she's ashamed
of her own country and is trying to become a full-fledged American
woman. "America is a wonderful country for a woman," she says
to me. I thought to myself—Yeah, for a big cow like you who
hasn't any more sex appeal . . . This is the country for woman's
rights. This is a matriarchy. A matriarchy of fat old dowagers with
whiskers on their chins, a matriarchy of blue noses and flat-
breasted heifers. Women are better off in the countries where they
are supposedly mistreated.

Last night Jack Brent came to town with his streamlined Packard. He calls me up from his suite at the Albemarle Hotel. Mr.
Brent speaking! Ahem! We pick up a cunt on the way and go to
Ticino's for dinner. In the front of the basement is a billiard table
where the laborers shoot some kind of crazy pool. This lends
atmosphere—for the Village artists who frequent the joint.

Anyway, here's how we started the meal—the cunt, Jack and I
. . . We start with six martini cocktails—Brent insists that they be
brought all at once. O. K. There they are—six of them staring us
in the face. Then the menu. Antipasto with steak! Olives and
macaroni! While we are lapping up the cocktails Brent orders a
few more drinks—to make sure we don't go dry. I venture to
suggest wine. He says—*later!* O. K. We order three sidecars and
two old-fashioneds. A vicious assortment. I'm hungry. It's about
9:30 p.m. Nothing but celery stalks so far. The cocktails make you
sick and you talk a lot of drunken shit between whiles. (For
instance, a long speech from Brent about a letter I wrote him in
1924—a letter in which I insulted him, *him,* Jack Brent, the
millionaire's son. Now he likes that letter. He shows it around.
Proud of it, in fact. He'd like me to insult him some more—that is,
if I could do it delicately.)

When the food arrives I demand some wine. I ask for red wine,
naturally. Brent doesn't like red wine—says it's no good. Jesus,
I'm wondering if there are to be more sidecars, or perhaps some
fandangled limousine of a drink. But no, he calls the waiter very
ostentatiously, runs down the wine list, and settles on a Graves—

the best! that is, the highest-priced. It happens to be really good. I leave the cocktails and sidecars to one side and ply the wine. Seeing me drink a big bottle all by myself Brent gets sore. He says he wants to drink some wine also. Good. I pour him out a glass. The cunt only drinks a mouthful and pushes the glass away. She's never had a good glass of wine in her life. Finally I call the waiter over. He's an intelligent dago and he seems to have good taste. I invite him to have a drink with us. He pours himself out a big tumblerful of the Graves. I can see Brent wincing. He wasn't ordering wine for me to pour it down the waiter's throat. But down it goes. Hurrah! That cheers me up a bit. I like to be friendly with the waiters.

After the steak and radishes, the macaroni and sidecars and gin fizzes and whiskey sours and wine and what not, we have some brandy. Brent wants Napoleon brandy no less. We down the brandy and it's like firewater. We're standing up on our hind legs now, rearing to go. I pull out a five-dollar bill, pretending to split the bill with him, but he pushes it aside. The bill comes to $18.00. Try to imagine what that is—$18.00! Almost a week's wages. And this guy hasn't tasted anything! He's been smoking a cigar all during the meal, and now he's lighting another, and when that's finished he'll light another from the dead end of the last one. Anyhow, we pile into the Packard and start towards Broadway. The lights fizzing just as always and always it looks marvellous—and always it's disappointing once you're in the thick of it. We stop off at a bar en route—to have a little drink before tackling the dance halls. Brent orders in French now. The bartender, a fat mick, looks at him blankly and asks what language he is speaking. Try and order a sidecar in French! Or any hard drink. Well, that down, we descend a few steps to find ourselves in the Silver Slipper where it is advertised that there are nothing but the world's most beautiful show girls as hostesses. There are nothing but hostesses here, half nude, and shivering because of lack of customers. They light up electrically as you enter. It costs only a quarter to *enter*. It costs about $20.00 *to leave*. They advertise "a nickel a dance," and it's true enough, but a dance lasts about two minutes, or less. The music never stops—just a little knock-knock when a new tune commences. Waltzing around with a ravishing show girl you don't notice the tunes being knocked off. It's like the click of a taximeter. Suddenly, however, she says: "Won't you please get another strip of tickets?" A strip costs a dollar which, as I say, you burn up in about eight and a half minutes. Sometimes you sit out a dance while your hostess drinks a Coca-Cola or an orange juice, or perhaps eats a banana layer cake. They are always hungry and thirsty, as you know. *And never drunk.* The law forbids even beer to be sold in these places. The girl is not allowed to sit at the table with you, but only at the railing by your side. She must sit on the railing and lean over to sip her drink. It's a wonder they permit them to smoke—or fuck. The one I picked asked me very innocently what I had come for and I said—"Why, to get a lay, of course." Whereupon she pretended to be highly insulted and wanted to walk off. "Go ahead," I said. But instead of going she clings to me like a leech.

Well, after I had used up about eight dollars of Brent's money I squandered a couple of my own. Then I got fed up. They are all willing to be laid, but they want a snack first and then a little ride and I suppose after that a little hush money, and with this and that, a little here and a little there, and here a little and there a little, why the dawn would be breaking just about the time you'd be trying to pull their pants off.

When we got outside we forgot where we had parked the car. You have to park blocks away from Broadway—there are so many cars lined up. We wandered around stupidly, up and down side streets, looking for Brent's streamlined Packard. We found it finally and just as we were about to pile in along comes a tough bimbo who sails up to two janes standing against a railing. Without a word he hauls off and socks one of them in the jaw. Then he snatches the bag from her hand and dumps the contents into the gutter. He gives her another crack for good measure and walks off. By this time I had already climbed into the car. I felt nervous and uneasy. Brent, however, like a chevalier, bends down and picks up the money lying in the street. Then, in his best manner, he goes up to the girl and handing her the dough, he says: "Lady, would you like me to take a sock at that guy for you? I will, if you say so." The guy, by the way, is almost out of sight now. Anyway, the "lady" makes a grab for the dough, counts it quickly, and then yells—"Hey, what do you mean holding out on me like that? Where's the other dollar?" With that Brent climbs into the car, starts the motor, and then just as he's giving her the gas, he leans out of the window and says—in his best manner—"Lady, go fuck yourself!" and we drive off.

Well, that's the third most interesting night I've had since I'm here, so you can imagine what the rest must be like. The other two I forget already, but I know there were three. Joe has just taken me to lunch; we sat three hours or more, talking about the old days when we hiked through the South together. He was just telling me about the time I was hustled out of the railroad station in Jacksonville at the point of a gun—an incident I had almost completely forgotten. But the thing I do remember vividly—and I will remember it all my life—is that whack over the ass I got when I was sleeping on a bench in the park, at Jacksonville. That I shall never forgive the city of Jacksonville! I will put it down in every book I write—with variations. My ass is still smarting!

Well, these reminiscences only serve to remind me to tell you that everything is just the same here and that I would still be leading a dog's life if I had to depend on America for inspiration. The reason I write you this long letter is because for ten days now I have been unable to write a line. New York crushes you. You can't breathe. It's not the noise and dust, nor the traffic, nor the crowds—it's the appalling flatness, ugliness, monotony and sameness of everything. The walls bear down on you. One wall is like another, and there are no advertisements of Pernod Fils or Amer Picon or Suze or Marie Brizard or Zigzag. The walls are bare and, in the case of the skyscrapers, they are like huge railroad tracks standing up, gleaming, metallic, straight as a die—walls broken only by millions of windows which are let up here and there like organ stops. As you come within range of a skyscraper you get caught up in a maelstrom. The wind eddies about the base of the building and almost lifts you off your feet. You stand and gape at these buildings night after night, half amused, half disgusted, half awed, and you say *"our* this," and *"our* that," and then you go to a cafeteria and order a ham sandwich with a cup of weak coffee and think what a grand time you didn't have.

I told you that I intended writing a final section to the book, to be called—"I the Human Being." Well, I wrote about six pages and had to quit. I feel that I am no longer a human being. I am just a biped, an animal what eats and sleeps—*its* and *slips,* as the Mocks say. "I slips well," you hear on the street. Or a guy says to a woman in broad daylight, corner of 45th Street and Broadway: "Now I tell you what to do, Rose . . . Saturday you go home and you give yourself a thorough cleaning out." Just like that! *Alors,* who goes there, *friend or enema?*

The other day I ventured a visit to the Radio City Theatre. Joe slept soundly throughout the performance. Maybe I told you about this before—about the giant octopi that float on a gauze screen while three thousand chorines dance the *Liebestraum* a mile off? Everything colossal. Colossally colossal. The theatre itself is magnificent—the last word in modern architecture. As soon as you cough it is ventilated—automatically. By thermostat. An average mean temperature of 72 degrees Fahrenheit, winter, spring or summer. No smoking. No smoking anywhere, except in the burlesk. The best you can do is to fart. And, as I said before, even that is immediately cleared off by thermostat device . . . In the lobby there is a piece of mosaic done by somebody or other in which the Muses are depicted. They have added three or four new ones to the original Nine, among them one to Engineering, one to Health, and one to Publicity. Believe it or not, beloved. Every morning, at half past nine punkt, the same radio announcer announces the same wonderful fishing tackle sold in Newark, N.J., by a rodman who makes bamboo poles and just the right tackle with a handsome trawler free of charge just cut out the coupon in the Ladies' Home Journal page 24 last column and don't forget the telephone number is Weehawken 238745 courtesy of the Genuine Diamond Watch Company are you listening the gong is just about to strike the half-hour it is now exactly nine-thirty Eastern Standard Daylight Time.

Well, tomorrow I make application for my passport, and where it says—"Why do you intend to visit France?"—I shall put down as I did the last time—*for pleasure!* Or maybe I'll put down: "Because I want to become a human being again." How's that? I am hoping to begin my next book on the boat. It will begin with my life in New York eight or nine years ago, starting off with the Orpheum Dance Palace the night I had 75 bucks in my pocket for the first time in my life and decided I would take a chance and took it. I am going to write this so simply and honestly that my grandchildren, if I have any, will be able to appreciate it. A long, long story and I intend to put in every detail. I've got the rest of my life ahead of me.

Coming by the Champlain, unless I advise you otherwise. Haven't earned a penny, haven't gotten a stick of recognition. This is the grandest country God every made. Especially the Grand Canyon. One of the greatest blessings ever showered upon mankind is Horlick's Frosted Milk Chocolate. *Or,* the beautiful Men's Room in the Pennsylvania Depot.

Am I happy to leave? No, not happy—*delirious!* From now on it'll be all 13th Arrondissement!

This is one of those incredible New York days when you stay in because you're broke and it's raining. If you're a lucky guy like me you have your friend Joe O'Regan stay with you and make watercolors while you fret and fume. The thing is, when you're in America, you must always obey the law. Take the Conroy Bottle Breaking Machine, for example. This machine, sold at the nominal cost of $125.00 f.o.b. docks or warehouse, enables you to keep within the law and at the same time avoid the risk of cutting your wrist. It breaks empty liquor bottles by a simple movement of the lever on top: thus, if your premises should be raided by Federal Agents all your bottles will be found perfectly broken in accordance with the last idiotic law and you will be spared the penalty of a heavy fine or a year in the penitentiary. Next door to the Conroy Bottle Breaking Machine Co. is the Suke-Yaki restaurant which offers Japanese food at 65¢ per head. You can have your shoes shined outside the restaurant by a nigger who advocates world peace. He advertises—"World Peace"—on his shoe box. No extra charge for the shine.

A little further down is the "Poets' Corner," a dingy Village rendezvous where the Communist poets sit and chew the fat over a cup of pale, greasy coffee. Here is where America's great poems are made. They are sold a little further up the street for ten cents a piece. You can read them before you buy them as they are all conveniently tacked on to the fence, corner of Washington Square and Thompson Street. Most of them are written in lead pencil and signed by the author who scratches himself while you read. "Please buy a poem!" he says in a cheery voice. "Only ten cents the poem!" If it rains of course there is no market. Then you must go directly to the Poets' Corner, downstairs in the basement, a few doors below June Mansfield's old hangout on Third Street—where the "young and evil" used to congregate. The painters, I must say, are a little better off. They fetch thirty-five and fifty, even seventy cents, for an oil. They are not afraid of the rain because, as you know, oil and water don't mix.

So you think I am shitting you about all this? You ask about the fancy prices paid by Esquire and Vanity Fair, etc. Well, ask! No poet ever gets into Vanity Fair or Esquire. These organs are reserved exclusively for he-men like Hemingway and Joe Schrank. They are magazines for MEN. Another think about these magazines is the wonderful pipeline system leading to the affiliated organs such as Harper's, Vogue, Atlantic Monthly, etc., etc. It's like boarding an open trolley and getting a transfer. *Or* like passing from one wet dream to another and waking utterly refreshed. All this has a bearing on what I am about to tell you—that is, about the treatment of snakes. You see, Joe O'Regan was a snake-fancier, as a boy. He lived with old man Moncure down in Virginia somewhere. Joe was telling me about this as we sat in McElroy's Saloon on Thirty-First Street where, after midnight, you can dance with some of the finest sots ever imported from Ireland. Across the street from McElroy's is the Hebrew National Restaurant where you may see an enlarged photograph of a dinner given by Lou Siegel to his playmates Eddie Cantor, George Jessel, Al Jolson and the other well-known comedians of Jewish vintage. This, for your information, is just opposite the Hotel Wolcott now made famous by my chapter called "The Tailor Shop," in memory of my old man and his defunct cronies—Corse Payton, Julian L'Estrange, Tom Ogden, Chucky Morton, et alia. The effect of passing the Wolcott and looking over towards the Hebrew National where Eddie Cantor somewhat enlarged makes googoo eyes at George Jessell is nothing less than horripilating. This is what has happened to good old Thirty-First Street in the space of a generation.

But, as I say, Joe and I were talking about scallops. There were a few empty scallop shells on my writing table when we pulled in last night. We pulled in rather broke and disheartened—had to while away the time watching a dance across the way, at the Carroll Club. The Carroll Club is a lovely mansion for poor working girls. On Saturday nights the Settlement workers throw a dance; fashionable young men from West End Avenue and the Bronx drive up in fresh-painted limousines and neck the girls behind the translucent screens which we look down upon from the 23rd story of our little apartment house. The poverty of New York is on a grand scale, as is everything else. Behind this dire poverty stand the hope and courage of 120,000,000 morons and idiots tattooed with the N. R. A. double eagle. Behind this stand the empty bottles which the Conroy Bottle Breaking Machine will break for you at no less than ordinary ground burial. Behind this stands the red Indian who was so despoiled and deprived of all rights that today he is bored with his huge estates and oil wells and clamoring to be treated like a white man.

It was raining, as I say, and Joe and I were standing at Whelan's Cigar Store watching other people watch us. This is at the L station corner of 33rd Street, Sixth Avenue and Broadway. Under the elevated stood a strange figure—a slim young man in dungarees and blue silk shirt with a red bandanna around his neck and a huge sombrero on his bean, rakishly set, of course. He seemed to be waiting for the rain to stop. We had about 75 cents between us, Joe and I, and we didn't know whether to engage the young cowboy in talk or not. Finally we whistled to him and he came over, looking rather startled and apprehensive. He had overslept, he said, and so he had just come down from Holyoke, Mass., where the circus was, and he was training spitz dogs or something. He had a pair of big iron spurs in his pocket which he showed us rather proudly. The rowels were rather dull, but he said they could be sharpened easily. He said he was looking for the Grand Central Depot, in order to find the Travellers' Aid Society. Said it was the biggest taown he had ever been in—just as though there might be dozens of other big towns in the world, even bigger. We asked him how he

liked New York. Said he couldn't say cause he had only been in it
a half hour and was looking how to get out of it. We took him to
the Mills Hotel, paid his fare for the night, and gave him instructions as to how to get to the ferry in the morning.

After we left him it struck me that this was the most interesting
experience I had had since being here. A fine upstanding youth, as
they say, with soft, winsome talk, a dumb animal that had strayed
from the fold. All New York owned and run by pushing, grabbing
Jews: a frozen clatter over your head day and night; grim, over-
weening buildings pushing you back into the concrete; the lights
blinking like mad, red to stop, green to go; suits in every window,
and an extra pair of trousers, if you choose—*Sanforized* too,
whatever the hell that means. I remember how we took his ten-
gallon hat, how we felt it, weighed it, rolled it, crumpled it, tried it
on, looked at the label, asked the price of it, etc., etc. That man
and that hat were worth more to me than all New York put
together—I mean the whole damned city and what it stands for
. . . even with cellophane around it. Here was one of our own kind,
a dumb animal lost and strayed, walking in the rain, zigzagging
under the L, ducking taxis, his blue shirt open at the chest, his
hair wet and glistening, trim figure, nineteen years old, muscles of
steel, eyes like a deer, horny hands, blue dungarees, the pockets
cut on the bias. Strike me dead if I didn't envy him! He was
heading back to Tennessee, where it would be all farm and no
more circus. In the morning the bums will wean him of his last few
pennies and he will stand on a corner looking helplessly for the
ferry we told him to take. His name was Self. Will Self. I want you
to remember that. It's a swell American name, good in any
language. Reminds me distantly of "The Ego and His Own," a fat,
pretentious piece of anarchism which I read in Chula Vista when I
was trying hard to be a cowboy myself—only the bedbugs wouldn't
let me.

So, as we were sitting in McElroy's Saloon Joe started to
reminisce—about Miami and the great tornado of 1927 or '8, just
after the boom. He's talking to me about a wench he had on the
beach under a row boat, during the cyclone. Just as he's a-straddle
of her along come the Miami gallon-nippers (a species of exaggerated mosquito) and they start nipping him in the ass. From this to
the sunrise in Key West and the shapes of the clouds, one back of
another, big, balloonlike, some like Buffalo Bill, some like Sitting
Bull, and all in violent colors. We're standing under an arc light in
St. Petersburg—the old men's retreat—and suddenly the mosquitos are biting us, millions and millions of them. We're playing a
nineteen-hole game of golf on the run, with the mosquitos chasing

us. And then the clear springs which come up out of nowhere, the fish eating out of your hand through the glass-bottomed boats. (Does this remind you a little of Blaise Cendrars?) Better still . . . when you dig a hole to drain off the water the water disappears and nobody knows where to. The St. Johns River is the only river in the United States which runs from south to north, i.e., uphill. Hence Ponce de Leon . . .

But it was with old Moncure, when they came up north to Madison Square Garden, that Joe found out about snakes. They were travelling with the carnival then. Joe says, and I take it on his authority, that snakes have been so molested from time immemorial that when they are treated with a little tenderness they respond very warmly. What Joe used to do was to run a king snake up his left sleeve, across the back of his vest, and down through the right sleeve—in order to feed it a raw egg. (I asked if it was customary to peel the egg first, but Joe says no.) Anyway, the king snake knows whether an egg is good or not. You can't give him a bad egg. He's clean, the snake. Eats no garbage, as do the heathen Chinese. No sirree. Once in a while he resorts to cannibalism, but he must be very hungry first. The thing to do, when he gets this way, is to put a younger king snake—a snake *cadet*—in the same cell with him. Don't put a rat in as the rat is apt to kill the snake. What Joe used to do was to wait for the big snake to gobble the little one. When the jaws were firmly locked about the little snake's neck Joe would get out his jackknife and, making a ring around the little snake's neck, he would let the big snake hold while he pulled off the little snake's skin. When you feed the snake a raw egg, you must cup the egg with your five fingers. This endears the snake to you, or you to him. When the snake has swallowed the egg he spits out the shell. This, I think, is the most wonderful part of the egg story. Imagine what a feat this is! First swallowing the egg whole, then crushing it, then digesting it, then spitting out the shell. I think any man who sincerely wanted to make friends with a snake should also go to the trouble of shelling the egg for the snake. Or parboiling it, at least. There are little delicacies which even a snake can learn to appreciate. More especially since the snake has no way of thanking you, except by rolling his eyes.

You see, I am having a very interesting time in New York. Like the other day, for example, when I revisited the scene of my childhood—at Paradise Point. We had to go there and back, eat, gas up, turn around and take a shower, all in five and a half hours. It's a little over a hundred miles to Paradise Point. All I had time for was a quick look at the bay—Peconic Bay, say O.K., void a little urine, pick up some dead crabs, and tumble back into the

rumble seat. That's how things are done in America. Even sacred
things, such as exploring Swann's Way. There I was, a hundred-
per-cent Proust, remembering everything in advance, getting all
tremulous and sweaty, and suddenly we're there—that's it!—and
bango, like a streak we're off again. Here is where I offer a new
point of view on memory and childhood. The strange thing about
this little excursion is this—the place looked even better to me
after a lapse of 35 years than before! This must be one of those
places which obey the Fraenkelian law—they live back ever more
beautiful, ever more wondrous. They grow younger with time.
When I was a kid it was just Peconic Bay to me, plus a few pretty
sea shells. Yesterday, or the day before, it was Capri, the Mediterranean, Majorca, Cyprus, what have you. The miracle is that
nobody comes here. The Jews have left it undiscovered. Not one
more house than thirty-five years ago. Not one more inhabitant.
Not one more duck farm, or any other kind of farm. Something
rare and strange about this. Especially in America where things
grow so fast and so large over night.

(Interruption: Joe is so excited over his watercolor that he is
painting on his knees. We have only one piece of paper left and he
is slaving in the margin. He is doing a corner of my room which I
will send you by second-class mail.)

   Walking down Broadway I noticed how lousy the street was with
whores. Not the old bag-swingers of 1908 and '10, but young ones
without stockings, lean, trim, racy ones with strips of monkey fur
or skunk slung around their necks. They come bounding out of the
side streets with a cigarette to their lips and they stand a moment
looking bewilderedly up and down the Appian Way. They look
right through you, not graciously and invitingly and sexually and
sensually, but with that boring, riveting eye like the acetylene
torch on the car tracks at night. There is only one look the
American woman can turn on, be she a whore or a duchess.
European women have a thousand looks. The American gal has
just one. And that's a searchlight which sprays your spine and
throws no heat. It speaks of cold cash and speed and sanitary
conditions. Drunk or sober, it's the same thing. It's not sex, but
the light of a powerful apparatus hidden in the hind lobe of the
brain, just above the medulla oblongata. It's like a music box in
which you drop a coin, like a chewing gum slot machine, like a
London gas meter. You drop the coin, the jiggers start, there's a
little flirr and movement, a whirr and then the light goes on, stays
on just long enough to read what's written and is off again. Don't

think they come up to you and solicit you. Ah no! They stand
there in the gloom of a stage exit and suddenly, when they espy
you, they leap forward, matching your stride with theirs, moving
in closer and closer, always parallel and abreast of you, until your
arms touch, and then your hips, and when you have rubbed each
other well, like a couple of old alley cats, they let you open your
trap and make a price, still walking, still nonchalant, blasé, indifferent, cold as cement, walking on rubber heels with stiff American
gait as though to get somewhere someday and why not now just
around the corner buy me a drink no then well so long and the hell
with you.

Since I was here last everything has become younger, the
whores included. The price is youth. Old whores are taken to the
slaughter-house and made into harnesses and straps and leather
handles. Broadway is to the young, where the females are concerned. The males may be middle-aged, bald, fat, amorphous,
cockeyed, lopsided, bile-ridden, rheumy, asthmatic, arthritic—*but
the women must be young!* They must be young and fresh and
tough and durable, like the new buildings, the new elevators, the
new cars, the stainless-steel knives and forks that never wear out
and are just as sharp and efficacious as Gorham silver blades.
Broadway is full of jowl-faced, lynx-eyed lawyers and politicians,
all smartly dressed, white-starched collars, the correct tie, the
latest patch pocket. Everybody has a crease in his trousers and
shoes highly polished. Nobody wears a last year's hat, crisis or no
crisis. Nobody is without a clean handkerchief softly laundered
and wrapped in a seal packerchief. When you have your hair
brushed by the barber he throws the brush away to be fumigated
and wrapped in cellophane again. The cloth he puts around your
neck is sent immediately to the laundry—by pneumatic air tubes
that deliver the following morning. Everything is a twenty-four-
hour service, whether it is necessary or not. Your things come
back so fast you don't have time to earn the money to pay for this
service you don't need. If it rains you get your shoes shined just
the same—because the polish is a protection against weather
stains. You get trimmed coming and going. You are in the sausage
machine and there is no way out—unless you take a boat and go
somewhere else. Even then you can't be sure because the whole
fucking world is going a hundred percent American. It's a disease.

All this leads me back to the great American novel—*Of Time
and the River*—now being advertised in all the Fifth Avenue buses.
This is one of those great American novels which is always
heralded as *the* great American novel but which somehow is
forgotten after a month or so because the props which made up

the scaffolding are so rotten that they fall apart. Like all the other great American novels this one is a space filler. *Time and the River* are lost in space. There are three dimensions, but the fourth is lacking. It is a *Comédie Humaine* with Hannibal, Missouri, as the vital center. It proliferates as cancer proliferates. It does not burn, belch, roar, sizzle, fume, steam, fire, smoke. It starts, as all the great American novels start, at the big toe—and works upward. In travelling up the tibia you get lost. You get lost in the follicles of that superfluous hair which the American women are always removing from their legs and arms. A really great book starts in the midriff and works outward. It starts vitally and ends vitally. It is vital through and through. The architecture comes about not through a desire to fill space but because hunger and faith demand an edifice, a testimony, a concrete symbol and resting place. Perhaps I am unfair to this great American author: I admit that I read only about forty pages. But in forty pages a man, or his soul—if he has one—must unlimber. True, there were emotional swells—but they were like bloated frescoes which one takes in out of the corner of his eye while running a marathon. Altogether too goddamned genealogical to suit my taste! I detest all books which run chronologically, which commence at the cradle and end with the grave. Even life doesn't run that way, much as people think it does. Life only commences at the hour of spiritual birth—which may be at eighteen or at forty-seven. And death is never the goal—but life! more life! Someone must throw a pitchfork into this river of space-time which the Americans have created; the rivers must be made to run uphill, against the grain. Like the St. Johns River! Here as fast as new rivers are created dikes are built to hem them in—to make them work, to make them pay. We need a flood, and only then will there be a rich silt to work with. We don't need genealogical novels, or the story of the American continent seen through the eyes of the Swiss Family Robinson. Somebody has got to throw a monkey wrench into the works. I feel that I'm the guy, Joey, to make the rivers run uphill. I owe it to the American buffalo and the red Indian, to the shades of Montezuma and the Quetzalcoatl. In order to accomplish this task I have already cut off my head. I am going to walk down the open street, Broadway preferably, with my head in hand and all the gas mains belching a sweet stench. I am going to walk along with my head in my hands and have a look at things astrologically. I already feel lighter, springier, gayer. Perhaps I will leave my head at the Villa Seurat and just walk with the rest of my body down Broadway. I will carry the book with me, a big iron book clasped to my belt. In it I will record strange things. I shall be the high priest of the great

American novel running uphill for the first time since the dawn of creation—and *ship some fine Westphalian hams to Jerusalem, please!*

Just had a letter from that old gal Juliet who asks—"Why didn't you look us up before? Why do you have to make your *permanent* home in Paris? Why do you have to sail on June the 14th? Why do you continue to be expatriated?" I feel like answering that letter here and now. So here goes, Joey . . .

Dear Juliet,

The reason I didn't look you up before this is because I had forgotten about you completely. It was only the other night, when I was a little soused and had ordered an expensive cigar, that seeing the label on the cigar I remembered you were alive and had a kid. The reason I make my *permanent* home in Paris is because I am a millionaire and can afford to have a home wherever I please. The reason I sail June the 14th is because another day here would drive me nuts; had you written me a few days earlier I could have saved myself the trouble of writing this letter by sending you a copy of the preceding pages which explain everything. You say that things are so exciting in America that it is difficult for you to imagine establishing yourself elsewhere. That's all right for you to say since you are only a mother and the wife of the editor of a third-rate swindle sheet. You live on the socio-economic plane. I am living on the astronomic plane which you can reach only if you have a pair of wings. You say that you read my book "not without interest," which is a curious negative way of putting it—but what about your husband, the editor, to whom I sent a copy for review at my own expense? Why hasn't that bastard given me a review? A stick at least? Isn't there enough sociology in it for his swindle sheet? My next book will be about the functional work habits of the cockroach during the Civil War—which I think will be up his street. It will describe the endocrine system with and without food, showing the relation between climatic changes and periods of unemployment. It will have a dull cover, such as the government tracts are bound in, and small type, and an errata at the back. It is too bad I never read any of your husband's verse. All my knowledge of him comes from Joe Gould. Joe Gould said he would piss on him one day and make a man of him. Is that true? Anyway, that's what they tell me. And now let me tell you something about the baby—about bringing it up properly. When you feed him his oats always pour a little lukewarm horse piss into the mush. This will put backbone into him and later, when he becomes an editor, he will not need to be pissed on by a neglected American author in order to become a man. If you want him to become an erudite read him Kenneth Burke's translation of *The City Man*—it makes a fine slumber song. And why do you insist on washing the baby's diapers? Use Kotex. It costs no more, and it's sanitary. Order a box to-day from the Smithsonian Institute. "By exercising care, courtesy and common sense," as Police Commissioner Valentine counsels, "you and yours may live long and happily." Please remember that. So long, Juliet . . . you were always a good cigar . . . but rather expensive. Signed: Henry Valentine Miller.

Did you like that, Joey? Maybe you can think up some more cunts we can write to. They don't need to write me. Just forward their names and addresses. This is the open season for letters. If I had money I wouldn't write another line. I would go to a bar and order a sandwich and a glass of beer. I would look up Stefano Fanti who calls me by name whenever I visit his joint. He makes me feel good. He says: "I let you buy all the drinks you want; when you get ready to leave *I buy you a drink.*" He says that to our face. No cunning in that. Right out with it. That's what I like about Europeans. They don't give you something for nothing. You must pay and pay through the nose. Here everything is free, cheap as a song, but it costs more than you can afford. It seems wonderful at first not to leave a tip when you go to a bar or a drugstore. No tips! Sounds like Utopia. But when you count your change you find that you paid three times as much for a drink as you would in Europe, *pourboire compris*. I figure I've paid these soda water jerkers royal tips all along. They've been fucking me—maybe not the jerkers themselves, but the proprietors then, i.e., The Great Atlantic & Pacific Tea Co.

It just occurs to me that it's a pity I was not sent over by the *Paris-Soir,* along with Blaise Cendrars and Claude Farrère. I would have earned my passage back by this time, to say nothing of the free champagne and the Corona-Coronas. Perhaps my style is not good enough for the *Paris-Soir*—but then, is Claude Farrère's? Can you imagine what that bird's going to say about the *Normandie?* And how does Cendrars manage to hold himself down? Does he dictate his copy? You see, I have all the equipment, including carbon paper. I would be the most inexpensive reporter they could possibly find. If they didn't like that letter I just wrote to Juliet they could cut it out. I remember how, in the early days, I used to buy *Le Journal* for breakfast—that was my morning exercise. I remember those cheesy articles dispatched by Maurice Dekobra— here and there an English phrase (misspelled) to lend a little local color. I remember the guy they sent to India, the guy who wrote so charmingly about the *pavillon des fleurs*. I remember the bike races reported by Paul Morand—or if not Morand then some other pretentious nitwit. All these things I could do with my left hand— *and at less than the cost of ordinary ground burial.* Of course, I would have to do them in English. That's it—I am condemned to write in English to a people who do not exist. I might just as well begin to study Chinese. I am sure the Chinese would be more appreciative. (Free ad: Read *The Hanging on Union Square!* Written in English by one, Tchiang, a Chinaman. *Ta, ta, ta, ta! Money gone, nobody home. Ta, ta, ta, ta!* That's from the poems. The novel is in colloquial pidgin English, fresh from Union Square and the Rand School of Social Sciences.) Mr. Tchiang is one of my favorite authors. I have forgotten who the others are. Ezra Pound probably. Someday I am going to read Ezra Pound. I am going to read the *Unfinished Cantos* at a gallop. And then I am going to read Gertrude Stein and Unamuno. If I have more time I shall get down to reading the *Fourth Eclogue*—and perhaps the three preceding *Eclogues*. And now I am going to call a brief halt and take a nap. It is four o'clock Eastern Standard Time; if I sleep fast I can wake up at exactly the same time in Nagasaki or Mozambique. I do hate to lose time, time being the only precious thing I possess. So I will snooze a while to restore my waning powers in order to go on with this letter which I am sure must be of great interest to you and the readers of *Paris-Soir*. Don't forget to remind me of the man I saw shining his own shoes. He was a bootblack and business was so bad that he had to shine his own shoes. I can't get over it. Times are really bad, I guess.

Passing the Woolworth Building today on the elevated line I couldn't help but notice how like a Nuremberg cheese cake this piece of architecture now seems. This is the skyscraper that only a few years ago they were praising the shit out of because of its modernity. Designed by one of the best American architects. And today it looks cheesy. Not only cheesy, but insignificant. It looks like an angel cake with birthday candles on it. The same for the Metropolitan Tower and the Singer Building. They look woebegone. They belong to the past, that past which has no place in America, which crumbles at a breath. I notice that the great cathedrals never seem outmoded. The pedant may see in them this century or that; but a man like myself who walks the streets aimlessly is completely indifferent to the centuries represented. For him they are timeless. They will inspire a hundred years from now, five hundred years from now, a thousand years from now—if the Germans haven't destroyed them. The feeling I have about America, about the whole continent—flora, fauna, architecture, peoples, customs—is this: *nothing vital was ever begun here . . . nothing of value*. As far as I can determine, nothing ever will get started, in this deep, vital sense. They can blow things up to the most colossal proportions, make a network of cities which will obliterate the now intervening countryside—still it will make no difference. It is a horizontal movement—*space-filling*—and consequently futile. Tomorrow the whole continent might sink into the sea—and what would be lost? Is there one priceless monument? One irreplaceable thing? Anything whose loss would create a feeling of real deprivation, such as the loss of Dante's great work, for example?

And now, Joey, I'm going to get serious for a moment. I'm going to say a few words about the aeroplane, about that obsession for the air which seems to have the Americans by the balls. I want to ask you what it means, this business of flying to the moon, or Mars, or Jupiter? I ask myself very seriously if this flying mania is not the symptom of a very great and very real distress, if it does not mean something more than just a conquest of the air, as they say. It's all right to say that the aviator is connecting one city with another, that he's cutting down the time element, establishing new modes of communication, etc. But that's not all—that's not the whole story. There is another and deeper element which enters into it, and that's the awakening of a mystic sense. The aviator rises above the earth and revolves with the earth, or almost. He moves with the stars in a new dimension, or he has the illusion of so doing. He feels a sense of power, not as of old—in touching the earth—but in freeing himself from the earth. This is dangerous. In another hundred years he will be thinking astrologically again. He will have developed the flying sense, he will be drunk with the feel of the cosmos, with new space-time ideas, just as Europe was drunk with the discovery of America. He will say to himself that it is his ambition to reach the moon, or Mars, or Jupiter, but he will never reach the moon—he will reach to himself again, to man, to a new fury of creative activity. Each time a new horizon is opened up, each time the imaginative horizon is enlarged, the earth becomes smaller and more habitable. Life does not spread: it blooms, it burgeons, it develops in intensity. Now men think it is important to get from one place to another more quickly. Tomorrow they will stand stock-still, content to go nowhere. They will stand stock-still and sing about travelling to incalculable realms. There is only one road for man, and that is towards God. Along this road, if he searches and prays, he meets himself. Then he opens wide his jaws and sings with all his might. Then he doesn't need God anymore—God then is everywhere distant as the farthest planet, close as his own skin. We are going towards God, I say, in the aeroplane. No aeroplane will ever reach God. No *man* will ever reach God. But we can have Hallelujah, and when a man has found himself it is Hallelujah all the time. I have found it without hiring an aeroplane. I found it standing in a pair of moccasins.

And now, brother Fredl, I want you to make ready a little song. Up, up, up in my flying machine! We are going to sing this standing on the higher ground. We will stand on the last stanza of *Faust* and get that ever-higher feeling. Towards the eternal feminine, which, after all, is only the drag and pull of Nature, which, when one becomes altogether Godlike, says: Be yourself! Touch the earth! Let us, therefore, rise in song and fall with the parachute. Goethe, standing on that last stanza, commanded a greater vista than any aviator has yet commanded. He was standing on the higher middle ground, the metaphysical tableland which is between heaven and earth. Poised on the eternal moment, calm, sure, prince of men, he surveyed past and future. He saw the spiral motion which obtains in all realms, commencing with the astral and finishing with the astral. He saw it in its unendingness. Goethe was an aviator a hundred years before his time. He learned to stand still— *and sing.*

II. The Empire State Building

And now, Joey, before hopping the boat I want to give you a little more precise information about the Empire State Building—a few facts and figures which will make your hair stand on end. It's like this . . . beyond the 13th story no more vertigo, because the speed of ducks flying towards the Equator is in inverse ratio to the sound of shot falling through space at 865,000,947 miles a second. The windows are rainproof, the walls fireproof. Lingerie and toilet articles on the 227th floor. Since this building was erected there have been 8,765,492,583 visitors to the mooring mast, all of them equipped with parachutes and false teeth. This is the tallest building in the world "irregardless of" the flagpole where throughout 365 days and nights Old Glory flies "irregardless of" snow, rain, sleet, hail, mist, fog, bank panics or no bank panics. The janitors, who comprise a force slightly larger than the standing armies of Europe, are equipped with holeproof socks and bullet-proof jockstraps. They have been tested for intelligence and are extremely courteous even when underpaid. The entire staff, with the exception of the night force, is fumigated each evening in order to avoid the outbreak of epidemics such as typhoid, yellow fever, dysentery and similar contagious diseases. This is the most wonderful building in the world with the exception of those still more wonderful buildings now in course of construction which will outdo everything past and present including the ones to come concerning which we can give as yet no precise figures as all the returns are not in yet. However, it looks like a landslide.

The most marvellous thing about this most marvellously marvellous building is the gift shop on the 267th floor where you change elevators to fly to the 318th floor situated at the base of the mooring mast which rises from here to the dizzy height of 563 stories. Here you may find every bauble and trinket known to civilized man, not least of which is a menagerie of figurines made entirely of chewing gum—*Wrigley's* chewing gum. The man whose inventive genius made possible this assemblage of chewing gum figurines was a *chiclero* from the jungle of Yucatan. After a long and honorable career he was discharged by the chewing gum magnates without notice. Said genius may be interviewed any day at the Barbizon-Plaza where courtesy dwells. Here, free of the chewing gum barons, he now makes his abode. Other remarkable gifts are picture postcards showing front, back and side views of every building in New York "irregardless of" size or content. Also views from the roof—and stereopticon slides. A word of caution to the casual visitor: *do not handle the objects!*

Despite its prodigious dimensions this giant skyscraper was erected in less than six months, thanks to the splendid aeroplane interfactories service through the co-operation of the Carpenters & Joiners Guild. It may interest you to know that by the terms of the contract the building called for completion at noon, the 12th of February. Due, however, to the splendid co-operation aforementioned, the building was entirely erect and all the windows washed at nine o'clock the morning of February 12th. The contract did not call for the windows to be washed: this was a gratuitous contribution of the Window Cleaners Union. We wish to dispel here and now any false rumors that may have been circulated by hostile unions as to the quality of light emitted through these windows. The light is absolutely pure and filtered, and the tower management guarantees faultless vision of not less than 75 miles under normal barometrical conditions. Such a guarantee could only be offered the public thanks to the latest installation of thermostats manufactured expressly for *Empire State*. In addition to faultless vision the thermostats also insure an even pressure on the eardrums when dropping from the top of the mooring mast to the subbasement which, it has been estimated, is approximately a half-mile below sea level. This is a device absolutely unique in the history of skyscrapers and will prove a boon to all those who suffer from phthisis and dyspnoeia, the latter sometimes referred to as internal catarrh.

The casual observer may have been impressed by a phenomenal sight whilst eating a steak sandwich at the base of the tower. The canaries which warble so melodiously in their platinum cages are not here to entertain the visitor while lunching, as one might imagine, but to overcome an inclination to fall asleep when gazing out the windows. These canaries, unlike their fellow canaries, do not warble to pass the time away. On the contrary, they warble to restore the sense of time which is endangered whenever the human organism is subjected to the unreality of altitudes to which his pedestrian habits make him maladapted. The canaries have been skilfully trained by a staff of expert endocrinologists working in conjunction with the best psychoanalysts of New York State. They warble just loud enough to cross the subliminal threshold of the acoustic nerve centers, thus lulling the transient visitor back to a triphammer rhythm of daily life whence he may look out upon a familiar world without fear of agoraphobia, hydrophobia, or any perverse or polymorphous disturbances. The canaries are released every night at nine o'clock sharp in order to be examined by diplomaed throat specialists. This amazing service is due in part to the memory of Gatti-Cazzazza who, in anticipation of this great need, ordered his confidential attorney to add a codicil to his last will and testament. The visitor will observe that on the underside of every cage the head of this great benefactor has been embossed in solid gold.

In anticipating the eventual decline of New York City as a financial and industrial center the owners of *Empire State,* heretofore known as Empire State Corporation, Inc., cede to the State of New York all vested rights and preoccupations with its skyscraper modus operandi. No cost will be spared by said management to keep the unemployed workers of this great and glorious State in a permanent condition of content. The halls on the ground floor, deliberately given a sombre cast in deference to the national crisis, will be redecorated in bright colors, with frescoes especially designed by artists of international repute to prevent melancholy or morbidity. These frescoes will depict the gay and turbulent life of New York when the factories were working overtime and sirloin steaks were selling at $5.79 a pound. Profiting by the experience of Greece and Babylon, of Egypt and China, New York State intends to keep its monuments in a fit state of preservation, applying with great therapeutic insight and benevolence the pragmatic wisdom of her great pioneers and inventors, the Ghouls and the Breakwaters.

This gigantic structure, replete in all its parts, will be in its old age the refuge of the poor and needy, a haven for the industrious paupers whose sweat and toil, or *without* whose sweat and toil, these things could not, *sui generis,* have been made *de facto* and *ad hoc.* It has been estimated that with the depopulation of the city and the loss of the migratory worker no more healthful site than the *Empire State* could be found in these precincts. The ugly buildings of preskyscraper age will be razed in order to afford an unobstructed view of the Statue of Liberty. Said statue will be scraped and varnished and, from the neck up, studded with precious stones which will gleam in the night, thus eliminating the cost of electric wiring. Positively no expense will be spared to make *Empire State* an enduring monument to progress and invention . . .

III. In Paris

On French soil at last! Home again! I must say a few words, before closing this letter, about the last lap of the voyage. I address this to all and sundry . . .

The moment we left Plymouth a great calm came over me. Plymouth itself is soothing to the nerves. England itself comes to a gentle resolution here at the land's end. She puts her best foot forward, and there's no boot and spur attached. It's green and gentle, dreamy, somnolescent. The earth seems to breathe, as at the very dawn of time. If only there were no English! They're hoving alongside now, the customs officials, the porters, and what not. They move slowly, smoothly, unostentatiously, with that irritating calm efficiency which always distinguished the English. I feel a hatred towards them instantly. Not hatred really, but a loathing. They seem like animated oysters. I feel the hard shell which conceals the flabby flesh: I feel their imperturbable possessivity. The oyster that tried to swallow the world! There is something ridiculous about them: they look subhuman. I look at the war vessels at anchor, the factories, the gas tanks, the lighthouse. They exist and therefore I assume the English made them—but it seems incredible. I can't think of the English as anything but ghouls and pirates—and such deucedly serious ones, you know. But the hell with them! I'm not getting off here . . .

Boulogne! The French! It comes with the tender—a clamor, a stridency, an anarchy, a nervous excitement entirely unjustified by the occasion. Nobody knows what's what, particularly the French. Even before one Frenchman steps aboard there is a confusion and a chaos such as only the most brilliant logic can produce. It's tonic and refreshing; at once the mind is exhilarated. It doesn't matter now *what* happens: something's happening, that's the important thing! We pull into the wharf amidst a tremendous flutter and jabber. You might almost imagine that they had been surprised by our arrival. Nothing works right. Nothing is in readiness. Or, so it seems. It's the French way, *and I love it!* They stand there looking at us as though it were a huge mistake, as though the tender had been sent out to fetch a load of cattle or green vegetables and behold! here comes a boatload of tourists laden with expensive luggage. What's to be done? Anyway, they smell the tips coming.

It seems to me I can see them smacking their lips. Perhaps I imagine it.

I'm standing at the rail, quietly enjoying the hubbub, the errors, the confusion, when suddenly I hear an officer shouting to a man on the quai, the man who directs the derrick which is to swing over our heads. I hear him shouting that the derrick should be adjusted so that it "coincides," etc. . . . This word "coincides" coming from the officer's lips gives me the most intense gratification. It has such a subtle, civilized ring. The language! At once I am in a mathematical world, a world where things are ordered Euclidically—and above all, *with justice*. Confusion and logic! A surface contradiction only. Fundamentally there is no contradiction. For that perfect equilibrium which the individual Frenchman represents there must be an external chaos matched by an internal order and precision all the more wonderful in that it is purely autonomous, that each one creates it for himself.

By the time the boat train reaches Creilly I am certain that we are in France. The coastal region gives one a dubious feeling; but the station at Creilly is beyond a doubt *French*. It is falling to pieces; it has never been repaired or painted since the day it was erected. It brings back to my memory the hotels I occupied during my long stay in France: the chairs that were held together by thongs, the tattered wallpaper, the patched carpet on the stairs, the broken windows, the armoires that could never be locked, the worn towels thin as tissue paper . . . Later, on my way to the Opera, this feeling comes over me again. A building is being torn down: I see the party wall, strips of blue-and-white wallpaper, flowers *en série,* the black mark of the chimney, the design of the stairway. A little farther off the name of a hotel strung along the façade in gilt letters a foot high, a name such as only the French could invent: *Hôtel d'Egypte et de Choiseul.* Choiseul—that means a street and a restaurant, and always evening; immediately after a cup of Brazilian coffee, drip by drip, with brass cups and a choice of pastry at the counter. Choiseul—it reminds me of Fustel de Coulanges, the little street near Val-de-Grâce. Choiseul—it reminds me never to ask Fred a question which demands a precise answer. It annoys him. So I never asked who or what Choiseul: it's a street and a restaurant towards evening, and immediately after a cup of Brazilian coffee, drip by drip . . .

Anyway, now at my elbow is a book which I picked up to glance at again: *Bubu de Montparnasse.* The quaint French edition, with illustrations in the old manner. Holding this book in my hands is like embracing an old friend. I riffle the pages absent-mindedly: it seems as if the trees were shedding their leaves. I see the Seine, the quais, the narrow, winding streets with HOTEL prominently displayed, and of course, a man in a sack suit and bowler, the man slightly stooped, his mustache drooping. It is the year 1890 or so, a very important epoch astrologically, as Eduardo has just explained to me. I was born in this time of the grand conjunction—the Pluto-Neptune conjunction! My whole life is wrapped up in a little chestnut which fell off a tree during the years immediately preceding the dawn of a new century. I am at Louveciennes now. The lights have suddenly gone out. They are probably out in Paris too. The door won't close anymore, the hinges are rusty, the toilet seat is cracked and the paint rubbed off, the dining room walls are covered with mold. Here the slightest inattention is costly, ruinous. Deterioration sets in quicker than in America. *Physical* deterioration. But the soul expands. Steadily, like a thermometer rising, the soul expands. Things are rotting away and in this quick rot the ego buries itself like a seed and blooms. No more the feeling of dry walls, of sharp divisions, of fracture and schism; here the body becomes the plant it is, it gives off its own moisture, creates its own ambiance, produces a flower. Every day now a new flower. The ego is rooted, the soil well manured. Instead of a million towering walls there is one great wall, the Chinese wall which the French have built out of their own blood. Within this wall a security and serenity unknown to America. Over there a fight each day to repair the dikes; each day one is fresh born, a babe which must mature by nightfall, and die.

America! How far away it seems now! Distance doesn't explain it. There's something else. When I think of New York I think of a gigantic infant playing with high explosives. Not *new* so much as *inhuman*. The whole of one's experience counts for naught. One awakes in the morning to look out on a virgin continent which has known no history. A clean jump, without transition, from barbarism to the dementia of Civilization. An external civilization, visible in knobs, bulbs, brackets, racks, screws, pulleys, steel, cement . . . How or why a skyscraper was erected thoroughly unimportant. It's there—that's all that matters! Facts! Facts! They hit you in the eye, they knock you cold, they trample on you. You walk amidst facts day in and day out. You sleep with the facts. You eat the facts. Supposing during a New York night all the marvels of Egypt, China, Carthage, Rome, Babylon were unrolled and left lying in the street. Supposing no one knew where they came from, how they got there, what they signified. *That's New York!* It's the inside of a watch functioning perfectly in an incredible chaos. Not one man has ever been outside and had a look at the watch itself. Not one man knows what a watch is. The watch keeps perfect time. What *kind of time?* A question no American ever asks himself. It's time—or rather, it's a watch. Or a mechanism that would resemble a watch if there were something in the consciousness of the American which could imagine a watch. But there is none . . .

Looking now at *Bubu de Montparnasse* I recapture the image of the boulevard Sébastopol as it fixed itself in the back of my eye during the taxi ride. Leaving the Gare du Nord I had failed to notice the direction we were taking. I had hardly taken a glance at Paris. Suddenly I realized that we were on the boulevard Sébastopol. I looked deliberately at the shops, at the crowds, at individual men and women. Late afternoon and the sky is overcast. The whole street is registered in the back of my eye in sombre tones. It's not the overcast sky which causes it—it's something *in* the sky, something everlasting, a permanent effluvia given off by each individual citizen and by his ancestors in the grave. The boulevard Sébastopol is almost black. A soot black and not the gleaming Egyptian black which mirrors the lobbies of the skyscrapers. I look at the people on the sidewalk. They are black too. Black and decrepit. They are in tatters, like the dismantled wall lined with chimney stain and faded wallflowers. Only midafternoon and they are already black. They have been this way since morning. They will go to bed black. They will wake up black. The sky will stay overcast, it will rain again, and there will be bargain counters on the street and little black bags in which to carry the marketing. They will walk with one shoe on and one shoe off. A sou will count, will be counted carefully, even though it has a hole in it. Nothing will be thrown in the gutter—not even a banana peel. This man will ask for a light—in order to save a match. Tomorrow the situation will get worse. Yet not one man will dream of saying: *"Away with it! Raze it clean!"* No one dares to dream of a new, fresh life, a life from scratch. No one dreams of a life without dirt, without poverty, without sorrow, misery, disease, death, disaster. All these elements are flowing through the street now in a black river, a sewer of despair that runs through the underworld where the ghosts and ancestors wander restlessly. So close are they, the men below, that the feet of those above are scraping the heads of those below. The graves are filled to overflowing, the dead are being disgorged. Somewhere at the edge there is a leak. Through this rift in the underworld there arises a gray vapor that turns the living world, living men, to soot black. The past breathes heavily down one's neck. It flutters and palpitates like a cape hiding a drowning man.

Between this and New York lies the ocean. The ocean is a clearance between the old and the new. When you take the boat you take a leap incalculable. If instead of a week the voyage lasted a month the boat itself, to say nothing of the passengers, would have disintegrated. We would arrive, either at Boulogne or New York, like a load of spoiled vegetables. No one would be able to gather himself together again. A death voyage without benefit of transfiguration.

Rolling along the boulevard Sébastopol in the late afternoon I feel somewhat spoiled. I am bringing my somewhat spoiled carcass to Paris. My soul I have not yet found . . .

It is only towards midnight, sitting in Roger's place, that I come to. We are sitting before the open window. The room is almost bare. I am looking out on the city of Paris—with two clear eyes. Just a windowful, *but it is Paris*. The boulevard Sébastopol must be there too. Perhaps one of those soft, jagged streets straggling through the thick foliage below is the boulevard Sébastopol. Perhaps the same men and women are milling about. Perhaps they are in rags. Perhaps they have no shoes. Even if what I say were so it could not be true anymore. Not now! Now the lens is adjusted. Now I see straight. I see nothing anymore which is external— neither the walls, the clothes, nor the body itself. I see one big globule swimming in the blood of the great animal called MAN. This globule is Paris. I see it round and full, always the whole globule at once. If, closing the shutter, through the tiniest little fent I catch the back of a man, I see how and where it relates to the whole globule. Let him stand up straight, or let him bend over—it will always be a back, the back of a man. His back will never break through the globule. The globule will stretch and expand, permit the utmost freedom of movement, the most fantastic movements, *but it will not break*. The globule is always stronger than a man's back, stronger than the man himself, stronger than ten million men all pushing at once and in the same spot.

We are sitting in the little studio before the open window. The train is puffing along—the belt line which girdles Paris. No roar and whizz as it passes by. Just puffing along. Through an opaque ether it seems to move, through an elastic atmosphere which is the same up on the trestle as deep in the lungs. One atmosphere throughout: as difficult for the locomotive as it is difficult for the human lungs. The city is palpitating in the summer heat. The globule itself seems to be shrinking. The breath of the city is hot down our backs. Here I am in a room with old friends. I feel everything close, permeable, tangible, alive and breathing. I feel friendship itself, the essence of it slowly escaping through the stopped bottle, rising towards the envelope of the great globule which is shrinking. I feel the friendliness of the wine and of the carved cutlass which stands in a corner by the window. I say now what I have never said in America: *I feel a profound contentment*.

A moment ago, when I touched the book, I observed to myself that this profound contentment had not deserted me. Never before have I touched a book in this way. I feel that I am touching an old friend. A friend? Yes, suddenly it dawns on me—I am touching my old friend, the boulevard Sébastopol! How come then that I did not recognize my old friend immediately? Was the taxi outside the globule, trying vainly to pierce the envelope? Was it the envelope giving all the way, giving and giving until it seemed we were smothered in ethereal darkness? Where was I then? Now I am inside the globule. I realized it suddenly, sitting before the open window in Roger's studio. I entered by osmosis. I seeped through between late afternoon and midnight. *Inside*—I know it now. Sitting by the window, that first glance outdoors, perhaps it was then, that very moment, that I managed to get inside, to get inside all together, body and soul, the whole man.

I can't help thinking again of America. I remember now a night in New York when we were all drunk and suddenly some one burst out with this momentous phrase—*"But all great art is local!"* Nobody can possibly know, in America, what a phrase like this means. To be local there must be a sense of place, and there must be a whole to which the parts refer. America *seems* new because there is never a point of comparison. In reality there is no America! There are just millions of things unrelated one to the other, except as one part of a machine is related to another. To the parts themselves nothing seems new; only an old watch which has stopped ticking can gaze in wonder at a new and moving part.

Yesterday I had to walk through the rue Bonaparte. I stopped off at a *bistrot* to inquire the whereabouts of a certain hotel. The same woman at the desk who greeted me years ago. She seems to recognize me. I seem to recognize her. Yes, I remember her well, remember her when her belly was swollen, when she used to laugh so heartily that I thought she would burst a blood vessel. I remember too that she used to give the students credit—and still laugh heartily. I remember giving her too much money one day and I remember that she kept the money for me until I came again. And now, though she seems to recognize me, not a word out of her. Just that big smile which she had for everybody—and the hell with you if you croak tomorrow! I like it! It's French.

A little while ago, walking up the road, I pass a man standing in a field. He has a hoe in his hand and he is pottering around with it. He seems alone and complete, a sort of Chinese rock-bottom man. He is on one side of the fence and I am on the other. If I had dropped dead there in the road he would have gone on hoeing. He would hoe me into the sod, I believe. Well, anyway, I like it! I almost wish I had dropped dead . . . just to test it out.

And that brings me back to Mannheim, to the day when he started talking about China. I remember his opening words— "Very cruel." I thought of this often during the voyage. I thought of my countrymen who are so hospitable, so frank and generous, so "without rancor," as Keyserling says. Yes, they are all that, but they are also cruel, a thousand times more cruel than the Chinese. They are the most inhuman torturers the world has ever seen. They are cruel in the way that children are cruel. They walk over you to reach for a new toy . . .

The Tailor Shop

The day used to start like this: "ask so-and-so for a little something on account, *but don't insult him!*" They were ticklish bastards, all these old farts we catered to. It was enough to drive any man to drink. There we were, just opposite the Olcott, Fifth Avenue tailors even though we weren't on the Avenue. A joint corporation of father and son, with mother holding the boodle.

Mornings, eight A.M. or thereabouts, a brisk intellectual walk from Delancey Street and the Bowery to just below the Waldorf. No matter how fast I walked old man Berger was sure to be there ahead of me, raising hell with the cutter because neither of the bosses was on the job. How was it we could never get there ahead of that old buzzard Berger? He had nothing to do, Berger, but run from the tailor to the shirt-maker and from the shirt-maker to the jeweler's; his rings were either too loose or too tight, his watch was either twenty-five seconds slow or thirty-three seconds fast. He raised hell with everybody, including the family doctor, because the latter couldn't keep his kidneys clear of gravel. If we made him a sack coat in August by October it was too large for him, or too small. When he could find nothing to complain about he would dress on the right side so as to have the pleasure of bawling the pants maker out because he was strangling his, H. W. Berger's, balls. A difficult guy. Touchy, whimsical, mean, crotchety, miserly, capricious, malevolent. When I look back on it all now, see the old man sitting down to table with his boozy breath and saying *shit why don't some one smile, why do you all look so glum,* I feel sorry for him and for all merchant tailors who have to kiss rich people's asses. If it hadn't been for the Olcott bar across the way and the sots he picked up there God knows what would have become of the old man. He certainly got no sympathy at home. My mother hadn't the least idea what it meant to be kissing

40

rich people's backsides. All she knew how to do was to groan and lament all day, and with her groaning and lamenting she brought on the boozy breath and the potato dumplings grown cold. She got us so damned jumpy with her anxiety that we would choke on our own spittle, my brother and I. My brother was a half-wit and he got on the old man's nerves even more than H. W. Berger with his "Pastor So-and-so's going to Europe . . . Pastor So-and-so's going to open a bowling alley," etc. "Pastor So-and-so's an ass," the old man would say, "and why aren't the dumplings hot?"

There were three Bergers—H. W., the grumpy one, A. F., whom the old man referred to in the ledger as Albert, and R. N., who never visited the shop because his legs were cut off, a circumstance, however, which did not prevent him from wearing out his trousers in due season. R. N. I never saw in the flesh. He was an item in the ledger which Bunchek the cutter spoke of glowingly because there was always a little schnapps about when it came time to try on the new trousers. The three brothers were eternal enemies; they never referred to one another in our presence. If Albert, who was a little cracked and had a penchant for dotted vests, happened to see a cutaway hanging on the rack with the words H. W. Berger written in green ink on the try-on notice, he would give a feeble little grunt and say—"feels like spring to-day, eh?" There was not supposed to be a man by the name of H. W. Berger in existence, though it was obvious to all and sundry that we were not making clothes for ghosts.

Of the three brothers I liked Albert the best. He had arrived at that ripe age when the bones become as brittle as glass. His spine had the natural curvature of old age, as though he were preparing to fold up and return to the womb. You could always tell when Albert was arriving because of the commotion in the elevator—a great cussing and whining followed by a handsome tip which accompanied the process of bringing the floor of the elevator to a dead level with the floor of our tailor shop. If it could not be brought to within a quarter of an inch exactitude there was no tip and Albert with his brittle bones and his bent spine would have a devil of a time choosing the right buttons to go with his dotted vest, his *latest* dotted vest. (When Albert died I inherited all his vests—they lasted me right through the war.) If it happened, as was sometimes the case, that the old man was across the street taking a little nip when Albert arrived, then somehow the whole day became disorganized. I remember periods when Albert grew so vexed with the old man that sometimes we did not see him for three days; meanwhile the vest buttons were lying around on little cards and there was talk of nothing but vest buttons, vest buttons, as if the vest itself didn't matter, only the buttons. Later, when Albert had grown accustomed to the old man's careless ways—they had been growing accustomed to each other for twenty-seven years—he would give us a ring to notify us that he was on the way. And just before hanging up he would add: "I suppose it's all right my coming in at eleven o'clock . . . it won't inconvenience you?" The purport of this little query was twofold. It meant—"I suppose you'll have the decency to be on hand when I arrive and not make me fiddle around for a half hour while you swill it down with your cronies across the street." *And,* it also meant—"At eleven o'clock I suppose there is little danger of bumping into a certain individual bearing the intials H. W.?" In the twenty-seven years during which we made perhaps 1,578 garments for the three Berger brothers it so happened that they never met, not in our presence at least. When Albert died R. N. and H. W. both had mourning bands put on their sleeves, on all the left sleeves of their sack coats and overcoats—that is, those which were not black coats—but nothing was said of the deceased, nor even *who* he was. R. N., of course, had a good excuse for not going to the funeral—his legs were gone. H. W. was too mean and too proud to even bother offering an excuse.

About ten o'clock was the time the old man usually chose to go down for his first nip. I used to stand at the window facing the hotel and watch George Sandusky hoisting the big trunks on to the taxis. When there were no trunks to be hoisted George used to stand there with his hands clasped behind his back and bow and scrape to the clients as they swung in and out of the revolving doors. George Sandusky had been scraping and bowing and hoisting and opening doors for about twelve years when I first came to the tailor shop and took up my post at the front window. He was a charming, soft-spoken man with beautiful white hair, and strong as an ox. He had raised this ass-kissing business to an art. I was amazed one day when he came up the elevator and ordered a suit from us. In his off hours he was a gentleman, George Sandusky. He had quiet tastes—always a blue serge or an Oxford gray. A man who knew how to conduct himself at a funeral or a wedding.

After we got to know each other he gave me to understand that he had found Jesus. With the smooth tongue he had, and the brawn, and the active help of said Jesus he had managed to lay aside a nest-egg, a little something to ward off the horrors of old age. He was the only man I ever met in that period who had not taken out life insurance. He maintained that God would look after those who were left behind just as He had looked after him, George Sandusky. He had no fear of the world collapsing upon his decease. God had taken care of everybody and everything up to date—no reason to suppose He would fall down on the job after George Sandusky's death. When one day George retired it was difficult to find a man to replace him. There was no one oily or unctuous enough to fill the bill. No one who could bow and scrape like George. The old man always had a great affection for George. He used to try to persuade him to take a drink now and then, but George always refused with that habitual and stubborn politeness which had endeared him to the Olcott guests.

The old man often had moods when he would ask anybody to take a drink with him, even such as George Sandusky. Usually late in the afternoon on a day when things were going wrong, when nothing but bills were coming in. Sometimes a week would pass without a customer showing up, or if one did show up it was only to complain, to ask for an alteration, to bawl the piss out of the coat maker, or to demand a reduction in the price. Things like this would make the old man so blue that all he could do was to put on his hat and go for a drink. Instead of going across the street as usual he would wander off base a bit, duck into the Breslin or the Broztell, sometimes getting as far off the path as the Ansonia where his idol, Julian Legree, kept a suite of rooms.

Julian, who was then a matinée idol, wore nothing but gray suits, every shade of gray imaginable, but only grays. He had that depressingly cheerful demeanor of the beefy-faced English actor who lounges about here and there swapping stories with woolen salesmen, liquor dealers and others of no account. His accent alone was enough to make men swarm about him; it was English in the traditional stage sense, warm, soapy, glutinous English which gives to even the most insignificant thought an appearance of importance. Julian never said anything that was worth recording but that voice of his worked magic on his admirers. Now and then, when he and the old man were doing the rounds, they would pick up a derelict such as Corse Payton who belonged across the river in the ten-twenty-thirties. Corse Payton was the idol of Brooklyn! Corse Payton was to art what Pat McCarren was to politics.

What the old man had to say during these discussions was always a source of mystery to me. The old man had never read a book in his life, nor had he ever been to a play since the days when the Bowery gave way to Broadway. I can see him standing there at the free lunch counter—Julian was very fond of the caviar and the sturgeon that was served at the Olcott—sponging it up like a thirsty dog. The two matinée idols discussing Shakespeare—whether *Hamlet* or *Lear* was the greatest play ever written. Or else arguing the merits of Bob Ingersoll.

Behind the bar at that time were three doughty Irishmen, three low-down micks such as made the bars of that day the congenial haunts they were. They were so highly thought of, these three, that it was considered a privilege to have such as Patsy O'Dowd, for example, call you a god-damned degenerate cock-sucking son of a bitch who hadn't sense enough to button up his fly. And if, in return for the compliment, you asked him if he wouldn't have a little something himself said Patsy O'Dowd would coldly and sneeringly reply that only such as yourself were fit to pour such rot-gut down your throat, and so saying he would scornfully lift your glass by the stem and wipe the mahogany because that was part of his job and he was paid to do it but be damned to you if you thought you could entice such as him to poison his intestines with the vile stuff. The more vicious his insults the more he was esteemed; financiers who were accustomed to having their asses wiped with silk handkerchiefs would drive all the way uptown, after the ticker closed down, in order to have this foul-mouthed bastard of an Irish mick call them god-damned degenerate cock-sucking sons of bitches. It was the end of a perfect day for them.

The boss of this jaunty emporium was a portly little man with aristocratic shanks and the head of a lion. He always marched with his stomach thrown forward, a little wine cask hidden under his vest. He usually gave a stiff, supercilious nod to the sots at the bar, unless they happened to be guests of the hotel, in which case he would pause a moment, extend three fat little fingers with blue veins and then, with a swirl of his mustache and a gingerly, creaky pirouette, he would whisk away. He was the only enemy the old man had. The old man simply couldn't stomach him. He had a feeling that Tom Moffatt looked down upon him. And so when Tom Moffatt came round to order his clothes the old man would tack on ten or fifteen per cent to cover the rents in his pride. But Tom Moffatt was a genuine aristocrat: he never questioned the price and he never paid his bills. If we dunned him he would get his accountant to find a discrepancy in our statements. And when it came time to order another pair of flannel trousers, or a cutaway, or a dinner jacket, he would sail in with his usual portly dignity, his stomach well forward, his mustache waxed, his shoes brightly polished and squeaky as always, and with an air of weary indifference, of aloof disdain, he would greet the old man as follows: "Well, have you straightened out that error yet?" Upon which the old man would fly into a rage and palm off a remnant or a piece of American goods on his enemy Tom Moffatt. A long correspondence ensued over the "little error" in our statements. The old man was beside himself. He hired an expert accountant who drew up statements three feet long—but to no avail. Finally the old man hit upon an idea.

Towards noon one day, after he had had his usual portion, after he had stood treat to all the woolen salesmen and the trimmings salesmen who were gathered at the bar, he quietly picked up the bar stubs and taking a little silver pencil which was attached to his watch chain he signed his name to the checks and sliding them across to Patsy O'Dowd he said: "Tell Moffatt to charge them up to my account." Then he quietly moved off and, inviting a few of his select cronies, he took a table in the dining room and commanded a spread. And when Adrian the frog presented the bill he calmly said: "Give me a pencil. There . . . them's my demiquivers. Charge it up to my account." Since it was more pleasant to eat in the company of others he would always invite his cronies to lunch with him, saying to all and sundry—"if that bastard Moffatt won't pay for his clothes then we'll eat them." And so saying he would commandeer a juicy squab, or a lobster à la Newburg, and wash it down with a fine Moselle or any other vintage that Adrian the frog might happen to recommend.

To all this Moffatt, surprisingly enough, pretended to pay no heed. He continued to order his usual allotment of clothes for winter, spring, fall and summer, and he also continued to squabble about the bill which had become easier to do now since it was complicated with bar checks, telephone calls, squabs, lobsters, champagne, fresh strawberries, Benedictines, etc., etc. In fact, the old man was eating into that bill so fast that spindle-shanks Moffatt couldn't wear his clothes out quickly enough. If he came in to order a pair of flannel trousers the old man had already eaten it the next day.

Finally Moffatt evinced an earnest desire to have the account straightened out. The correspondence ceased. Patting me on the back one day as I happened to be standing in the lobby he put on his most cordial manner and invited me upstairs to his private office. He said he had always regarded me as a very sensible young man and that we could probably straighten the matter out between ourselves, without bothering the old man. I looked over the accounts and I saw that the old man had eaten way into the minus side. I had probably eaten up a few raglans and shooting jackets myself. There was only one thing to do if we were to keep Tom Moffatt's despised patronage and that was to find an error in the account. I took a bundle of bills under my arm and promised the old geezer that I would look into the matter thoroughly.

The old man was delighted when he saw how things stood. We kept looking into the matter for years. Whenever Tom Moffatt came round to order a suit the old man would greet him cheerily and say: "Have you straightened out that little error yet? Now here's a fine Barathea weave that I laid aside for you . . ." And Moffatt would frown and grimace and strut back and forth like a turkey cock, his comb bristling, his thin little legs blue with malice. A half hour later the old man would be standing at the bar swilling it down. "Just sold Moffatt another dinner jacket," he would say. "By the way, Julian, what would you like to order for lunch today?"

It was towards noon, as I say, that the old man usually went down for an appetizer; lunch lasted anywhere from noon till four or five in the afternoon. It was marvelous the companionship the old man enjoyed in those days. After lunch the troupe would stagger out of the elevator, spitting and guffawing, their cheeks aflame, and lodge themselves in the big leather chairs beside the cuspidors. There was Ferd Pattee who sold silk linings and trimmings such as skeins of thread, buttons, chest padding, canvas, etc. A great hulk of a man, like a liner that's been battered by a typhoon, and always walking about in a somnambulistic state; so tired he was that he could scarcely move his lips, yet that slight movement of the lips kept everybody about him in stitches. Always muttering to himself—about cheeses particularly. He was passionate about cheese, about schmierkäse and limburger especially—the mouldier the better. In between the cheeses he told stories about Heine and Schubert, or he would ask for a match just as he was about to break wind and hold it under his seat so that we could tell him the color of the flame. He never said good-bye or see you tomorrow; he commenced talking where he had left off the day before, as though there had been no interruption of time. No matter whether it was nine in the morning or six in the evening he walked with the same exasperating slow shambling gait, muttering in his vici-kids, his head down, his linings and trimmings under his arm, his breath foul, his nose purple and translucent. Into the thickest traffic he would walk with head down, schmierkäse in one pocket and limburger in the other. Stepping out of the elevator he would say in that weary monotonous voice of his that he had some new linings and the cheese was fine last night were you thinking of returning the book he had loaned you and better pay up soon if you want more goods or like to see some dirty pictures please scratch my back there a little higher that's it excuse me I'm going to fart now have you the time I can't waste all day here better tell the old man to put on his hat it's time to go for a drink. Still mumbling and grumbling he turns on his big scows and presses the elevator button while the old man with a straw hat on the back of his head is making a slide for the home plate from the back of the store, his face lit up with love and gratitude and saying: "Well, Ferd, how are you this morning? It's good to see you." And Ferd's big heavy mask of a face relaxes for a moment into a broad amiable grin. Just a second he holds it and then, lifting his voice he bellows at the top of his lungs—so that even Tom Moffatt across the way can hear it—"BETTER PAY UP SOON WHAT THE HELL DO YOU THINK I'M SELLING THESE THINGS FOR?"

And as soon as the elevator has started down out comes little Rubin from the busheling room and with a wild look in his eye he says to me: "Would you like me to sing for you?" He knows damned well that I would. So, going back to the bench, he picks up the coat that he's stitching and with a wild Cossack shout he lets loose.

If you were to pass him in the street, little Rubin, you would say "dirty little kike," and perhaps he was a dirty little kike but he knew how to sing and when you were broke he knew how to put his hand in his pocket and when you were sad he was sadder still and if you tried to step on him he spat on your shoe and if you were repentant he wiped it off and he brushed you down and put a crease in your trousers like Jesus H. Christ himself couldn't do.

They were all midgets in the busheling room—Rubin, Rapp and Chaimowitz. At noon they brought out big round loaves of Jewish bread which they smeared with sweet butter and slivers of lax. While the old man was ordering squabs and Rhine wine Bunchek the cutter and the three little bushelmen sat on the big bench among the goose irons and the legs and sleeves and talked earnestly and solemnly about things like the rent or the ulcers that Mrs. Chaimowitz had in her womb. Bunchek was an ardent member of the Zionist party. He believed that the Jews had a happy future ahead of them. But despite it all he could never properly pronounce a word like "screw." He always said: "He *scruled* her." Besides his passion for Zionism Bunchek had another obsession and that was to make a coat one day that would hug the neck. Nearly all the customers were round-shouldered and pot-bellied, especially the old bastards who had nothing to do all day but run from the shirt-maker to the tailor and from the tailor to the jeweler's and from the jeweler's to the dentist and from the dentist to the druggist. There were so many alterations to be made that by the time the clothes were ready to be worn the season had passed and they had to be put away until next year, and by next year the old bastards had either gained twenty pounds or lost twenty pounds and what with sugar in their urine and water in the blood it was hell to please them even when the clothes did fit.

Then there was Paul Dexter, a $10,000 a year man but always out of work. Once he almost had a job, but it was at $9,000 a year and his pride wouldn't permit him to accept it. And since it was important to be well groomed, in the pursuit of this mythical job, Paul felt it incumbent upon him to patronize a good tailor such as the old man. Once he landed the job everything would be settled in full. There was never any question about that in Paul's mind. He was thoroughly honest. But he was a dreamer. He came from Indiana. And like all dreamers from Indiana he had such a lovable disposition, such a smooth, mellow, honeyed way that if he had committed incest the world would have forgiven him. When he had on the right tie, when he had chosen the proper cane and gloves, when the lapels were softly rolled and the shoes didn't squeak, when he had a quart of rye under his belt and the weather wasn't too damp or dismal then there flowed from his personality such a warm current of love and understanding that even the trimmings salesmen, hardened as they were to soft language, melted in their boots. Paul, when all circumstances were favorably conjoined, could walk up to a man, any man on God's green earth and, taking him by the lapel of his coat, drown him in love. Never did I see a man with such powers of persuasion, such magnetism. When the flood began to rise in him he was invincible.

Paul used to say: "Start with Marcus Aurelius, or Epictetus, and the rest will follow." He didn't recommend studying Chinese or learning Provençal: he began with the fall of the Roman Empire. It was my great ambition in those days to win Paul's approbation, but Paul was difficult to please. He frowned when I showed him *Thus Spake Zarathustra*. He frowned when he saw me sitting on the bench with the midgets trying to expound the meaning of *Creative Evolution*. Above all, he loathed the Jews. When Bunchek the cutter appeared, with a piece of chalk and a tape measure slung around his neck, Paul became excessively polite and condescending. He knew that Bunchek despised him, but because Bunchek was the old man's right hand man he rubbed him down with oil, he larded him with compliments. So that eventually even Bunchek had to admit that there was something to Paul, some strange mark of personality which, despite his shortcomings, endeared him to every one.

Outwardly Paul was all cheerfulness. But at bottom he was morose. Every now and then Cora, his wife, would sail in with eyes brimming with tears and implore the old man to take Paul in hand. They used to stand at the round table near the window conversing in a low voice. She was a beautiful woman, his wife, tall, statuesque, with a deep contralto voice that seemed to quiver with anguish whenever she mentioned Paul's name. I could see the old man putting his hand on her shoulder, soothing her, and promising her all sorts of things no doubt. She liked the old man, I could see that. She used to stand very close to him and look into his eyes in a way that was irresistible. Sometimes the old man would put his hat on and the two of them would go down the elevator together, arm in arm, as if they were going to a funeral. Off looking for Paul again. Nobody knew where to find him when he had a drinking fever on. For days on end he would disappear from sight. And then one day he would turn up, crestfallen, repentant, humiliated, and beg everybody's forgiveness. At the same time he would hand in his suit to be dry cleaned, to have the vomit stains removed, and a bit of expert repairing done at the knees.

It was after a bout that Paul talked most eloquently. He used to sit back in one of the deep leather chairs, the gloves in one hand, the cane between his legs, and discourse about Marcus Aurelius. He talked even better when he came back from the hospital, after he had had the fistula repaired. The way he lowered himself into the big leather chair made me think then that he came expressly to the tailor shop because nowhere else could he find such a comfortable seat. It was a painful operation either to sit down or to get up. But once accomplished Paul seemed to be in bliss and the words rolled off his tongue like liquid velvet. The old man could listen to Paul all day long. He used to say that Paul had the gift of gab, but that was only his inarticulate way of saying that Paul was the most lovable creature on God's earth and that he had a fire in his bowels. And when Paul was too conscience-stricken to order another suit the old man would coax him into it, saying to Paul all the while, "nothing's too good for you, Paul . . . nothing!"

Paul must have recognized something of a kindred nature in the old man too. Never have I seen two men look at each other with such a warm glow of admiration. Sometimes they would stand there looking into each other's eyes adoringly until the tears came. In fact, neither of them was ashamed of showing his tears, something which seems to have gone out of the world now. I can see Paul's homely freckled face and his rather thick, blubbery lips twitching as the old man told him for the thousandth time what a great guy he was. Paul never spoke to the old man about things he wouldn't understand. But into the simple, everyday things which he discoursed about so earnestly he put such a wealth of tenderness that the old man's soul seemed to leave his body and when Paul was gone he was like a man bereaved. He would go then into the little cubby-hole of an office and he would sit there quietly all by himself staring ecstatically at the row of pigeon coops which were filled with letters unanswered and bills unpaid. It used to affect me so, to see him in one of these moods, that I would sneak quietly down the stairs and start to walk home, down the Avenue to the Bowery and along the Bowery to the Brooklyn Bridge, and then over the bridge past the string of cheap flops that extended from City Hall to Fulton Ferry. And if it were a summer's evening, and the entrance ways crowded with loungers, I would look among these wasted figures searchingly, wondering how many Pauls there were among them and what it is about life that makes these obvious failures so endearing to men. The others, the successful ones, I had seen with their pants off; I had seen their crooked spines, their brittle bones, their varicose veins, their tumors, their sunken chests, their big bread-baskets which had grown shapeless with years of swilling it. Yes, all the silk-lined duffers I knew well—we had the best families in America on our roster. And what a pus and filth when they opened their dirty traps! It seemed as though when they had undressed before their tailor they felt compelled to unload the garbage which had accumulated in the plugged up sinks which they had made of their minds. All the beautiful diseases of boredom and riches. Talked about themselves *ad nauseam*. Always "I", "I". I and my kidneys. I and my gout. I and my liverworts. When I think of Paul's dreadful hemorrhoids, of the marvelous fistula they repaired, of all the love and learning that issued from his grievous wounds, then I think that Paul was not of this age at all but sib brother to Moses Maimonides, he who under the Moors gave us those astounding learned treatises on "Hemorrhoids, warts, carbuncles," etc.

In the case of all these men whom the old man so cherished death came quickly and unexpectedly. In Paul's case it happened while he was at the seashore. He was drowned in a foot of water. Heart failure, they said. And so, one fine day Cora came up the elevator, clad in her beautiful mourning garb, and wept all over the place. Never had she looked more beautiful to me, more svelte, more statuesque. Her ass particularly—I remember how caressingly the velvet clung to her figure. Again they stood near the round table at the front window, and this time she wept copiously. And again the old man put on his hat and down the elevator they went, arm in arm.

A short time later the old man, moved by some strange whim, urged me to call on Paul's wife and offer my condolences. When I rang the bell at her apartment I was trembling. I almost expected her to come out stark naked, with perhaps a mourning band around her breasts. I was infatuated with her beauty, with her years, with that somnolent, plant-like quality she had brought from Indiana and the perfume which she bathed in. She greeted me in a low-cut mourning gown, a beautiful clinging gown of black velvet. It was the first time I had ever had a tête-à-tête with a woman bereft, a woman whose breasts seemed to sob out loud. I didn't know what to say to her, especially about Paul. I stammered and blushed, and when she asked me to sit beside her on the couch I almost fell over in my embarrassment.

Sitting there on the low sofa, the place flooded with soft lights, her big, heaving loins rubbing against me, the Malaga pounding my temples and all this crazy talk about Paul and how good he was, I finally bent over and without saying a word I raised her dress and slipped it into her. And as I got it into her and began to work it around she took to moaning like, a sort of delirious sorrowful guilt punctuated with gasps and little shrieks of joy and anguish, saying over and over again—"I never thought you would do this . . . I never thought you would do this!" And when it was all over she ripped off the velvet dress, the beautiful low-cut mourning gown, and she put my head down on her and she told me . . . . and with her two strong arms she squeezed me almost in half and moaned and sobbed. And then she got up and she walked around the room naked for a while. And then finally she got down on her knees beside the sofa where I was stretched out and she said in a low tearful voice—"You promise me you'll love me always, won't you? You promise me?" And I said Yes with one hand working around in her crotch. Yes I said and I thought to myself what a sap you've been to wait so long. She was so wet and juicy down there, and so child-like, so trustful, why anybody could have come along and had what's what. She was a push-over.

Always merry and bright! Regularly, every season, there were a few deaths. Sometimes it was a good egg like Paul, or Julian Legree, sometimes a bartender who had picked his nose with a rusty nail—hail and hearty one day, dead the next—but regularly, like the movements of the seasons themselves, the old buzzards dropped off, one by one. *Alors,* nothing to do but draw a red line slantwise down the right-hand side of the ledger and mark "dead." Each death brought a little business—a new black suit or else mourning bands on the left sleeve of every coat. Those who ordered mourning bands were cheap-skates, according to the old man. And so they were.

As the old 'uns died off they were replaced by young blood. *Young blood!* That was the war-cry all along the Avenue, wherever there were silk-lined suits for sale. A fine bloody crew they were, the young bloods. Gamblers, race-track touts, stock-brokers, ham actors, prize fighters, etc. Rich one day, poor the next. No honor, no loyalty, no sense of responsibility. A fine bunch of gangrened syphilitics they were, most of 'em. Came back from Paris or Monte Carlo with dirty postcards and a string of big blue rocks in their groin. Some of them with balls as big as a lamb's fry.

One of them was the Baron Carola von Eschenbach. He had earned a little money in Hollywood posing as the Crown Prince. It was the period when it was considered riotously funny to see the Crown Prince plastered with rotten eggs. It must be said for the Baron that he was a good double for the Crown Prince. A death's head with arrogant nose, a waspish stride, a corseted waist, lean and ravished as Martin Luther, dour, glum, fanatical, with that brassy, fatuous glare of the Junker class. Before going to Hollywood he was just a nobody, the son of a German brewer in Frankfort. He wasn't even a baron. But afterwards, when he had been knocked about like a medicine ball, when his front teeth had been pushed down his throat and the neck of a broken bottle had traced a deep scar down his left cheek, afterwards when he had been taught to flaunt a red neck-tie, twirl a cane, clip his mustache short, like Chaplin, then he became somebody. Then he stuck a monocle in his eye and named himself Baron Carola von Eschenbach. And all might have gone beautifully for him had he not fallen for a red-haried walk-on who was rotting away with syphilis. That finished him.

Up the elevator he came one day in a cutaway and spats, a bright red rose in his buttonhole and the monocle stuck in his eye. Blithe and dapper he looked, and the card he took out of his wallet was handsomely engraved. It bore a coat of arms which had been in the family, so he said, for nine hundred years. "The family skeleton," he called it. The old man was highly pleased to have a baron among his clients, especially if he paid cash, as this one promised to do. And then too it was exhilarating to see the baron come sailing in with a pair of soubrettes on his arm—each time a different pair. Even more exhilarating when he invited them into the dressing room and asked them to help him off with his trousers. It was a European custom, he explained.

Gradually he got acquainted with all the old cronies who hung out in the front of the shop. He showed them how the Crown Prince walked, how he sat down, how he smiled. One day he brought a flute with him and he played the Lorelei on it. Another day he came in with a finger of his pig-skin glove sticking out of his fly. Each day he had a new trick up his sleeve. He was gay, witty, amusing. He knew a thousand jokes, some that had never been told before. He was a riot.

And then one day he took me aside and asked me if I could lend him a dime—for carfare. He said he couldn't pay for the clothes he had ordered but he expected a job soon in a little movie house on Ninth Avenue, playing the piano. And then, before I knew it, he began to weep. We were standing in the dressing room and the curtains were drawn fortunately. I had to lend him a handkerchief to wipe his eyes. He said he was tired of playing the clown, that he dropped in to our place every day because it was warm there and because we had comfortable seats. He asked me if I couldn't take him to lunch—he had had nothing but coffee and buns for the last three days.

I took him to a little German restaurant on Third Avenue, a bakery and restaurant combined. The atmosphere of the place broke him down completely. He could talk of nothing but the old days, the old days, the days before the war. He had intended to be a painter, and then the war came. I listened attentively and when he got through I proposed that he come to my home for dinner that evening—perhaps I could put him up with us. He was overwhelmed with gratitude. Sure, he would come—at seven o'clock *punkt*. Fine!

At the dinner table my wife was amused by his stories. I hadn't said anything about his being broke. Just that he was a baron—the Baron von Eschenbach, a friend of Charlie Chaplin's. My wife—one of my first ones—was highly flattered to sit at the same table with a baron. And Puritanical bastard that she was, she never so much as blushed when he told a few of his risqué stories. She thought they were delightful—*so European*. Finally, however, it came time to spill the beans. I tried to break the news gently, but how can you be gentle about a subject like syphilis? I didn't call it syphilis at first—I said "venereal disease." *Maladie intime, quoi!* But just that little word "venereal" sent a shudder through my wife. She looked at the cup he was holding to his lips and then she looked at me imploringly, as though to say—"how could you ask a man like that to sit at the same table with us?" I saw that it was necessary to bring the matter to a head at once. "The baron here is going to stay with us for a while," I said quietly. "He's broke and he needs a place to flop." My word, I never saw a woman's expression change so quickly. *"You!"* she said, *"you* ask *me* to do that? And what about the baby? You want us all to have syphilis, is that it? It's not enough that *he* has it—you want the baby to have it too!"

The baron of course was frightfully embarrassed by this outburst. He wanted to leave at once. But I told him to keep his shirt on. I was used to these scenes. Anyway, he got so wrought up that he began to choke over his coffee. I thumped him on the back until he was blue in the face. The rose fell out of his button-hole on to the plate. It looked strange there, as though he had coughed it up out of his own blood. It made me feel so god-damned ashamed of my wife that I could have strangled her on the spot. He was still choking and sputtering as I led him to the bath-room. I told him to wash his face in cold water. My wife followed us in and watched in murderous silence as he performed his ablutions. When he had wiped his face she snatched the towel from his hands and, flinging the bath-room window open, flung it out. That made me furious. I told her to get the hell out of the bath-room and mind her own business. But the baron stepped between us and flung himself at my wife supplicatingly. "You'll see, my good woman, and you, Henry, you won't have to worry about a thing. I'll bring all my syringes and ointments and I'll put them in a little valise—there, under the sink. You mustn't turn me away, I have nowhere to go. I'm a desperate man. I'm alone in the world. You were so good to me before—why must you be cruel now? Is it my fault that I have the syph? Anybody can get the syph. It's human. You'll see, I'll pay you back a thousand times. I'll do anything for you. I'll make the beds, I'll wash the dishes . . . I'll cook for you . . ." He went on and on like that, never stopping to take a breath for fear that she would say No. And after he had gotten all through with his promises, after he had begged her forgiveness a hundred times, after he had knelt down and tried to kiss her hand which she drew away abruptly, he sat down on the toilet seat, in his cutaway and spats, and he began to sob, to sob like a child. It was ghastly, the sterile, white-enamelled bath-room and the splintering light as if a thousand mirrors had been shattered under a magnifying glass, and then this wreck of a baron in his cutaway and spats, his spine filled with mercury, his sobs coming like the short puffs of a locomotive getting under way. I didn't know what the hell to do. A man sitting on the toilet like that and sobbing—it got under my skin. Later I became inured to it. I got hard-boiled. I feel quite certain now that had it not been for the 250 bed patients whom he was obliged to visit twice a day at the hospital in Lyons Rabelais would never have been so boisterously gay. I'm sure of it.

Anyhow, apropos the sobs . . . A little later, when another kid was on the way and no means of getting rid of it, though still hoping, still hoping that something would happen, a miracle perhaps, and her stomach blown up like a ripe watermelon, about the sixth or seventh month, as I say, she used to succumb to fits of melancholy and, lying on the bed with that watermelon staring her in the eye, she would commence to sob fit to break your heart. Maybe I'd be in the other room, stretched out on the couch, with a big, fat book in my hands, and those sobs of hers would make me think of the Baron Carola von Eschenbach, of his gray spats and the cutaway with braided lapels, and the deep red rose in his buttonhole. Her sobs were like music to my ears. Sobbing away for a little sympathy she was, and not a drop of sympathy in the house. It was pathetic. The more hysterical she grew the more deaf I became. It was like listening to the boom and sizzle of surf along the beach on a summer's night: the buzz of a mosquito can drown out the ocean's roar. Anyway, after she had worked herself up to a state of collapse, when the neighbors couldn't stand it any longer and there were knocks on the door, then her aged mother would come crawling out of the bed-room and with tears in her eyes would beg me to go in there and quiet her a bit. "Oh, leave her be," I'd say, "she'll get over it." Whereupon, ceasing her sobs for a moment, the wife would spring out of bed, wild, blind with rage, her hair all down and tangled up, her eyes swollen and bleary, and still hiccoughing and sobbing she would commence to pound me with her fists, to lambast me until I became hysterical with laughter. And when she saw me rocking to and fro like a crazy man, when her arms were tired and her fists sore, she would yell like a drunken whore—"Fiend! Demon!"—and then slink off like a weary dog. Afterwards, when I had quieted her down a bit, when I realized that she really needed a kind word or two, I would tumble her on the bed again and throw a good fuck into her. Blast me if she wasn't the finest piece of tail imaginable after those scenes of grief and anguish! I never heard a woman moan and gibber like she could. "Do *anything* to me!" she used to say. "Do what you want!" I could stand her on her head and ...., ..., I could drag her past the parson's house, as they say, any god-damn thing at all—she was simply delirious with joy. Uterine hysteria, that's what it was! *And I hope God take me,* as the good master used to say, *if I am lying in a single word I say.*

(God, mentioned above, being defined by St. Augustine, as follows: "An infinite sphere, the centre of which is everywhere, the circumference nowhere.")

However, *always merry and bright!* If it was before the war and the thermometer down to zero or below, if it happened to be Thanksgiving Day, or New Year's, or a birthday, or just any old excuse to get together, then off we'd trot, the whole family, to join the other freaks who made up the living family tree. It always seemed astounding to me how jolly they were in our family despite the calamities that were always threatening. Jolly in spite of everything. There was cancer, dropsy, cirrhosis of the liver, insanity, thievery, mendacity, buggery, incest, paralysis, tape-worms, abortions, triplets, idiots, drunkards, ne'er-do-wells, fanatics, sailors, tailors, watch-makers, scarlet fever, whooping cough, meningitis, running ears, chorea, stutterers, jail-birds, dreamers, story-tellers, bartenders—and finally there was Uncle George and Tante Melia. The morgue and the insane asylum. A merry crew and the table loaded with good things;—with red cabbage and green spinach, with roast pork and turkey and sauerkraut, with kartoffeln-klösze and sour black gravy, with radishes and celery, with stuffed goose and peas and carrots, wiith beautiful white cauliflower, with apple sauce and figs from Smyrna, with bananas as big as a black-jack, with cinnamon cake and Streussel Kuchen, with chocolate layer cake and nuts, all kinds of nuts, walnuts, butternuts, almonds, pecans, hickory nuts, with lager beer and bottled beer, with white wines and red, with champagne, kümmel, malaga, port, with schnapps, with fiery cheeses, with dull, innocent store cheese, with flat Holland cheeses, with limburger and schmier-käse, with home made wines, elderberry wine, with cider, hard and sweet, with rice pudding and tapioca, with roast chestnuts, mandarines, olives, pickles, with red caviar and black, with smoked sturgeon, with lemon meringue pie, with lady fingers and chocolate eclairs, with macaroons and cream puffs, with black cigars and long thin stogies, with Bull Durham and Long Tom and meerschaums, with corn-cobs and tooth-picks, wooden tooth-picks which gave you gum-boils the day after, and napkins a yard wide with your initials stitched in the corner, and a blazing coal fire and the windows steaming, everything in the world before your eyes except a fingerbowl.

Zero weather and crazy George, with one arm bitten off by a horse, dressed in dead men's remnants. Zero weather and Tante Melia looking for the birds she left in her hat. Zero, zero, and the tugs snorting below in the harbor, the ice floes bobbing up and down, and long thin streams of smoke curling fore and aft. The wind blowing down at seventy miles an hour; tons and tons of snow all chopped up into tiny flakes and each one carrying a dagger. The icicles hanging like cork-screws outside the window, the wind roaring, the panes rattling. Uncle Henry is singing "Hurrah for the German Fifth!" His vest is open, his suspenders are down, the veins stand out on his temples. *Hurrah for the German Fifth!*

Up in the loft the creaking table is spread; down below is the warm stable, the horses whinnying in the stalls, whinnying and champing and pawing and stomping, and the fine aromatic smell of manure and horse piss, of hay and oats, of steaming blankets and dry cruds, the smell of malt and old wood, of leather harness and tan-bark floats up and rests like incense over our heads.

The table is standing on horses and the horses are standing in warm piss and every now and then they get frisky and whisk their tails and they fart and whinny. The stove is glowing like a ruby, the air is blue with smoke. The bottles are under the table, on the dresser, in the sink. Crazy George is trying to scratch his neck with an empty sleeve. Ned Martini, the ne'er-do-well, is fiddling with the phonograph; his wife Carrie is guzzling it from the tin growler. The brats are downstairs in the stable, playing stink-finger in the dark. In the street, where the shanties begin, the kids are making a sliding-pond. It's blue everywhere, with cold and smoke and snow. Tante Melia is sitting in a corner fingering a rosary. Uncle Ned is repairing a harness. The three grandfathers and the two great-grandfathers are huddled near the stove talking about the Franco-Prussian war. Crazy George is lapping up the dregs. The women are getting closer together, their voices low, their tongues clacking. Everything fits together like a jig-saw puzzle— faces, voices, gestures, bodies. Each one gravitates within his own orbit. The phonograph is working again, the voices get louder and shriller. The phonograph stops suddenly. I oughtn't to have been there when they blurted it out, but I was there and I heard it. I heard that big Maggie, the one who kept a saloon out in Flushing, well that Maggie had slept with her own brother and that's why George was crazy. She slept with everybody—except her own husband. And then I heard that she used to beat George with a leather belt, used to beat him until he foamed at the mouth. That's what brought on the fits. And then Mele sitting there in the corner—she was another case. She was queer even as a child. So was the mother, for that matter. It was too bad that Paul had died. Paul was Mele's husband. Yes, everything would have been all right if that woman from Hamburg hadn't shown up and corrupted Paul. What could Mele do against a clever woman like that— against a shrewd strumpet! Something would have to be done about Mele. It was getting dangerous to have her around. Just the other day they caught her sitting on the stove. Fortunately the fire was low. But supposing she took it into her head to set fire to the house—when they were all asleep? It was a pity that she couldn't hold a job any more. The last place they had found for her was such a nice berth, such a kind woman. Mele was getting lazy. She had had it too easy with Paul.

The air was clear and frosty when we stepped outdoors. The stars were crisp and sparkly and everywhere, lying over the bannisters and steps and window-ledges and gratings, was the pure white snow, the driven snow, the white mantle that covers the dirty, sinful earth. Clear and frosty the air, pure, like deep draughts of ammonia, and the skin smooth as chamois. Blue stars, beds and beds of them, drifting with the antelopes. Such a beautiful, deep, silent night, as if under the snow there lay hearts of gold, as if this warm German blood was running away in the gutter to stop the mouths of hungry babes, to wash the crime and ugliness of the world away. Deep night and the river choked with ice, the stars dancing, swirling, spinning like tops. Along the broken street we straggled, the whole family. Walking along the pure white crust of the earth, leaving tracks, foot-stains. The old German family sweeping the snow with a Christmas tree. The whole family there, uncles, cousins, brothers, sisters, fathers, grandfathers. The whole family is warm and winey and no one thinks of the other, of the sun that will come in the morning, of the errands to run, of the doctor's verdict, of all the cruel, ghastly duties that foul the day and make this night holy, this holy night of blue stars and deep drifts, of arnica blossoms and ammonia, of asphodels and carborundum.

No one knew that Tante Melia was going completely off her nut, that when we reached the corner she would leap forward like a reindeer and bite a piece of the moon. At the corner she leapt forward like a reindeer and she shrieked. "The moon, the moon!" she cried, and with that her soul broke loose, jumped clean out of her body. Eighty-six million miles a minute it travelled. Out, out, to the moon, and nobody could think quick enough to stop it. Just like that it happened. In the twinkle of a star.

And now I'm going to tell you what those bastards said to me . . .

They said—*Henry, you take her to the asylum to-morrow. And don't tell them that we can afford to pay for her.*

Fine! *Always merry and bright!* The next morning we boarded the trolley together and we rode out into the country. If Mele asked where we were going I was to say—"to visit Aunt Monica." But Mele didn't ask any questions. She sat quietly beside me and pointed to the cows now and then. She saw blue cows and green ones. She knew their names. She asked what happened to the moon in the day-time. And did I have a piece of liverwurst by any chance?

During the journey I wept—I couldn't help it. When people are too good in this world they have to be put under lock and key. There's something wrong with people who are too good. It's true Mele was lazy. She was born lazy. It's true that Mele was a poor housekeeper. It's true Mele didn't know how to hold on to a husband when they found her one. When Paul ran off with the woman from Hamburg Mele sat in a corner and wept. The others wanted her to do something—put a bullet in him, raise a rumpus, sue for alimony. Mele sat quiet. Mele wept. Mele hung her head. What little intelligence she had deserted her. She was like a pair of torn socks that are kicked around here, there, everywhere. Always turning up at the wrong moment.

Then one day Paul took a rope and hanged himself. Mele must have understood what had happened because now she went completely crazy. The day before they found her eating her own dung. The day before that they found her sitting on the stove.

And now she's very tranquil and she calls the cows by their first name. The moon fascinates her. She has no fear because I'm with her and she always trusted me. I was her favorite. Even though she was a half-wit she was good to me. The others were more intelligent, but their hearts were bad.

When brother Adolphe used to take her for a carriage ride the others used to say—"Mele's got her eye on him!" But I think that Mele must have talked just as innocently then as she's talking to me now. I think that Mele, when she was performing her marriage duties, must have been dreaming innocently of the beautiful gifts she would give to everybody. I don't think that Mele had any knowledge of sin or of guilt or remorse. I think that Mele was born a half-witted angel. I think Mele was a saint.

Sometimes when she was fired from a job they used to send me to fetch her. Mele never knew her way home. And I remember how happy she was whenever she saw me coming. She would say innocently that she wanted to stay with us. Why couldn't she stay with us? I used to ask myself that over and over. Why couldn't they make a place for her by the fire, let her sit there and dream, if that's what she wanted to do? Why must everybody *work*—even the saints and the angels? Why must half-wits set a good example?

I'm thinking now that after all it may be good for Mele where I'm taking her. No more work. Just the same, I'd rather they had made a corner for her somewhere.

Walking down the gravel path towards the big gates Mele becomes uneasy. Even a puppy knows when it is being carried to a pond to be drowned. Mele is trembling now. At the gate they are waiting for us. The gate yawns. Mele is on the inside, I am on the outside. They are trying to coax her along. They are gentle with her now. They speak to her so gently. But Mele is terror-stricken. She turns and runs towards the gate. I am still standing there. She puts her arms through the bars and clutches my neck. I kiss her tenderly on the forehead. Gently I unlock her arms. The others are going to take her again. I can't bear seeing that. I must go. I must run. For a full minute, however, I stand and look at her. Her eyes seem to have grown enormous. Two great round eyes, full and black as the night, staring at me uncomprehendingly. No maniac can look that way. No idiot can look that way. Only an angel or a saint.

Mele wasn't a good housekeeper I said, but she knew how to make fricadellas. Here is the recipe, while I think of it: a distemper composed of a humus of wet bread (from a nice urinal) plus horse meat (the fetlocks only) chopped very fine and mixed with a little sausage meat. Roll in palm of hands. The saloon that she ran with Paul, before the Hamburg woman came along, was just near the bend in the Second Avenue L, not far from the Chinese pagoda used by the Salvation Army.

When I ran away from the gate I stopped beside a high wall and burying my head in my arms, my arms against the wall, I sobbed as I had never sobbed since I was a child. Meanwhile they were giving Mele a bath and putting her into regulation dress; they parted her hair in the middle, brushed it down flat and tied it into a knot at the nape of the neck. Thus no one looks exceptional. All have the same crazy look, whether they are half crazy or three-quarters crazy, or just slightly cracked. When you say "may I have pen and ink to write a letter" they say "yes" and they hand you a broom to sweep the floor. If you pee on the floor absent-mindedly you have to wipe it up. You can sob all you like but you mustn't violate the rules of the house. A bug-house has to be run in orderly fashion just as any other house.

Once a week Mele would be allowed to receive. For thirty years the sisters had been visiting the bug-house. They were fed up with it. When they were tiny tots they used to visit their mother on Blackwell's Island. The mother always said to be careful of Mele, to watch over her. When Mele stood at the gate with eyes so round and bright her mind must have travelled back like an express train. Everything must have leaped to her mind at once. Her eyes were so big and bright, as if they saw more than they could comprehend. Bright with terror, and beneath the terror a limitless confusion. That's what made them so beautifully bright. You have to be crazy to see things so lucidly, so all at once. If you're great you can stay that way and people will believe in you, swear by you, turn the world upside down for you. But if you're only partly great, or just a nobody, then what happens to you is lost.

Mornings a brisk intellectual walk under the screaming elevated line, walking north from Delancey Street towards the Waldorf where the evening before the old man had been lounging around in Peacock Alley with Julian Legree. Each morning I write a new book, walking from the Delancey Street station north towards the Waldorf. On the fly-leaf of each book is written in vitriol: *The Island of Incest*. Every morning it starts with the drunken vomit of the night before; it makes a huge gardenia which I wear in the buttonhole of my lapel, the lapel of my double-breasted suit which is lined with silk throughout. I arrive at the tailor shop with the black breath of melancholy, perhaps to find Tom Jordan in the busheling room waiting to have the spots removed from his fly. After having written 369 pages on the trot the futility of saying Good Morning prevents me from being ordinarily polite. I have just this morning finished the 23rd volume of the ancestral book, of which not even a comma is visible since it was all written extemporaneously without even a fountain pen. I, the tailor's son, am now about to say Good Morning to Endicott Mumford's crack woolen salesman who stands before the mirror in his underwear examining the pouches under his eyes. Every limb and leaf of the family tree dangles before my eyes: out of the crazy black fog of the Elbe there floats this changing island of incest which produces the marvellous gardenia that I wear in my buttonhole each morning. I am just about to say Good Morning to Tom Jordan. It trembles there on my lips. I see a huge tree rising out of the black fog and in the hollow of the trunk there sits the woman from Hamburg, her ass squeezed tightly through the back of the chair. The door is on the latch and through the chink I see her green face, the lips set tight, the nostrils distended. Crazy George is going from door to door with picture post-cards, the arm that was bitten off by a horse lost and buried, the empty sleeve flapping in the wind. When all the pages have been torn from the calendar except the last six Crazy George will ring the doorbell and, with icicles in his mustache, he will stand on the threshold, cap in hand, and shout—"Merry Christmas!" This is the craziest tree that ever rose out of the Elbe, with every limb blasted and every leaf withered. This is the tree that shouts regularly once a year— "Merry Christmas!" Despite the calamities, despite the flow of cancer, dropsy, thievery, mendacity, buggery, paralysis, tapeworms, running ears, chorea, meningitis, epilepsy, liverworts, et cetera.

I am just about to say Good Morning. It trembles there on my lips. The 23 volumes of the Domesday Book are written with incestuous fidelity, the covers bound in finest morocco and a lock and key for each volume. Tom Jordan's blood-shot eyes are pasted on the mirror; they shudder like a horse shaking off a fly. Tom Jordan is always either taking off his pants or putting on his pants. Always buttoning or unbuttoning his fly. Always having the stains removed and a fresh crease put in. Tante Melia is sitting in the cooler, under the shade of the family tree. Mother is washing the vomit stains out of last week's dirty wash. The old man is stropping his razor. The Jews are moving up from under the shadow of the bridge, the days are getting shorter, the tugs are snorting or croaking like bull-frogs, the harbor is jammed with ice cakes. Every chapter of the book which is written in the air thickens the blood; the music of it deafens the wild anxiety of the outer air. Night drops like a boom of thunder, deposits me on the floor of the pedestrian highway leading nowhere eventually, but brightly ringed with gleaming spokes along which there is no turning back nor standing still.

From the shadow of the bridges the mob moves up, closer and closer, like a ring-worm, leaving a huge festering sore that runs from river to river along 14th Street. This line of pus, which runs invisibly from ocean to ocean, and age to age, neatly divides the Gentile world that I knew from the ledger from the Jewish world that I am about to know from life. Between these two worlds, in the middle of the pus line that runs from river to river, stands a little flower pot filled with gardenias. This is as far as the mastodons roam, where the buffaloes can graze no more; here the cunning, abstract world rises like a cliff in the midst of which are buried the fires of the revolution. Each morning I cross the line, with a gardenia in my button-hole and a fresh volume written in the air. Each morning I wade through a trench filled with vomit to reach the beautiful island of incest; each day the cliff rises up more toweringly, the window-lines straight as a railroad track and the gleam of them even more dazzling than the gleam of polished skulls. Each morning the trench yawns more menacingly.

I should be saying Good Morning now to Tom Jordan, but it hangs there on my lips tremblingly. What morning is this that I should waste in salutation? Is it *good,* this morning of mornings? I am losing the power to distinguish morning from morning. In the ledger is the world of the fast disappearing buffalo; next door the riveters are sewing up the ribs of the coming skyscrapers. Cunning Oriental men with leaden shoes and glass craniums are plotting the paper world of tomorrow, a world made entirely of merchandise which rises box on box like a paper box factory, f. o. b. Canarsie. To-day there is still time to attend the funeral of the recent dead; to-morrow there will be no time, for the dead will be left on the spot and woe to him who sheds a tear. This is a good morning for a revolution if only there were machine guns instead of fire-crackers. This morning would be a splendid morning if yesterday's morning had not been an utter fiasco. The past is galloping away, the trench widens. To-morrow is further off than it was yesterday because yesterday's horse has run wild and the men with leaden shoes cannot catch up with him. Between the good of the morning and the morning itself there is a line of pus which blows a stench over yesterday and poisons the morrow. This is a morning so confused that if it were only an old umbrella the slightest sneeze would blow it inside out.

My whole life is stretching out in an unbroken morning. I write from scratch each day. Each day a new world is created, separate and complete, and there I am among the constellations, a god so crazy about himself that he does nothing but sing and fashion new worlds. Meanwhile the old universe is going to pieces. The old universe resembles a busheling room in which pants are pressed and stains removed and buttons sewn on. The old universe smells like a wet seam receiving the kiss of a red hot iron. Endless alterations and repairs, a sleeve lengthened, a collar lowered, a button moved closer, a new seat put in. But never a new suit of clothes, never a creation. There is the morning world, which starts from scratch each day, and the busheling room in which things are endlessly altered and repaired. And thus it is with my life through which there runs the sewer of night. All through the night I hear the goose irons hissing as they kiss the wet seams; the rinds of the old universe fall on the floor and the stench of them is sour as vinegar.

The men my father loved were weak and lovable. They went out, each and every one of them, like brilliant stars before the sun. They went out quietly and catastrophically. No shred of them remained—nothing but the memory of their blaze and glory. They flow now inside me like a vast river choked with falling stars. They form the black flowing river which keeps the axis of my world in constant revolution. Out of this black, endless, ever-expanding girdle of night springs the continuous morning which is wasted in creation. Each morning the river overflows its banks, leaving the sleeves and buttonholes and all the rinds of a dead universe strewn along the beach where I stand contemplating the ocean of the morning of creation.

Standing there on the ocean's shore I see crazy George leaning against the wall of the undertaker's shop. He has on a funny little cap, a celluloid collar and no tie; he sits on the bench beside the coffin, neither sad nor smiling. He sits there quietly, like an angel that has stepped outside of a Jewish painting. The man in the coffin, whose body is still fresh, is decked out in a modest pepper and salt suit just George's size. He has a collar and tie on and a watch in his vest pocket. George takes him out, undresses him and, while he changes his clothes, lays him on the ice. Not wishing to steal the watch he lays the watch on the ice beside the body. The man is lying on the ice with a celluloid collar around his neck. It is getting dark as George steps out of the undertaker's shop. He has a tie now and a good suit of clothes. At the corner drug store he stops off to buy a joke book which he saw in the window; he memorizes a few jokes standing in the subway. They are Joe Miller's jokes.

At precisely the same hour Tante Melia is sending a Valentine greeting to the relatives. She has a gray uniform on and her hair is parted in the middle. She writes that she is very happy with her new-found friends and that the food is good. She would like them to remember however that she asked for some *Fastnacht Kuchen* the last time—could they send some by mail, by parcel post? She says that there are some lovely petunias growing up around the garbage can outside the big kitchen. She says that she took a long walk on Sunday last and saw lots of reindeer and rabbits and ostriches. She says that her spelling is very poor, but that she was never a good hand at writing anyway. Everybody is very kind and there is lots of work to do. She would like some *Fastnacht Kuchen* as soon as possible, by air-mail if possible. She asked the director to make her some for her birthday but they forgot. She says to send some newspapers because she likes to look at the advertisements. There was a hat she saw once, from Bloomingdale's, she thought, and it was marked down. Maybe they could send the hat along with the *Fastnacht Kuchen?* She thanks them all for the lovely cards they sent her last Christmas—she still remembers them, especially the one with the silver stars on it. Everybody thought it was lovely. She says that she will soon be going to bed and that she will pray for all of them because they were always so good to her.

It's growing dusky, always about the same hour, and I'm standing there gazing at the ocean's mirror. Ice-cold time, neither fast nor slow, but a stiff lying on the ice with a celluloid collar—and if only he had an erection it would be marvelous . . . too marvelous! In the dark hall-way below Tom Jordan is waiting for the old man to descend. He has two blowsers with him and one of them is fixing her garter; Tom Jordan is helping her to fix her garter. Same hour, toward dusk, as I say, Mrs. Lawson is walking through the cemetery to look once again at her darling son's grave. Her dear boy Jack, she says, though he was thirty-two when he kicked off seven years ago. They said it was rheumatism of the heart, but the fact is the darling boy had knocked up so many venereal virgins that when they drained the pus from his body he stank like a shit-pump. Mrs. Lawson doesn't seem to remember that at all. It's her darling boy Jack and the grave is always tidy; she carries a little piece of chamois in her hand-bag in order to polish the tomb-stone every evening.

Same dusky time, the stiff lying there on the ice, and the old man is standing in a telephone booth with the receiver in one hand and something warm and wet with hair on it in the other. He's calling up to say not to hold the dinner, that he's got to take a customer out and he'll be home late, not to worry. Crazy George is turning the leaves of Joe Miller's Joke Book. Down further, towards Mobile, they're practising the St. Louis Blues without a note in front of 'em and people are getting ready to go crazy when they hear it yesterday, to-day, to-morrow. Everybody's getting ready to get raped, drugged, violated, soused with the new music that seeps out of the sweat of the asphalt. Soon it'll be the same hour everywhere, just by turning a dial or hanging suspended over the earth in a balloon. It's the hour of the kaffee-klatchers sitting around the family table, each one operated on for a different thing, the one with the whiskers and the heavy rings on her fingers having had a harder time than any one else because she could afford it.

It's staggeringly beautiful at this hour when every one seems to be going his own private way. Love and murder, they're still a few hours apart. Love and murder, I feel it coming with the dusk: new babies coming out of the womb, soft, pink flesh to get tangled up in barbed wire and scream all night long and rot like dead bone a thousand miles from nowhere. Crazy virgins with ice-cold jazz in their veins egging men on to erect new buildings and men with dog collars around their necks wading through the muck up to the eyes so that the czar of electricity will rule the waves. What's in the seed scares the living piss out of me: a brand new world is coming out of the egg and no matter how fast I write the old world doesn't die fast enough. I hear the new machine guns and the millions of bones splintered at once; I see dogs running mad and pigeons dropping with letters tied to their ankles.

Always merry and bright, whether north from Delancey Street or south towards the pus line! My two soft hands in the body of the world, ploughing up the warm entrails, arranging and disarranging, cutting them up, sewing them together again. The warm body feeling which the surgeon knows, together with oysters, warts, ulcers, hernias, cancer sprouts, the young kohlrabies, the clips and the forceps, the scissors and tropical growths, the poisons and gases all locked up inside and carefully covered with skin. Out of the leaking mains love gushing like sewer gas: furious love with black gloves and bright bits of garter, love that champs and snorts, love hidden in a barrel and blowing the bung-hole night after night. The men who passed through my father's shop reeked with love: they were warm and winey, weak and indolent, fast yachts trimmed with sex, and when they sailed by me in the night they fumigated my dreams. Standing in the center of New York I could hear the tinkle of the cow-bells, or, by a turn of the head, I could hear the sweet sweet music of the death-rattle, a red line down the page and on every sleeve a mourning band. By twisting my neck just a little I could stand high above the tallest skyscraper and look down on the ruts left by the huge wheels of modern progress. Nothing was too difficult for me if only it had a little grief and anguish in it. *Chez nous* there were all the organic diseases—and a few of the inorganic. Like rock crystal we spread, from one crime to another. A merry whirl, and in the center of it my twenty-first year already covered with verdigris.

And when I can remember no more I shall always remember the night I was getting a dose of clap and the old man so stinking drunk he took his friend Tom Jordan to bed with him. Beautiful and touching this—to be out getting a dose of clap when the family honor was at stake, when it was *at par,* you might say. Not to be there for the shindig, with mother and father wrestling on the floor and the broomstick flying. Not to be there in the cold morning light when Tom Jordan is on his knees and begging to be forgiven but not being forgiven even on his knees because the inflexible heart of a Lutheran doesn't know the meaning of forgiveness. Touching and beautiful to read in the paper next morning that about the same hour the night before the pastor who had put in the bowling alley was caught in a dark room with a naked boy on his lap! But what makes it excruciatingly touching and beautiful is this, that not knowing these things, I came home next day to ask permission to marry a woman old enough to be my mother. And when I said "get married" the old lady picks up the bread knife and goes for me. I remember, as I left the house, that I stopped by the bookcase to grab a book. And the name of the book was—*The Birth of Tragedy*. Droll that, what with the broomstick the night before, the bread knife, the dose of clap, the pastor caught red-handed, the dumplings growing cold, the cancer sprouts, et cetera . . . I used to think then that all the tragic events of life were written down in books and that what went on outside was just diluted crap. I thought that a beautiful book was a diseased portion of the brain. I never realized that a whole world could be diseased!

Walking up and down with a package under my arm. A fine bright morning, let's say, and the spittoons all washed and polished. Mumbling to myself, as I step into the Woolworth Building—"Good morning, Mr. Thorndike, fine morning this morning, Mr. Thorndike. Are you interested in clothes, Mr. Thorndike?" Mr. Thorndike is not interested in clothes this morning; he thanks me for calling and throws the card in the waste basket. Nothing daunted I try the American Express Building. "Good morning, Mr. Hathaway, fine morning this morning!" Mr. Hathaway doesn't need a good tailor—he's had one for thirty-five years now. Mr. Hathaway is a little peeved and damned right he is thinks I to myself stumbling down the stairs. A fine, bright morning, no denying that, and so to take the bad taste out of my mouth and also have a view of the harbor I take the trolley over the bridge and call on a cheap skate by the name of Dyker. Dyker is a busy man. The sort of man who has his lunch sent up and his shoes polished while he eats. Dyker is suffering from a nervous complaint brought on by . . . . He says we can make him a pepper and salt suit if we stop dunning him every month. The girl was only sixteen and he didn't want to knock her up. Yes, patch pockets, please! Besides, he has a wife and three children. Besides, he will be running for judge soon—judge of the Surrogate Court.

Getting towards matinee time. Hop back to New York and drop off at the Burlesk where the usher knows me. The first three rows always filled with judges and politicians. The house is dark and Margie Pennetti is standing on the runway in a pair of dirty white tights. She has the most wonderful ass of any woman on the stage and everybody knows it, herself included. After the show I walk around aimlessly, looking at the movie houses and the Jewish delicatessen stores. Stand awhile in a penny arcade listening to the siren voices coming through the megaphone. Life is just a continuous honeymoon filled with chocolate layer cake and cranberry pie. Put a penny in the slot and see a woman undressing on the grass. Put a penny in the slot and win a set of false teeth. The world is made of new parts every afternoon: the soiled parts are sent to the dry cleaner, the used parts are scrapped and sold for junk.

Walk uptown past the pus line and stroll through the lobbies of the big hotels. If I like I can sit down and watch other people walking through the lobby. Everybody's on the watch. Things are happening all about. The strain of waiting for something to happen is delirious. The elevated rushing by, the taxis honking, the ambulance clanging, the riveters riveting. Bell hops dressed in gorgeous livery looking for people who don't answer to their names. In the golden toilet below men standing in line waiting to take a leak; everything made of plush and marble, the odors refined and pleasant, the flush flushing beautifully. On the sidewalk a stack of newspapers, the headlines still wet with murder, rape, arson, strikes, forgeries, revolution. People stepping over one another to crash the subway. Over in Brooklyn a woman's waiting for me. Old enough to be my mother and she's waiting for me to marry her. The son's got T. B. so bad he can't crawl out of bed any more. Tough titty going up there to her garret to make love while the son's in the next room coughing his lungs out. Besides, she's just getting over an abortion and I don't want to knock her up again—not right away anyhow.

The rush hour! and the subway a free for all Paradise. Pressed up against a woman so tight I can feel the hair on her twat. So tightly glued together my knuckles are making a dent in her groin. She's looking straight ahead, at a microscopic spot just under my right eye. By Canal Street I manage to get my penis where my knuckles were before. The thing's jumping like mad and no matter which way the train jerks she's always in the same position vis-à-vis my dickie. Even when the crowd thins out she stands there with her pelvis thrust forward and her eyes fixed on the microscopic spot just under my right eye. At Borough Hall she gets out, without once giving me the eye. I follow her up to the street thinking she might turn round and say hello at least, or let me buy her a frosted chocolate, assuming I could buy one. But no, she's off like an arrow, without turning her head the eighth of an inch. How they do it I don't know. Millions and millions of them every day standing up without underwear and getting a dry fuck. What's the conclusion—a shower? a rub down? Ten to one they fling themselves on the bed and finish the job with their fingers.

Anyway, it's going on towards evening and me walking up and down with an erection fit to burst my fly. The crowd gets thicker and thicker. Everybody's got a newspaper now. The sky's choked with illuminated merchandise every single article of which is guaranteed to be pleasant, healthful, durable, tasty, noiseless, rainproof, imperishable, the *ne plus ultra* without which life would be unbearable were it not for the fact that life is already unbearable because there is no life. Just about the hour when old Henschke is quitting the tailor shop to go to the card club uptown. An agreeable little job on the side which keeps him occupied until two in the morning. Nothing much to do—just take the gentlemen's hats and coats, serve drinks on a little tray, empty the ash trays and keep the match boxes filled. Really a very pleasant job, everything considered. Towards midnight prepare a little snack for the gentlemen, should they so desire it. There are the spittoons, of course, and the toilet bowl. All such gentlemen, however, that there's really nothing to it. And then there's always a little cheese and crackers to nibble on, and sometimes a thimbleful of Port. Now and then a cold veal sandwich for the morrow. Real gentlemen! No gainsaying it. Smoke the best cigars. Even the butts taste good. Really, a very, very pleasant job!

Getting towards dinner time. Most of the tailors have closed shop for the day. A few of them, those who have nothing but brittle old geezers on the books, are waiting to make a try-on. They walk up and down with their hands behind their backs. Everybody has gone except the boss tailor himself, and perhaps the cutter or the bushelman. The boss tailor is wondering if he has to put new chalk marks on again and if the check will arrive in time to meet the rent. The cutter is saying to himself—"why yes, Mr. So-and-So, why to be sure . . . yes, I think it should be just a little higher there . . . yes, you're quite right . . . it *is* a little off on the left side . . . yes, we'll have that ready for you in a few days . . . yes, Mr. So-and-So . . ., yes, yes, yes, yes, yes . . ." The finished clothes and the unfinished clothes are hanging on the rack; the bolts are neatly stacked on the tables; only the light in the busheling room is on. Suddenly the telephone rings. Mr. So-and-So is on the wire and he can't make it this evening but he would like his tuxedo sent up right away, the one with the new buttons which he selected last week, and he hopes to Christ it doesn't jump off his neck any more. The cutter puts on his hat and coat and runs quickly down the stairs to attend a Zionist meeting in the Bronx. The boss tailor is left to close the shop and switch out all the lights if any were left on by mistake. The boy that he's sending up with the tuxedo right away is himself and it doesn't matter much because he will duck round by the trade entrance and nobody will be the wiser. Nobody looks more like a millionaire than a boss tailor delivering a tuxedo to Mr. So-and-So. Spry and spruce, shoes shined, hat cleaned, gloves washed, mustache waxed. They start to look worried only when they sit down for the evening meal. No appetite. No orders to-day. No checks. They get so despondent that they fall asleep at ten o'clock and when it's time to go to bed they can't sleep any more.

Walking over the Brooklyn Bridge . . . Is this the world, this walking up and down, these buildings that are lit up, the men and women passing me? I watch their lips moving, the lips of the men and women passing me. What are they talking about—some of them so earnestly? I hate seeing people so deadly serious when I myself am suffering worse than any of them. *One* life! and there are millions and millions of lives to be lived. So far I haven't had a thing to say about my own life. Not a thing. Must be I haven't got the guts. Ought to go back to the subway, grab a Jane and rape her in the street. Ought to go back to Mr. Thorndike in the morning and spit in his face. Ought to stand on Times Square with my pecker in my hand and piss in the gutter. Ought to grab a revolver and fire point-blank into the crowd. The old man's leading the life of Reilly. He and his bosom pals. And I'm walking up and down, turning green with hate and envy. And when I turn in the old woman'll be sobbing fit to break her heart. Can't sleep nights listening to her. I hate her too for sobbing that way. The one robs me, the other punishes me. How can I go into her and comfort her when what I most want to do is to break her heart?

Walking along the Bowery . . . and a beautiful snot-green pasture it is at this hour. Pimps, crooks, cokies, panhandlers, beggars, touts, gunmen, chinks, wops, drunken micks. All gaga for a bit of food and a place to flop. *Walking and walking and walking.* Twenty-one I am, white, born and bred in New York, muscular physique, sound intelligence, good breeder, no bad habits, etc. etc. Chalk it up on the board. Selling out at par. Committed no crime, except to be born here.

In the past every member of our family did something with his hands. I'm the first idle son of a bitch with a glib tongue and a bad heart.

Swimming in the crowd, a digit with the rest. Tailored and retailored. The lights are twinkling—on and off, on and off. Sometimes it's a rubber tire, sometimes it's a piece of chewing gum. The tragedy of it is that nobody sees the look of desperation on my face. Thousands and thousands of us, and we're passing one another without a look of recognition. The lights jigging like electric needles. The atoms going crazy with light and heat. A conflagration going on behind the glass and nothing burns away. Men breaking their backs, men bursting their brains, to invent a machine which a child will manipulate. If I could only find the hypothetical child who's to run this machine I'd put a hammer in its hands and say: Smash it! Smash it!

Smash it! Smash it! That's all I can say. The old man's riding around in an open barouche. I envy the bastard his peace of mind. A bosom pal by his side and a quart of rye under his belt. My toes are blistering with malice. Twenty years ahead of me and this thing growing worse by the hour. It's throttling me. In twenty years there won't be any soft, lovable men waiting to greet me. Every bosom pal that goes now is a buffalo lost and gone forever. Steel and concrete hedging me in. The pavement getting harder and harder. The new world eating into me, expropriating me. Soon I won't even need a name.

Once I thought there were marvelous things in store for me. Thought I could build a world in the air, a castle of pure white spit that would raise me above the tallest building, between the tangible and the intangible, put me in a space like music where everything collapses and perishes but where I would be immune, great, god-like, holiest of the holies. It was *I* imagined this, *I* the tailor's son! I who was born from a little acorn on an immense and stalwart tree. In the hollow of the acorn even the faintest tremor of the earth reached me: I was part of the great tree, part of the past, with crest and lineage, with pride, *pride*. And when I fell to earth and was buried there I remembered *who* I was, *where* I came from. Now I am lost, *lost,* do you hear? You don't hear? I'm yowling and screaming—don't you hear me? Switch the lights off! Smash the bulbs! Can you hear me now? *Louder!* you say. *Louder!* Christ, are you making sport of me? Are you deaf, dumb and blind? Must I yank my clothes off? Must I dance on my head?

All right, then! I'm going to dance for you! A merry whirl, brothers, and let her whirl and whirl and whirl! Throw in an extra pair of flannel trousers while you're at it. And don't forget, boys, I dress on the right side. You hear me? Let 'er go. *Always merry and bright!*

Peace! It's Wonderful!

It was only the other night while entertaining an American writer who had come to visit France after a long absence that I realized poignantly what has happened to me since I left my native land. Like all my compatriots who come to see me he asked quite naturally what it was that had kept me here so long. (It is seven years since I am living in Paris.) I felt that it was useless to answer him in words. I suggested instead that we take a stroll through the streets. We started out from the corner of the Rue de la Gaîté and the Avenue du Maine where we had been sitting; I walked him down the Rue de l'Ouest to the Rue du Château, then over the railroad bridge back of the Gare Montparnasse down the Boulevard Pasteur to the Avenue de Breteuil and thence to a little café facing the Invalides where we sat in silence for a long while. Perhaps that silence which one finds in the streets of Paris at night, perhaps that alone was a sufficient answer to his query. It is something difficult to find in a big American city.

At any rate, it was not chance which had directed my footsteps. Walking with my friend through the deserted streets I was reliving my first days in Paris, for it was in the Rue de Vanves that my new life really began. Night after night without money, without friends, without a language I had walked these streets in despair and anguish. The streets were everything to me, as they must be to every man who is lost in a big city. Walking through them again with my countryman I congratulated myself silently that I had begun my life in Paris behind the scenes, as it were. If I *had* led a Bohemian life, as some imagine, it was through bitter necessity. *A Bohemian life!* What a strange phrase that is when you think of it! There is so little that is Bohemian about it. In any case, the important thing is that in the Rue de Vanves I touched bottom. Like it or not, I was obliged to create a new life for myself. And

72

this new life I feel is mine, absolutely mine, to use or to smash, as I see fit. In this life I am God, and like God I am indifferent to my own fate. I am everything there is—so why worry?

Just as a piece of matter detaches itself from the sun to live as a wholly new creation so I have come to feel about my detachment from America. Once the separation is made a new orbit is established, and there is no turning back. For me the sun had ceased to exist; I had myself become a blazing sun. And like all the other suns of the universe I had to nourish myself *from within*. I speak in cosmological terms because it seems to me that is the only possible way to think if one is truly alive. I think this way also because it is just the opposite of the way I thought a few years back when I had what is called hopes. Hope is a bad thing. It means that you are not what you want to be. It means that part of you is dead, if not *all* of you. It means that you entertain illusions. It's a sort of spiritual clap, I should say.

Before this inward change came about I used to think that we were living in extraordinarily difficult times. Like most men I thought that *our* time was the worst possible time. And no doubt it is—for those, I mean, who still say "our time." As for myself, I've thrown away the calendar by which one reckons the lean and the fat years. For me it is all gravy, one continuous, marvellous stream of time without beginning or end. Yes, the times are bad, permanently bad—unless one becomes immune, *becomes God*. Since I have become God I go the whole hog always. I am absolutely indifferent to the fate of the world: I have my own world and my own private fate. I make no reservations and no compromises. I accept. *I am*—and that is all.

That is why, perhaps, when I sit at my typewriter I always face East. No backward glances over the shoulder. The orbit over which I am travelling leads me farther and farther away from the dead sun which gave me birth. Once I was confronted with a choice—either to remain a satellite of that dead thing or create a new world of my own, with my own satellites. I made my choice. Having made it there is no standing still. One becomes more and more alive, or more and more dead. To get a piqûre is useless; a blood transfusion is useless. A new man is made out of the whole cloth, by a change of heart which alters every living cell of the body. Anything less than a change of heart is sure catastrophe. Which, if you follow the reasoning, explains why the times are always bad. For, unless there be a change of heart there can be no act of will. There may be a show of will, with tremendous activity accompanying it (wars, revolutions, etc.), but that will not change the times. Things are apt to grow worse, in fact.

Over many centuries of time a few men have appeared who, to my way of thinking, really understood why the times are permanently bad. They proved, through their own unique way of living, that this sad "fact" is one of man's delusions. But nobody, apparently, understands them. And it is eminently right that it should be thus. If we want to lead a creative life it is absolutely just that we should be responsible for our own destiny. To imagine a way of life that could be patched is to think of the cosmos as a vast plumbing affair. To expect others to do what we are unable to do ourselves is truly to believe in miracles, miracles that no Christ would dream of performing. The whole social-political scheme of existence is crazy—because it is based on vicarious living. A real man has no need of governments, of laws, of moral or ethical codes, to say nothing of battleships, police clubs, high-powered bombers and such things. Of course a real man is hard to find, but that's the only kind of man worth talking about. Why talk about trash? It is the great mass of mankind, the mob, the people, who create the permanently bad times. The world is only the mirror of ourselves. If it's something to make one puke, why then puke, me lads, it's your own sick mugs you're looking at!

Sometimes it almost seems that the writer takes a perverse delight in finding the times out of joint, finding everything awrack and awry. Perhaps the artist is nothing more than the personification of this universal maladjustment, this universal disequilibrium. Perhaps that explains why in the neutral, sterilized countries (Scandinavia, Holland, Switzerland), so little art is forthcoming, or why in the countries undergoing profound social and political changes (Russia, Germany, Italy), the art products are of negligible value. But, whether there is little art or bad art, art, it should be understood, is only a makeshift, a substitute for the real thing. There is only one art which, if we practised it, would destroy what is called "art." With every line I write I kill off the "artist" in me. With every line it is either murder in the first degree or suicide. I do not want to give hope to others, nor to inspire others. If we knew what it meant to be inspired we would not inspire. We would simply *be*. As it is we neither inspire nor aid one another: we deal out cold justice. For myself I want none of this stinking cold justice; I want either warm-hearted magnanimity or absolute neglect. To be honest, I want something more than any man can give me. I want everything! I want everything—or nothing. It's crazy, I know, but that's what I mean.

Is it good here in France? It's wonderful. Marvellous. For *me* it's marvellous, because it's the only place in the world I know of where I can go on with my murder-and-suicide business—until I

strike a new zodiacal realm. For a French writer it may be bad
here, but then I am not a French writer. I should hate to be a
French or a German or a Russian or an American writer. It must
be hell. I am a cosmological writer, and when I open my trap I
broadcast to the whole world at once. (Like Father Divine: *Peace!
It's Wonderful!*) Acting as I do I am apt to get it in the neck. I am
apt to get sucked good and proper, and I know it. But that's my
temperament, and I'll stand or fall by it. Eventually I shan't even
bother to be a cosmological writer: *I shall be just a man.* But first
there's a lot of slaughtering to be done.

Every man who aspires to be a good French writer (or a bad
one), or a (good or bad) German writer, or a (good or bad) Russian
writer, any man, I mean, who hopes to make a living by giving
regular doses of medicine to his sick countrymen, helps to perpetuate a farce which has been going on since the beginning of history.
Such writers, and they are practically all we have, it seems, are
the lice which keep us from knowing Paradise or Hell. They keep
us in a perpetual Purgatory where we scratch without let. Whereas
even the earth wobbles on its axis, or will change its axis from
time to time, these blokes keep us forever on an even keel. In
every great figure who has flashed across the horizon there is, or
was, a large element of treachery, or hatred, or love, or disgust.
We have had traitors to race, country, religion, but we have not
yet bred any real traitors, *traitors to the human race,* which is
what we need. The chances are slim, I know. I mention it merely
to show how the wind blows.

As I say, one needs either a heaven or a hell in which to
flourish—until one arrives at that Paradise of his own creation,
that middle realm which is not a bread-and-butter Utopia of which
the masses dream but an interstellar realm in which one rolls along
his orbit with sublime indifference. Dante was the best cartogra-
pher of the soul which Europe ever produced, everything clear as
a whistle and etched in black and white; but since his time not
only Europe, but the whole universe, has moved into new spiritual
dimensions. Man is still the center of the cosmos, but having
stretched the cosmos almost to the bursting point—the scientists
actually predict that the universe will explode!—man himself is
practically invisible. Artificial wings won't help, nor artificial eyes,
nor escalators, nor pemmican. The whole damned universe has to
be taken apart, brick by brick, and reconstructed. Every atom has
to be rearranged. Perhaps just to sit quiet and take deep breathing
exercises would be better than popping one another off with slugs
of dynamite. Because the strange thing is that just doing nothing,
just taking it easy, loafing, meditating, things tend to right them-

selves. As it is we are all terrified by the thought of losing our freedom. And yet it is freedom, *the idea of freedom,* which is what we dread most. Freedom means the strict inner precision of a Swiss watch—combined with absolute recklessness. Whence gayety and indifference, at present non-existent. Of course only lunatics dream of such a condition. And so we all remain sane and bite into one another like lice. And the lousier it gets the more progress we make. *Peace! It's Wonderful!*

I should say that every since the dawn of history—all through the great civilizations, that is to say—we have been living like lice. Once every thousand years or so a man arises who is not a louse— and then there is even more hell to pay. When a MAN appears he seems to get a stranglehold on the world which it takes centuries to break. The sane people are cunning enough to find these men "psychopathic." These sane ones seem to be more interested in the technique of the stranglehold than in applying it. That's a curious phenomenon, one that puzzles me, to be frank. It's like learning the art of wrestling in order to have the pleasure of letting someone pin you to the mat.

What do I mean to infer? Just this—that art, the art of living, involves the act of creation. The work of art is nothing. It is only the tangible, visible evidence of a way of life, which, if it is not crazy is certainly *different* from the accepted way of life. The difference lies in the act, in the assertion of a will, and individuality. For the artist to attach himself to his work, or identify himself with it, is suicidal. An artist should be able not only to spit on his predecessor's art, or on all works of art, but on his own too. He should be able to be an artist all the time, and finally not be an artist at all, but a piece of art.

In addition to the deep breathing exercises perhaps mercurial inunctions ought also to be recommended—*for the time being.*

An Open Letter to Surrealists Everywhere

Below the belt all men are brothers. Man has never known *solitude* except in the upper regions where one is either a poet or a madman—or a criminal. "To-day," writes Paul Eluard, "the solitude of poets is breaking down. They are now men among men, they have brothers." It is unfortunately too true, and that is why the poet is becoming more and more rare. I still prefer the anarchic life; unlike Paul Eluard I cannot say that the word "fraternisation" exalts me. Nor does it seem to me that this idea of brotherhood arises from a poetic conception of life. It is not at all what Lautréamont meant when he said that poetry must be made by all. The brotherhood of man is a permanent delusion common to idealists everywhere in all epochs: it is the reduction of the principle of individuation to the least common denominator of intelligibility. It is what leads the masses to identify themselves with movie stars and megalomaniacs like Hitler and Mussolini. It is what prevents them from reading and appreciating and being influenced by and creating in turn such poetry as Paul Eluard gives us. That Paul Eluard is desperately lonely, that he strives with might and main to establish communication with his fellow-man, I understand and subscribe to with all my heart. But when Paul Eluard goes down into the street and becomes a man he is not making himself understood and liked for what he is—*for the poet that he is,* I mean. On the contrary, he is establishing communication with his fellow-men by capitulation, by renunciation of his individuality, his high role. If he is accepted it is only because he is willing to surrender those qualities which differentiate him from his fellow-men and make him unsympathetic and unintelligible to them. It is not at all strange that madmen are put under lock and key and saviours crucified and prophets stoned. At any rate, one

77

thing is certain: it is not in this way that poetry will be made by all.

(Query: And why should poetry be made by all? Why?)

In every age, just as in every life worthy of the name, there is the effort to re-establish that equilibrium which is disturbed by the power and tyranny which a few great individuals exercise over us. This struggle is fundamentally personal and religious. It has nothing to do with liberty and justice, which are idle words signifying nobody knows precisely what. It has to do with making poetry, or, if you will, with making life a poem. It has to do with the adoption of a creative attitude towards life. One of the most effective ways in which it expresses itself is in killing off the tyrannical influences wielded over us by those who are already dead. It consists not in denying these examplars, but in absorbing them, assimilating them, and eventually surpassing them. Each man has to do this for himself. There is no feasible scheme for universal liberation. The tragedy which surrounds the life of almost every great figure is forgotten in the admiration which we bestow on the man's work. It is forgotten that the glorious Greeks, whom we never cease admiring, treated their men of genius more shamefully, more cruelly perhaps than any other people we know of. It is forgotten that the mystery which attaches itself to Shakespeare's life is a mystery only because the English do not wish to admit that Shakespeare was driven mad by the stupidity, non-understanding and intolerance of his countrymen, that he finished his days in a mad-house.

Life is either a feast or a famine, as the old Chinese proverb goes. Right now it is pretty much of a famine. Without having recourse to the wisdom of such a sage as Freud, it is obvious that in times of famine men behave differently than when there is abundance. In times of famine one prowls the streets with a rapacious eye. One looks at his brother, sees in him a succulent morsel, and straightaway he waylays and devours him. This is done in the name of the revolution. The fact is that it doesn't matter much in what name it is done. When men get brotherly they also get slightly cannibalistic. In China, where famines are more frequent and more devastating, the people have become so hysterical (beneath the renowned Oriental mask) that when they see a man being executed they quite often forget themselves and laugh.

The famine which we are living through is a peculiar one in that it occurs in the midst of plenty. It is more of a *spiritual* famine, we might say, than a physical one. People are not fighting for bread this time, but for a *right* to their piece of bread, which is a distinction of some importance. Bread, figuratively speaking, is everywhere, but most of us are hungry. Shall I say—especially the poets? I ask because it is in the tradition of poets to starve. It is a little strange therefore to find them identifying their habitual physical hunger with the spiritual hunger of the masses. Or is it vice versa? Anyway, now we are all starving, except the rich, to be sure, and the smug bourgeoisie who have never known what it is to starve, either spiritually or physically.

Originally men killed one another in the direct pursuit of booty—food, weapons, implements, women, and so on. There was sense to it, even though there was no charity or sympathy. Now we have become sympathetic and charitable and brotherly, but we go on killing just the same, and we kill without the least hope of attaining our ends. We kill one another for the benefit of those to come, that they may enjoy a life more abundant. *(The hell we do!)*

There has been mention throughout this book on Surrealism [*Surrealism,* by Herbert Read (Faber and Faber Ltd.)] of our great indebtedness to Freud et alia. But there is one thing which Freud and all his tribe have made painfully clear and which is singularly missing in this account of our supposed indebtedness. It is something like this . . . Every time we fail to strike or to kill the person who threatens to humiliate or degrade or enslave or enchain us we pay the penalty for it in collective suicide, which is war, or in fratricidal slaughter, which is revolution. Every day that we fail to live out the maximum of our potentialities we kill the Shakespeare, Dante, Homer, Christ which is in us. Every day that we live in harness with the woman whom we no longer love we destroy our power to love and to have the woman whom we merit. The age we live in is the age which suits us: it is we who make it, not God, not Capitalism, not this or that, call it by any name you like. The evil is in us—and the good too! But as the old bard said—"the good is oft interred with our bones."

The basic effectiveness of the psycho-analytic doctrine lies in the recognition of the creative aspect of responsibility. Neurosis is not a new phenomenon in the history of human maladies, nor is its most wonderful bloom, schizophrenia. This is not the first time that the cultural soil, and even the sub-soil, has become exhausted. This is a famine which goes to the roots, and it is not at all paradoxical, on the contrary, it is absolutely logical, that it should occur in the midst of plenty. In the midst of this rotting plenty it is altogether fitting and natural that we the living dead should sit like lepers with outstretched arms and beg a little charity. *Or,* get up and kill one another, which is a little more diverting, but which comes to the same thing in the end. That is, nullity.

When at last each man realizes that nothing is to be expected

from God, or society, or friends, or benevolent tyrants, or democratic governments, or saints, or saviours, or even from the holiest
of holies, *education,* when each man realizes that he must work
with his own hands to save himself, and that he need expect no
mercy, perhaps then . . . *Perhaps!* Even then, seeing what manner
of men we are, I doubt. The point is that we are doomed. Maybe
we are going to die to-morrow, maybe in the next five minutes. Let
us take stock of ourselves. We can make the last five minutes
worth while, entertaining, even gay, if you will, or dissipate them
as we have the hours and the days and months and years and
centuries. No god is coming to save us. No system of government,
no belief will provide us with that liberty and justice which men
whistle for with the death-rattle.

The renascence of wonder, which Mr. Read writes about, will
be brought about, if it *is* brought about, by a few individuals for
whom this phrase has vital significance, by those, in short, who
are unable not to act in accordance with a truth perceived. What
distinguishes the majority of men from the few is their inability to
act according to their beliefs. The hero is he who raises himself
above the crowd. He is not a hero because he lays down his life
for his country, or for a cause or principle. Indeed, in making such
a sacrifice he is often cowardly rather than heroic. To run with the
herd, and die with the herd, is the natural animal instinct which
man shares with other beasts. To be a pacifist is not necessarily
heroic either. "For if a man," to quote from the devil himself, "is
unprepared or unable to fight for his life, just Providence has
already decreed his end." To fight for one's life, though Herr
Hitler did not mean it this way, usually means to lose one's life.
To get men to rally round a cause, a belief, an idea, is always
easier than to persuade them to lead their own lives. We live in the
swarm and our fine principles, our glorious ideas, are but blinders
which we put over our eyes in order to make death palatable. We
have not advanced a peg beyond the primitive man's idea of the
fertility of death. Since the dawn of civilization we have been
killing one another off—*on principle.* The fact is—I must repeat it
again because the Surrealists are guilty of the same mistake as all
other warring idealists—that human beings have an imperative
need to kill. The distinguishing trait of the civilized man is that he
kills *en masse.* Sadder than that, however, is the fact that *he lives
the life of the masses.* His life is lived according to totem and
taboo, as much now as in the past, even more, perhaps.

The role which the artist plays in society is to revive the
primitive, anarchic instincts which have been sacrificed for the
illusion of living in comfort. If the artist fails we will not necessarily

have a return to an imaginary Eden filled with wonder and cruelty. I am afraid, on the contrary, that we are much more apt to have a condition of perpetual work, such as we see in the insect world. Myself I do not believe that the artist will fail. On the other hand, it doesn't matter a damn to me whether he fails or not. It is a problem beyond my scope. If I choose to remain an artist rather than go down in the street and shoulder a musket or sling a stick of dynamite it is because my life as an artist suits me down to the ground. It is not the most comfortable life in the world but I know that it is *life,* and I am not going to trade it for an anonymous life in the brotherhood of man—which is either sure death, or quasi-death, or at the very best cruel deception. I am fatuous enough to believe that in living my own life in my own way I am more apt to give life to others (though even that is not my chief concern) than I would if I simply followed somebody else's idea of how to live my life and thus become a man among men. It seems to me that this struggle for liberty and justice is a confession or admission on the part of all those engaging in such a struggle that they have failed to live their own lives. Let us not deceive ourselves about "humanitarian impulses" on the part of the great brotherhood. The fight is for life, to have it more abundantly, and the fact that millions are now ready to fight for something they have ignominiously surrendered for the greater part of their lives does not make it more *humanitarian.*

"I came not to bring peace, but a sword!" said the great humanitarian. That is not the utterance of a militarist, nor is it the utterance of a pacifist: it is the utterance of one of the greatest artists that ever lived. If his words mean anything they mean that the struggle for life, for *more* life, must be carried on day by day. It means that life itself is struggle, *perpetual struggle.* This sounds almost banal, and in fact it has become banal, thanks to the frog-like perspective of Darwin and such like. Banal because our struggle has become banal, because our struggle is for food and shelter—not even that, by God, but *for work.* Men are struggling for the right to work! It sounds almost incredible but that is precisely what it amounts to, the great goal of the civilized man. What an heroic struggle! Well, for my part, I will say that whatever else I may want, I know I don't want *work.* To live as an artist I stopped work some ten or twelve years ago. I made it extremely uncomfortable for myself. I cannot even say that it was a matter of choice, my decision. I had to do it, or die of boredom. Naturally I was not paid to stop work and live as an artist. The time came quickly enough when I had to beg for a crust of bread. They said strange things to me, those whom I asked for food or shelter.

Brother, said one man, why didn't you save your money for a rainy day? Said another: brother, open your heart to God that you may be saved. And another: join the union and we will find you a job so that you may eat and have a place to sleep. None of them gave me money, which is all I had asked for. I realized that I was ostracized and I understood quickly enough that this was just, because if one chooses to live his own life in his own way he must pay the penalty.

I cannot help seeing in men what I know them to be from my own experience of life. Their illusions and delusions are poignantly touching to me, but they do not convince me that I should offer my life for them. It seems to me that the men who would create a Fascist world are the same at heart as those who would create a Communist world. They are all looking for leaders who will provide them with enough work to give them food and shelter. I am looking for something more than that, something which no leader can give me. I am not against leaders *per se*. On the contrary, I know how necessary they are. They will be necessary so long as men are insufficient unto themselves. As for myself, I need no leader and no god. I am my own leader and my own god. I make my own bibles. *I believe in myself*—that is my whole credo.

An age such as ours is the most difficult one of all for an artist. There is no place for him. At least, that is what one hears on all sides. Nevertheless, some few artists of our time have made a place for themselves. Picasso made a place for himself. Joyce made a place for himself. Matisse made a place for himself. Céline made a place for himself. Should I rattle off the whole list? Perhaps the greatest of them all has not yet made a place for himself. But *who* is he? *Where* is he? If he is the greatest of all he will make himself heard. He will not be able to conceal himself.

Those who are perpetually talking about the inability to communicate with the world—have they made every effort? Have they learned what it is to "compromise"? Have they learned how to be as wise and cunning as the serpent, as well as strong and obstinate as a bull? Or are they braying like donkeys, whining about some ideal condition in the ever-receding future when every man will be recognized and rewarded for his labors? Do they really expect such a day to dawn, these simple souls?

I feel that I have some right to speak about the difficulty of establishing communication with the world since my books are banned in the only countries where I can be read in my own tongue. I have enough faith in myself however to know that I eventually will make myself heard, if not understood. Everything I write is loaded with the dynamite which will one day destroy the barriers erected about me. If I fail it will be because I did not put enough dynamite into my words. And so, while I have the strength and the gusto I will load my words with dynamite. I know that the timid, crawling ones who are my real enemies are not going to meet me face to face in fair combat. *I know these birds!* I know that the only way to get at them is to reach up inside them, through the scrotum; one has to get up inside and twist their sacred entrails for them. That's what Rimbaud did. That's what Lautréamont did. Unfortunately, those who call themselves their successors have never learned this technique. They give us a lot of piffle about the revolution—first the revolution of the word, now the revolution in the street. How are they going to make themselves heard and understood if they are going to use a language which is emasculated? Are they writing their beautiful poems for the angels above? Is it communication with the dead which they are trying to establish?

You want to communicate. All right, communicate! Use any and every means. If you expect the world to fall for your lingo because it is the right lingo, or even the *left* lingo, you are going to be cruelly deceived. It's like the "pug" who goes into the ring expecting to get it over with quickly. Generally he gets flattened stiff as a board. He thinks he'll deliver an uppercut or a swift one to the solar plexus. He forgets to defend himself. He lays himself wide open. Everybody who's gone out to fight has had to first learn something about the strategy of the ring. The man who refuses to learn how to box becomes what is called, in the language of the ring, "a glutton for punishment." Speaking for myself, I'll say that I've taken all the punishment I could assimilate. From now on I use my head, my bean, as they say. I watch for an opening. I do a little fancy stepping. I duck. I feint. I spar a bit, I bide my time. When the moment comes I let go with all my might.

I am against revolutions because they always involve a return to *status quo*. I am against the *status quo* both *before* and *after* revolutions. I don't want to wear a black shirt or a red shirt. I want to wear the shirt that suits my taste. And I don't want to salute like an automaton either. I prefer to shake hands when I meet someone I like. The fact is, to put it simply, I am positively against all this crap which is carried on first in the name of this thing, then in the name of that. I believe only in what is active, immediate and personal.

I was writing Surrealistically in America before I had ever heard the word. Of course I got a good kick in the pants for it. I wrote for ten years in America without once having a manuscript accepted. I had to beg, borrow and steal in order to get by. Finally I got out of the country. As a foreigner in Paris, without friends, I went through an even worse ordeal, though in another sense it was a thousand times better than the American experience. I grew so desperate that finally I decided to explode—and I did explode. The naive English critics, in their polite, asinine way, talk about the "hero" of my book (*Tropic of Cancer*) as though he were a character I had invented. I made it as plain as could be that I was talking in that book about myself. I used my own name throughout. I didn't write a piece of fiction: I wrote an autobiographical document, a *human* book.

I mention this only because this book marks a turning point in my literary career—I should say, *in my life*. At a certain point in my life I decided that henceforth I would write about myself, my friends, my experiences, what I knew and what I had seen with my own eyes. Anything else, in my opinion, is literature, and *I am not interested in literature*. I realized also that I should have to learn to content myself with what was within my grasp, my scope, my personal ken. I learned not to be ashamed of myself, to talk freely about myself, to advertise myself, to elbow my way in here and there when necessary. The greatest man America ever produced was not ashamed to peddle his own book from door to door. He had faith in himself and he has given tremendous faith to others. Goethe too was not ashamed to beg a friend to put in a good word for him with the critics. Gide and Proust were not ashamed to publish their first books at their own expense. Joyce had the courage to search for years for the person who would publish his *Ulysses*. Was the world better then? Were people more kind, more intelligent, more sympathetic, more understanding? Did Milton get a reasonable price for his *Paradise Lost?* I could go on multiplying instance after instance. What's the use?

Justice you ask for! Well, every day life metes out an inexorable justice. It's not ideal, it may not even be intelligent—from the viewpoint of a Marxian dialectician. But it's justice. The English are particularly noted for shouting about liberty and justice. They make a great point always about "fair play," even in war. As though war were a game played according to rules. But in crucial matters the English have never indulged in "fair play." If they had they would not own the vast empire on which the sun never sets, as they so fatuously boast. No, the English may *talk* about fair play, but in practice they have always employed the most dastardly tactics.

I know little about history, politics, literature, art, science, philosophy, religion, etc. I know only what I have seized through experience. I put no trust in the men who explain life to us in terms of history, economics, art, etc. They are the fellows who bugger us up, juggling their abstract ideas. I think it is a piece of the most cruel deception to urge men to place their hopes of justice in some external order, some form of government, some social order, some system of ideal rights. I read every day somewhere or other about the Marxian dialectic, as though not to understand this lingo were a blot on the intelligence of man. Well, I must confess, and very willingly, that I have never read a line of Karl Marx. I have never felt *compelled* to read him. And the more I listen to his disciples the more I realize that I have lost nothing. Karl Marx, so they say, explains the structure of our capitalistic society. I don't need an explanation of our capitalistic society. Fuck your capitalistic society! Fuck your Communistic society and your Fascist society and all your other societies! Society is made up of individuals. It is the individual who interests me—not the society.

What strikes one as pathetic, lamentable, deplorable and ridiculous, in riffling the pages of this English book on Surrealism, is the effort "to get together." It's like a courtship between the serpent and the eagle, this momentary truce between the English and the French. André Breton, the great fish out of water, solemnly pontificates as usual. Reviving the language of Dr. Johnson, distorting it through his Freudian French, he seems to be giving the English elementary instruction in the art of tapping the Unconscious. In Hugh Sykes Davies he has an able disciple; this lad, blown up out of all proportion by his learning, is on the point of bursting. He needs only another breathful from André Breton.

No, the Dadaists were more entertaining. They had humor, at least. The Surrealists are too conscious of what they are doing. It's fascinating to read about their intentions—but when are they going to pull it off? On the other hand, take this from the Dada Manifesto 1918:

"I am neither for nor against and I do not explain for I hate good sense."

"Dialectic is an amusing machine which carries us—in a stupid manner—to opinions which we would have had in any case."

"God can afford not to be successful: Dada also."

And now to quote again from the devil: *"The greatness of any active organization which is the embodiment of an idea lies in the spirit of religious fanaticism and intolerance with which it attacks all others, being fanatically convinced that it alone is right. If an idea is right in itself, and, being armed with such weapons, wages warfare on this earth, it is invincible and persecution only increases its internal strength."*

One would like to ask where Hitler got this sound and crazy

notion. From Jerome? From Augustine? From Luther? Anyway, humanity is always marching in the van triumphant. To get the right idea! What a beautiful, senseless dream of a clean solution! But don't lose sight of the "religious fanaticism and intolerance!" That's important . . .

Last night I was glancing over that essay in indirect criticism called *The Laic Mystery*. It's a step in a direction which the English have never taken and never will, even though the whole nation becomes Surrealist. Here's a bit at random . . .

"Nothing is more touching than an animal trying to regain the secret of human speech which it has discovered and then lost."

"Without puns and puzzles there is no serious art. That is to say there is nothing but serious art."

This may be irrelevant, but it's Surrealistically true: Diamond Jim Brady was a capitalist who was on the level. He had a good heart. He was magnanimous. So-and-So, on the other hand, was a rapacious idiot even before he had grown senile. He would be a disgrace to any society in any time. If you follow the logic you get a free ride.

We are always talking about society as though it were made up of two classes, those who have and those who have not. In addition to class lines, the men of civilized society are divided by intelligence (the lowest going far below the intelligence of the savage), temperament, race, language, occupation, belief, principles, a thousand and one things. Cut a slice anywhere any time and you have a history of the evolution of the human race from start to finish.

Coming back to Freud . . . From a letter I once wrote to a painter who had just been analyzed and wondered why he couldn't paint any more:

"As far as we know, man has never been free of disease. Health and disease have always co-existed. The interest of the medical man has been and still is in disease, *not in health*. No physician has ever proposed to give man health—only to eradicate disease. His whole attention centers upon disease. Health is kept in the background, like an ideal, but one moves realistically in a curve towards this ideal. One does not move towards the ideal of health directly, drastically, fanatically. Part of the great fear of disease which is in us has its origin in the unconscious desire of the physician to exploit disease.

"This much is indisputable, that disease is a constant and vital factor of life, that in stressing *health* we are stressing an untenable ideal, a delusion. Moreover, despite all our warfare against disease we have made no real progress; we have merely set up new configurations of health-disease. Also falsely, casuistically, we have minimized the importance, the *benefits,* of disease. In short, we have interpreted the history of the warfare between health and disease as we have interpreted all other histories—according to our intuitions, our prejudices. (I trust it is not necessary to specify the very genuine contributions to civilization made by the great plagues, or by such admittedly tainted individuals as Buddha, Jesus, St. Francis, Joan of Arc, Nietzsche, Dostoievski, Napoleon, Genghis Khan et alii.)

"Coming to the more immediate problem, the all-important conflict between the artist and the collectivity . . . the growing attitude among the public that the artist is a leper, the attitude of the analysts that art is merely the expression of a neurotic conflict, the intensification and objectification of a condition found in other strata of society, the confused attitude among artists themselves as to the nature and purpose of art, together with the very definite belief on the part of many artists that 'art is a cure' . . . The question, it seems to me, which each one must pose for himself is this: which reality is more vital, more life-giving, more valid, more durable—the reality of science or the reality of art? (I realize that the question itself is open to criticism. We enter immediately into the realm of metaphysics, from which there is no escape, except into life.) But, assuming a divergence between the scientific and the poetic attitudes towards life, is it not clear enough that to-day the schism has grown impassable? To-day with the mass of mankind completely under the hypnotic sway of the scientific-minded, art is fighting for its life, for its very right to exist.

"I want to discover if you consider the work of the analyst to be an effort to adjust man to reality, and if so, whether you consider such an adjustment more important than the recreation of reality, through art. Do you prefer a smooth levelling down, a smooth functioning on the part of the individual in society to a state of tension, eruption, fertility? Naturally you will say NO. The implication is, however, that the artist sows discord, strife. To try to eradicate the disturbing elements of life by 'adjustment' is tantamount to expropriating the artist. Fear, love, hate, all the varying, contradictory expressions or reactions of the personality, are what compose the very warp and woof of life. You can't pull one of them out without the whole edifice crumbling.

"Here, no doubt, you will answer me by saying—This is precisely what the analyst is trying to do, to get people to accept life as a struggle, a conflict, a game. But, immediately the analyst enters the field in the role of medicine man, the question *why* our life presents such a pattern interests him exceedingly less than *how to combat it.* I say that with the increasing sway of the analyst there will occur an increasing prevalence of neurosis. Neurosis will become universal. It will take its legitimate place in the hierarchy of our diseases, just as tuberculosis, cancer, etc., took their place in the pattern of our ancestors' diseases. A niche will be made for it, and the more we pretend to fight it the more strongly will it become entrenched.

"Why do we not rid ourselves of tuberculosis, syphilis, cancer, etc., when we know so well how to combat them? Why do we not *prevent* instead of *cure?* Because cancer, syphilis, tuberculosis, neurosis, are as definite and fixed a part of our life as the machine, the aeroplane, the skyscraper, etc. This is the psychic and substantial configuration that we want. The moment we want another one we shall have it—*just by wanting!* And the aim of the artist, as I see it, is to make people *want* another, a *different* picture. The sane, the wise, the adjusted souls are always ready to reply—'But this is the way life is . . . you can't alter it . . . you're mad!' And the artist always answers: 'You are right. I want only the impossible, only the marvellous. To-morrow you will see that what I proclaimed was not impossible. But then it will be too late, for to-morrow we will see again with different eyes and again you will cry *Impossible!* You live to-morrow and yesterday; I live only to-day. Therefore, I live eternally. I am timeless. And since this is obviously untrue, you are right and I continue to be wrong. It is out of my wrongness that your right is created. To be right is to be either late or ahead of time. The only span between us is time!'

"Art, as I see it, is the expression of this chasm, this desynchronization: it is the projection of the universal picture of individuation. Man against the universe. *Against,* please notice. The work of art, *the poem,* is the symbol of his latitude and longitude, of his temporal position in time and space.

"Will analysis, or revolution, or anything else dissolve this picture? Is understanding a goal in itself, or is understanding a byproduct? Do we want a closer rapport between artist and collectivity, or do we want an increasing tension? Do we want art to become more communicative, or do we want it to be more fecundating? Do we want every man to become an artist and thus eliminate art? Unconsciously I think that every great artist is trying with might and main to destroy art. By that I mean that he is desperately striving to break down this wall between himself and the rest of humanity. Not for the sake of the brotherhood of man, because at bottom he is tyrant (like Mohammed, Buddha, Christ, Tamerlane), but in the hope of debouching into some more quick and vivid realm of human experience. He is not struggling to isolate himself from his fellow-men, since it is his very isolation which drives him to create, but rather to emancipate himself from false relations with his fellow-men, from false relations with nature and with all the objects which surround him. Art is only one of the manifestations of the creative spirit. What every great artist is manifesting in his work is a desire to lead a richer life; his work itself is only a description, an intimation, as it were, of those possibilities. The worst sin that can be committed against the artist is to take him at his word, to see in his work a fulfillment instead of an horizon. Da Vinci, who troubles us more than any other artist, who left so much unfinished . . . fortunately! . . . has left us the symbol of this desire in that upraised index finger which speaks to us more laconically than the famous Mona Lisa smile. Da Vinci was the forerunner of those anatomists of the soul who are now moving into the foreground with megaphones and amplifiers.

"Freud's contribution to the cause of human enlightenment (as the stupid saying goes) is creative and anarchic, in keeping with his race and temperament; there is the same uncompromising spirit in him as in his forerunners, the same arid, monotonous, luminous quality of the desert, the geometric line, the theorem, the axiom— and naturally, *the golden hypothesis*. The Absolute is in his blood. An anal rectitude, a frigid punctilio, a gray sprightliness in which there is neither joy nor sensuality. Unable to reconcile himself to the world (to the philosophy of the day, that is), he turned the world upside down. He created a fiction which helped to pass the time away. Which helped, if you please, not to adjust him to the world but to adjust the world to his own imaginings. His theory of psycho-analysis is a piece of art, like any other piece of art, and it will lead a pure isolated existence. The truth of it is incommunicable. What will happen to-morrow in the name of the holy cause may have little or nothing to do with his creation. Even Hitler, so rumor has it, was willing to use it for his own ends, as he does with astrology. The significance of Freud's creation is purely aesthetic. As he draws quietly nearer to the grave he is not only honestly dubious about the future, but downright pessimistic. There is a sort of wistful questioning, a doubting, one might say, as to the efficacy of his penetrative researches into the mysteries of the human psyche. (Is there not something slightly humorous about this, as if perhaps the old bird had never given himself a chance to think it all out?) However, no panaceas! That much is clear. And if at the end the great Sigmund Freud happens to find himself enmeshed in his own creative lie is there any denying the fact that thousands of individuals, believing implicitly in the efficacy of his therapy, have found greater enjoyment of life? In turning the world upside down I sometimes think that Freud more than anyone else must have been astonished to find that it tended to remain upside down. The disciples of Freud, as is the way with disciples, are struggling to put the world back on its feet again. The role of the disciple is always to betray the master. The moral is that no matter how great the master the world will not remain permanently upside down.

"There have always been and always will be men in the world who are healers, just as there will always be an order of priests, an order of prophets, an order of warriors, an order of kings, an order of poets. In our day the interest in physical maladies is on the wane. (The importance of surgery is only one of the many proofs of the fact.) Our world is suffering from mental disorders—from the insanities and neuroses of one form and another. Just as literature swings at times from the poetic to the prosodic, so nowadays we have the swing from the physical disorders to the mental, with the inevitable emergence of new types of genius cropping out among the mental healers. All that the creative personality demands is a new field for the exercise of its powers; out of the dark, inchoate forces, these personalities will, by the exercise of their creative faculties, impose upon the world a new ideology, a new and vital set of symbols. What the collective mass desires is the concrete, visible, tangible substance . . . which the theories of Freud, Jung, Rank, Stekel, et alii provide. This they can pore over, chew, masticate, tear to pieces or prostrate themselves before. Tyranny always works best under the guise of liberating ideas. The tyranny of ideas is merely another way of saying the tyranny of a few great personalities.

"There is a vast parallelism between the religious figures of the past and the psychologists of to-day. The underlying theme is *salvation,* whether it be called 'finding God' or 'adapting oneself to reality.' ('May not one succeed in systematizing confusion and so assist the total discrediting of the world of reality?' asks Dali.) When the symbols by which man relates himself to the universe are exhausted he must perforce find new ones, vital ones, which will reintegrate him to the universe. This process which is one of oscillation, is known as a macro-microcosmizing of the universe. According to whichever way the pendulum happens to swing, man tends either to become himself, God, or to become mere *dreck.* To-day the world has become so inflated that God has been completely squeezed out. The exploration of the Unconscious, which is now under way, is a confession of the bankruptcy of the spirit. When we almost reach the Absolute, when we can no longer work in it, or with it, we let in the air . . . and establish a relative balance again.

"Recently at a Surindépendent showing I had a terrific feeling of this desire on the part of modern man to explore this uncharted world of the Unconscious. I am speaking more particularly of the Surrealist section of the exhibit. It was a strange afternoon, dark, foggy, ominous, like one of those days in the early Middle Ages when signs and portents were so frequently observed in the heavens, the ominous ones always occurring in mid-day. I arrive at the big hall towards four o'clock. No lights have been lit to illuminate these marvels. They swim around me in a sort of oceanic twilight. Looking about me I can discover only three people in this vast hall. I wander from zone to zone, as if under the ocean, and gradually I discover that I am the only spectator left. The darkness gets more intense. I have to approach within a foot of the pictures in order to make them out. It seems suddenly very strange to me that there should be hundreds of pictures in this vast gallery and no audience. And then jokingly, also a little desperately, I add, half-aloud; 'You're the whole audience; the show is for *you!*' Immediately the thought formulates itself—it seems to me singularly right that it should be thus, that only I am there to voice an unheard appreciation. After a bit I observe that the guardians are prowling about in my wake, also examining the pictures . . . and with more than usual interest, it would seem. I observe them more attentively, and would you believe it, I notice that it is to the Surrealist paintings that they instinctively turn. Maybe then these robots, whose appreciation nobody gives a fuck about, maybe then these half-wits and myself are the only valid audience for a Surrealist show! Excellent! Anyway, I see it as strangely significant, symbolic if you like. Not only the absence of the crowd, but the frost and the fog . . . and the utter lack of illumination. One might very well imagine that a plague had swept the country and that only a few monkish souls, the guardians and myself included, were left to enjoy the benefits of a vanished civilization. A strange question then presented itself to my mind. Were these Surrealist specimens part of our vanished civilization and thus forgotten without ever being known, or were they already existing in a time which had not yet commenced and therefore invisible to the ordinary eye? I wondered how and if Dali would recover his remarkable etherized horse and whether, through handling or neglect, it would undergo a metamorphosis which would so astonish everybody as to produce something in the nature of a miracle. If, for example, the horse suddenly got detached from the frame and managed to hide away in the chandelier swinging high above.

If they had discovered that it was a real horse, only somewhat abnormal, which the painter Dali had drugged in order to plaster him over his canvas. How would the damp and the mould affect him—the horse, I mean? All sorts of enigmas presented themselves to my mind in quick fashion.

"And what was it I witnessed in this festival of the Unconscious? What were the masters of this unexplored realm bringing up from the depths? For one thing, the organs of the human body, the parts we look at without shuddering only in the butcher's shop. I saw the insides coming out and smearing themselves in extrovert fashion over the feeble mass of skin and bones. I saw the hungry, gnawing innards of man so long hidden away, despised, ignored, denigrated, blasphemed, I saw them issuing forth in bold assertiveness, weaving a bloody and hysterical, but *marvellously* bloody and hysterical, legend on the frost-sweated walls of Versailles. Amongst these hysterical phantoms of the deep I feel absolutely at home. A thousand times more at home than in the butcher's shop or the funeral parlor. I float among them in the deepening twilight in a genuine ecstasy. Dali's horse with the motorized sex organs is far more real than reality, which of course is in the nature of an oxymoron, if you happen to be the victim of pedantry. This horse with the female head, its motored sex borrowed from Darwin, Edison, Freud & Co., Inc., its mythological and atavistic remnants and fragments, the baited hook like a spur driven through the rectum, the color and odor of it, the nostalgia it evokes (Troy, Bucephalus, Man of War, The Dime Museum, Laotse, Meissonier, Heliogabolus, Montezuma, Infanticide, Lady of the Lake, to mention a few), the incongruous and anomalous parts, the absurd which is devastating, together with the sense of space which is absent and yet devours you, all of it, sex, nonsense, poison, nostalgia, Darwinian hypothesis, and electric light bulbs, not overlooking the penny arcades and the statues forgotten to be pulled down, make up a totality of reality so enticing that one feels like walking into the canvas, folding up and dying there. And if, cher ami, as you once remarked walking down the Rue de la Gaieté, it is impossible or futile to paint the Unconscious, then please accept in my name this replica of the Unconscious which will have to serve until detachments are brought up and the trenches consolidated. This perhaps is not even a representation of the Unconscious, but a necessity of the Unconscious. And, let me add, that whenever between Idea and Representation there occurs such an inviolable marriage we may without let or fear take one for the other or vice versa.

"As in olden times, when the Christian myth had man by the

balls so that he was powerless to paint anything but madonnas, angels, demons and their like, so now it seems to me that in the paintings of the Surrealists we have the embryonic spawn of the coming angels, demons and madonnas, etc. I see some dim relationship between the bankruptcy of the conscious intellectual forces (the insanity of our present world) and the emergence of this great new empire of darkness (the insanity of the future) which, in its demand to be explored and charted, will revive the sensory powers of man so that he may look upon the world about him with renewed exaltation and more vivid consciousness. I see it as a desire to deflate the abstract, materialistic universe of the scientific-minded man, a desire to fill in the chinks of his hole-and-theory conception of Nature so that we may live, if necessary, even in a space no bigger than a padded cell and feel at one with the universe. The artist is now giving a first coat of paint to that tautly stretched canvas which the scientist has been so busy stretching that he has forgotten the use he intended to put it to. The whole world has almost forgotten what the canvas was meant for. The artists too had almost forgotten, most of them at any rate. A few of them, however, have started in to lay down a nice thick coat of unconscious; they have covered up a few of the gaping holes already.

"I come back again to the path-finders, the great pioneers, such as Father Freud, Jung the Mystic, et alii, and I say that what they are striving for is not to create a technique of psychoanalysis, nor even a philosophic-scientific theory. Nothing of the kind. What they are doing is to offer themselves to us as examples of the potentialities which reside in each and all of us. They are trying to eliminate themselves as doctors, scientists, philosophers, theoreticians, trying to reveal to us the miraculous nature of man, the vast possibilities which stretch before him. They do not want disciples and expounders, they do not want to be imitated—they want merely to point the way. We ought, I say, to turn our backs on their theories, we ought to smash their theories. We ought to make all these theories unnecessary. Let each one turn his gaze inward and regard himself with awe and wonder, with mystery and reverence; let each one promulgate his own laws, his own theories; let each one work his own influence, his own havoc, his own miracles. Let each one as an individual, assume the roles of artist, healer, prophet, priest, king, warrior, saint. No division of labor. Let us recombine the dispersed elements of our individuality. Let us reintegrate.

"The religious leader, like the analyst, awakens men to a consciousness of the Id, the great unknown reservoir and fundament of humanity. In making men conscious of this identity of substratum, this brotherhood below the belt, this lurking humanity, so to speak, he sets in motion an oppositional force, divinity. If you make a psychological graph of the human mind you have something like an iceberg, with one-third visible and two-thirds invisible, below the surface of the sea, below the threshold of consciousness. What distinguishes the great icebergs from the little ones is height and profundity—the measure of the one is the measure of the other. The same force which thrusts one iceberg higher up also thrusts it deeper down than the others. Isolation is the index of profundity. Of what use then for the analysts to stress adaptation to reality? What reality? Whose reality? The reality of iceberg Prime or icebergs X, Y, Z? We are all swimming in the ocean depths and flying in the stratosphere. Some dive a little lower, some climb a little higher—but it's always air and water, always reality, even if it's a completely crazy reality. The analyst stresses the lower depths reality, the religious leader the stratospheric spiritual reality. Neither of them is adequate. Both are distorting the picture of reality in the passionate pursuit of truth. The artist is not interested in truth or beauty *per se*. The artist puts the picture into whack *because he is thoroughly disinterested*. His vision goes round the obstacle; it refuses to exhaust itself in straight line attacks. His work, which is simply the expression of his struggle to adapt himself to a reality of his own making, sums up all other approaches to reality and gives them significance.

"Experience alone is valueless, and idea alone is valueless. To give either validity one must employ them together plastically. In short, we are never going to be cured of our diseases (physical or mental), we are never going to reach a heaven (either real or imaginary) and we are never going to eliminate our evil, thwarting instincts (whatever these may be). In the realm of ideas the best we shall ever have will be a philosophy of life (not a science of life, which is a contradiction in terms); in the realm of experience we shall never have a better expression than the living out of our animal nature (not our cultural patterns). The highest aim of man, as thinker, is to achieve a pattern, a synthesis, to grasp life poetically; the chief and highest aim of man as animal is to live out his instincts, obey his instincts, take him where they will. So long as he cannot operate as a savage or less than savage, and think as a god, or better than a god, he will suffer, he will propose to himself remedies, governments, religions, therapies. Back of all his behaviour is fear—fear of death. Could he overcome this he might live as god and beast. The fear of death has created a whole cosmogony of lesser fears which plague us in a thousand different ways. We are forever tinkering with the little fears, the minor aches. That is what gives life its melodic minors, as we know. The bigger the personality the greater the simplification, the greater the diapason, the tension, the polarity, the juice, the vitality. One can take fear, isolate it, and against it counterpoint a grand symphony of life. Or one can refuse to acknowledge it, fight a million trivial battles every day of his life, and achieve that stale hash which the majority of men serve up to themselves in lieu of solid nutriment."

PERHAPS WE ARE ONLY CHARGED WITH THE LIQUIDATION OF SOME SPIRITUAL INHERITANCE WHICH IT IS IN EVERY ONE'S INTEREST TO REPUDIATE, AND THAT IS ALL. (André Breton)

Surrealism starts out innocently enough as a revolt against the insanity of every-day life. It is expressed marvellously in one of Breton's early pronunciamentoes: "I am resolved to render powerless that *hatred of the marvellous* which is so rampant among certain people." Naturally he is not referring to concierges alone. He means everybody (who is not living as a poet), from the President of France on down to the chimney-sweep. It is a big order. It is a defi to the whole world practically. But there is no confusion behind the idea. It is clear as a bell.

"THE MARVELLOUS IS ALWAYS BEAUTIFUL. ANYTHING THAT IS MARVELLOUS IS BEAUTIFUL. INDEED NOTHING BUT THE MARVELLOUS IS BEAUTIFUL."

If one takes a sweeping glance at the paraphernalia which distinguishes our civilization from those of the past—I mean our battleships, factories, railways, torpedoes, gas-masks, etc.—one realizes that this *is* our civilization and not something else which we imagine civilization to be. Civilization is drugs, alcohol, engines of war, prostitution, machines and machine slaves, low wages, bad food, bad taste, prisons, reformatories, lunatic asylums, divorce, perversion, brutal sports, suicides, infanticide, cinema, quackery, demagogy, strikes, lockouts, revolutions, putsches, colonization, electric chairs, guillotines, sabotage, floods, famine, disease, gangsters, money barons, horse racing, fashion shows, poodle dogs, chow dogs, Siamese cats, condoms, pessaries, syphilis, gonorrhea, insanity, neuroses, etc., etc.

When Dali talks of systematizing confusion does he mean this, this confusion which is truly marvellous, though perhaps not so beautiful? All this marvellous confusion is systematized. If one added another drop of confusion to it the bubble would burst. Surrealism is an expression of this universal confusion. Christianity was also the expression of a universal confusion.

But the point is that the early Christians were not mad. No more than the Surrealists are to-day. They were simply unhappy, unfit for the struggle which life demanded of them. The Christians invented a life hereafter where they would have pie in the sky, as we say. The Surrealists are almost as other worldly. "Is a man ready to risk everything so that at the very bottom of the crucible into which we propose throwing our poor abilities . . . he may have the joy of getting a glimpse of the light which will cease to flicker?"

There is no doubt about it, Surrealism is the secret language of our time, the only spiritual counterpart to the materialistic activities of the socialist forces which are now driving us to the wall. The seeming discrepancies between the language of Breton and Lenin, or Marx, are only superficial. Surrealism will give a new, deeper, truer, more immediate spiritual doctrine to the economic, social and political revolutionists. The Church has not been defeated after all. Christianity is *not* dead. It is about to triumph . . . after 2,000 years of futile struggle. The world *is* going to be turned upside down—and this time it may stay upside down. Unless "doubt's duck with the vermouth lips" comes along and upsets all calculations . . .

Before me, as I write this, lies the latest issue of the *Minotaure*, that most valuable index of the times. The cover design is by Dali, and as best I make out, represents a modern conception of the Minotaur. In the margin is a series of pen points all of different design. The most striking feature of Dali's Minotaur is the hollow thorax in which he has lodged a vicious looking lobster. Striking because the vitals have been entirely hollowed out! In the cusp of each thigh is an object, the right leg containing a glass cup and spoon, the left one a dark bottle with a cork in it. The left leg seems also to button and unbutton. The right one holds a key and just above the ankle a manacle bites through the tendons and flesh. But the chief feature, as I said, is the missing vitals—with the lobster still muscling in.

Riffling the pages of this magazine, I see that it deals entirely with disintegration—with nerve ends, necrophilism, sadism, eschatology, fetichism, embryology. *Ici on charcute l'embryon.* It is a perfect picture of our time, a pretty little fireside picture which corroborates the impression I had upon reading Céline's speech in honor of Emile Zola. This speech of Céline's is entirely about the death instincts in man, about his hallucinating desire for self-destruction. There are no young men to-day, he says. They are born old. We are in the grip of a sadist-masochist obsession and there will be no liberation until we are all wiped out. Hitler is nothing to the monsters who are to come. He adds that the worst ones will probably be bred here in France. With all of which I thoroughly agree.

By the year 2000 A.D. we will be completely under the sway of Uranus and Pluto. The word Communism will be an obsolete expression known only to philologists and etymologists. We shall be breaking ground for the new anarchy which will come in with the advent of the new zodiacal sign, Aquarius. Circa 2160 A.D. There won't be any A.D. any more, as the symbol will cease to mean anything. We shall have a wholly new calendar before we definitely enter the sign of Aquarius. I predict it now.

A man lives with dead suns inside him or he goes out like a flame and lives the life of the moon. Or he disintegrates entirely and throws a flaming comet across the horizon. But all the while, everywhere in the world, the lobster is muscling in and gnawing out the vitals. The Minotaur is we ourselves standing on the threshold of a new era. We must be devoured whilst devouring. The bottle, the key, the little coffee cup and spoon, these are the last relics hidden in the flesh. When they unbutton the leg of our once sacred body in the years to come, they will find these little treasures and prize them. The ethnologists, what I mean. These birds, ditto the archaeologists, we shall have with us always. Things will go on this way, ruins and relics, new battleships, new skyscrapers, peace treaties, holy wars, repartitions, alignments, discoveries, inventions, more ruins, more relics, progress everywhere all the time amidst famine, floods, pestilence, on and on like that for thousands of years until we have passed through every sign of the zodiac. Then one fine day we shall burst the belt and be out in the wide world of space in a bright new realm, the ahistorical realm in which art will have disappeared completely— because life itself will have become an art. All things point steadily towards this miracle, believe it or not. The miracle is MAN, man full blown and travelling with his mother the earth in a new field of constellations. Now he is busy weighing the stars and measuring the distance between them; *then* he will be of the stars and there will be no need to record, neither with instruments, nor with paper and ink, nor with signs and symbols. The meaning of destiny is to throw away the truss which the zodiacal belt represents and live it out *ad hoc* and *post rem*. That is what Breton means when he says with apocalyptic precision: "We should carry ourselves as though we were really *in the world!*"

Madness is tonic and invigorating. It makes the sane more sane. The only ones who are unable to profit by it are the insane. Very often the Surrealists give us the impression that they are insane in a very sane way—that it is "ice-box madness," as my friend Lawrence Durrell puts it, and not real madness.

When we look at the Surrealistic products of such men as Hieronymus Bosch or Grunewald or Giotto we notice two elements which are lacking in the works of the Surrealists to-day; *guts and significance*. Without vital guts there can be no true madness; without a healthy scepticism there can be no real significance in a work of art, or in life, for that matter. Breton says somewhere that "it had to be with lunatics that Columbus set out to discover America." That is a sad joke. Columbus set out with a bunch of desperate, hopeless men. Far from being dreamers, far from being fanatical believers, his men were ignorant, superstitious and filled with greed. The voyage may have been risky, but the idea was not. It wasn't even a gamble. And in the last analysis, Columbus never set out to discover America: he set out to discover a short route to India.

And another thing . . . it is a mistake to speak about Surreal*ism*. There is no such thing: there are only Surrealists. They have existed in the past and they will exist in the future. The desire to posit an ism, to isolate the germ and cultivate it, is a bad sign. It means impotency. It is on a par with that impotency which makes of a man a Christian, a Buddhist, or a Mohammedan. A man who is full of God is outside the faith.

It seems to me that it is a very simple error which the Surrealists are guilty of; they are trying to establish an Absolute. They are trying with all the powers of consciousness to usher in the glory of the Unconscious. They believe in the Devil but not in God. They worship the night but refuse to acknowledge the day. They talk of magic, but they practise voodooism. They await the miracle, but they do nothing to assist it, to bring about an accouchement. They talk of ushering in a general confusion, but they live like the bourgeoisie. A few of them have committed suicide, but not one of them has as yet assassinated a tyrant. They believe in the revolution but there is no real revolt in them.

It is true, they have dug up some interesting old post-cards; it is true they have pulled off some interesting seances; it is true they have staged some amusing riots; it is true they have managed to edit one of the most de luxe reviews to be found anywhere in the world; it is true that from time to time there have been included in their group some of the best artists in the world. But, *as Surrealists* have they given us the greatest masterpieces, either in music, literature, or painting? Have they been able to retain among their numbers *one* great figure in the world of art?

They say they are against the current order, but have their lives been endangered by their actions . . . as was the case with Villon, Rabelais, Sade, Voltaire, to mention but a few? Why are they allowed to shoot their mouths off without fear of arrest? Because the authorities know they are harmless, and they are harmless because they lack guts, and lacking guts they are unable to convince those to whom they address their appeals. The failure to "communicate" is entirely their own. Jesus managed to communicate; so did Gautama the Buddha; so did Mohammed; so did St. Francis; so did a host of lesser men. There is no great mystery behind the lives of these men. In each case the simple fact is that the man acted upon his belief, *regardless of the consequences.* Each one had a revelation to make and he made it. Society was no more favorable then to the ideas which they brought forward than society is to-day to the Surrealist doctrine. Paul Eluard says somewhere: "Mind can only triumph in its most perilous activities. *No daring is fatal.*" In his poetry Paul Eluard proves the truth of this. But there is something beyond mind, and that is *the whole being of man,* which he expresses in action. What is disastrous is the divorce between mind and action. The ultimate can only be expressed in conduct. Example moves the world more than doctrine. The great exemplars are the poets of action, and it makes little difference whether they be forces for good or forces for evil. There is one thing which the surrealists stress repeatedly, and that is the necessity for poetry in life. Despite what anybody says, poetry *is* communicable—because it is of the nature of the marvellous and man is precisely the one creature on earth which can be moved by the marvellous. His religions prove it; his art proves it; history proves it. Everything of value that has been accomplished by man has been accomplished in spite of reason, in spite of logic, in spite of honor, justice and all other shibboleths. The marvellous, and only the marvellous, is what hypnotizes man. That is what makes him a gullible fool, an idiot, a criminal, a martyr, a saint, a hero, a death-eater. In his moments of genius he is mad; if he is not mad enough he goes insane, and then he is unable to distinguish between what is marvellous and what is not marvellous. The Surrealists are the last of all people to go insane. They have too great a need, too great a thirst, for the marvellous. When Lautréamont, in a moment of high lucidity, said, "Nothing is incomprehensible," he was saying something marvellous. But only a poet has a right to say this. The ignorance of the poet is not a negative thing; it is a crucible in which all knowledge is refunded. In this state of true and humble ignorance everything is clear and knowledge is therefore superfluous. Knowledge is a sifting, a categorizing, a comparing, an analyzing. Knowledge was never essential to the poet. The poet comprehends because he feels; his passion is to embrace the world, not with his mind, but with his heart. The world is always in a wrong condition for the man who knows too much; as one becomes more ignorant one accepts more graciously. Knowledge makes everything finally incomprehensible. One only begins to comprehend when one begins to stop trying to know.

The Surrealists are trying to open a magic chamber of man's being through knowledge. That is where the fatal mistake lies. They are looking backwards instead of forwards. To discredit the world of reality, as they suggest, is an act of will, not of fate. What is really discredited is done silently, unostentatiously, and alone. People band together to proclaim an ideal, or a principle, to establish a movement, to organize a cult. But if they believed, each and every one wholeheartedly, they would have no need of numbers, nor of creeds, nor of principles, etc. The fear of standing alone is the evidence that the faith is weak. Man is happier when he is in a crowd; he feels safe and justified in what he is doing. But crowds have never accomplished anything, except destruction. The man who wants to organize a movement is invoking aid to help tear down something which he is powerless to combat single-handed. When a man is truly creative he works single-handed and he wants no help. A man acting alone, on faith, can accomplish what trained armies are incapable of accomplishing. To believe in one's self, in one's own powers, is apparently the most difficult thing in the world. Unfortunately there is nothing, absolutely nothing, more efficacious than believing in one's self. When a movement dies there is left only the memory of the man who originated the movement, the man who believed in what he was saying, what he was doing. The others are without name; they contributed only their faith in an idea. And that is never enough.

And just as I get this off my chest, someone walks in and hands me another book edited by Herbert Read, Called *Unit 1*. *Unit 1* is the name of a group of eleven English artists who have banded together to stand by each other and defend their beliefs. *"Unit One,"* says Paul Nash, "may be said to stand for the expression of a truly contemporary spirit, for that which is recognized as peculiarly *of to-day* in painting, sculpture and architecture."

Mr. Read, who writes the Introduction, goes on to say that "the modern artist is essentially an individualist; his general desire is not to conform to any pattern, to follow any lead, to take any instructions—but to be as original as possible, to be himself and to express himself in his art." If what Mr. Read says is so then this group is not composed of modern artists nor of individuals, but of rank imitators, men without originality who have banded together in self-defense. Looking at the reproductions one sees the ghosts of Brancusi, Picasso, Braque, Chirico, Max Ernst et alii. *Unit One* is not a group of "New" artists, we are informed. No, they are British artists of established reputation. Which is tantamount to saying there is no British art!

The most revelatory feature of this little book is the statements of the artists themselves, made in answer to a questionnaire submitted to them. There is something about the British mentality which baffles me. You ask a pertinent question and the man begins to talk about the wax in his ear, or about the rainfall in Uganda last summer. In the main questionnaires are idiotic, and this one is no exception to the rule. Nevertheless the questionnaire gives the artist an opportunity to talk about art, not about apple sauce. The British artists, like the British general, is muddle-headed. Perhaps it's the perpetual fog in which he is obliged to work. Perhaps it's the British diet. God knows what is responsible, but the fact remains that these eleven individuals talk like grammar-school students. It is difficult to get a clear idea of what they are driving at because none of them has a clear idea in his head.

Take this, for example, from John Armstrong, a painter: "It began to seem clear that my painting could not stand on its own legs, much less climb on them, that perhaps no painting ever had, that art had always to have a shove from behind from religion or politics, and a lift by the scruff of the neck from architecture in order to achieve anything."

Or this from Douglas Cooper who answers for Edward Burra: "Hieronymus Bosch was a moralist; he was trying to educate the people of his time: he was not merely dreaming, he was giving plastic expression to what were in his era undeniable truths: so, too, is Burra. Both are phantasists, but whereas Bosch throughout his whole life was concerned with educating his public (for Flemish art in the fifteenth century was primarily literary) Burra freed by 'the march of progress' from any such necessity, relied entirely on his imagination, and has been carried into the realms of the surreal." (The fact that both names begin with B seems to serve as the liaison. Why no mention was made of Burra's obvious master, Chirico, is a mystery to me. Perhaps Mr. Cooper was being "delicate.")

Or the profundity of Edward Wadsworth: "We change with age, but without change we are dead." . . . "Art evolves with the human race." . . . "The artists of this country have added—from time to time—their contribution to the ideography of Occidental painting, and they will continue to do so if they combine their craftsmanship with a more universal point of view of what they want to say."

It seems to me that there is a sort of cultivated feeble-mindedness here. To any one who has had the privilege of conversing with British people this comes as no shock. As my friend Lawrence Durrell says: "They have confused the inner struggle with the outer one. They want to bread poultice a primary chancre." As a matter of fact, they don't even have to go that far: they want to pretend there is no chancre. The reason why there is no British painter, poet, musician or sculptor worthy of the name is because ever since the Elizabethan Age the British have been walking around with blinders over their eyes. They have created an unreality which is the exact opposite of the "surreal," as one of these artists puts it. It may be too that the effort expended in producing a Shakespeare—which seems to be the crowning achievement of British genius—was so tremendous that not a crumb of originality was left for the men who came after. And even Shakespeare, greatest of the lot, was not exactly a model of originality.

The suave, self-patronizing way in which Paul Nash takes cognizance of this lack of originality also seems typically British to me. "The kind of art practised by the individuals of *Unit One*," says he blithely, "is no doubt traceable to origins; its counterpart is to be found in many countries to-day; that, however, is no reason for underestimating its value." If that is not a reason, the only reason, for underestimating its value, then I should like to know what is the reason. A statement like this might have been made by a British diplomat who, as we all know, has a genius for saying nothing. I find the same sort of wool-gathering in Herbert Read's Introduction to the Book *Surrealism*. Obliged to make some mention of Wyndham Lewis, here is now he drags him in: "English plastic arts had to wait for the inspiration of Picasso to show any real revival. In the last twenty years we have produced potentially great artists—Wyndham Lewis is the typical example—but they have suffered from a disastrous form of individualism. The English sin has always been eccentricity (sic!); by which I do not mean a lack of social coherence." What the last phrase means I haven't the slightest idea. But I do know what he means by "potentially great artists": artists who were nipped in the bud! On the other hand, why the English plastic arts had to wait for the inspiration of Picasso is not at all clear to me. Why? Because they did? At any rate, by means of this scurrilous and wishy-washy sort of legerdemain Wyndham Lewis, who is the only English artist of importance, outside of D. H. Lawrence, whom the English produced in the last couple of generations, is flippantly pushed into the background. It is obvious that Wyndham Lewis is not in the swing, that he chooses to remain, as always, the Enemy. That alone speaks well of him, in my opinion. For whenever an English artist of any value has arisen he has been marked as Public Enemy No. 1. Including the great Shakespeare! It may be comforting for the pygmies who are banding together to-day to believe that a proper understanding of the Marxian dialectic, together with a dash of Freud, may solve this time old difficulty, but I am afraid they are doomed to bitter disappointment. In order for England to have art, the English will have to undergo a radical transformation. They may even have to change the climate! Or else wait another five hundred years or so for a real inspiration. The question is, where did Picasso get his inspiration from?

Scarcely anything has been as stimulating to me as the theories and the products of the Surrealists. I say scarcely anything because I feel impelled to make mention of a few other things equally stimulating: China, for instance, everything associated with the name; the work of Otto Rank and Minkowski, the poet of schizophrenia; Keyserling, yes Count Herman Keyserling; the language and the ideas of Elie Faure; and, of course, D. H. Lawrence, and Nietzsche, and Dostoievski. Even Emerson and Rimbaud; even Goethe. And not least of all, Lewis Carroll.

If, as Goethe says somewhere—"only that which is fecund is true"—then in all these men whom I have cited, and in the whole idea of China, there must be truth. But truth is everywhere, in everything. It is useless to search for truth, as it is useless to search for beauty or for power. As it is useless also to search for God. Beauty, truth, power, God, all these come without searching, without effort. The struggle is not for these; the struggle is deeper than that. The struggle is to synchronize the potential being with the actual being, to make a fruitful liaison between the man of yesterday and the man of to-morrow. It is the process of growth which is painful, but unavoidable. We either grow or we die, and to die while alive is a thousand times worse than to "shuffle off this mortal coil." In a thousand different languages, in a thousand different ways, men everywhere are trying to express the same idea: that one must fight to keep vitally alive. Fight in order to realize one's potential self. Guilt, sin, conscience—there is no eradicating these factors of human consciousness. They are part and parcel of consciousness itself. The stress on the Unconscious forces of man does not necessarily imply the elimination of consciousness. On the contrary it imples the expansion of consciousness. There can be no return to an instinctive life, and in fact, even among primitive men I see no evidence of a purely instinctive life. The strict taboos, which belong to the order of consciousness, permit a greater release of the instinctive life. Civilized man has his taboos also, but the penalty, instead of being quick death, is a slow and poisonous one. By contrast with primitive people, civilized people seem dead, quite dead. They are not really more dead, to be sure, but they give the semblance of death because the tension, the polarity, is breaking down. Through this breakdown the stress shifts from the collective life to the individual life. The life of the primitive man is a collective life par excellence; but the life of the civilized man is not wholly individualistic. The goal is unmistakable, but the powers are lacking. Paradoxically enough, the more man approaches self-mastery the more fear he develops. As his sphere of influence widens his sense of isolation, of aloneness, increases. For thousands of years man has run with the herd; for thousands of years he has been—and still is—a predatory animal, killing with the pack. Civilization has not eliminated the instinct to kill, nor will it ever. But civilization has done another thing, almost unwittingly: it has encouraged the development of man's ego, of his individuality. I say civilization, but in reality I mean a *few men*, a few great, extraordinary individuals whose spiritual development has so far outstripped that of the ordinary man that they remain unique and exert over the great majority of men a tyranny which is to all intents and purposes obsessive. The cold, sterile crystallization of the truths which they perceived and acted upon forms the framework of what is called civilization. Just as with primitive man, so with the civilized man it is fear again which operates most powerfully, which dominates his consciousness. In the neurotic individual this fear comes to supreme expression; the paralyzed neurotic is the symbol of the thwarting power of civilization. He it is who is the victim of so-called "progress." He stands out in our midst as a warning, a sort of flesh-and-blood totem representing the powers of evil.

It is just here that a phrase of André Breton's—"the crisis of consciousness"—comes to my mind with significant force. Neurosis, is, in a way, precisely this—*the crisis of consciousness*. The neurotic is the victim of a new way of life which we must take or perish. For the neurotic is the victim of a soul struggle which takes place in the amphitheatre of the mind. It is a Narcissistic struggle with the self, and whichever way the issue turns it is he himself who is the victim. It is a sacrificial struggle waged by our highest types, and we the spectators are either going to eliminate these sufferers from our midst, in creating a more equilibrated individual, or we are going to imitate them and perish as they are perishing.

Analysis is not going to bring about a cure of neurosis. Analysis is merely a technique, a metaphysic, if you wish, to illustrate and explain to us the nature of a malady which is universal among civilized beings. Analysis brings no curative powers in its train; it merely makes us conscious of the existence of an evil, which, oddly enough, is consciousness.

This may sound confusing, but actually it is very clear and very simple. Everything that lives, that has being, whether it be a star, a plant, an animal, or a human being—even God Almighty—has direction. This idea might be explained equally well mathematically or by physics or psychologically. Or finally, *religiously*. Along the road which each of us is travelling there is no turning back. It is forward or dead stop, which is living death. This forward movement, or direction, is nothing but consciousness. It is movement along a gamut which makes itself known to us in the form of opposites, by duality, in other words. Everything is a question of degree, as we say. It is all one, and yet it is not one. It is two. The mystic, who is more dual than other men, arrives momentarily at a solution of the enigma by achieving a state of ecstasy in which he is at one with the universe. Needless to say, in such moments he has no need of God, or anything beyond him. He is beyond himself, so to speak, in the sense that his consciousness has so far expanded as to embrace the two opposite poles of his being. Struggle is unthinkable. He knows the meaning, in this trance-like state, of the ineffable. Everything is clear and acceptable; he is one with destiny. He is, in such moments, direction itself. That is, consciousness.

The condition of ecstasy is, as we know, not a permanent state of being. It is an experience which permits us to undergo a radical transformation, a fruitful metamorphosis, a renewal. The man who is with God, who sees God and talks to him, returns to the world of reality profoundly altered. By means of his experience he in turn alters reality itself. He puts a little more of God into it, so to speak. So that the vital problems which yesterday plagued us no longer exist. More difficult problems now confront us. Always problems, however. Every Utopia confers upon us a new hell. The chasm widens and deepens. The isolation becomes more intense.

The example which the lives of the mystics afford us is that progress and direction are two totally different things. Back of the idea of progress, which is the false idea underlying all civilizations—and the reason why they perish—is the notion of conquering over Nature. Neither offers a way out. There is no way out, as a matter of fact. We must accept the dilemma, if we are to accept life itself.

Herbert Read, in the closing paragraph of his Introduction to *Surrealism* speaks of "the renascence of wonder." It is a phrase which I should like to put beside that of Paul Eluard—"no daring is fatal." Wonder and daring! Dionysian concepts which are restored to us as we journey towards the night of the *Unconscious*. The day face of the world is unbearable, it is perhaps true. But this mask which we wear, through which we look at the world of reality, who has clapped it on us? Have we not grown it ourselves? The mask is inevitable: we cannot meet the world with naked skins. We move within grooves, formerly taboos, now conventions. Are we to throw away the mask, the lying day face of the world? *Could we,* even if we chose? It seems to me that only the lunatic is capable of making such a gesture—and at what a price! Instead of the conventional but flexible groove, which irks more or less, he adopts the obsessional mould which clamps and imprisons. He has completely lost contact with reality, we say of the insane man. But has he liberated himself? Which is the prison—reality or anarchy? Who is the gaoler?

"We make for ourselves," writes Amiel, "in truth, our own spiritual world monsters, chimeras, angels; we make objective what ferments in us. All is marvellous for the poet, all is divine for the saint; all is great for the hero; all is wretched, miserable, ugly and bad for the base and sordid soul. The bad man creates around him a pandemonium, the artist an Olympus, the elect soul a paradise, which each of them sees for himself alone. *We are all visionaries, and what we see is our soul in things . . .*"

All is marvellous for the poet! Yes, the more one is a poet the more marvellous everything becomes. Everything! That is to say, not just the life to come, not merely what is unknown and dimly apprehended, not the ideal, not truth, beauty, madness, but what is here and now, the flux of life, the dead as well as the alive, the common, the sordid, the worthless, the ugly, the boring, all, all, because the transforming vision alters the aspect of the world. The Surrealists themselves have demonstrated the possibilities of the marvellous which lie concealed in the commonplace. They have done it by juxtaposition. But the effect of these strange transpositions and juxtapositions of the most unlike things has been to freshen the vision. Nothing more. For the man who is vitally alive it would be unnecessary to rearrange the objects and conditions of this world. The vision precedes the arrangement, or rearrangement. The world doesn't grow stale. Every great artist by his work reaffirms this fact. The artist is the opposite of the politically-minded individual, the opposite of the reformer, the opposite of the idealist. The artist does not tinker with the universe: he recreates it out of his own experience and understanding of life. He knows that the transformation must proceed from within outward, not vice versa. The world problem becomes the problem of the Self. The world problem is the projection of the inner problem. It is a process of expropriating the world, of becoming God. The striving toward this limit, the expansion of the Self, in other words, is what truly brings about the condition of the marvellous. Knowledge is not involved, nor power. But vision.

It is but natural that the tremendous emphasis on the marvellous which the *Surrealists* have given to the movement should be the reaction against the crippling, dwarfing harmony imposed by French culture. In the fake Hellenism of French culture the sense of the marvellous, the sense of magic, of wonder, awe, mystery, was doomed to perish. In France "the lying cultural mask" which Nietzsche speaks of has become real; it is no longer a mask. Employing a ritual and ceremonial less rigid, less elaborate than the Chinese, the French nevertheless have come to resemble them in spirit more closely than any European nation. French life has become stylized. It is not a life rhythm but a death rhythm. The culture is no longer vital . . . it is decayed. And the French, securely imprisoned within this cultural wall, are rotting away. That is why, so it seems to me, the individual Frenchman appears to possess more vitality than his surrounding neighbors. In each and every Frenchman it is the cultural mould which manifests itself. Before you can kill off the individual Frenchman you have to kill off the culture which produced him. Nowhere else in Europe is this true. With the others the mould has already broken and what we smell in them is an amorphous, anonymous culture which is extinct. To be a good European now means to become a polyglot and nomadic cultural nobody. (Goethe was the last good European.)

If it serves to destroy this death grip Surrealism will serve a valuable function. But it rather seems to me that Surrealism is merely the reflection of the death process. It is one of the manifestations of a life becoming extinct, a virus which quickens the inevitable end. Even so it is a movement in the right direction. Europe must die, and France with it. Sooner or later a new life must begin, a life from the roots.

"As yet," writes Keyserling, "only the few are conscious of the extent to which the course of the historic process is a phenomenon resembling that of counterpoint in music. Just *because* the masses have triumphed to an unheard of degree for the time being, we are approaching a decidedly aristocratic epoch. Just *because* quantity alone is the decisive factor to-day, the qualitative will soon mean more than ever before. Just *because* the mass appears to be everything, all great decisions will soon be taken within the smallest circle. They, and they alone, as the Ark during the Flood, are the safeguards of the future.

"For this reason we who are spiritual should consciously assume the counterpoint attitude to everything which is going on to-day. Let the culture of making-all-things-easy overspread the earth like a flood. An age whose day is past is being drowned in the deluge. We will not even try to stem the tide. Let us recognize the fact that for a long time to come everything within view, and in the first instance the state, will have to serve the process of liquidation. But at the same time let us remain proudly conscious of this other fact: that to-day everything depends on those who keep aloof, who are officially inconspicuous and not in view of the many. All the future is theirs."

There remain the death-eaters, those who are coming more and more into control as the bright future opens up. Destined to hasten the collapse of a world already defunct they are galvanizing the dead youth of the world into a temporary enthusiasm. Everywhere youth is being called to the colors; as in every epoch the young are being groomed for the ritual slaughter. The cause! The sacred cause! For the sake of "the cause" the demons will soon be unleashed and we shall all be commanded to fly at each other's throats. It is as clear as can be. Under the sign of DEATH all sides, all forces, are secretly making common cause. *Death:* that is the real motive, the real urge. Whoever doubts that we are going to escape this death-feast is an imbecile. In this stupid infatuation for death the Surrealists are no different from the others. We are all going down together—red shirts, black shirts, pacifists, militarists, dadaists, Surrealists, nonconformists, all kins of ists and isms together. Down into the bottomless pit.

Now, my dear fellows, my dear Belgian, Swedish, Japanese, Dutch, British, French, American, Rhodesian, Arthurian, Cro-Magnon, Neanderthalian Surrealists, now is the time to grab hold of that most wonderful prehensile tail which has been dragging in the mud for countless centuries. Get hold of it, if you can, and swing for your lives! It's one chance out of a million, and I wish you luck, you poor bleeding bastards.

Un Etre Étoilique

As I write these lines Anaïs Nin has begun the fiftieth volume of her diary, the record of a twenty year struggle towards self-realization. Still a young woman she has produced on the side, in the midst of an intensely active life, a monumental confession which when given to the world will take its place beside the revelations of St. Augustine, Petronius, Abélard, Rousseau, Proust, and others.

Of the twenty years recorded half the time was spent in America, half in Europe. The diary is full of voyages; in fact, like life itself it might be regarded as nothing but voyage. The epic quality of it, however, is eclipsed by the metaphysical. The diary is not a journey towards the heart of darkness, in the stern Conradian sense of destiny, not a *voyage au bout de la nuit,* as with Céline, nor even a voyage to the moon in the psychological sense of escape. It is much more like a mythological voyage towards the source and fountain head of life—I might say an *astrologic* voyage of metamorphosis.

The importance of such a work for our time hardly needs to be stressed. More and more, as our era draws to a close, are we made aware of the tremendous significance of the human document. Our literature, unable any longer to express itself through dying forms, has become almost exclusively biographical. The artist is retreating behind the dead forms to rediscover in himself the eternal source of creation. Our age, intensely productive, yet thoroughly un-vital, un-creative, is obsessed with a lust for investigating the mysteries of the personality. We turn instinctively towards those documents—fragments, notes, autobiographies, diaries—which appease our hunger for more life because, avoiding the circuitous expression of art, they seem to put us directly in contact with that which we are seeking. I say they "seem to," because there are no short cuts such as we imagine, because the most direct expression, the most permanent and the most effective is always that of art. Even in the most naked confessions there exists the same ellipsis of art. The diary is an art form just as much as the novel or the play. The diary simply requires a greater canvas; it is a chronological tapestry which, in its ensemble, or at whatever point it is abandoned, reveals a form and language as exacting as other literary forms. A work like *Faust,* indeed, reveals more discrepancies, irrelevancies and enigmatic stumbling blocks than a diary such as Amiel's, for example. The former represents an artificial mode of synchronization; the latter has an organic integration which even the interruption of death does not disturb.

The chief concern of the diarist is not with truth, though it may seem to be, any more than the chief concern of the conscious artist is with beauty. Beauty and truth are the by-products in a quest for something beyond either of these. But just as we are impressed by the beauty of a work of art, so we are impressed by the truth and sincerity of a diary. We have the illusion, in reading the pages of an intimate journal, that we are face to face with the soul of its author. This is the illusory quality of the diary, its art quality, so to speak, just as beauty is the illusory element in the accepted work of art. The diary has to be read differently from the novel, but the goal is the same: self-realization. The diary, by its very nature, is quotidian and organic, whereas the novel is timeless and conventional. We know more, or seem to know more, immediately about the author of a diary than we do about the author of a novel. But as to what we *really* know of either it is hard to say. For the diary is not a transcript of life itself any more than the novel is. It is a medium of expression in which truth rather than art predominates. But it is not *truth.* It is not for the simple reason that the very problem, the obsession, so to say, is truth. We should look to the diary, therefore, not for the truth about things but as an expression of this struggle to be free of the obsession for truth.

It is this factor, so important to grasp, which explains the tortuous, repetitive quality of every diary. Each day the battle is begun afresh; as we read we seem to be treading a mystic maze in which the author becomes more and more deeply lost. The mirror of the author's own experiences becomes the well of truth in which ofttimes he is drowned. In every diary we assist at the birth of Narcissus, and sometimes the death too. This death, when it occurs, is of two kinds, as in life. In the one case it may lead to dissolution, in the other to rebirth. In the last volume of Proust's great work the nature of this rebirth is magnificently elaborated in the author's disquisitions on the metaphysical nature of art. For it

is in *Le Temps Retrouvé* that the great fresco wheels into another
dimension and thus acquires its true symbolic significance. The
analysis which had been going on throughout the preceding volumes reaches its climax finally in a vision of the whole; it is almost
like the sewing up of a wound. It emphasizes what Nietzsche
pointed out long ago as "the healing quality of art." The purely
personal, Narcissistic element is resolved into the universal; the
seemingly interminable confession restores the narrator to the
stream of human activity through the realization that life itself is
an art. This realization is brought about, as Proust so well points
out, through obeying the still small voice within. It is the very
opposite of the Socratic method, the absurdity of which Nietzsche
exposed so witheringly. The mania for analysis leads finally to its
opposite, and the sufferer passes on beyond his problems into a
new realm of reality. The therapeutic aspect of art is then, in this
higher state of consciousness, seen to be the religious or metaphysical element. The work which was begun as a refuge and
escape from the terrors of reality leads the author back into life,
not *adapted* to the reality about, but *superior* to it, as one capable
of recreating it in accordance with his own needs. He sees that it
was not life but himself from which he had been fleeing, and that
the life which had heretofore been insupportable was merely the
projection of his own phantasies. It is true that the new life is also
a projection of the individual's own phantasies but they are invested now with the sense of real power; they spring not from
dissociation but from integration. The whole past life resumes its
place in the balance and creates a vital, stable equilibrium which
would never have resulted without the pain and the suffering. It is
in this sense that the endless turning about in a cage which
characterized the author's thinking, the endless fresco which
seems never to be brought to a conclusion, the ceaseless fragmentation and analysis which goes on night and day, is like a gyration
which through sheer centrifugal force lifts the sufferer out of his
obsessions and frees him for the rhythm and movement of life by
joining him to the great universal stream in which all of us have
our being.

A book is a part of life, a manifestation of life, just as much as a
tree or a horse or a star. It obeys its own rhythms, its own laws,
whether it be a novel, a play, or a diary. The deep, hidden rhythm
of life is always there—that of the pulse, the heart beat. Even in
the seemingly stagnant waters of the journal this flux and reflux is
evident. It is there in the whole of the work as much as in each
fragment. Looked at in its entirety, especially for example in such
a work as that of Anaïs Nin's, this cosmic pulsation corresponds

to the death and rebirth of the individual. Life assumes the aspect of a labyrinth into which the seeker is plunged. She goes in unconsciously to slay her old self. One might say, as in this case, that the disintegration of the self had come about through a shock. It would not matter much what had produced the disintegration; the important thing is that at a given moment she passed into a state of two-ness. The old self, which had been attached to the father who abandoned her and the loss of whom created an insoluble conflict in her, found itself confronted with a nascent other self which seems to lead her further and further into darkness and confusion. The diary, which is the story of her retreat from the world into the chaos of regeneration, pictures the labyrinthine struggle waged by these conflicting selves. Sinking into the obscure regions of her soul she seems to draw the world down over her head and with it the people she meets and the relationships engendered by her meetings. The illusion of submergence, of darkness and stagnation, is brought about by the ceaseless observation and analysis which goes on in the pages of the diary. The hatches are down, the sky shut out. Everything—nature, human beings, events, relationships—is brought below to be dissected and digested. It is a devouring process in which the ego becomes a stupendous red maw. The language itself is clear, painfully clear. It is the scorching light of the intellect locked away in a cave. Nothing which this mind comes in contact with is allowed to go undigested. The result is harrowing and hallucinating. We move with the author through her labyrinthine world like a knife making an incision into the flesh. It is a surgical operation upon a world of flesh and blood, a Caesarian operation performed by the embryo with its own private scissors and cleaver.

Let me make a parenthetical remark here. *This diary is written absolutely without malice.* The psychologist may remark of this that the pain inflicted upon her by the loss of her father was so great as to render her incapable of causing pain to others. In a sense this is true, but it is a limited view of the matter. My own feeling is rather that we have in this diary the direct, naked thrust which is of the essence of the great tragic dramas of the Greeks. Racine, Corneille, Molière may indulge in malice—not the Greek dramatists. The difference lies in the attitude toward Fate. The warfare is not with men but with the gods. Similarly, in the case of Anaïs Nin's journal: the war is with herself, with God as the sole witness. The diary was written not for the eyes of others, but for the eye of God. She has no malice any more than she has the desire to cheat or to lie. To lie in a diary is the height of absurdity. One would have to be really insane to do that. Her concern is not with others, except as they may reveal to her something about herself. Though the way is tortuous the direction is always the same, always inward, further inward, towards the heart of the self. Every encounter is a preparation for the final encounter, the confrontation with the real Self. To indulge in malice would be to swerve from the ordained path, to waste a precious moment in the pursuit of her ideal. She moves onward inexorably, as the gods move in the Greek dramas, on towards the realization of her destiny.

There is a very significant fact attached to the origin of this diary and that is that it was begun in artistic fashion. By that I do not mean that it was done with the skill of an artist, with the conscious use of a technique; no, but it was begun as something to be read by some one else, as something to influence some one else. In that sense as an artist. Begun during the voyage to a foreign land, the diary is a silent communion with the father who has deserted her, a gift which she intends to send him from their new home, a gift of love which she hopes will reunite them. Two days later the war breaks out. By what seems almost like a conspiracy of fate the father and child are kept apart for many years. In the legends which treat of this theme it happens, as in this case, that the meeting takes place when the daughter has come of age.

And so, in the very beginning of her diary, the child behaves precisely like the artist who, through the medium of his expression, sets about to conquer the world which has denied him. Thinking originally to woo and enchant the father by the testimony of her grief, thwarted in all her attempts to recover him, she begins little by little to regard the separation as a punishment for her own inadequacy. The difference which had marked her out as a child, and which had already brought down upon her the father's ire, becomes more accentuated. The diary becomes the confession of her inability to make herself worthy of this lost father who has become for her the very paragon of perfection.

In the very earliest pages of the diary this conflict between the old, inadequate self which was attached to the father and the budding, unknown self which she was creating manifests itself. It is a struggle between the real and the ideal, the annihilating struggle which for most people is carried on fruitlessly to the end of their lives and the significance of which they never learn. Scarcely two years after the diary is begun comes the following passage:

"Quand aucun bruit ne se fait entendre, quand la nuit a recouvert de son sombre paletot la grande ville dont elle me cache l'éclat trompeur, alors il me semble entendre une voix mystérieuse qui me parle; je suppose qu'elle vient de moi-même car elle pense comme moi . . . Il me semble que je cherche quelque chose, je ne sais pas quoi, mais quand mon esprit libre dégage des griffes puissantes de ce mortel ennemi, le Monde, il me semble que je trouve ce que je voulais. Serait-ce l'oubli? le silence? Je ne sais, mais cette même voix, quand je crois être seule, me parle. Je ne puis comprendre ce qu'elle dit mais je me dis que l'on ne peut jamais être seule et oubliée dans le monde. Car je nomme cette voix: Mon Génie: mauvais ou bon, je ne puis savoir . . .''

Even more striking is a passage in the same volume which begins: "Dans ma vie terrestre rien n'est changé . . .'' After recounting the petty incidents which go to make up her earthly life, she adds, *but:*

"Dans la vie que je mène dans l'infini cela est différent. Là, tout est bonheur et douceur, car c'est un rêve. Là, il n'y a pas d'école aux sombres classes, mais il y a Dieu. Là, il n'y a pas de chaise vide dans la famille, qui est toujours au complet. Là, il n'y a pas de bruit, mais de la solitude qui donne la paix. La, il n'y a pas d'inquiétude pour l'avenir, car c'est un autre rêve. Là, il n'y a pas de larmes, car c'est un sourire. Voilà l'infini où je vis, *car je vis deux fois.* Quand je mourrai sur la terre, il arrivera, comme il arrive a deux lumières allumées à la fois, quand l'une s'éteint l'autre se rallume, et celà avec plus de force. Je m'éteindrai sur la terre, mais je me rallumerai dans l'infini . . .''

She speaks of herself mockingly at times as *"une étoilique"*—a word which she has invented, and why not, since as she says, we have the word *lunatique.* Why not *"étoilique"?* "To-day," she writes, "I described very poorly *le pays des merveilles où mon esprit était. Je volais dans ce pays lointain où rien n'est impossible. Hier je suis revenue, à la réalité, à la tristesse. Il me semble que je tombais d'une grande splendeur à une triste misère.*"

One thinks inevitably of the manifestoes of the Surrealists, of their unquenchable thirst for the marvellous, and that phrase of Breton's, so significant of the dreamer, the visionary: "we should conduct ourselves as though we were really *in the world!*" It may seem absurd to couple the utterances of the Surrealists with the writings of a child of thirteen, but there is a great deal which they have in common and there is also a point of departure which is even more important. The pursuit of the marvellous is at bottom nothing but the sure instinct of the poet speaking and it manifests itself everywhere in all epochs, in all conditions of life, in all forms of expression. But this marvellous pursuit of the marvellous, if not understood, can also act as a thwarting force, can become a thing of evil, crushing the individual in the toils of the Absolute. It can become as negative and destructive a force as the yearning for God. When I said a while back that the child had begun her great work in the spirit of an artist I was trying to emphasize the fact that, like the artist, the problem which beset her was to conquer the world. In the process of making herself fit to meet her father again (because to her the world was personified in the Father) she was unwittingly making herself an artist, that is, a self-dependent creature for whom a father would no longer be necessary. When she does encounter him again, after a lapse of almost twenty years, she is a full-fledged being, a creature fashioned after her own image. The meeting serves to make her realize that she has emancipated herself; more indeed, for to her amazement and dismay she also realizes that she has no more need of the one she was seeking. The significance of her heroic struggle with herself now reveals itself symbolically. That which was beyond her, which had dominated and tortured her, which *possessed* her, one might say, no longer exists. She is de-possessed and free at last to live her own life.

Throughout the diary the amazing thing is this intuitive awareness of the symbolic nature of her role. It is this which illuminates the most trivial remarks, the most trivial incidents she records. In reality there is nothing trivial throughout the world record; everything is saturated with a purpose and significance which gradually becomes clear as the confession progresses. Similarly there is nothing chaotic about the work, although at first glance it may give that impression. The fifty volumes are crammed with human figures, incidents, voyages, books read and commented upon, reveries, metaphysical speculations, the dramas in which she is enveloped, her daily work, her preoccupation with the welfare of others, in short with a thousand and one things which go to make up her life. It is a great pageant of the times patiently and humbly delineated by one who considered herself as nothing, by one who had almost completely effaced herself in the effort to arrive at a true understanding of life. It is in this sense again that the human document rivals the work of art, or in times such as ours, *replaces* the work of art. For, in a profound sense, this *is* the work of art which never gets written—because the artist whose task it is to create it never gets born. We have here, instead of the consciously or technically finished work (which to-day seems to us more than ever empty and illusory), the unfinished symphony which achieves consummation because each line is pregnant with a soul struggle. The conflict with the world takes place within. It matters little, for the artist's purpose, whether the world be the size of a pinhead or an incommensurable universe. *But there must be a world!* And this world, whether real or imaginary, can only be created out of despair and anguish. For the artist there is no other world. Even if it be unrecognizable, this world which is created out of sorrow and deprivation is true and vital, and eventually it expropriates the "other" world in which the ordinary mortal lives and dies. It is the world in which the artist has his being, and it is in the revelation of his undying self that art takes its stance. Once this is apprehended there can be no question of monotony or fatigue, of chaos or irrelevance. We move amidst boundless horizons in a perpetual state of awe and humility. We enter, with the author, into unknown worlds and we share with the latter all the pain, beauty, terror and illumination which exploration entails.

Of the truly great authors no one has ever complained that they over-elaborated. On the contrary, we usually bemoan the fact that there is nothing further left us to read. And so we turn back to what we have and we re-read, and as we re-read we discover marvels which previously we had ignored. We go back to them again and again, as to inexhaustible wells of wisdom and delight. Almost invariably, it is curious to note, these authors of whom I speak are observed to be precisely those who have given us *more* than the others. They claim us precisely because we sense in them an unquenchable flame. Nothing they wrote seems to us insignificant—not even their notes, their jottings, not even the designs which they scribbled unconsciously in the margins of their copy books. Whereas with the meagre spirits everything seems superfluous, themselves as well as the works they have given us.

At the bottom of this relentless spirit of elaboration is care—*Sorgen*. The diarist in particular is obsessed with the notion that everything must be preserved. And this again is born out of a sense of destiny. Not only, as with the ordinary artist, is there the tyrannical desire to immortalize one's self, but there is also the idea of immortalizing the world in which the diarist lives and has his being. Everything must be recorded because everything must be preserved. In the diary of Anaïs Nin there is a kind of desperation, almost like that of a shipwrecked sailor thrown up on a desert island. From the flotsam and jetsam of her wrecked life the author struggles to create anew. It is a heart-breaking effort to recover a lost world. It is not, as some might imagine, a deliberate retreat from the world; it is an involuntary separation from the world! Every one experiences this feeling in more or less degree. Every one, whether consciously or unconsciously, is trying to recover the luxurious, effortless sense of security which he knew in the womb. Those who are able to realize themselves do actually achieve this state; not by a blind, unconscious yearning for the uterine condition, but by transforming the world in which they live into a veritable womb. It is this which seems to have terrified Aldous Huxley, for example, when standing before El Greco's painting, "The Dream of Philip 2nd." Mr. Huxley was terrified by the prospect of world converted into a fish-gut. But El Greco must have been supremely happy inside his fish-gut world, and the proof of his contentment, his ease, his satisfaction, is the world-feeling which his pictures create in the mind of the spectator. Standing before his paintings one realizes that *this is a world!* One realizes also that it is a world dominated by vision. It is no longer a man looking *at* the world, but a man inside his own world ceaselessly reconstructing it in terms of the light within. That it is a world englobed, that El Greco seems to Aldous Huxley, for example, much like a Jonah in the belly of the whale, is precisely the comforting thing about El Greco's vision. The lack of a boundless infinity, which seems so to disturb Mr. Huxley, is on the contrary, a most beneficent state of affairs. Every one who has assisted at the creation of a world, any one who has made a world of his own, realizes that it is precisely the fact that his world has definite limits which is what is good about it. One has to first lost himself to discover the world of his own, the world which, because it is rigidly limited, permits the only true condition of freedom.

Which brings us back to the labyrinth and the descent into the womb, into the night of primordial chaos in which "knowledge is refunded into ignorance." This laborious descent into the infernal regions is really the initiation for the final descent into the eternal darkness of death. He who goes down into the labyrinth must first strip himself of all possessions, as well as of prejudices, notions, ideals, ideas, and so on. He must return into the womb naked as the day he was born, with only the core of his future self, as it were. No one, of course, offers himself up to this experience unless he is harried by vision. The vision is first and foremost, always. And this vision is like the voice of conscience itself. It is a double vision, as we well know. One sees forwards and backwards with equal clarity. But one does not see what is directly under the nose; one does not see the world which is immediately about. This blindness to the everyday, to the normal or abnormal circumstances of life, is the distinguishing feature of the restless visionary. The eyes, which are unusually endowed, have to be trained to see with normal vision. Superficially this sort of individual seems to be concerned only with what is going on about him; the daily communion with the diary seems at first blush to be nothing more than a transcription of this normal, trivial, everyday life. And yet nothing can be further from the truth. The fact is that this extraordinary cataloguing of events, objects, impressions, ideas, etc. is only a keyboard exercise, as it were, to attain the faculty of seeing what is so glibly recorded. Actually, of course, few people in this world see what is going on about them. Nobody really sees until he understands, until he can create a pattern into which the helter-skelter of passing events fits and makes a significance. And for this sort of vision a personal death is required. One has to be able to see first with the eyes of a Martian, or a Neptunian. One has to have this extraordinary vision, this clairvoyance, to be able to take in the multiplicity of things with ordinary eyes. Nobody sees with his eyes alone; we see with our souls. And this problem of putting the soul into the eye is the whole problem of a diarist such as Anaïs Nin. The whole vast diary, regarded from this angle, assumes the nature of the record of a second birth. It is the story of death and transfiguration.

Or one might put it still more figuratively and say it was the story of an egg which was splitting in two, that this egg went down into the darkness to become a single new egg made of the ingredients of the old. The diary then resembles a museum in which the world that made up the old split egg goes to pieces. Superficially it would seem as though every crumbling bit had been preserved in the pages of the diary. Actually not a crumb remains; everything that made up the former world not only goes to pieces but is devoured again, re-digested and assimilated in the growth of a new entity, the new egg which is one and indivisible. This egg is indestructible and forms a vital component element of that world which is constantly in the making. It belongs not to a personal world but to the cosmic world. In itself it has very definite limits, as has the atom or the molecule. But taken in relation with other similar identities it forms, or helps to form, a universe which is truly limitless. It has a spontaneous life of its own which knows a true freedom because its life is lived in accordance with the most rigid laws. The whole process does indeed seem to be that union with nature of which the poets speak. But this union is achieved parabolically, through a spiritual death. It is the same sort of transfiguration which the myths relate of; it is what makes intelligible to us such a phrase as "the spirit which animates a place." Spirit in taking possession of a place, so identifies itself with it that the natural and the divine coalesce.

It is in this same way that human spirits take possession of the earth. It is only in the understanding of this, which by some is considered miraculous, that we can look without the least anguish upon the deaths of millions of fellow men. For we do distinguish not only between the loss of a near one and a stranger, but also, and how much more, between the loss of a near one and the loss of a great personality, a Christ, a Buddha, or a Mahomet. We speak of them, quite naturally, as though they never had died, as though they were still with us, in fact. What we mean is that they have so taken possession of the world that not even death can dislodge them. Their spirit does truly pass into the world and animate it. And it is only the animation of such spirits which gives to our life on earth significance. But all these figures had to die first in the spirit. All of them renounced the world first. That is the cardinal fact about them.

In the later volumes of the diary we note the appearance of titles. For instance, and I give them in chronological order, the following: "The Definite Disappearance of the Demon"; "Death and Disintegration"; "The Triumph of White Magic"; "The Birth of Humor in the Whale"; "Playing at Being God"; "Fire"; "Audace"; "Vive la dynamite"; "A God who Laughs". The use of titles to indicate the nature of a volume is an indication of the gradual emergence from the labyrinth. It means that the diary itself has undergone a radical transformation. No longer a fleeting panorama of impressions, but a consolidation of experience into little bundles of fibre and muscle which go to make up the new body. The new being is definitely born and travelling upward towards the light of the every-day world. In the previous volumes we had the record of the struggle to penetrate to the very sanctum of the self; it is a description of a shadowy world in which the outline of people, things and events becomes more and more blurred by the involutional inquisition. The further we penetrate into the darkness and confusion below, however, the greater becomes the illumination. The whole personality seems to become a devouring eye turned pitilessly on the self. Finally there comes the moment when this individual who has been constantly gazing into a mirror sees with such blinding clarity that the mirror fades away and the image rejoins the body from which it had been separated. It is at this point that normal vision is restored and that the one who had died is restored to the living world. It is at this moment that the prophecy which had been written twenty years earlier comes true—"*Un de ces jours je pourrais dire: mon journal, je suis arrivée au fond!*"

Whereas in the earlier volumes the accent was one of sadness, of disillusionment, of being *de trop*, now the accent becomes one of joy and fulfillment. Fire, audacity, dynamite, laughter—the very choice of words is sufficient to indicate the changed condition. The world spreads out before her like a banquet table: something to *enjoy*. But the appetite, seemingly insatiable, is controlled. The old obsessional desire to devour everything in sight in order that it be preserved in her own private tomb is gone. She eats now only what nourishes her. The once ubiquitous digestive trace, the great whale into which she had made herself, is replaced by other organs with other functions. The exaggerated sympathy for others which had dogged her every step diminishes. The birth of a sense of humor denotes the achievement of an objectivity which alone the one who has realized himself attains. It is not indifference, but toleration. The totality of vision brings about a new kind of sympathy, a free, non-compulsive sort. The very pace of the diary changes. There are now long lapses, intervals of complete silence in which the great digestive apparatus, once all, slows up to permit the development of complementary organs. The eye too seems to close, content to let the body *feel* the presence of the world about, rather than pierce it with a devastating vision. It is no longer a world of black and white, of good and evil, or harmony and dissonance; no, now the world has at last become an orchestra in which there are innumerable instruments capable of rendering every tone and color, an orchestra in which even the most shattering dissonances are resolved into meaningful expression. It is the ultimate poetic world of *As Is*. The inquisition is over, the trial and torture finished. A state of absolution is reached. This is the true catholic world of which the Catholics know nothing. This is the eternally abiding world which those in search of it never find. For with most of us we stand before the world as before a mirror; we never see our true selves because we can never come before the mirror unawares. We see ourselves as actors, but the spectacle for which we are rehearsing is never put on. To see the true spectacle, to finally participate in it, one must die before the mirror in a blinding light of realization. We must lose not only the mask and the costume but the flesh and bone which conceals the secret self. This we can only do by illumination, by voluntarily going down into death. For when this moment is attained we who imagined that we were sitting in the belly of the whale and doomed to nothingness suddenly discover that the whale was a projection of our own insufficiency. The whale remains, but the whale becomes the whole wide world, with stars and seasons, with banquets and festivals, with everything that is wonderful to see and touch, and being that it is no longer a whale but something nameless because something that is inside as well as outside us. We may, if we like, devour the whale too—piecemeal, throughout eternity. No matter how much is ingested there will always remain more whale than man; because what man appropriates of the whale returns to the whale again in one form or another. The whale is constantly being transformed as man himself becomes transformed. There is nothing but man and whale, and the man is *in* the whale and possesses the whale. Thus, too, whatever waters the whale inhabits man inhabits also, but always as the inner inhabitant of the whale. Seasons come and go, whale-like seasons, in which the whole organism of the whale is affected. Man, too, is affected, as that inner inhabitant of the whale. But the whale never dies, nor does man inside him, because that which they have established together is undying—their relationship. And it is in this that they live, through and by which they live: not the waters, nor the seasons, nor that which is swallowed nor that which passes away. In this passing beyond the mirror, as it were, there is an infinity which no infinity of images can give the least idea of. One lives within the spirit of transformation and not in the act. The legend of the whale thus becomes the celebrated book of transformations destined to cure the ills of the world. Each man who climbs into the body of the whale and works therein his own resurrection is bringing about the miraculous transfiguration of the world which, because it is human, is none the less limitless. The whole process is a marvellous piece of dramatic symbolism whereby he who sat facing his doom suddenly awakes and lives, and through the mere act of declaration—the act of declaring his livingness—causes the whole world to become alive and endlessly alter its visage. He who gets up from his stool in the body of the whale automatically switches on an orchestral music which causes each living member of the universe to dance and sing, to pass the endless time in endless recreation.

And here I must return once again to El Greco's "Dream of Philip the 2nd" which Mr. Huxley so well describes in his little essay. For in a way this diary of Anaïs Nin's is also a curious dream of something or other, a dream which takes place fathoms deep below the surface of the sea. One might think that in this retreat from the daylight world we are about to be ushered into an hermetically sealed laboratory in which only the ego flourishes. Not at all. The ego indeed seems to completely disappear amidst the furniture and trappings of this subterranean world which she has created about her. A thousand figures stalk the pages, caught in their most intimate poses and revealing themselves as they never reveal themselves to the mirror. The most dramatic pages are those perhaps in which the gullible psychoanalysts, thinking to unravel the complexities of her nature, are themselves unravelled and left dangling in a thousand shreds. Every one who comes under her glance is lured, as it were, into a spider web, stripped bare, dissected, dismembered, devoured and digested. All without malice! Done automatically, as a part of life's processes. The person who is doing this is really an innocent little creature tucked away in the lining of the belly of the whale. In nullifying herself she really becomes this great leviathan which swims the deep and devours everything in sight. It is a strange *dédoublement* of the personality in which the crime is related back to the whale by a sort of self-induced amnesia. There, tucked away in a pocket of the great intestinal tract of the whale, she dreams away throughout whole volumes of something which is not the whale, of something greater, something beyond which is nameless and unseizable. She has a little pocket mirror which she tacks up on the wall of the whale's intestinal gut and into which she gazes for hours on end. The whole drama of her life is played out before the mirror. If she is sad the mirror reflects her sadness; if she is gay the mirror reflects her gayety. But everything the mirror reflects is false, because the moment she realizes that her image is sad or gay she is no longer sad or gay. Always there is another self which is hidden from the mirror and which enables her to look at herself in the mirror. This other self tells her that it is only her image which is sad, only her image which is gay. By looking at herself steadily in the mirror she really accomplishes the miracle of not looking at herself. The mirror enables her to fall into a trance in which the image is completely lost. The eyes close and she falls backward into the deep. The whale too falls backward and is lost into the deep. This is the dream which El Greco dreamed that Philip the 2nd dreamed. It is the dream of a dream, just as a double mirror would reflect the image of an image. It can as well be the dream of a dream of a dream, or the image of an image of an image. It can go back like that endlessly, from one little Japanese box into another and another and another without ever reaching the last box. Each lapse backward brings about a greater clairvoyance; as the darkness increases the inner eye develops in magnitude. The world is boxed off and with it the dreams that shape the world. There are endless trap-doors, but no exits. She falls from one level to another, but there is never a final ocean floor. The result is often a sensation of brilliant crystalline clarity, the sort of frozen wonder which the metamorphosis of a snow-flake awakens. It is something like what a molecule would experience in decomposing into its basic elements, if it had the ability to express its awareness of the transformation going on. It is the nearest thing to ultimate sensation without completely losing identity. In the ordinary reader it is apt to produce a sensation of horror. He will find himself suddenly slipping into a world of monstrous crimes committed by an angel who is innocent of the knowledge of crime. He will be terrified by the mineralogical aspect of these crimes in which no blood is spilt, no wounds left unhealed. He will miss the normally attendant elements of violence and so be utterly confounded, utterly hallucinated.

There are some volumes, in which attention is focussed almost entirely on one or two individuals, which are like the raw pith of some post-Dostoievskian novel; they bring to the surface a lunar plasm which is the logical fruit of that drive towards the dead slag of the ego which Dostoievski heralded and which D. H. Lawrence was the first to have pointed out in precise language. There are three successive volumes, of this sort, which are made of nothing but this raw material of a drama which takes place entirely within the confines of the female world. It is the first female writing I have ever seen: it rearranges the world in terms of female honesty. The result is a language which is ultra-modern and yet which bears no resemblance to any of the masculine experimental processes with which we are familiar. It is precise, abstract, cloudy and unseizable. There are larval thoughts not yet divorced from their dream content, thoughts which seem to slowly crystallize before your eyes, always precise but never tangible, never once arrested so as to be grasped by the mind. It is the opium world of woman's physiological being, a sort of cinematic show put on inside the genito-urinary tract. There is not an ounce of man-made culture in it; everything related to the head is cut off. Time passes, but it is not clock time; nor is it poetic time such as men create in their passion. It is more like that aeonic time required for the creation of gems and precious metals; an embowelled sidereal time in which the female knows that she is superior to the male and will eventually swallow him up again. The effect is that of starlight carried over into day-time.

The contrast between this language and that of man's is forcible; the whole of man's art begins to appear like a frozen edelweiss under a glass bell reposing on a mantelpiece in the deserted home of a lunatic. In this extraordinary unicellular language of the female we have a blinding, gem-like consciousness which disperses the ego like star-dust. The great female corpus rises up from its sleepy marine depths in a naked push towards the sun. The sun is at zenith—permanently at zenith. Space broadens out like a cold Norwegian lake choked with ice-floes. The sun and moon are fixed, the one at zenith, the other at nadir. The tension is perfect, the polarity absolute. The voices of the earth mingle in an eternal resonance which issues from the delta of the fecundating river of death. It is the voice of creation which is constantly being drowned in the daylight frenzy of a man-made world. It comes like the light breeze which sets the ocean swaying; it comes with a calm, quiet force which is irresistible, like the movement of the great Will gathered up by the instincts and rippling out in long silky flashes of enigmatic dynamism. Then a lull in which the mysterious centralized forces roll back to the matrix, gather up again in a sublime all-sufficiency. Nothing lost, nothing used up, nothing relinquished. The great mystery of conservation in which creation and destruction are but the antipodal symbols of a single constant energy which is inscrutable.

It is at this point in the still unfinished symphony of the diary that the whole pattern wheels miraculously into another dimension; at this point that it takes its cosmic stance. Adopting the universal language, the human being in her speaks straight out from under the skin to Hindu, Chinaman, Jap, Abyssinian, Malay, Turk, Arab, Tibetan, Eskimo, Pawnee, Hottentot, Bushman, Kaffir, Persian, Assyrian. The fixed polar language known to all races: a serpentine, sybilline, sibilant susurrus that comes up out of the astral marshes: a sort of cold, tinkling, lunar laughter which comes from under the soles of the feet: a laughter made of alluvial deposit, of mythological excrement and the sweat of epileptics. This is the language which seeps through the frontiers of race, color, religion, sex; a language which soaks through the litmus paper of the mind and saturates the quintessential human spores. The language of bells without clappers, heard incessantly throughout the nine months in which every one is identical and yet mysteriously different. In this first tinkling melody of immortality lapping against the snug and cosy walls of the womb we have the music of the still-born sons of men opening their lovely dead eyes one upon another.

Via Dieppe-Newhaven

The thing was that I wanted to be among English-speaking people again, for a little while at least. I had nothing against the French; on the contrary, I had at last made a bit of a home for myself in Clichy and everything would have been swell if it hadn't been for the fact that I had just gone through a crisis with my wife. She was living in Montparnasse and I was living with my friend Fred, who had taken an apartment, in Clichy just outside the Porte. We had agreed to separate; she was going back to America as soon as the money arrived for the boat fare.

So far so good. I had said good-bye to her and I thought everything was finished. Then one day when I walked into the grocer's the old woman informed me that my wife had just been in with a young man and that they had taken away a good supply of groceries which they had charged up to my account. The old woman seemed a bit perplexed and a little worried too. I told her it was O.K. And it was O.K. too, because I knew my wife didn't have any money, and after all a wife has to eat just like any other person. About the young man, that was O.K. too: he was just a fairy who felt sorry for her and I supposed he had put her up for the time being in his apartment. In fact, everything was O.K. except that she was still in Paris, and when in Christ's name was she going to beat it, that's what I was wondering about.

A few more days passed and then she dropped in one late afternoon to have dinner with us. Why not? We could always scrape up a bit of food whereas in Montparnasse among the riff-raff she was obliged to hang out where food was almost unobtainable. After the dinner she got hysterical: she said she was suffering from dysentery ever since she had left me and that it was my fault, that I had tried to poison her. I walked her to the Metro station at the Porte without saying a word. I was sore as hell, so god-damned

125

sore that I couldn't talk. She was sore too, sore because I refused
to argue the matter with her. I thought to myself, walking back,
well this is the last straw, she surely won't come back again. I
poisoned her. Good, if she wants to think that way let her! That
ought to settle the issue.

A few days later I had a letter from her asking for a little cash
with which to meet the rent. Seems she wasn't living with the fairy
at all, but in a cheap hotel back of the Gare Montparnasse. I
couldn't give her the money immediately as I didn't have any
myself so I let a few days intervene before going to her hotel and
settling the bill. While I was trotting round to her hotel a pneuma-
tique had come for me saying that she simply must have the money
or she'd be kicked out. If I had had a little money I wouldn't have
put her to all these humiliations, but the point is I didn't have any.
However, she didn't believe me. And even if it were true, she said,
I could at least have borrowed it for her. Which was also true. But
I was never good on borrowing large sums; all my life I had been
used to asking for hand-outs, for chicken feed, and feeling damned
grateful when I got that. She seemed to have forgotten that. It was
natural enough that she should because she was bitter and her
pride had been wounded. And to do her justice I must add that had
the situation been reversed the money would have been forthcoming; she always knew how to raise money for me but never for
herself. That I've got to admit.

I was getting pretty wrought up about the whole thing. I felt like
a louse. And the worse I felt the less I was able to do. I even
suggested that she come back and stay with us until the money
which she was expecting for the boat trip should come. But this
she wouldn't hear of, naturally. Or was it natural? I was so damned
perplexed and humiliated and confused that I didn't know any
more what was natural and what wasn't. Money. Money. All my
life it had been a question of money. I would never be able to solve
the problem and I didn't hope to.

After turning round and round like a rat in a trap I got the
brilliant idea of beating it myself. Just walk out on the problem,
that's always the easiest way. I don't know how the idea came to
me but suddenly I had decided that I would go to London. If you
had offered me a chateau in Touraine I would have said no. For
some reason or other I had made up my mind that it must be
London and no other place. The reason I gave myself was that
she'd never think of looking for me in London. She knew I hated
the place. But the real reason, as I soon discovered, was that I
wanted to be among English-speaking people; I wanted to hear
English spoken twenty-four hours of the day, and nothing but

English. In my weak condition that was like falling back on the bosom of the Lord. Talking and listening to English meant just that less strain. God knows, when you're in a jam to talk a foreign language, or even just to listen to it—because you can't shut your ears even if you try to—is a subtle form of torture. I had absolutely nothing against the French, nor against the language they spoke. Up until she arrived on the scene I had been living in a sort of Paradise. Suddenly everything had gone sour. I found myself muttering things against the French, and against the language particularly, which I would never have dreamed of thinking in my sober senses. I knew it was my own fault, but that only made it worse. Well, London then. A little vacation and perhaps by the time I returned she would have left. That's all there was to it.

I rustled up the dough for a visa and a return trip ticket. I bought a visa for a year thinking that if by any chance I should change my mind about the English I might go back a second or a third time to England. It was getting on towards Christmas and I began to think what a jolly old place London might be during the holidays. Perhaps I would find a different sort of London than the one I knew, a Dickensian London such as tourists always dream of. I had the visa and the ticket in my pocket and just about enough dough to last me for ten days. I was feeling almost jubilant about the trip.

When I got back to Clichy it was almost dinner time. I walked into the kitchen and there was my wife helping Fred with the dinner. They were laughing and joking as I walked in. I knew that Fred wouldn't say anything to her about my going to London and so I sat down to the table and laughed and joked a bit myself. It was a jolly meal, I must say, and everything would have gone off splendidly if Fred hadn't been obliged to go to the newspaper office after dinner. I had been canned a few weeks ago but he was still working, though expecting the same fate any day. The reason I was canned was that, even though I was an American, I had no right to be working on an American newspaper as a proof-reader. According to French theory the job could just as well have been held by a Frenchman who knew English. That griped me a bit and no doubt contributed to my feeling sour towards the French the last few weeks. Anyway, that was over and done with and I was a free man again and I would soon be in London talking English all day long and far into the night if I wanted to. Besides, my book was coming out very soon and that might change everything. All in all things weren't half as black as they had seemed a few days back. Thinking how nicely I was going to duck the whole thing I got a bit careless and ran out, in a moment of exuberation, to buy a bottle of Chartreuse which I knew she liked better than anything. That was a fatal mistake. The Chartreuse made her mellow and then hysterical and then reproving. We sat there at the table, the two of us, and I guess we rehearsed a lot of things that should have been forgotten. Finally I got to such a point of guilt and tenderness that I blurted out the whole thing—about the trip to London, the money I had borrowed, and so on and so forth. I forked the whole thing out and laid it on the table. There it was, I don't know how many pounds and shillings, all in bright new English money. I told her I was sorry and to hell with the trip and to-morrow I would try to get a refund on the tickets and give that to her too.

And here again I must render her justice. She really didn't want to take the money. It made her wince, I could see that, but finally she accepted it reluctantly and stuffed it away in her bag. As she was leaving she forgot the bag and I was obliged to run down the stairs after her and hand it to her. As she took the bag she said good-bye again and this time I felt that it was the last good-bye. She said good-bye and she stood there on the stairs looking up at me with a strange sorrowful smile. If I had made the least gesture I know she would have thrown the money out of the window and rushed back into my arms and stayed with me forever. I took a long look at her, walked slowly back to the door, and closed it. I went back to the kitchen table, sat there a few minutes looking at the empty glasses, and then I broke down and sobbed like a child.

It was about three in the morning when Fred came back from work. He saw right away that something had gone wrong. I told him what had happened and then we sat down and ate, and after we had eaten we drank some good Algerian wine and then some Chartreuse and after that a little cognac. It was a damned shame, in Fred's opinion, and I was a fool to have forked up all the money. I agreed, but I felt good about it just the same.

"And what about London? Do you mean to tell me you're not going to London?" he says.

"No," I said, "I've given up the idea. Besides, I couldn't go now even if I wanted to. Where's the dough to come from?"

Fred didn't seem to think the lack of dough was any grave obstacle. He thought he could borrow a couple of hundred francs at the office and on pay-day, which was only a few days off, he would wire me more. We sat there discussing the thing until dawn, and of course drinking a bit too. When I hit the hay I could hear the Westminster chimes—and a few rusty sleigh bells too. I saw a beautiful blanket of snow lying over dirty London and everybody greeting me with a hearty "Merry Christmas"—*in English,* to be sure.

I made the Channel crossing at night. It was a miserable night and we stayed indoors shivering with the cold. I had a hundred franc note and some change—that was all. The idea was that as soon as I found a hotel I was to cable and Fred would cable back some more dough. I sat at the long table in the salon listening to the conversation going on around me. The thought uppermost in my mind was how to make the hundred francs stretch as far as possible, because the more I thought about it the less sure I was that Fred would raise the dough immediately. The scraps of conversation I picked up also had to do with money. Money. Money. The same thing everywhere and all the time. It seems that England had just that day paid her debt to America, much against her will. She had kept her word, as they were saying all about me. England always kept her word. And more of that and more, until I felt like strangling them for their bloody honesty.

I hadn't intended to break the hundred franc note until absolutely necessary, but with this silly conversation going on about England keeping her word and knowing that they had spotted me as an American I finally got so jumpy that I ordered a beer and a ham sandwich. That brought me directly into contact with the steward. He wanted to know what I thought about the situation. I could see that he thought it was a bloody crime what we had done to England. I felt sore that he should make me responsible for the situation just because I happened to be born an American. So I told him I didn't know anything about the situation, that it was none of my affair, and furthermore that it was a matter of absolute indifference to me whether England paid her debts or didn't pay her debts. He didn't relish this very much. A man ought to have an interest in the affairs of his country, even if his country is in the wrong, that's what he thought. I told him I didn't give a damn about America or Americans. I told him I didn't have an ounce of patriotism in me. At that moment a man who had been pacing up and down beside the table stopped to listen to me. I had a feeling that he was a spy or a detective. I piped down almost at once and turned to the young man beside me who had also called for a beer and a sandwich.

Apparently he had been listening to me with some interest. He wanted to know where I came from and what I was going to do in England. I told him I was taking a little vacation, and then, impulsively, I asked him if he could recommend a very cheap hotel. He said he had been away from England quite a long while and that he didn't know London very well anyhow. Said he had been living in Australia the last few years. Just then the steward happened along and the young man interrupted himself to ask the steward if he knew of any good cheap little hotel in London. The steward called the waiter over and asked him the same question, and just as he put the question to the waiter the man who looked like a spy came along and paused a moment to listen in. From the serious way in which the subject was discussed I could see at once that I had made a mistake. One shouldn't ask questions like that of a steward or a waiter. I felt that they were looking me over suspiciously, that they were giving my pocket-book the X-ray. I tossed off the beer at one gulp and, as though to prove that money was the least of my worries I called for another and then, turning to the young man at my elbow, I asked him if he wouldn't let me buy him a drink too. When the steward came back with the drinks we were deep in the wilds of Australia. He started to say something about a hotel but I told him immediately to forget about it. It was just an idle question, I added. That seemed to stump him. He stood there a few moments not knowing what to do, then suddenly, moved by some friendly impulse, he blurted out that he would be glad to put me up in his own home at Newhaven if I cared to spend the night there. I thanked him warmly and told him not to worry about it any more, that I would go on to London just the same. It really isn't important, I added. And the moment I said it I knew that that too was a mistake, because somehow, despite myself, I had made the thing seem quite important to everybody.

There was still a bit of time to kill and so I listened to the young Englishman who had had a strange time of it in Australia. He was telling me of his life as a sheep herder, how they castrated I don't know how many thousands of sheep in a day. One had to work fast. So fast, in fact, that the most expedient thing to do was to grab the testicles with your teeth and then a quick slit with the knife and spit them out. He was trying to estimate how many thousand pair of testicles he had bitten off in this hand to mouth operation during his sojourn in Australia. And as he was going through his mental calculations he wiped his mouth with the back of his hand.

"You must have had a strange taste in your mouth," I said, instinctively wiping my own mouth.

"It wasn't as bad as you might imagine," he answered calmly. "You get used to everything—in time. No, it wasn't a bad taste at all . . . the idea is worse than the actual thing. Just the same, I never thought when I left my comfortable home in England that I would be spitting out those things for a living. A man can get used to doing most anything when he's really up against it."

I was thinking the same thing. I was thinking of the time I burned brush in an orange grove in Chula Vista. Ten hours a day in the broiling sun running from one fire to another and the flies biting like mad. And for what? To prove to myself that I was a man, I suppose, that I could take it on the chin. And another time working as a gravedigger: to show that I wasn't afraid of tackling anything. The gravedigger! With a volume of Nietzsche under his arm, and trying to memorize the last part of Faust to and from work. Well, as the steward says, *"the English never twist you!"* The boat is coming to a stop. Another swig of beer to drown the taste of sheep's nuts and a handsome little tip for the waiter just to prove that Americans pay their debts too sometimes. In the excitement I find myself quite alone, standing behind a bulky Englishman with a checkered cap and a big ulster. Landing in any other country the checkered cap would look ridiculous, but as it's his own country he can do as he pleases, and what's more I almost admire him for it, it makes him seem so big and independent. I'm beginning to think that they're not such a bad race after all.

On deck it's dark and drizzly. The last time I pulled into England, that was coming up the Thames, it was also dark and drizzly and the faces were ashen gray and the uniforms were black and the houses were grim and grimy. And up High Holborn Street every morning I remember there passed me the most respectable, lamentable, dilapidated paupers God ever made. Gray, watery paupers with bowlers and cutaways and that absurd air of respectability which only the English can muster in adversity. And now the language is coming to me a little stronger and I must say I don't like it at all: it sounds oily, slimy, servile, unctuous. I feel the class line cutting through the accents. The man with the checkered cap and the ulster has suddenly become a pompous ass; he seems to be talking Choctaw to the porters. I hear Sir all the time. Can I do this, *Sir?* Which way, *Sir?* Yes, *Sir.* No, *Sir.* Bugger me if it doesn't make me a bit creepy, all this yes sir and no sir. *Sir my ass,* I say under my breath.

At the Immigration Office. Waiting my turn on the line. The rich bastards go first, as usual. We move up inch by inch. Those who've passed through are having their baggage inspected on the quay. The porters are bustling about loaded down like donkeys. Only two people ahead of me now. I have my passport in my hand and my train ticket and my baggage checks. Now I'm standing square in front of him, offering him my passport. He looks at the big white sheet beside him, finds my name and checks it off.

"How long do you intend to stay in England, Mr. Miller?" he says, holding the passport in his hand as though ready to give it back to me.

"A week or two," I answer.

"You're going to London, are you?"

"Yes."

"What hotel are you stopping at, Mr. Miller?"

I have to smile at this. "Why, I don't know," I respond, still smiling. "Perhaps you can recommend me a hotel."

"Have you any friends in London, Mr. Miller?"

"No."

"Just what are you going to do in London, if I may ask?"

"Why, I'm going to take a little vacation." Still smiling.

"I suppose you have enough money for your stay in England?"

"I think so," says I, still nonchalant, still smiling. And thinking to myself what a cinch it is to bluff it through with questions like that.

"Do you mind showing me your money, Mr. Miller?"

"Of course not," and reaching into my jeans I haul out the remains of the hundred franc note. The people next to me are laughing. I try to laugh too, but I'm not very successful. As for my inquisitor, he gives a feeble little chuckle and looking me sqaure in the eye he says with all the sarcasm he can put into it: "You didn't expect to stay very long in London on that, did you, Mr. Miller?"

Always this *Mr. Miller* tacked on to every phrase! I'm beginning to dislike the son-of-a-bitch. What's more it's beginning to get uncomfortable.

"Look here," I say, still amiable and still outwardly nonchalant, "I don't intend to have a vacation on that. As soon as I get a hotel I expect to wire for money. I left Paris in a great hurry and . . ."

He cuts me short. Can I give him the name of my bank in Paris, he wants to know.

"I haven't got a bank account," I'm obliged to answer. That makes a very bad impression I realize at once. I can feel the hostility growing up all about me. People who were holding their bags are putting them down now, as though they knew they were in for a long siege. The passport which he had been holding in his hands like a little testament he puts on the counter before him and holds it there, like a damaging piece of evidence, with outstretched finger-tips.

"Where were you going to get the money from, Mr. Miller?" he asks more blandly than ever.

"Why, from a friend of mine, the man who lives with me in Paris."

"Has he a bank account?"

"No, but he's got a job. He works on the Chicago Tribune."

"And you think he will send you the money for your vacation?"

"I don't think so, I *know* so," I answered tartly. "I'm not trying

to give you a cock and bull story. I told you I left in a hurry. I left
with the understanding that he'd send me the money as soon as I
arrived in London. Besides, it's *my* money, not his."

"You left your money with him rather than put it in a bank, is
that it, Mr. Miller?"

"Well," I said, beginning to lose my temper, "it isn't a hell of a
lot of money and besides, I don't see the point of all this. If you
don't believe me I'll stay right here and you can send a cable and
find out for yourself."

"Just a minute, Mr. Miller. You say the two of you live together
. . . do you live in a hotel or in an apartment?"

"An apartment."

"And the apartment is in your name?"

"No, in his. That is, it belongs to the both of us, but it's in his
name because he's a Frenchman and it makes it easier."

"And he keeps your money for you?"

"No, not usually. You see, I left under rather unusual circumstances. I . . ."

"Just a minute, Mr. Miller," and he motions to me to step back
from the ranks a bit. At the same time he calls one of his assistants
over and hands him my passport. The latter takes the passport and
goes behind a screen some distance off. I stand there watching the
others go through.

"You might go and have your baggage inspected meanwhile," I
hear him say as if in a trance. I move off to the shed and open my
luggage. The train is waiting for us. It looks like a team of Eskimo
dogs straining at the leash. The locomotive is puffing and steaming.
Finally I walk back and take my stand in front of my interlocutor.
The last few passengers are being hustled through the examination.

Now the tall thin man from behind the screen comes forward
with the passport in his hand. He seems determined in advance
that I'm a malefactor.

"You're an American citizen, Mr. Miller?"

"Obviously," I answer. With this guy I know there's going to
be no mercy. He hasn't a speck of humor in him.

"How long have you been in France?"

"Two or three years, I guess. You can see the date there for
yourself . . . *Why?* What's that got to do with it?"

"You were thinking of spending several months in England,
were you?"

"No, I wasn't. I was thinking of spending a week or ten days
there, that's all. But now . . ."

"So you bought a visa for a year, thinking to spend a week."

"I bought a return trip ticket too, if that interests you."

"One could always throw the return ticket away," he says with a malicious twist of the mouth.

"One could if he were an idiot. I don't get the point. And anyway, look here, I'm tired of all this nonsense. I'm going to stay in Newhaven overnight and take the next boat back. I don't have to spend my vacation in England."

"Not so fast, Mr. Miller. I think we ought to look into this a little more closely."

As he said this I heard the whistle blow. The passengers were all aboard and the train was just starting. I thought of my trunk which I had checked through to London. Nearly all my manuscripts were in it, and my typewriter too. A nice mess, I thought to myself. All because of that chicken feed I slapped down on the counter.

The little fat fellow with the bland imperturbable mask now joined us. He seemed to be expecting a treat.

Hearing the train roll out of the station I resigned myself to the inquisition. Thinks I to myself, now that they've fucked me, let's see how far they can prolong the agony. First of all, however, I demanded my passport back. If they wanted to grill me a little more O.K. There was nothing to do at that hour of the night and before turning in at Newhaven I thought I'd go through with the song and dance.

To my amazement the tall thin fellow refused to return my passport. That made me furious. I demanded to know if there was an American Consul on hand. "Listen," I said, "you may think what you like, but that passport belongs to me and I want it back."

"There's no need to get excited, Mr. Miller. You'll have your passport before you leave. But first there are a few questions I'd like to put to you . . . I see that you are a married man. Is your wife living with you—and your friend? Or is she in America?"

"I don't see that that's any of your business," I said. "But since you brought the subject up I'm going to tell you something now. The reason I came away with so little money is because I gave the money for my trip to my wife before leaving. We're separating and she's going back to America in a few days. I gave her the money because she was broke."

"How much money did you give her, if I may ask?"

"You're asking so damned many questions that you have no right to ask I don't see why you shouldn't ask that too. If you want to know, I gave her about 60 pounds. Let's see. I may still have the exchange slip in my wallet . . ." And I made a gesture as if to reach for my wallet and look for the slip.

"Wasn't that rather foolish to give your wife all that money and come to England penniless, or almost so?"

I gave him a sour smile. "My dear man, I've tried to explain to you that I'm not coming to England as a pauper. If you had let me go to London and wire for the money everything would have been all right. I suppose it's a waste of time to say a thing like this to you but try to understand me, will you? *I'm a writer.* I do things impulsively. I don't have bank accounts and I don't plan things years in advance. When I want to do something I do it. For some reason or other you seem to think that I want to come to England to . . . frankly, I don't know what the hell's in your mind. I just wanted to come to England to hear English, if you can believe it— and partly too to escape my wife. Does that make sense to you?"

"I should say it does," says the tall thin fellow. "You want to run away from your wife and let her become a public charge. How do you know she won't follow you to England? And how will you take care of her in England—without money?"

I felt as though I were talking to a stone wall. What was the use of rehearsing the whole thing again? "Listen," I said, "as far as I'm concerned I don't care what happens to her. If she becomes a public charge that's her affair, not mine."

"You're working for the Chicago Tribune, you say?"

"I never said anything of the kind. I said my friend, the man who was to send me the money, *he's* working on the Chicago Tribune."

"You never worked for the newspaper then?"

"Yes, I used to work for them, but I don't now. They fired me a few weeks ago."

He snapped me up immediately. "Oh, then you *did* work for the newspaper in Paris?"

"Didn't I just say so? Why? Why do you ask?"

"Mr. Miller, could I see your carte d'identité . . . I suppose you *have* a carte d'identité, living in Paris, as you say."

I fished it out for him. The two of them looked it over together.

"You have a non-worker's card—yet you worked for the Chicago Tribune as a proof-reader. How do you explain that, Mr. Miller?"

"No, I suppose I can't explain that to you. I suppose it's useless to explain to you that I'm an American citizen and that the Chicago Tribune is an American newspaper and that therefore . . ."

"Excuse me, but why were you dismissed from the newspaper?"

"That's just what I was coming to. You see, the French officials, those who have to do with the red tape, seem to take the same attitude as you do. Perhaps I could have remained on the Tribune if I hadn't also been a bad proof-reader. That's the real reason why I was fired, if you want to know."

"You seem rather proud of the fact."

"I am. I think it's a mark of intelligence."

"And so, not having a job on the Tribune any more you thought you'd come to England for a little vacation. And you provided yourself with a visa for a year and a return trip ticket."

"Also to hear English and to escape my wife," I added.

Here the little round-faced fellow spoke up. The tall fellow seemed ready to relinquish the tussle.

"You're a writer, Mr. Miller?"

"Yes."

"You mean you write books and stories?"

"Yes."

"Do you write for the magazines in America?"

"Yes."

"Which ones . . . can you name a few?"

"Certainly. The American Mercury, Harper's, Atlantic Monthly, Scribner's, the Virginia Quarterly, The Yale Review . . ."

"Just a minute." He walked back to the counter and bending down he pulled out a big fat directory. "American Mercury . . . American Mercury . . ." he kept mumbling as he thumbed the pages. "Henry V. Miller, isn't it? Henry V. Miller . . . Henry V. Miller . . . Was it this year or last year, Mr. Miller?"

"It may be three years ago—*for the Mercury,*" I said blandly.

Apparently he had no book on hand that went back that far. Couldn't I give him the name of a magazine I had written for in the last year or two? I said no, I had been too busy writing a book the last year or so.

Had the book been published? What was the name of the American publisher?

I said it had been published by an Englishman.

What was the name of the publisher?

"The Obelisk Press."

He scratched his head. "An *English* publisher?" He couldn't seem to remember any English house by that name. He called his side-kick who had disappeared behind the screen with my passport. "Ever hear of the Obelisk Press?" he yelled.

At this point I thought it timely to tell him that my English publisher published from Paris. That seemed to make him hopping mad. An English publisher in Paris! It was a violation of the rules of nature. Well, anyway, what were the names of the books?

"There's only one," I said. "It's called *Tropic of Cancer.*"

At this I thought he would throw a fit. I didn't know what had come over him for the moment. Finally he seemed to bring himself under partial control and, in the suavest, the most sarcastic voice imaginable, he said: "Come, Mr. Miller, you don't mean to tell me that you write *medical* books too?"

It was my turn to be flabbergasted. The two of them were standing there boring me through with their mean gimlet-like eyes.

"The *Tropic of Cancer*," I said slowly and solemnly, "is *not* a medical book."

"Well, what is it then?" they asked simultaneously.

"The title," I answered, "is a symbolic title. The Tropic of Cancer is a name given in text-books to a temperate zone lying above the Equator. Below the Equator you have the Tropic of Capricorn, which is the south temperate zone. The book, of course, has nothing to do with climatic conditions either, unless it be a sort of mental climate. Cancer is a name which has always intrigued me: you'll find it in zodiacal lore too. Etymologically it comes from chancre, meaning crab. In Chinese symbolism it is a sign of great importance. The crab is the only living creature which can walk backwards and forwards and sideways with equal facility. Of course my book doesn't treat of all this explicitly. It's a novel, or rather an autobiographical document. If my trunk were here I might have shown you a copy. I think you'd be interested in it. By the way, the reason it was published in Paris is because it's too obscene for England or America. Too much cancer in it, if you know what I mean . . ."

This brought the discussion to a close. The tall slim fellow packed his brief case, put on his hat and coat and waited impatiently for the little fellow to get ready. I asked for my passport again. The tall slim fellow went behind the screen and got it for me. I opened it and I saw that he had drawn a big black X through my visa. That infuriated me. It was like a black mark against my good name. "Where's a place to put up for the night in this burg?" I asked, putting as much snot and venom in it as I could muster.

"The constable here will take care of that," says the big fellow, giving me a wry smile and turning on his heel. And with that I see a very tall man dressed in black with a big helmet and a cadaverous face coming towards me out of the gloom of the far corner.

"What do you mean?" I yelled. "Do you mean that I'm under arrest?"

"No, I wouldn't say *that*, Mr. Miller. The constable will put you up for the night and in the morning he'll put you on the boat for Dieppe." And he started to walk away again.

"O.K." I said. "But you're going to see me back here, maybe next week."

By this time the constable was at my side and had me by the arm. I was white with rage, but that firm grasp of the arm told me it was useless to say anything more. It was like the hand of death itself.

As we walked towards the door I explained very calmly to the constable that my trunk had gone on to London and that it contained all my manuscripts as well as other things.

"We can take care of that, Mr. Miller," he says in a quiet, low, steady voice. "Just step this way with me," and he made for the telegraph office. I gave him the necessary dope and he assured me in his quiet, easy voice that I'd have my things in the morning, the first thing in the morning. I knew from the way he spoke that he was a man of his word. Somehow I had an instant respect for him. I did wish, however, that he'd let go my arm. Shit, I wasn't a criminal, and even if I did want to make a break for it where would I go? I couldn't jump in the sea, could I? However, it was no use starting things with him. He was a man who obeyed orders and it was enough just to take one look at him to know that he had been trained like a dog. He escorted me gently and firmly to the hoosegow. We had to pass through a number of vacant, dim-lit rooms or halls to get to the joint. Each time we opened a door he paused and, taking out a bunch of keys, locked the door behind us. It was impressive. I began to get a bit of a thrill out of it. It was ridiculous and awesome at the same time. Christ knows what he would have done if I had been a really dangerous criminal. I suppose he'd have manacled me first. Anyway, finally we got to the hoosegow, which was a sort of big gloomy waiting room very dimly lit. There wasn't a soul in the place, nothing but a few long empty benches, as far as I could make out.

"Here's where we spend the night," said the constable in the same quiet, steady voice. Really a gentle voice it was. I was beginning to take a liking to him. "There's a wash room in there," he added, pointing to a door just in back of me.

"I don't need to wash up," I said. "What I'd really like to do is to take a crap."

"You'll find the place in there," he answered, and opening the door he turned on the light for me.

I went in, took my coats off and sat down. Suddenly, as I was sitting there I looked up and to my amazement there was the constable sitting by the doorway on a little stool. I wouldn't say he was watching me, but certainly he had one eye on me, as they say. At once my bowels were paralyzed. *That,* I thought to myself, that beats everything! And then and there I made a mental note to write about the incident.

As I was buttoning up I expressed a little of my amazement. He took what I said in good part, replying very simply that it was part of his duty. "I've got to keep you under observation until I hand you over to the captain in the morning," he said. "Those are the orders."

"Do people try to run away sometimes?" I asked.

"Not very often," he said. "But things are very bad now, you know, and lots of people are trying to get into England who don't belong here. People who are looking for work, you know."

"Yes, I know," I said. "Things are in a mess."

I was pacing slowly up and down in the big waiting room. Suddenly I felt rather chilly. I went over to the big bench where my overcoat was lying and flung it around my shoulders.

"Would you like me to build you a fire, sir?" the constable suddenly asked.

I thought it was damned considerate of him to ask a question like that and so I said "Why, I don't know. How about *you?* Do you want a fire too?"

"It isn't that, sir," he said. "You see the law entitles you to a fire, if you wish it."

"The hell with that!" I said. "The question is, would it be a bother to make one? Perhaps I can help you."

"No, it's my duty to make you a fire if you wish it. I have nothing to do but look after you."

"Well, if that's the case, let's have a fire," I said. I sat down on the bench and watched him getting it started. Pretty decent, I thought to myself. So the law entitles you to a fire. Well, I'll be God-damned!

When the fire was made the constable suggested that I stretch out on the bench and make myself comfortable. He dug up a cushion from somewhere and a blanket. I lay there looking at the fire and thinking what a strange world it is after all. I mean how on the one hand they manhandle you and on the other hand they nurse you like a baby. All written down in the same book, like debit and credit columns in a ledger. The government is the invisible bookkeeper who makes the entries, and the constable is just a sort of human blotter who dries the ink. If you happen to get a kick in the ass or a couple of teeth pushed down your throat that's gratis and no record is made of it.

The constable was sitting on the little stool by the fireside reading the evening paper. He said he would just sit there and read a bit until I fell asleep. He said it in a neighborly way, without the slightest malice or sarcasm. A different species entirely from the other two bastards whom I had just left.

I watched him reading the paper for a while and then I started to talk to him, in a human way, what I mean, not like he was the constable and me the prisoner. He was not an unintelligent man, nor did he lack sensibility. He struck me, in fact, very much like a fine greyhound, something anyway with blood and breeding. Whereas those other two farts, who were also doing their duty by the government, impressed me as a couple of sadistic jakes, as mean, low, cringing bastards who enjoyed doing their dirty work for the government. I'm sure if the constable were to kill a man in the line of duty you could forgive him for it. But those other pimps! Bah! I spat into the fire with disgust.

I was curious to know if the constable ever did any serious reading. To my surprise he told me that he had read Shaw and Belloc and Chesterton—and some of Somerset Maugham's work. *Of Human Bondage* was a great book, he thought. I thought so too and I scored another strike for the constable on my mental blackboard.

"And you're a writer too?" he said, very gently, almost timidly, I thought.

"A bit of a one," I said diffidently. And then impulsively, falteringly, stutteringly, I launched into an account of *Tropic of Cancer*. I told him about the streets and the cafes. I told him how I had tried to put it all in the book and whether I had succeeded or not I didn't know. "But it's a *human* book," I said, getting up from the bench and moving very close to him. "And I tell you one thing, constable, you impress me as being very human too. I've enjoyed this evening with you and I want you to know that I have a respect and admiration for you. And if you don't think it's immodest of me why I'd like to send you a copy of my book when I get back to Paris."

He wrote his name and address in my notebook and told me he would read the book with great pleasure. "You're a very interesting man," he said, "and I'm worry we had to meet under such painful circumstances."

"Well, let's not talk about that," I said. "What do you say we do a wink of sleep now? Eh?"

"Why yes," he said, "you can make yourself comfortable on the bench there. I'll just sit here and doze a bit. By the way," he added, "would you like me to order breakfast for you in the morning?"

I thought to myself well that's a pretty swell guy, about as decent as they make 'em. And with that I closed my eyes and dozed off.

In the morning the constable took me aboard the boat and handed me over to the captain. There were no passengers aboard yet. I waved good-bye to the constable and then I stood at the prow of the boat and took a good look at England. It was one of those quiet, peaceful mornings with a clear sky overhead and the gulls flying. Always, looking at England from the sea, I am impressed by the gentle, peaceful, somnolent quality of the landscape. England comes so gently down to the sea, it's almost touching. Everything seems so still, so civilized. I stood there looking at Newhaven with tears in my eyes. I wondered where the steward lived and whether he was up and eating his breakfast or pottering around the garden. In England every man *ought* to own a garden: it's meant to be that way, you feel it immediately. As I say, it couldn't have been a better day and England couldn't have looked lovelier, more inviting, than she looked at this moment. I thought of the constable again and how he fitted into the landscape. I want him to know, if he ever reads this, how much I regret the fact, seeing how gentle and sensitive he was, that I had to take a crap in front of him. If I had ever dreamed that he was going to sit there and keep an eye on me I would have held it in until we got to sea. I want him to know that. As for the other two bastards, I want to warn them here and now that if ever I encounter them again in this life I am going to spit in their eye. And may the curse of Job be on them for the rest of their lives. May they die in agony in a foreign land!

One of the most beautiful mornings I have ever known. The little village of Newhaven nestling in the white chalk cliffs. The end of the land, where civilization slips quietly into the sea. I stood there in a reverie for a long while, and a profound peace came over me. In such moments it seems that everything that happens to you happens for the best. Standing there quiet and peaceful like that I got to thinking of our own New Haven (Connecticut), where I had gone once to visit a man in jail. He was a man who had worked for me as a messenger and we had become friends. And then one day in a fit of jealousy he had shot his wife and then himself. Fortunately both of them recovered. After they had transferred him from the hospital to the prison I went to see him one day; we had a long talk through a steel mesh. When I left the prison I suddenly remarked how beautiful it was outdoors and, acting on the impulse, I went to a beach nearby and took a dip. It was one of the strangest days I ever spent at the ocean. When I dove off the springboard I had a feeling that I was taking leave of the earth forever. I didn't try to drown myself, but I didn't care a hoot if I were to drown. It felt marvellous to dive off the earth, to leave behind me all that man-made muck which we glorify with the word civilization. Anyway, as I came up and swam around I seemed to be looking at the world with new eyes. Nothing was like it had been before. People looked curiously separate and detached; they were sitting around like seals drying themselves in the sun. What I'm trying to say is that they seemed absolutely devoid of significance. They were just part of the landscape, like the rocks and the trees and the cows in the meadows. How they had ever assumed such a colossal importance on this earth was a mystery to me. I saw them plainly and distinctly as natural objects, as animals or plants. I felt that day that I could commit the most dastardly crime with a clear conscience. A crime without reason. Yes, it was that that I felt strongly: to kill some innocent person without reason.

As soon as the boat turned its nose toward Dieppe my thoughts began to take a different turn. I had never been out of France before and here I was returning in disgrace with that black mark against my visa. What would the French think? Perhaps they would begin to cross-examine me too. What was I doing in France? How did I make my living? Was I taking bread out of the mouths of French workers? Was I apt to become a public charge?

Suddenly I got into a panic. Supposing they refused to let me return to Paris? Supposing they transferred me to another boat and shipped me back to America? I got into a terrible funk. America! To be shipped back to New York and dumped there like a load of rotten apples! No, if they were going to try that stunt I'd jump overboard. I couldn't bear the thought of returning to America. It was Paris I wanted to see again. Never again would I grumble over my lot. It wouldn't matter if I had to live the rest of my life in Paris as a beggar. Better a beggar in Paris than a millionaire in New York!

I rehearsed a marvellous speech, in French, which I intended to make to the officials. It was such an elaborate, melodramatic speech that the crossing of the Channel passed like a dream. I was trying to conjugate a verb in the subjunctive when suddenly I saw the land popping up and the passengers flocking to the rail. Now it's coming, I thought. Brace up, me bucko, and unloose the subjunctives!

I stood apart from the others instinctively, as though not to contaminate them. I didn't know just what the procedure would be in stepping off—whether there's be an *agent* to meet me or whether somebody would just pounce on me with the grappling hooks as I hit the gangplank. It was all much more simple than my

anxiety led me to anticipate. As the boat pulled into the wharf the
captain came forward and, grasping me by the arm just as the
constable had done, he led me to the rail where I was in plain view
of the men ashore. When he had caught the eye of the man on the
quay whom he was seeking he raised his left hand aloft with the
index finger pointing heavenward and then motioned to me. It was
like saying *One!* One head of cabbage to-day! One head of cattle! I
was more amazed than ashamed. It was so direct and logical, too,
that you could hardly quarrel about it. After all, I was on a boat
and the boat was pulling in and I was the man they were looking
for and why send a cablegram or telephone when all you need to
do is raise your arm and point like that? What could be simpler,
less expensive?

When I observed the man whom I was being delivered to my
heart sank. He was a big brute of a fellow with black handlebars
for moustache and an enormous derby which half crushed his big
appetizing ears. Even at long range his hands looked like big hams.
And he too was dressed all in black. Clearly things were against
me.

Walking down the gangplank I was struggling desperately to
recall fragments of the speech which I had rehearsed only a few
moments ago. I couldn't remember a blooming phrase. All I kept
saying to myself was—"Oui, monsieur, je suis un Américain—
mais je ne suis pas un mendiant. Je vous jure, monsieur, je ne suis
pas un mendiant."

"Votre passeport, s'il vous plaît!"

"Oui, monsieur!"

I knew I was destined to say "Oui, monsieur" over and over
again. Each time it came out of me I cursed myself for saying it.
But what are you going to do? That's the first thing that's drummed
into you when you come to France. *Oui, monsieur! Non, monsieur!* You feel like a cockroach at first. And then you get used to
it and you say it unconsciously, and if the other fellow doesn't say
it you notice it and you hold it against him. And when you're in
trouble that's the first thing that pops out of your mouth. *"Oui,
monsieur!"* You say it like an old billy-goat.

Anyway, I had only said it once or twice, because like the
constable this chap was also a silent man. His duty consisted, as I
happily discovered, in nothing more than escorting me to the office
of another official who again demanded my passport and my carte
d'identité. Here I was politely asked to sit down. I did so with a
great feeling of relief and at the same time, taking a last look at the
big brute who had dismissed me, I asked myself—where have I
seen that man before?

After the grilling of the night before one great difference made itself felt immediately: *Respect for one's individuality!* I think now that even if he had put me on a boat for America I would have accepted my fate tranquilly. There was an inner order to the language, for one thing. He said nothing capricious, nothing insolent, nothing mean or foul or vindictive. He was talking the language of his people and there was form in it, an inner form which had come out of a deep experience of life. It was all the more striking, this clarity, in comparison with the external chaos in which he moved. In fact, it was almost ridiculous, this disorder which enveloped him. It was not altogether ridiculous because what inspired it was human, human foibles, human fallibilities. It was a disorder in which you feel at home, which is a purely French disorder. He had, after a few entirely perfunctory questions, left me undisturbed. I still had no idea what my fate was to be, but I knew definitely that whatever his verdict it would not be capricious or malevolent. I sat there in silence observing the way he went about his work. Nothing seemed to work just right, neither the pen, nor the blotter, nor the ink, nor the ruler. It was as though he had just opened the office and I was his first client. But he had had other offices before, thousands of them, and so he was not greatly perturbed if things didn't go smoothly all at once. The important thing, as he had learned, was to get it all down correctly in the proper books. And to have the necessary stamps and seals which were to give the case its legal, orthodox aspect. *Who was I? What had I done? Ca ne me regarde pas!* I could almost hear him saying it to himself. All he had asked me was—where were you born? where do you live in Paris? when did you come to France? With those three facts in his hand he was constructing a beautiful little dossier in my name to which he would finally sign his name with the proper flourish and then affix the stamps with the proper seal. That was his job and he understood it thoroughly.

It took him quite a little while to go about this task, I must admit. But time now was all in my favor. I would have sat there until the next morning quietly watching him if it had been necessary. I felt that he was working in my interest and in the interest of the French people and that our interests were one because clearly we were both intelligent and reasonable and why would either of us want to cause any one any trouble? I suppose he was a man whom the French would call a *quelconque,* which is not quite the same as a nobody in English, because Mr. Anybody or Everybody in France is quite another species from Mr. Nobody in America or England. A *quelconque* is not a nobody in France. He is a man like any other man, but he has a history and a tradition and a race behind him which often makes him more than the so-called Somebodies in other countries. Like this patient little man working on my dossier these men are often shabbily dressed: they look ragged about the edges and sometimes, be it said, they are not very clean either. But they know how to mind their own business, which is a very great deal.

As I say, it took him a little while to transcribe this data from one record to another. There were carbons to be adjusted, receipts to be detached, little labels to be pasted on, and so forth. Meanwhile the pencil had to be sharpened, a new stub had to be inserted in the penholder, the scissors had to be found, and they were found finally in the waste basket, the ink had to be changed, a new blotter dug up . . . there were lots of things to be done. And to complicate matters he discovered at the last minute that my French visa had expired. Perhaps it was out of delicacy that he merely *suggested* that it would be a good thing if I were to renew my visa—in case I intended to travel out of France again, he said. I was only too delighted to fall in line with the suggestion, feeling at the same time however that it would be a long time before I would ever think of leaving France again. I gave my consent more out of politeness and consideration for his valiant efforts on my behalf.

When everything had been put in order and my passport and carte d'identité were safely in my pocket again I very respectfully suggested that we have a little drink together at the bar across the way. He very graciously accepted the invitation and together we sauntered leisurely out to the *bistrot* opposite the station. He asked me if I liked living in Paris. A little more exciting than this hole, eh? he added. We didn't have time for much of a conversation as the train was due to leave in a few minutes. I thought perhaps at the end he would say—"how did you ever come to get into such a mess?"—but no, not the slightest allusion to the subject.

We walked back to the quay and as the whistle blew we shook hands cordially and he wished me a bon voyage. As I took my seat he was still standing there. He waved his hand and again he said: "Au revoir, Monsieur Miller, et bon voyage!" This time the *Monsieur Miller* sounded good to my ears, and perfectly natural. In fact it sounded so good and natural that it brought tears to my eyes. Yes, as the train rolled out of the station I distinctly remember two big tears rolling down my cheeks and falling on to my hands. I felt safe again and among human beings. The "bon voyage" was ringing in my ears. *Bon voyage! Bon voyage!*

A light drizzle was falling over Picardy. It made the thatched roofs look invitingly black and the grass a little greener. Now and then a patch of ocean veered into sight, to be swallowed up immediately by rolling sand dunes, then farms and meadows and brooks. A silent, peaceful countryside where each man minds his own business.

Suddenly I felt so god-damned happy I wanted to stand up and shout or sing. But all I could think of was *"bon voyage!"* What a phrase that! All our lives we're knocking about here and there mumbling that phrase which the French have given us, but do we ever take the *bon voyage?* Do we realize that even when we walk to the bistrot, or to the corner grocer, that it's a voyage from which we may never return? If we keenly felt that, that each time we sailed out of the house we were embarking on a voyage, would it make our lives a little different? While we make the little trip to the corner, or to Dieppe, or to Newhaven, or wherever it may be, the earth too is making her little trip, where nobody knows, not even the astronomers. But all of us, whether we move from here to the corner or from here to China, are making a voyage with our mother the earth, and the earth is moving with the sun and with the sun the other planets too are moving . . . Mars, Mercury, Venus, Neptune, Jupiter, Saturn, Uranus. The whole firmament is moving and with it, if you listen closely, you will hear *"Bon Voyage!" "Bon Voyage!"* And if you get still as a needle and don't ask a lot of foolish questions you will realize that to make a voyage is only an idea, that there is nothing in life but voyage, voyage within voyage, and that death is not the last voyage but the beginning of a new voyage and nobody knows why or whither, but *bon voyage* just the same! I wanted to stand up and sing that in the key of Ut-Mineur. I saw the whole universe like a network of tracks, some deep and invisible like the planetary grooves, and in this vast misty slithering to and fro, in the ghost-like passage from one realm to another, I saw all things animate and inanimate waving to one another, the cockroaches to the cockroaches, the stars to the stars, man to man, and God to God. All aboard for the big trek to nowhere, but *Bon Voyage* just the same! From osmosis to cataclysm, all a vast, silent, and perpetual movement. To stand still within the big crazy movement, to move with the earth however she wobbles, to join up with the cockroaches and the stars and the gods and men, that's voyaging! And out there in space where we are moving, where we leave our invisible tracks, out there is it possible that I hear a faint, sarcastic echo, a slimy, anaemic little English voice asking incredulously—"Come, Mr. Miller, you don't mean to say that you write *medical* books too?" Yes, by Jesus, now I can say it with a clean conscience. Yes, Mr. Nobody from Newhaven, I *do* write medical books too, marvellous medical books which cure all the ills of time and space. In fact, I am writing now, this very minute, the one great purgative of the human consciousness: *the sense of voyage!*

And just as I imagined I saw the idiot from Newhaven cocking his ear to hear me better a big shadow loomed in front of him and blotted him out. Just as I was about to say to myself—"Where have I seen this face before?"—it dawned on me like a flash. The man with the moustache at Dieppe, that face I had seen somewhere before, I recognized it now: it was the face of Mack Swain! He was The Big Bad Wolf and Charlie was Samson Agonistes. That's all. I just wanted to straighten it out in my mind. *Et bon voyage. Bon voyage à tout le monde!*

The Universe of Death

In selecting Proust and Joyce I have chosen the two literary figures who seem to me most representative of our time. Whatever has happened in literature since Dostoievski has happened on the other side of death. Lawrence apart, we are no longer dealing with living men, men for whom the Word is a living thing. Lawrence's life and works represent a drama which centers about the attempt to escape a living death, a death which, if it were understood, would bring about a revolution in our way of living. Lawrence experienced this death creatively, and it is because of his unique experience that his "failure" is of a wholly different order from that of Proust or Joyce. His aborted efforts towards self-realization speak of heroic struggle, and the results are fecundating—for those, at any rate, who may be called the "aristocrats of the spirit."

Despite all that may be said against him, as an artist, or as a man, he still remains the most alive, the most vitalizing of recent writers. Proust had to die in order even to commence his great work; Joyce, though still alive, seems even more dead than Proust ever was. Lawrence on the other hand, is still with us: his death, in fact, is a mockery of the living. Lawrence killed himself in the effort to burst the bonds of living death. There is evidence for believing, if we study for example such a work as *The Man Who Died,* that had it been given him to enjoy the normal span of life he would have arrived at a state of wisdom, a mystic way of life, in which the artist and the human being would have been reconciled. Such men have indeed been rare in the course of our Western civilization. Whatever in the past may have operated to prevent our men of genius from attaining such a state of perfection we know that in Lawrence's case the poverty, the sterility of the cultural soil into which he was born, was certainly the death-dealing cause. Only a part of the man's nature succeeded in

148

blossoming—the rest of him was imprisoned and strangled in the dry walls of the womb. With Proust and Joyce there was no struggle: they emerged, took a glance about, and fell back again into the darkness whence they come. Born creative, they elected to identify themselves with the historical movement.

If there be any solution of life's problems for the mass of mankind, in this biological continuum which we have entered upon, there is certainly little hope of any for the individual, i. e., the artist. For him the problem is not how to identify himself with the mass about, for in that lies his *real* death, but how to fecundate the masses by his dying. In short, it is his almost impossible duty now to restore to this unheroic age a *tragic* note. This he can do only by establishing a new relationship with the world, by seizing anew the sense of death on which all art is founded, and reacting creatively to it. Lawrence understood this, and it is for this reason that his work, however conventional it may appear extrinsically, has vitality.

The fact remains, nevertheless, that not even a Lawrence was able to exercise any visible influence upon the world. The times are stronger than the men who are thrown up. We are in a deadlock. We have a choice, but we are unable to make it. It was the realization of this which impelled me to end my long introduction to *The World of Lawrence,* of which this is the final section, with the title *Universe of Death.*

So far as the creative individual goes life and death are of equal value: it is all a question of counterpoint. What is of vital concern, however, is how and where one meets life—or death. Life can be more deadly than death, and death on the other hand can open up the road to life. It is against the stagnant flux in which we are now drifting that Lawrence appears brilliantly alive. Proust and Joyce, needless to say, appear more representative: they *reflect* the times. We see in them no revolt: it is surrender, suicide, and the more poignant since it springs from creative sources.

It is in the examination, then, of these two contemporaries of Lawrence that we see the process all too clearly. In Proust the full flower of psychologism—confession, self-analysis, arrest of living, making of art the final justification, but thereby divorcing art from life. An intestinal conflict in which the artist is immolated. The great retrospective curve back towards the womb: suspension in death, living death, for the purposes of dissection. Pause to question, but no questions forthcoming, the faculty having atrophied. A worship of art for its own sake—not for man. Art, in other words, regarded as a means of salvation, as a redemption from suffering, as a compensation for the terror of living. *Art a substi-*

tute for life. The literature of flight, of escape, of a neurosis so brilliant that it almost makes one doubt the efficacy of health. *Until* one casts a glance at that "neurosis of health" of which Nietzsche sings in *The Birth of Tragedy.*

In Joyce the soul deterioration may be traced even more definitely, for if Proust may be said to have provided the tomb of art, in Joyce we can witness the full process of decomposition. "Whoso," says Nietzsche, "not only comprehends the word Dionysian, but also grasps his *self* in this word, requires no refutation of Plato or of Christianity or of Schopenhauer—*he smells the putrefaction.*" *Ulysses* is a paean to "the late-city man," a thanatopsis inspired by the ugly tomb in which the soul of the civilized man lies embalmed. The most astoundingly varied and subtle means of art are herein exploited to glorify the dead city. The story of *Ulysses* is the story of a lost hero recounting a lost myth; frustrated and forlorn the Janus-faced hero wanders through the labyrinth of the deserted temple, seeking for the holy place but never finding it. Cursing and vilifying the mother who bore him, deifying her as a whore, bashing his brains out with idle conundrums, such is the modern Ulysses. Through the mystery-throngs he weaves his way, a hero lost in a crowd, a poet rejected and despised, a prophet wailing and cursing, covering his body with dung, examining his own excrement, parading his obscenity, lost, lost, a crumbling brain, a dissecting instrument endeavoring to reconstruct the soul. Through his chaos and obscenity, his obsessions and complexes, his perpetual, frantic search for God, Joyce reveals the desperate plight of the modern man who, lashing about in his steel and concrete cage, admits finally that there is no way out.

In these two exponents of modernity we see the flowering of the Hamlet-Faust myth, that unscotchable snake in the entrails which, for the Greeks, was represented by the Oedipus myth, and for the whole Aryan race by the myth of Prometheus. In Joyce not only is the withered Homeric myth reduced to ashes, but even the Hamlet myth, which had come to supreme expression in Shakespeare, even this vital myth, I say, is pulverized. In Joyce we see the incapacity of the modern man even to doubt: it is the simulacrum of doubt, not its substance, that he gives us. With Proust there is a higher appreciation of doubt, of the inability to act. Proust is more capable of presenting the metaphysical aspect of things, partly because of a tradition so firmly anchored in the Mediterranean culture, and partly because his own schizoid temperament enabled him to examine objectively the evolution of a vital problem from its metaphysical to its psychological aspect. The progression from nerves to insanity, from a tragic confrontation of the duality in man to a pathologic split in the personality, is mirrored in the transition from Proust to Joyce. Where Proust held himself suspended over life in a cataleptic trance, weighing, dissecting, and eventually corroded by the very scepticism he had employed, Joyce had already plunged into the abyss. In Proust there is still a questioning of values; with Joyce there is a denial of all values. With Proust the schizophrenic aspect of his work is not so much the cause as the result of his world-view. With Joyce there is no world-view. Man returns to the primordial elements; he is washed away in a cosmological flux. Parts of him may be thrown up on foreign shores, in alien climes, in some future time. But the whole man, the vital, spiritual ensemble, is dissolved. This is the dissolution of the body and soul, a sort of cellular immortality in which life survives chemically.

Proust, in his classic retreat from life, is the very symbol of the modern artist—the sick giant who locks himself up in a cork-lined cell to take his brains apart. He is the incarnation of that last and fatal disease: *the disease of the mind*. In *Ulysses* Joyce gives us the complete identification of the artist with the tomb in which he buries himself. *Ulysses* has been spoken of as seeming like "a solid city." Not so much a solid city, it seems to me, as a dead world-city. Just as there is, beneath the hollow dynamism of the city, an appalling weariness, a monotony, a fatigue insuperable, so in the works of Proust and Joyce the same qualities manifest themselves. A perpetual stretching of time and space, an obedience to the law of inertia, as if to atone, or compensate, for the lack of a higher urge. Joyce takes Dublin with its worn-out types; Proust takes the microscopic world of the Faubourg St. Germain, symbol of a dead past. The one wears us out because he spreads himself over such an enormous artificial canvas; the other wears us out by magnifying his thumb-nail fossil beyond all sensory recognition. The one uses the city as a universe, the other as an atom. The curtain never falls. Meanwhile the world of living men and women is huddling in the wings clamoring for the stage.

In these epics everything is of equal prominence, equal value, whether spiritual or material, organic or inorganic, live or abstract. The array and content of these works suggest to the mind the interior of a junk-shop. The effort to parallel space, to devour it, to install oneself in the time process—the very nature of the task is foreboding. The mind runs wild. We have sterility, onanism, logomachy. *And*—the more colossal the scope of the work the more monstrous the failure!

Compared to these dead moons how comforting the little works which stick out like brilliant stars! Rimbaud, for example! His *Illuminations* outweighs a shelf of Proust, Joyce, Pound, Eliot, etc. Times there are, to be sure, when the colossal work compels admiration, when, as with Bach or Dante, it is ordered by an inner plan, by the organic mechanism of faith. Here the work of art assumes the form and dimensions of a cathedral, a veritable tree of life. But with our latter-day exponents of head-culture the great monuments are lying on their sides, they stretch away like huge petrified forests, and the landscape itself becomes *nature-morte*.

Though we do, as Edmund Wilson says, "possess Dublin seen, heard, smelt and felt, brooded over, imagined, remembered," it is, in a profound sense, no possession at all: it is possession through the dead ends of the brain. As a naturalistic canvas *Ulysses* makes its appeal to the sense of smell only: it gives off a sublime mortuary odor. It is not the reality of nature here, still less the reality of the five senses. *It is the sick reality of the mind.* And so, if we possess Dublin at all, it is only as a shade wandering through an excavated Troy or Knossus; the historical past juts out in geological strata.

In referring to *Work in Progress* Louis Gillet, an admirer of Joyce, says: "One sees how the themes are linked together in this strange symphony; men are, to-day, as at the beginning of the world, the playthings of nature; they translate their impressions into myths which comprise the fragments of experience, the shreds of reality which are held in the memory. And thus is made a legend, a sort of extra-temporal history, formed of the residue of all histories, which one might call (in using a title of Johann Sebastian Bach) a cantata for all time."

A noble ring to these words, but absolutely false. This is not how legends are made! The men who are capable of creating an "extra-temporal history" are not the men who create legends. The two are not co-eval in time and space. The legend is the soul emerging into form, a singing soul which not only carries hope, but which contains a promise and a fulfillment. In the "extra-temporal," on the other hand, we have a flat expanse, a muddy residue, a sink without limits, without depths, without light and shadow—an abyss into which the soul is plunged and swallowed up. It marks the end of the great trajectory: the tapeworm of history devours itself. If this be legend, it is legend that will never survive, and most certainly never be sung. Already, almost coincidentally with their appearance, we have, as a result of *Ulysses* and *Work in Progress,* nothing but dry analyses, archaeological burrowings, geological surveys, laboratory tests of the Word. The commentators, to be sure, have only begun to chew into Joyce.

The Germans will finish him! They will make Joyce palatable, understandable, clear as Shakespeare, *better* than Joyce, *better* than Shakespeare. Wait! The mystagogues are coming!

As Gillet has well said—*Work in Progress* represents "a picture of the flowing reminiscences, of the vain desires and confused wishes which wander in our sleepy, loosened soul, which comprises the crepuscular life of thought . . ." But *who* is interested in this language of night? *Ulysses* was obscure enough. But *Work in Progress* . . .? Of Proust at least we may say that his myopia served to render his work exciting, stimulating: it was like seeing the world through the eyes of a horse, or a fly. Joyce's deformity of vision, on the other hand, is depressing, crippling, dwarfing: it is a defect of the soul, and not an artistic, metaphysical device. Joyce is growing more blind every day—blind in the pineal eye. For passion he is substituting books; for men and women rivers and trees—or wraiths. Life to Joyce, as one of his admirers says, is a mere tautology. Precisely. We have here the clue to the whole symbolism of defeat. And, whether he is interested in history or not, Joyce *is* the history of our time, of this age which is sliding into darkness. Joyce is the blind Milton of our day. But whereas Milton glorified Satan, Joyce, because his sense of vision has atrophied, merely surrenders to the powers of darkness. Milton was a rebel, a demonic force, a voice that made itself heard. Milton blind, like Beethoven deaf, only grew in power and eloquence; the inner eye, the inner ear, became more attuned to the cosmic rhythm. Joyce, on the other hand, is a blind and deaf *soul:* his voice rings out over a waste land and the reverberations are nothing but the echoes of a lost soul. Joyce is the lost soul of this soulless world; his interest is not in life, in men and deeds, not in history, not in God, but in the dead dust of books. He is the high priest of the lifeless literature of to-day. He writes a hieratic script which not even his admirers and disciples can decipher. He is burying himself under an obelisk for whose script there will be no key.

It is interesting to observe in the works of Proust and Joyce, and of Lawrence as well, how the milieu from which they sprang determined the choice of the protagonist as well as the nature of the disease against which they fought. Joyce, springing from the priest class, makes Bloom, his "average" man or double, the supreme object of ridicule. Proust, springing from the cultured middle-class, though himself living only on the fringe of society, *tolerated,* as it were, makes Charlus, his king figure, a bitter object of ridicule. And Lawrence, springing from the common classes, makes the type Mellors, who appears in a variety of ideal roles, but usually as the man of the soil, his hope of the future—treating him, however, no less unsparingly. All three have idealized in the person of the hero those qualities which they felt themselves to lack supremely.

Joyce, deriving from the mediaeval scholar, with the blood of the priest in him, is consumed by his inability to participate in the ordinary, everyday life of human beings. He creates Bloom, the shadow of Odysseus, Bloom the eternal Jew, the symbol of the outcast Irish race whose tragic story is so close to the author's heart. Bloom is the projected wanderer of Joyce's inner restlessness, of his dissatisfaction with the world. He is the man who is misunderstood and despised by the world, rejected by the world because he himself rejected the world. It is not so strange as at first blush it may seem that, searching for a counterpart to Daedalus, Joyce chose a Jew; instinctively he selected a type which has always given proof of its ability to arouse the passions and prejudices of the world.

In giving us Dublin Joyce gave us the scholar-priest's picture of the world as is. Dirty Dublin! Worse even than London, or Paris. The worst of all possible worlds! In this dirty sink of the world-as-is we have Bloom, the fictive image of the man in the street, crass, sensual, inquisitive but unimaginative—the educated nincompoop hypnotized by the abracadabra of scientific jargon. Molly Bloom, the Dublin slut, is an even more successful image of the common run. Molly Bloom is an archetype of the eternal feminine. She is the rejected mother whom the scholar and priest in Joyce had to liquidate. She is the veridic whore of creation. By comparison, Bloom is a comic figure. Like the ordinary man, he is a medal without a reverse. And like the ordinary man, he is most ludicrous when he is being made *cocu*. It is the most persistent, the most fundamental image of himself which the "average" man retains in this woman's world of to-day where his importance is so negligible.

Charlus, on the other hand, is a colossal figure, and Proust has handled him in colossal fashion. As symbol of the dying world of caste, ideals, manners, etc., Charlus was selected, whether with thought or not, from the forefront of the enemy's ranks. Proust, we know, was outside that world which he has so minutely described. As a pushing little Jew, he fought or wormed his way inside—and with disastrous results. Always shy, timid, awkward, embarrassed. Always a bit ridiculous. A sort of cultivated Chaplin! And, characteristically, this world which he so ardently desired to join he ended by despising. It is a repetition of the Jew's eternal fight with an alien world. A perpetual effort to become part of this hostile world and then, because of inability to become assimilated, rejecting it or destroying it. But if it is typical of the mechanism of the Jew, it is no less typical of the artist. And, true artist that he was, thoroughly sincere, Proust chose the best example of that alien world for his hero, Charlus. Did he not, in part, become like that hero himself later on, in his unnatural effort to become assimilated? For Charlus, though he had his counterpart in reality, quite as famous as the fictive creation, Charlus is, nevertheless, the image of the later Proust. He is, indeed, the image of a whole world of aesthetes who have now incorporated under the banner of homosexualism.

The beautiful figure of the grandmother, and of the mother, the sane, touching, moral atmosphere of the household, so pure and integrated, so thoroughly Jewish, stands opposed to the glamorous, the romantic, alien world of the Gentile which attracts and corrodes. It stands out in sharp contrast to the milieu from which Joyce sprang. Where Joyce leaned on the Catholic Church and its traditional masters of exegesis, thoroughly vitiated by the arid intellectualism of his caste, we have in Proust the austere atmosphere of the Jewish home contaminated by a hostile culture, the most strongly rooted culture left in the Western world—French Hellenism. We have an uneasiness, a maladjustment, a war in the spiritual realm which, projected in the novel, continued throughout his life. Proust was touched only superficially by French culture. His art is eminently un-French. We have only to think of his devout admiration for Ruskin. Ruskin! of all men!

And so, in describing the decay of his little world, this microcosm which was for him *the* world, in depicting the disintegration of his hero, Charlus, Proust sets before us the collapse of the outer and the inner world. The battleground of love, which began normally enough with Gilberte, becomes transferred, as in the world to-day, to that plane of depolarized love wherein the sexes fuse, the world where doubt and jealousy, thrown out of their normal axes, play diabolical roles. Where in Joyce's world a thoroughly normal obscenity slops over into a slimy, glaucous fluid in which life sticks, in Proust's world vice, perversion, loss of sex breaks out like a pox and corrodes everything.

In their analysis and portrayal of disintegration both Proust and Joyce are unequalled, excepting perhaps by Dostoievski and Petronius. They are both *objective* in their treatment—technically classic, though romantic at heart. They are naturalists who present the world as they find it, and say nothing about the causes, nor derive from their findings any conclusions. They are defeatists, men who escape from a cruel, hideous, loathsome reality into ART. After writing the last volume, with its memorable treatise on art, Proust goes back to his death-bed to revise the page on Albertine. This episode is the core and climax of his great work. It forms the arch of that Inferno into which the mature Proust descended. For if, retiring ever deeper into the labyrinth, Proust had cast a glance back at that which he left behind, he must have seen there in the figure of woman that image of himself in which all life was mirrored. It was an image which tantalized him, an image which lied to him from every reflection, because he had penetrated to an underworld in which there were nothing but shadows and distortions. The world he had walked out on was the masculine world in process of dissolution. With Albertine as the clue, with this single thread in his hand which, despite all the anguish and sorrow of knowledge he refuses to let slip, he feels his way along the hollows of the nerves, through a vast, subterranean world of remembered sensations in which he hears the pumping of the heart but knows not whence it comes, or what it is.

It has been said that *Hamlet* is the incarnation of doubt, and *Othello* the incarnation of jealousy, and so they may be, *but*—the episode of Albertine, reached after an interval of several centuries of deterioration, seems to me a dramaturgic study of doubt and jealousy so infinitely more vast and complex than either *Hamlet* or *Othello* that the Shakespearean dramas, by comparison, resemble the feeble sketches which later are to assume the dimensions of a great fresco. This tremendous convulsion of doubt and jealousy which dominates the book is the reflection of that supreme struggle with Fate which characterizes our entire European history. To-day we see about us Hamlets and Othellos by the thousands—such Hamlets, such Othellos, as Shakespeare never dreamed of, such as would make him sweat with pride could he turn over in his grave. This theme of doubt and jealousy, to seize upon its most salient aspects only, is in reality only the reverberation of a much greater theme, a theme more complex, more ramified, which has become heightened, or *muddied,* if you like, in the interval of time between Shakespeare and Proust. Jealousy is the little symbol of that struggle with Fate which is revealed through doubt. The poison of doubt, of introspection, of conscience, of idealism, overflowing into the arena of sex, develops the marvellous bacillus of jealousy which, to be sure, will ever exist, but which in the past, when life ran high, was held in place and served its proper role and function. Doubt and jealousy are those points of resistance on which the great whet their strength, from which they rear their towering structures, their *masculine* world. When doubt and jealousy run amok it is because the body has been defeated, because the spirit languishes and the soul becomes unloosed. Then it is that the germs work their havoc and men no longer know whether they are devils or angels, nor whether women are to be shunned or worshiped, nor whether homosexuality is a vice or a blessing. Alternating between the most ferocious display of cruelty and the most supine acquiescence we have conflicts, revolutions, holo-causts—*over trifles, over nothing.* The last war, for example. The loss of sex polarity is part and parcel of the larger disintegration, the reflex of the soul's death, and coincident with the disappear-ance of great men, great deeds, great causes, great wars, etc.

Herein lies the importance of Proust's epic work, for here in the Albertine episode we have the problem of love and jealousy depicted in Gargantuan fashion, the malady become all-inclusive, turning in on itself through the inversion of sex. The great Shake-spearean dramas were but the announcement of a disease which had just begun to run its staggering course; in Shakespeare's time it had not yet eaten into every layer of life, it could still be made the subject of heroic drama. There was man and there was the disease, and the conflict was the material for drama. But now the toxin is in the blood. For such as us, who have been eaten away by the virus, the great dramatic themes of Shakespeare are but swashbuckling oratory and pasteboard sets. Their impression is nil. We have become inoculated. And it is in Proust that we can sense the deterioration of the heroic, the cessation of conflict, the surrender, the thing become itself.

I repeat that we have in our midst to-day greater Hamlets, greater Othellos, than Shakespeare ever dreamed of. We have now the ripe fruit of the seeds planted by the masters of old. Like some marvellous unicellular organism in endless process of exfoliation these types reveal to us all the varieties of body cells which formerly entered into the making of blood, bone, muscle, hair, teeth, nails, etc. We have now the monstrous flower whose roots were watered by the Christian myth. We are living amidst the ruins of a world in collapse, amidst the husks which must rot away to make new loam.

This formidable picture of the world-as-disease which Proust and Joyce have given us is indeed less a picture than a microscopic study which, because we see it magnified, prevents us from recog-nizing it as the world of everyday in which we are swimming. Just as the art of psycho-analysis could not have arisen until society was sick enough to call for this peculiar form of therapy, so we could not have had a faithful image of our time until there arose in our midst monsters so ridden with the disease that their works resemble the disease itself.

Seizing upon the malodorous quality in Proust's work Edmund Wilson, the American critic, is moved to doubt the authenticity of the narrative. "When Albertine finally leaves him," he writes, "the emotional life of the book becomes progressively asphyxiated by the infernal fumes which Charlus has brought with him—until such a large percentage of the characters have tragically, grue-somely, irrevocably turned out to be homosexual that we begin for the first time to find the story a little incredible." Of course it is incredible—from a realistic point of view! It is incredible, as are all authentic revelations of life, because it is too true. We have modulated into a higher realm of reality. It is not the author whom we should take to task, but life. The Baron de Charlus, like Albertine again, is precisely the illuminating figure on which to rivet attention. Charlus is Proust's supreme creation, his "hero," if this work can be said to have a hero. To call the Baron's behavior, or that of his satellites and imitators, *incredible*, is to deny the validity of Proust's whole edifice. Into the character of Charlus (derived from many accurately studied prototypes), Proust poured all that he knew of the subject of perversion, and that subject dominates the entire work—justly. Do we not know that he originally contemplated labelling the whole work by the title given to the cornerstone of his work—*Sodom and Gomorrah!* Sodom and Gomorrah! Do I not detect here a little of the smell of Ruskin?

At any rate, it is indisputable that Charlus is his grand effort. Like Stavrogin for Dostoievski, Charlus was the supreme test. Like Stavrogin also, observe how the figure of Charlus permeates and dominates the atmosphere when off scene, how the poison of his being shoots its virus into the other characters, the other scenes, the other dramas, so that from the moment of his entry, or even before, the atmosphere is saturated with his noxious gases. In analyzing Charlus, in ridiculing and pillorying him Proust, like Dostoievski, was endeavoring to expose himself, to understand himself perhaps.

When, in *The Captive*, Marcel and Albertine are discussing Dostoievski, Marcel feebly endeavoring to give a satisfactory response to Albertine's questions, how little did Proust realize, I wonder, that in creating the Baron de Charlus he was giving her the answer which then he seemed incapable of. The discussion, it may be recalled, centered about Dostoievski's propensities for depicting the ugly, the sordid, particularly his prepossession for the subject of *crime*. Albertine had remarked that crime was an obsession with Dostoievski, and Marcel, after venturing some rather weak remarks about the multiple nature of genius, dismisses the subject with something to the effect that *that* side of Dostoiev-ski really interested him but little, that in truth he found himself incapable of understanding it.

Nevertheless, when it came to the delineation of Charlus, Proust showed himself capable of performing a prodigious piece of creative imagination. Charlus seems so removed from Proust's actual experience of life that people often wonder where he gathered the elements for his creation. Where? In his own soul! Dostoievski was not a criminal, not a murderer, Dostoievski never *lived* the life of Stavrogin. But Dostoievski was obsessed with the *idea* of a Stavrogin. He *had* to create him in order to live out his *other* life, his life as a creator. Little matter that he may have *known* a Stavrogin in the course of his manifold experiences. Little matter that Proust had under his eye the *actual* figure of Charlus. The originals, if not discarded, were certainly radically recast, transformed, in the light of inner truth, inner vision. In both Dostoievski and Proust there existed a Stavrogin, a Charlus, far more real than the actual figures. For Dostoievski the character of Stavrogin was bound up with the search for God. Stavrogin was the ideal image of himself which Dostoievski jealously preserved. More than that—Stavrogin was the god in him, the fullest portrait of God which Dostoievski could give.

Between Stavrogin and Charlus, however, there is an enormous gulf. It is the difference between Dostoievski and Proust, or if you like, the difference between the man of God whose hero is himself and the modern man for whom not even God can be a hero. All of Dostoievski's work is pregnant with conflict, *heroic* conflict. In an essay on *Aristocracy* Lawrence writes—"Being alive constitutes an aristocracy which there is no getting beyond. He who is most alive, intrinsically, is King, whether men admit it or not . . . More life! More *vivid* life! Not more safe cabbages, or meaningless masses of people. All creation contributes, and must contribute to this: towards the achieving of a vaster, vivider, cycle of life. That is the goal of living. He who gets nearer the sun is leader, the aristocrat of aristocrats. Or he who, like Dostoievski, gets nearest the moon of our not-being."

Proust, early in life, relinquished this conflict. As did Joyce. Their art is based on submission, on surrender to the stagnant flux. The Absolute remains outside their works, dominates them, destroys them, just as in life idealism dominates and destroys the ordinary man. But Dostoievski, confronted by even greater powers of frustration, boldly set himself to grapple with the mystery; he crucified himself for this purpose. And so, wherever in his works there is chaos and confusion, it is a *rich* chaos, a meaningful confusion; it is positive, vital, soul-infected. It is the aura of the beyond, of the unattainable, that sheds its lustre over his scenes and characters—not a dead, dire obscurity. Needless to say, with

Proust and Joyce there is an obscurity of another order. With the former we enter the twilight zone of the mind, a realm shot through with dazzling splendors, but always the pale lucidity, the insufferable, obsessional lucidity of the mind. With Joyce we have the night mind, a profusion even more incredible, more dazzling than with Proust, as though the last intervening barriers of the soul had been broken down. But again, *a mind!*

Whereas with Dostoievski, though the mind is always there, always effective and powerfully operative, it is nevertheless a mind constantly held in leash, subordinated to the demands of the soul. It works as mind should work—that is, as machinery, and not as generative power. With Proust and Joyce the mind seems to resemble a machine set in motion by a human hand and then abandoned. It runs on perpetually, or will, until another human hand stops it. Does anybody believe that for either of these men death could be anything but an accidental interruption? *When* did death occur for them? Technically one is still alive. But were they not both dead before they commenced to write?

It is in Joyce that one observes that peculiar failing of the modern artist—the inability to communicate with his audience. Not a wholly new phenomenon, admitted, but always a significant one. Endowed with a Rabelaisian ability for word invention, embittered by the domination of a church for which his intellect had no use, harassed by the lack of understanding on the part of family and friends, obsessed by the parental image against which he vainly rebels, Joyce has been seeking escape in the erection of a fortress composed of meaningless verbiage. His language is a ferocious masturbation carried on in fourteen tongues. It is a dervish executed on the periphery of meaning, an orgasm not of blood and semen, but of dead slag from the burnt out crater of the mind. The Revolution of the Word which his work seems to have inspired in his disciples is the logical outcome of this sterile dance of death.

Joyce's exploration of the night world, his obsession with myth, dream, legend, all the processes of the unconscious mind, his tearing apart of the very instrument itself and the creating of his own world of phantasy, is very much akin to Proust's dilemma. Ultracivilized products, both, we find them rejecting all question of soul; we find them sceptical of science itself, though bearing witness through their works of an unadmitted allegiance to the principle of causality, which is the very cornerstone of science. Proust, imagining himself to be making of his life a book, of his suffering a poem, exhibits through his microscopic and caustic analysis of man and society the plight of the modern artist for whom there is no faith, no meaning, no life. His work is the most triumphant monument to disillusionment that has ever been erected.

At the root of it was his inability, confessed and repeatedly glorified, to cope with reality—the constant plaint of the modern man. As a matter of fact, his life was a living death, and it is for this reason that his case interests us. For, intensely aware of his predicament, he has given us a record of the age in which he found himself imprisoned. Proust has said that the idea of death kept him company as incessantly as the idea of his own identity. That idea relates, as we know, to that night when, as he says himself, "his parents first indulged him." That night which "dates the decline of the will" also dates his death. Thenceforth he is incapable of living in the world—of *accepting* the world. From that night on he is dead to the world, except for those brief intermittent flashes which not only illuminate the dense fog which is his work but which made his work possible. By a miracle, familiar enough now to the psychiatrist, he stepped beyond the threshold of death. His work like his life, was a biological continuum punctuated by the meaningless interruption of statistical death.

And so it is no surprise when, standing on the two uneven flagstones and re-experiencing to the ultimate degree those sensational truths which had assailed him several times during the course of his life, he proceeds with a clarity and subtlety unrivalled to develop those thoughts which contain his final and highest views of life and art—magnificent pages dedicated to a lost cause. Here, when he speaks of the artist's instincts, his necessity to obey the small, inner voice, to eschew realism and simply to *"translate"* what is there ever surging upward, ever struggling for expression, here we realize with devastating intensity that for him, Proust, life was not a living, but a feasting upon sunken treasures, a life of retrospect; we realize that for him what joy remained was nothing but the joy of the archeologist in rediscovering the relics and ruins of the past, of musing among these buried treasures and reimagining the life that had once given form to these dead things. And yet, sad as it is to contemplate the grandeur and nobility of these pages, moving as it is to observe that a great work had been built up out of suffering and disease, it is also tonic to realize that in these same passages there had been dealt the death-blow to that school of realism which, pretending to be dead, had resuscitated itself under the guise of psychologism. After all Proust was concerned with a view of life; his work has meaning and content, his characters do live, however distorted they are made to seem by his laboratory method of dissection and analysis. Proust was preeminently a man of the 19th century, with all the tastes, the ideology, and the respect for the powers of the conscious mind which dominated the men of that epoch. His work now seems like the labor of a man who has revealed to us the absolute limits of such a mind.

The breakdown which, in the realm of painting, gave rise to the school of Impressionism is evident also in Proust's literary method. The process of examining the medium itself, of subjecting the external world to microscopic analysis, thereby creating a new perspective and hence the illusion of a new world, has its counterpart in Proust's technique. Weary of realism and naturalism, as were the painters, or rather finding the existent picture of reality unsatisfying, *unreal,* owing to the explorations of the physicists, Proust strove, through the elaborate diffraction of incident and character, to displace the psychologic realism of the day. His attitude is coincident with the emergence of the new analytical psychology. Throughout those veritably ecstatic passages in the last volume of his work—the passages on the function of art and the role of the artist—Proust finally achieves a clarity of vision which presages the finish of his own method and the birth of a wholly new kind of artist. Just as the physicists, in their exploration of the material nature of the universe, arrived at the brink of a new and mysterious realm, so Proust, pushing his powers of analysis to the utmost limits, arrived at that frontier between dream and reality which henceforth will be the domain of the truly creative artists.

It is when we come to Joyce, who succeeds Proust by a short interval, that we notice the change in the psychologic atmosphere. Joyce who in his early work gives us a romantic confessional account of the "I", suddenly moves over into a new domain. Though smaller in scope, the canvas which Joyce employs gives the illusion of being even more vast than Proust's; we lose ourselves in it, not as with Proust, in dream fashion, but as one loses himself in a strange city. Despite all the analysis, Proust's world is still a world of nature, of monstrous yet live fauna and flora. With Joyce we enter the inorganic world—the kingdom of minerals, of fossil and ruin, of dead dodos. The difference in technique is more than remarkable—it is significant of a wholly new order of sensation. We are done now with the 19th century sensibility of Proust; it is no longer through the nerves that we receive our impressions, no longer a personal and sub-conscious memory ejecting its images. As we read *Ulysses* we have the impression that the mind has become a recording machine: we are aware of a double world as we move with the author through the great labyrinth of the city.

It is a perpetual day dream in which the mind of the sick scholar runs amok.

And, just as Proust's animus was directed against that little society which had first snubbed him, so with Joyce the satire and the bitterness is directed towards the philistine world of which he remains the eternal enemy. Joyce is not a realist, nor even a psychologist; there is no attempt to build up character—there are caricatures of humanity only, *types* which enable him to vent his satire, his hatred, to lampoon, to vilify. For at bottom there is in Joyce a profound hatred for humanity—the scholar's hatred. One realizes that he has the neurotic's fear of entering the living world, the world of men and women in which he is powerless to function. He is in revolt not against institutions, but against mankind. Man to him is pitiable, ridiculous, grotesque. And even more so are man's ideas—not that he is without understanding of them, but that they have no validity for him; they are ideas which would connect him with a world from which he has divorced himself. His is a medieval mind born too late: he has the taste of the recluse, the morals of an anchorite, with all the masturbative machinery which such a life entrains. A Romantic who wished to embrace life realistically, an idealist whose ideals were bankrupt, he was faced with a dilemma which he was incapable of resolving. There was only one way out—to plunge into the collective realm of phantasy. As he spun out the fabric of his dreams he also unloaded the poison that had accumulated in his system. *Ulysses* is like a vomit spilled by a delicate child whose stomach has been overloaded with sweetmeats. "So rich was its delivery, its pent-up outpouring so vehement," says Wyndham Lewis, "that it will remain eternally a cathartic, a monument like a record diarrhoea." Despite the maze of facts, phenomena and incident detailed there is no grasp of life, no *picture* of life. There is neither an organic conception, nor a vital sense of life. We have the machinery of the mind turned loose upon a dead abstraction, *the city,* itself the product of abstractions.

It is in comparing this city-world, vague, diffuse, amorphous, with that narrower, but more integrated and still perfumed, if wholly decadent, world of Proust's that we realize the change which has come over the world in but a few years. The things men discussed in that artificial world of the Faubourg St. Germain no longer bear resemblance to that which passes for conversation in the streets and pubs and brothels of Dublin. That fragrance which emanates from the pages of Proust, what is it but the fragrance of a dying world, the last faint perfume of things running to seed?

When, via *Ulysses,* we penetrate Dublin and there detect the flora and fauna stratified in the memory of a highly civilized, highly sensitive being such as Joyce, we realize that the absence of fragrance, the deodorization, is the result of death. What seem to be alive and walking, loving, talking, drinking people are not people, but ghosts. The drama is one of liquefaction; it is not even static, as in Proust's case. Analysis is no longer possible because the organism is defunct. Instead of the examination of a dying, though still intact, organism, as with Proust, we find ourselves inspecting cell life, wasted organs, diseased membranes. A study in etiology, such as the Egyptologists give us in their post-mortems of post-mortems. A description of life via the mummy. The great Homeric figure of Ulysses, shrunk to the insignificant shadow now of Bloom, now of Daedalus, wanders through the dead and for-saken world of the big city; the anaemic, distorted and desiccated reflections of what were once epic events which Joyce is said to have plotted out in his famous ground-plan remain but simulacra, the shadow and tomb of ideas, events, people.

When one day the final interpretation of *Ulysses* is given us by the "anatomists of the soul" we shall have the most astounding revelations as to the significance of this work. Then indeed we shall know the full meaning of this "record diarrhoea." Perhaps then we shall see that not Homer but *defeat* forms the real ground-plan, the invisible pattern of his work.

In the famous chapter of question and answer is it wittingly or unwittingly that Joyce reveals the empty soul quality of the modern man, this wretch who is reduced to a bundle of tricks, this encyclopaedic ape who displays the most amazing technical facil-ity? *Is Joyce this man who can imitate any style—even the text-book and the encyclopaedia?* This form of humor, in which Rabe-lais also indulged, is the specific remedy which the intellectual employs to defeat the moral man: it is the dissolvent with which he destroys a whole world of meaning. With the Dadaists and the Surrealists the powerful stress on humor was part of a conscious and deliberate attitude toward breaking down the old ideologies. We see the same phenomenon in Swift and Cervantes. But observe the difference between the humor of Rabelais, with whom the author of *Ulysses* is so frequently and unjustly compared, and Joyce. Mark the difference between that formidable Surrealist, Jonathan Swift, and the feeble iconoclasts who to-day all them-selves Surrealists! Rabelais' humor was still healthy; it had a stomachic quality, it was inspired by the Holy Bottle. Whereas with our contemporaries it is all in the head, above the eyes—a vicious, envious, mean, malign, humorless mirth. To-day they are laughing out of desperation, out of despair. Humor? Hardly. A reflexive muscular twitch, rather—more gruesome than mirth-provoking. A sort of Onanistic laughter . . . In those marvellous passages where Joyce marries his rich excretory images to his sad mirth there is a poignant, wistful undercurrent which smells of reverence and idolatry. Reminiscent, too reminiscent, of those devout medieval louts who kneeled before the Pope to be anointed with dung.

In this same chapter of riddle and conundrum there is a profound despair, the despair of a man who is giving the works to the last myth—*Science.* That disintegration of the ego which was sounded in *Ulysses,* and is now being carried to the extreme limits in *Work in Progress,* does it not correspond faithfully to the outer, world disintegration? Do we not have here the finest example of that phenomenon touched on before—*schizophrenia?* The dissolution of the macrocosm goes hand in hand with the dissolution of the soul. With Joyce the Homeric figure goes over into its opposite; we see him splitting off into multitudes of characters, heroes, legendary figures, into trunks, arms, legs, into river, tree and rock and beast. Working down and down and down into the now stratified layers of the collective being, groping and groping for his lost soul, struggling like an heroic worm to re-enter the womb. What did he mean, Joyce, when on the eve of *Ulysses* he wrote that he wanted "to forge in the smithy of his soul the uncreated conscience of his race?" When he cried out—"No, mother, let me be; let me live!"—was that a cry of anguish from a soul imprisoned in the womb? That opening picture of the bright morning sea, the image of navel and scrotum, followed by the harrowing scene with the mother—everywhere and throughout the mother image. "I love everything that flows," he says to one of his admirers, and in his new book there are hundreds of rivers, including his own native Liffey. What a thirst! What a longing for the waters of life! If only he could be cast up again on a distant shore, in another clime, under different constellations! Sightless bard . . . lost soul . . . eternal wanderer. What longing, groping, seeking, searching for an all-merciful bosom, for the night in which to drown his restless, fruitless spirit! Like the sun itself which, in the course of a day, rises from the sea and disappears again, so *Ulysses* takes its cosmic stance, rising with a curse and falling with a sigh. But like a sun that is up-to-date the split-hero of *Ulysses* wanders, not over the waters of life and death, but through the eternal, monotonous, mournful, empty, lugubrious streets off the big city—dirty Dublin, the sink of the world.

If the *Odyssey* was a remembrance of great deeds *Ulysses* is a forgetting. That black, restless, never-ending flow of words in which the twin-soul of Joyce is swept along like a clot of waste matter passing through the drains, this stupendous deluge of pus and excrement which washes through the book languidly seeking an outlet, at last gets choked and, rising like a tidal wave, blots out the whole shadowy world in which this shadowy epic was conceived. The chapter before the last, which is the work of a learned desperado, is like the dynamiting of a dam. The dam, in the unconscious symbology of Joyce, is the last barrier of tradition and culture which must give way if man is to come into his own. Each idiotic question is a hole drilled by a madman and charged with dynamite; each idiotic answer is the detonation of a devastating explosion. Joyce, the mad baboon, herein gives the works to the patient ant-like industry of man which has accumulated about him like an iron ring of dead learning.

When the last vestige has been blown up comes the flood. The final chapter is a free fantasia such as has never been seen before in all literature. It is a transcription of the deluge—except that there is no ark. The stagnant cesspool of the cultural drama which comes again and again to nought in the world-city, this drama which was personified by the great whore of Babylon, is echoed in the timeless reverie of Molly Bloom whose ears are stuffed by the lapping of the black waters of death. The very image of Woman, Molly Bloom bulks large and enduring. Beside her the others are reduced to pygmies. Molly Bloom is water, tree, and earth. She is mystery, she is the devourer, the ocean of night in which the lost hero finally plunges, and with him the world.

There is something about Molly Bloom, as she lies a-dreaming on her dirty, crummy bed, which carries us back to primordial images. She is the quintessence of the great whore which is Woman, of Babylon the vessel of abominations. Floating, unresisting, eternal, all-contained, she is like the sea itself. Like the sea she is receptive, fecund, voracious, insatiable. She begets and she destroys; she nourishes and she devastates. With Molly Bloom, *con anonyme,* woman is restored to prime significance—as womb and matrix of life. She is the image of nature itself, as opposed to the illusory world which man, because of his insufficiency, vainly endeavors to displace.

And so, with a final, triumphant vengeance, with suicidal glee, all the threads which were dropped throughout the book are recapitulated; the pale, diminutive hero, reduced to an intestinal worm and carried like a tickling little phallus in the great body of the female, returns to the womb of nature, shorn of everything but the last symbol. In the long retrospective arc which is drawn we have the whole trajectory of man's flight from unknown to unknown. The rainbow of history fades out. The great dissolution is accomplished. After that closing picture of Molly Bloom a-dreaming on her dirty bed we can say, as in Revelation—*And there shall be no more curse!* Henceforth no sin, no guilt, no fear, no repression, no longing, no pain of separation. The end is accomplished—man returns to the womb.

A Night with Jupiter

Every once in a while, when I'm riding the crest of euphoria, I get the notion that I'm immune—to disease, accidents, poverty, even death. I was coming home one night, after having spent a wonderful evening with my friend Moricand, the astrologer, and just as I was about to turn off the avenue d'Orléans into the rue d'Alésia I thought of two things simultaneously: a) to sit down and have a glass of beer, b) to look up and see where Jupiter was at that precise chronological moment. I had just passed the Café Bouquet d'Alésia which faces the church and as there were still a few moments before closing time I saw no reason why I should not sit down on the terrace and enjoy a quiet beer all to myself. There was always a red glow about the church which fascinated me—and at the same time from where I sat I could look at my benevolent planet, Jupiter. I never thought to see where Saturn was, or Mars. Well, I was sitting there like that, feeling wonderful inside and out, when the couple who lived below me happened to come along. We shook hands and then they asked if I would object to their sitting beside me and joining me in a little drink. I was in such a state of elation that, despite the fact that the man, who was an Italian refugee, bored me to death, I said—"Sure, nothing could be better." And with that I began to tell them how marvelous everything was. The man looked at me as though I were a bit cracked, because at that particular moment everything was rotten in the world and he felt particularly rotten about it because it was his business to write about historical events and processes. When he pressed me as to why I felt so good and I told him for no particular reason he looked at me as though I had done him a personal injury. But that didn't deter me in the least. I ordered another round of drinks, not to get high, because the beer was innocuous and besides I was drunk already, drunk with exaltation, but because I

168

wanted to see them look a little more cheerful even if world events did look putrid. Well, I guess I had three beers—and then I suggested we go home. It was a short walk back to the Villa Seurat and in that brief span of time I grew positively radiant. Like an idiot I confessed to them that I was in such a superb state of being that if the Creator himself had willed it he would find it impossible to harm me. And on that note I shook hands with them and climbed the stairs to my studio.

As I was undressing I got the idea of going up to the roof and having a last look at Jupiter. It was a warm night and I had on nothing but my carpet slippers. To get up to the roof I had to climb a vertical iron ladder to the balcony of the studio. Well, to make it short, I had my fill of Jupiter. I was ready to hit the hay. The lights were out but the moonlight came through the long window above the balcony. I walked in a trance to the iron ladder, put my foot out instinctively, missed it and fell through the glass door below. In falling I remember distinctly how delicious it felt to fall backwards into space. I picked myself up and began hopping around like a bird to see if any bones had been broken. I could hop all right but I was gasping, as though some one had stuck a knife in my back. I reached around with one hand and felt a big piece of glass sticking in my back, which I promptly pulled out. I felt another piece in my backside and pulled that out too, and then another in my instep. Then I began to laugh. I laughed because evidently I was not killed and I could still hop about like a bird. The floor was getting rather bloody and no matter where I stepped there was more glass.

I decided to call the Italian downstairs and have him look me over, bandage up the cuts, and so on. When I opened the door I found him coming up the stairs. He had heard the crash and wondered what had happened to me. Previously, while we were at table one day, a rabbit had fallen off the roof and crashed through the sky-light on to our table. But this time it was no rabbit, he knew that.

"You'd better call a doctor," he said, "you're full of cuts and bruises."

I told him I'd rather not—just find some alcohol and some cotton to wash the cuts. I said I'd sleep it off, it couldn't be very serious.

"But you're bleeding like a pig," he said, and he began to wring his hands frantically.

He woke the fellow up across the hall and asked him to telephone a doctor. No luck. One said, "Take him to the hospital"; another said, "It's too late, I've just gone to bed, call So-and-so."

"I don't want any bloody French doctor," I said. "You find some alcohol and put some bandages over the cuts—I'll be O.K."

Finally they found some wood alcohol and a roll of absorbent cotton. I stood in the bathtub and they sponged me off.

"You're still bleeding," said the Italian, who for some reason couldn't stand the sight of blood.

"Get some adhesive tape and plug the cuts up with cotton," I said. The blood was running down my legs and I didn't like to see it going to waste like that.

Well, they did their best and then they helped me into bed. When I touched the bed I realized that I was full of bruises. I couldn't move. Soon I fell asleep and I guess I must have slept an hour or more when suddenly I awoke and felt something slippery in the bed. I put my hand on the sheet and it was wet with blood. That gave me a start. I got out of bed, turned on the lights and threw the covers back. I was horrified when I saw the pool of blood I had been lying in. Jesus! My own blood and running out of me like a sewer. That brought me to my senses. I ran next door and knocked. "Get up quick!" I yelled. "I'm bleeding to death!"

Luckily the fellow had a car. I couldn't put any clothes on, I was stiff and sore and too frightened to bother. I slung a bath robe around me and let him race me to the American hospital in Neuilly. It was almost daylight and everybody was asleep apparently. It seemed hours until the interne came down and deigned to staunch my wounds.

While he was sewing me up here and there and feeling my bones and ligaments we fell into a curious conversation about Surrealism. He was a youngster from Georgia and he had never heard of Surrealism until he came to Paris. He wanted to know what it was all about. Well, it's hard enough to explain what Surrealism means under ordinary circumstances but when you've lost a lot of blood and had an anti-tetanus injection and a man is trying to sew up your rectum and another man is looking at you and wondering why you don't yell or faint it's almost impossible to get the old dialectic working properly. I made a few Surrealistic explanations which I saw at once meant nothing to him and then I closed my eyes and took a cat nap until he had finished his job.

The Surrealistic touch came after we started back in the car. My young friend, who was a Swiss, and a very neurotic one at that, suddenly had an imperious desire to eat breakfast. He wanted to take me to some café on the Champs-Elysées where they had excellent croissants. He said a coffee would do me good, and a little cognac with it.

"But how can I walk into a café in this bathrobe?" I asked. I didn't have the trousers to my pajamas—they had ripped them off, as doctors always do, why I don't know. They rip them off and throw them in the waste basket, when it would be just as easy to pull them off and save them for the laundry.

Arnaud, my friend, saw nothing strange whatever about having breakfast in a bathrobe on the Champs-Elysées. "They can see that you've had an accident," he said. "The bathrobe is full of blood."

"That makes it all right, does it?" I asked.

"It's all right with me," he said. "As for them, *je m'en fous!*"

"If you don't mind," I insisted weakly, "I'd rather wait till we get to our own neighborhood."

"But the croissants there are no good," he said, clinging stubbornly to his obsession like a petulant child.

"Damn the croissants!" I said. "I'm weak, I want to get to bed."

Finally he reluctantly consented to do as I had suggested. "But my palate was just set for those delicious croissants," he said. "I'm hungry. . . . I'm famished."

On the rue de la Tombe-Issoire we stopped at a *bistro* and had breakfast. We had to stand up at the bar. I ate half a croissant and felt like caving in. The workmen dropping in thought we had been on a spree. One burly chap was just about to give me a hearty slap on the back, the very thought of which almost threw me into a faint. Arnaud leisurely devoured one croissant after another. They were not so bad after all, he averred. Just when I thought we were ready to go he asked for another cup of coffee. I stood there in agony while he slowly sipped it—it was too hot to polish off at one gulp.

When I got back to my place I threw the bloody sheets on the floor and laid myself gently on the mattress. The bruises were so painful now that I groaned with pleasure. I fell into a sound sleep—a coma.

When I came to my friend Moricand was sitting beside the bed. Arnaud has telephoned him, he said. He seemed amazed that I was able to talk.

"It happened between one-thirty and two in the morning, did it not?" he asked.

Yes, I thought that was about the time. *Why,* I wanted to know. What was he getting at?

He made a serious face. Then he solemnly extracted a paper from his inside pocket. "This," he said, waving the paper before my eyes, "is the astrological picture of the accident. I was curious, you know. You seemed in such an excellent mood last night when you left me. Well, here it is . . .'' and he leaned over to explain the black and red lines which contained so much meaning for him.

"You were lucky not to have killed yourself," he said. "When I came in and saw the blood everywhere I thought surely you were dead. Everything was against you at that hour last night. If you had gone to bed immediately you might have escaped it. Another man would have died, that's a certainty. But you, as I told you often, are very lucky. You have two rudders: when the one gives out the other one comes into play. What saved you was Jupiter. Jupiter was the only planet in your horoscope which was not badly aspected.'' He explained the set-up to me in detail. It was very much like being walled in. If all the doors had been shut I would have died. He showed me the picture of Balzac's death, an amazing diagram of Fate, as beautiful and austere as a chess problem.

"Can't you show me Hitler's death chart?" I said, smiling weakly.

"Mon vieux," he responded with alacrity, "that would indeed give me great pleasure, could I do that. Unfortunately I see nothing catastrophic in sight for him yet. But when he falls, mark my words, he will go out quickly—like a light. Now he is still climbing. When he reaches the top it will be for just a little while and then *Pam!* he will go like that! There are bad days ahead. We're going to suffer a great catastrophe. I wish I had a Jupiter like yours. But I have that infernal Saturn. I don't see any hope . . .''

Remember to Remember

(Excerpt)

When I ran across Alfred Perlès on the Rue Delambre one rainy night a friendship was begun which was to color the entire period of my stay in France. In him I found the friend who was to sustain me through all my ups and downs. There was something of the *"voyou"* about him, let me say at once. My temptation, I must confess, is to exaggerate his failings. He had one virtue, however, which compensated for all his failings: he knew how to be a friend. Sometimes, indeed, it seemed to me that he knew nothing else. His whole life seemed centered about the cardinal fact that he was not just my friend, your friend, a friend, but *the* friend. He was capable of anything were it necessary to prove his friendship. I mean *anything*.

Fred was the sort of person I had been unconsciously looking for all my life. I had gravitated to Paris from Brooklyn and he from Vienna. We had been through the school of adversity long before reaching Paris. We were veterans of the street, on to all the tricks which keep a man afloat when all resources seem to be exhausted. Rogue, scallywag, buffoon that he was, he was nevertheless sensitive to the extreme. His delicacy, which manifested itself at incongruous moments, was extraordinary. He could be rude, impudent and cowardly without in the least diminishing himself. In fact, he deliberately cultivated a diminished state; it permitted him to indulge in all sorts of liberties. He pretended that all he wanted were the bare necessities of life, but he was an aristocrat in his tastes, and a spoiled darling to boot.

This potpourri of good and bad traits seemed to endear him to most every one. With women he would allow himself to be treated like a lap-dog, if that gave them pleasure. He would do anything they asked of him so long as he could gain his end which, of course, was to get them to bed. If you were a friend he would

173

share his women with you, in the same way that he would share his last crust of bread. Some people found this hard to forgive in him, this ability to share *everything*. He expected others to act the same way, of course. If they refused he was ruthless. Once he took a dislike to a person nothing could win him over. He never changed his opinion of a person once he had made it. With Fred one was either a friend or an enemy. What he despised particularly were pretentiousness, ambitiousness and miserliness. He did not make friends easily, because of his shyness and timidity, but those with whom he became friends remained friends for life.

One of his irritating traits was his secretiveness. He delighted in holding things back, not so much out of inability to reveal himself but in order to always have a surprise up his sleeve. He always chose the right moment to let the cat out of the bag; he had an unerring instinct for disconcerting one at the most embarrassing moment. He delighted in leading one into a trap, particularly where it concerned his supposed ignorance or supposed vices. One could never pin him down about anything, least of all about himself.

By the time I caught up with him he seemed to have lived the proverbial nine lives of a cat. Knowing him superficially, one would be inclined to say he had wasted his life. He had written a few books in German, but whether they had been published or not no one knew. He was always vague about the past anyway, except when he was drunk, and then he would expand for a whole evening over a detail which he felt in the mood to embellish. He never threw out chunks of his life, just these unrelated details which he knew how to elaborate with the skill and cunning of a criminal lawyer. The truth is, he had led so many lives, had assumed so many identities, had acted so many parts, that to give any hint of totality would have meant reconstructing a jig-saw puzzle. He was as bewildering to himself, to be honest, as he was to others. His secret life was not his *private* life, for he had no private life. He lived continually *en marge*. He was *"limitrophe,"* one of his favorite words, to everything, but he was not *limitrophe* to himself. In the first book he wrote in French (*Sentiments Limitrophes*) there were microscopic revelations of his youth which verged on the hallucinatory. A passage which reveals how he came alive at the age of nine (on his native health, the Schmelz) is a masterly piece of cortical dissection. One feels at this point in the narrative, which is an autobiography *aux faits divers,* that he was close to being endowed with a soul. But a few pages later he loses himself again and the soul remains in limbo.

Close association over a period of years with a man of his type has its rewards as well as its draw-backs. Looking back on those years with Fred I can think only of the good which resulted from our alliance. For it was an alliance even more than a friendship, if I may put it that way. We were allied to meet the future which every day presented its hydra-headed threat of annihilation. We got to believe, after a time, that there was no situation we could not meet and overcome. Often we must have seemed more like confederates than friends.

In everything he was the clown, even in making love. He could make me laugh when I was boiling with rage. I don't seem to recall a single day in which we did not laugh heartily, often until the tears came to our eyes. The three principal questions we put to each other every time we met were: 1.) Is there food? 2.) Was it a good lay? 3.) Are you writing? Everything centered around these three exigencies. It was the writing which concerned us most, but we always behaved as though the other two were more important. Writing was a constant, like the weather. But food and lays were quixotic: one could never be sure of either. Money, when we had it, we shared to the last penny. There was no question whom it belonged to. "Is there any dough?" we would ask, just as we would ask, "Is there food?" It was or it wasn't, that was all there was to it. Our friendship began on this note and it remained thus till we separated. It's such a simple, efficacious way of living, I wonder it isn't tried out on a universal scale.

There were three possessions he clung to, despite all the pawning and liquidating of the dark days: his typewriter, his watch and his fountain pen. Each was of the finest make, and he took care of them as an engineer would take care of his locomotive. He said they were gifts, gifts from women he had loved. Maybe they were. I know he treasured them. The typewriter was the easiest thing for him to part with, temporarily, of course. For a time it seemed as though it were in the hock shop more than *chez nous*. It was a good thing, he used to say. It forced him to write with the pen. The pen was a Parker pen, the finest I had ever seen. If you asked to use it, he would unscrew the top before handing it to you. That was his little way of saying, "Be gentle with it!" The watch he seldom carried about with him. It hung on a nail over his work table. It kept perfect time.

When he sat down to work these three articles were always present. They were his talismen. He couldn't write with another machine or another pen. Later, when he acquired an alarm clock, he still wound his watch regularly. He always looked to *it* for the time, not to the alarm clock. When he changed residence, which was fairly frequent, he always disposed of some precious relic which he had been holding on to for years. He enjoyed being forced to move. It meant reducing his baggage, because all he allowed himself was one valise. Everything had to get in that valise or be discarded. The things he clung to were souvenirs—a post card from an old friend, a photo of an old love, a pen knife picked up at the flea market. Always the trifles. He would throw away a sweater or a pair of pants to make room for his favorite books. Of course I always rescued the things I knew he didn't want to get rid of. I would steal back to his room and make a bundle of them; a few days later I would show up and hand them to him. The expression on his face then was like that of a child recovering an old toy. He would actually weep with joy. To prove, though, that he really didn't need them he would dig out some precious object and make me a present of it. It was like saying, "All right, I'll keep the sweater (or the pants), since you insist on it, but here's my valuable camera. I really have no use for it any more." Whatever the gift, I was hardly likely to have any use for it either, but I would accept it as though it were a royal gift. In a sentimental mood he would sometimes offer me his fountain pen—the type-writer I couldn't use because it had a French keyboard. The watch I accepted several times.

Having a job on the newspaper, he had only a few hours in the afternoon to give to his writing. In order not to worry himself about how much or how little he was accomplishing, he made it a rule to write just two pages a day, no more. He would stop in the middle of a sentence if it were the bottom of that second page. He always seemed extremely cheerful to have accomplished this much. "Two pages a day, 365 days in the year, that makes 730," he would say. "If I can do 250 in a year I'll be satisfied. I'm not writing a *roman fleuve.*" He had sense enough to know that, with the best intentions in the world, one seldom has the moral courage to write every day of the week. He made allowance for bad days: vile moods, hang-overs, fresh lays, unexpected visits, and so on. Even if the interruption lasted a week he would never try to write more than the two pages he had fixed as his stint. "It's good not to exhaust yourself," he would say chirpingly. "It leaves you fresh the next day." "But don't you feel like going on, don't you feel like writing six or seven pages sometimes?" I would ask. He would grin. "Sure I do, but I restrain myself." And then he would quote me a Chinese proverb about the master knowing how to *refrain* from working miracles. In his breast-pocket, of course, he always carried a notebook. At work he no doubt made notes with that flawless Parker pen of his, or continued where he had left off (bottom of page two).

It was characteristic of him to create the impression that everything was easy. Even writing. "Don't try too hard," that was his motto. In other words, "Easy does it." If you intruded upon him while he was at work he showed no irritation whatever. On the contrary, he would get up smiling, invite you to stay and chat with him. Always imperturbable, as though nothing could really interrupt what he was doing or thinking. At the same time he was discreet about intruding on the other person. Unless he was moody. Then he would burst in on me, or any one, and say: "You've got to drop what you're doing, I want to talk to you. Let's go somewhere and have a drink, eh? I can't work to-day. You shouldn't work either, it's too beautiful, life is too short." Or perhaps he had just taken a fancy too a girl and he needed some money. "You've got to help me find some dough," he would say. "I promised to meet her at 5:30 sharp. It's important." That meant I would have to go out and hit somebody up. I knew plenty of Americans, so he said, and Americans always had money hidden away. "Don't be shy about it," he would say. "Get a hundred francs while you're at it, or three hundred. Pay day will be here soon."

On pay day we were always most broke, it seemed. Everything went for debts. We would allow ourselves one good meal and trust in Providence to carry us through till the next pay day. We had to pay these little debts or there would be no more credit. But over a meal sometimes we would get a little high and decide to let it all ride. We would have our fling and wonder how to make up for it on the morrow. Often a stranger would turn up in the nick of time, one of those old friends from America who wanted to see the sights. We always handled the money for these visitors from America "so that they wouldn't be cheated." Thus, in addition to borrowing a bit, we would put aside a little extra on the sly.

Now and then an old friend of his would turn up, some one he had known in Italy, Jugoslavia, Prague, Berlin, Majorca, Morocco. Only then would one realize that the amazing tales he seemed to invent when drunk had a basis in fact. He was not one to boast of his travels or adventures. Usually he was shy and discreet about his personal experiences; only when drunk would he reveal choice morsels of the past. And then it was as though he were talking about some one else, some one he had known and identified himself with.

One day an Austrian friend turned up from God knows where. He was in a bad state morally and physically. Over a good meal he confessed that he was wanted by the police. We kept him in hiding for about two months, allowing him to go out of the house only at night when accompanied by Fred or myself. It was quite a wonderful period for the three of us. Not only did I get an insight into Fred's past but I got an insight into my own past. We were living then in Clichy, not very far from Céline's famous clinic. There was a cemetery a few blocks from the house to which we repaired in the evenings, always with one eye open for an *agent*.

After a time Erich, our guest, grew tired of reading and begged for something to do. I was at that time deep in Proust. I had marked off whole pages of *Albertine Disparue* which he eagerly agreed to copy for me on the typewriter. Every day there was a fresh pile of script lying on my work table. I can never forget how grateful he was for giving him this task to perform. Nearing the end, and observing that he had become thoroughly absorbed in the text, I invited him to give me his observations *viva voce*. I was so fascinated by his elaborate analyses of the passages selected that finally I persuaded him to go over the excerpts and make detailed annotations. At first he suspected that I was stringing him along, but when I had convinced him of the importance of his contribution his gratitude knew no bounds. He went to it like a ferret, pursuing every imaginable thread which would amplify the problem significantly. To see him work one would think he had received a commission from Gallimard. He worked more diligently and painstakingly than Proust himself, it seemed to me. All to prove that he really was capable of doing an honest day's work.

I can't remember any period of my life when the time flew more quickly than it did at Clichy. The acquisition of two bicycles worked a complete metamorphosis in our routine. Everything was planned so as not to interfere with our afternoon rides. At four on the dot Fred would have finished his two pages. I can see him now, in the courtyard, oiling and polishing his machine. He gave it the same loving care that he bestowed on his typewriter. He had every gadget that could be tacked on to it, including a speedometer. Sometimes he would sleep only three or four hours in order to take a long spin, to Versailles or St. Germain-en-Laye, for example. When the Tour de France was on we would go to the movies every night in order to follow the progress of the race. When the six day races came to the Vel d'Hiv we were there, ready to stay up all night.

Once in a while we dropped in at the Medrano. When my friend Renaud came up from Dijon we even ventured to go to the Bal Tabarin and the Moulin Rouge, places we loathed. The cinema was the principal source of relaxation, however. What I shall always remember about the cinema is the excellent meal we stowed away before entering the place. A meal and then a few leisurely moments at a bar, over a *café arrosé de rhum*. Then a quick hop to the nearest *pissotière* amidst the hum of traffic and the stir of idle throngs. During the entr'acte another dash to the *bistrot,* another visit to the urinal. Waiting for the curtain to go up we munched a peanut bar or lapped up an Eskimo. Simple pleasures, asinine, it seemed sometimes. On the way home a conversation begun in the street would often continue until dawn. Sometimes, just before dawn, we would cook ourselves a meal, polish off a couple of bottles of wine, and then, ready to hit the hay, would curse the birds for making such a racket.

Some of the more scabrous episodes belonging to this idyllic period I have recorded in *Quiet Days in Clichy* and *Mara-Marignan,* texts which are unfortunately unpublishable in England or America. It is strange that I always think of this period as "quiet days." They were anything but quiet, those days. Yet never did I accomplish more. I worked on three or four books at once. I was seething with ideas. The Avenue Anatole France on which we lived was anything but picturesque; it resembled a monotonous stretch of upper Park Avenue, New York. Perhaps our ebullience was due to the fact that for the first time in many a year we were enjoying what might be called a relative security. For the first time in ages I had a permanent address, for about a year.

When I moved to the Villa Seurat a wholly new atmosphere was created. Fred, after trying out a half dozen different quarters of the city, finally lodged himself nearby in the Impasse du Rouet. Here lived our mutual friends David Edgar and Hans Reichel. After a time Lawrence Durrell arrived from Greece. His appearance in our midst was truly sensational. He was electrifying. Fresh from the Mediterranean world, he was only too eager to throw himself into what he thought was the "decadent" life of Paris. Instead of debauches, however, he found a world of Rabelaisian jollity. If I had laughed long and heartily with Fred I laughed still more in Durrell's presence. It was only necessary for the three of us to meet in order to burst into guffaws. Everything about Fred, but particularly the clown and the mime, caused Durrell to go off into peals of laughter. He looked upon our life in the Villa Seurat as an endless three ring circus. Edgar, who was then in the worst phase of his neurotic career, was frequently with us; he acted as a sort of buffer, inveigling us against our will into the bogs of theosophy, astrology, anthroposophy and into other mephitic realms. Edgar seldom laughed. He went into long monologues in which he drew charts and diagrams explaining the evolution of man, his illnesses, and the glorious future which awaited him. We loved Edgar dearly, and when we were in difficulties it was to Edgar we turned, but unless we could rout him out of his obsessions, laugh him down, we were licked. Drink failed to relax him. Even if we carried him off to a night club, he was apt to go on analyzing, dissecting, construing. Sometimes on my way home of an evening—or it could be on my way home from lunch—I would run across him in a café, seated before an innocent glass of beer. It was impossible, ever, to get away from Edgar quickly, no matter how urgent the reason. If you insisted on leaving quickly he would accompany you home. He always seemed to have a book hidden away which he sprang on you just as you were getting fidgety. It was always a new book, one he had just finished reading, and which it was imperative for his friends to share with him. Sometimes, to give him credit, they were good books, stimulating, to say the least. The trouble was, however, that before he turned a book over to you, he had already read aloud to you the best passages—and with elaborate, hair-splitting exegeses delivered with passionate earnestness, all extemporaneous, to be sure. Often I would say "No! No, I refuse to read it! I'm not a damned bit interested, Edgar, I'm sorry." He wouldn't be offended by such outbursts, not Edgar. He would wait until you had cooled down, then slyly and insidiously work up to the point once again. When you had reached the phase of non-resistance, he would gently put it in your pocket or under your arm. If you hadn't glanced at it by the time he saw you again he would pick it up and begin reading aloud once more. "But that's no way to seduce us," we would object. "You're a damned proselytizer, do you know it?" Edgar would smile blandly. "But seriously," he would begin, "once you get into it you will see . . ." "I can tell from the cover that it's no good," Fred would say. "The book smells bad." Edgar would be absolutely imperturbable. He would listen to you rant for twenty minutes, then go to work on you quietly, as if nothing had been said. In the end, of course, Edgar won out. In the end we were obliged to take over his language and incorporate it into our own. A stranger in our midst would have found our discussions absolutely unintelligible: we had achieved a code language almost as rarefied as the physicist's.

How I laugh when I read of the Villa Seurat *cult!* It was the English, of course, with their utter lack of humor, who began this talk of a cult or group. It is so strange that, separated only by the Channel, the English are able to make France seem like a distant realm. The then young English writers, who made occasional trips to the Continent, gave me the impression of being utterly unreal. Sometimes I would ask Durrell to translate for me what they had said, so complicated, so outlandish was their speech. What they were searching for I never understood. They always impressed me as nearsighted people shorn of their glasses. Durrell and Fred could imitate their mannerisms perfectly. Often, when they had left, we would put on a performance in which we pretended to stutter and stammer, to lisp, to perspire freely, to walk with a mincing gait, to ask ridiculous questions, to get deeply involved in abstruse problems, and so on. During these sessions even Edgar would laugh until the tears rolled down his face.

If there *was* a group in the Villa Seurat it was across the way, at the home of a foreign woman who held soirées once a week. There one could meet all the intellectual bores of Paris, people of every stripe and denomination. Now and then, when we were hungry, we would drop in. There was always plenty to eat and drink, and the sandwiches were extremely delicious. Sometimes there would be dancing. The "great minds" would go into a huddle and the others would disport themselves. The hostess seemed quite indifferent to what went on. All she demanded was that we enjoy ourselves. Her idea of enjoyment was rather simple. As long as you were active, either with the mouth or the feet, she believed you were enjoying yourself.

The real enjoyment came when, obliged to go abroad, she turned her flat over to Fred. There were no more soirées after that, just continuous festivities from morn to night. The cellar and the larder were soon exhausted, the furniture began to fall apart, precious vases filled up with cigarette and cigar stubs which gave off a vile odor, the plumbing got out of order, the piano needed tuning and repairing, the rugs had burnt holes in them, the dirty dishes were strewn all over the kitchen, and in general the place became an unholy mess. For two days and nights there was an extra piano standing outside the door, in the middle of the street. It had been delivered while we were in the midst of dinner one evening. For the pure hell of it, Fred had instructed the moving man to leave it outdoors, that we would haul it in ourselves when we were good and ready. In the midst of the meal the man and wife to whom the piano belonged arrived. They were shocked, of course, and almost on the verge of calling the police. But Fred had a smooth line of talk for them, plied them with strong drinks, insisted that they eat something, and finally cajoled them into believing that all was for the best. Then it began to rain. We went outside and put the lid of the piano down. It was a concert grand, and an excellent make, if I remember well. Fortunately, the man, who was just recovering from an operation for hemorrhoids, had to hurry home. Something had gone amiss; he could neither sit down nor stand up for any length of time. Besides, the drinks had gone to his head. We called a cab and bustled the two of them in it, promising them most faithfully that we would get the piano indoors in jig time. An hour later, both of us pie-eyed by this time, we sat down in the middle of the street, the rain beating down on the keys, and pretended to play a duet. The noise was horrific. Windows were thrown up and threats and imprecations hurled at us from all directions. We then tried to find a few friends to help us get the damned thing indoors. That took another hour or two. Finally there were six of us struggling with might and main to squeeze it through the doorway. It was no go. The piano was all legs, it seemed. When we eventually desisted from this insane attempt the only thing to do was to leave the piano where it was, upside down on the sidewalk. There it remained for another thirty-six hours, during which time we had several visits from the police . . .

My eye falls on *Le Quatuor en Ré Majeur* on the shelf by my elbow. I open it at random, musing on this droll companion of other days. In a few lines he gives a portrait of himself. It seems extremely apposite after the above . . . "Je suis timide et d'humeur inégale," the passage begins. *"Himmelhoch jauchzend, zu Tode betrübt.* De brusques accès de mélancolie et d'effrayants élans de joie alternent en moi, sans transition aucune. Le cynisme n'est pas mon fort. Si je m'en sers quand même, comme tout à l'heure, par exemple, c'est précisement parceque je suis timide, parceque je crains le ridicule. Toujours prêt à fondre en larmes, j'éprouve le besoin de tourner en dérision mes sentiments les plus nobles. Une espèce de masochisme, sans doute.

"Et puis, il y a autre chose aussi qui explique mes velléites d'arrogance: je sais que tout à l'heure, je vais être obligé de me degonfler; alors, pour mieux me degonfler, je me gonfle d'abord; me gonfle de culot factice, de forfanterie, tellement ma couardise sentimentale et naturelle me dégoute de moi-même. Et comme ma sentimentalité porte surtout sur les femmes et sur l'amour, c'est sur ces sujets que ma hablerie artificielle s'acharne le plus furieusement."

"Culot" is the pass-word here. He calls it *"culot factice,"* as though that helped matters. What a gall he had, when I think of it. Natural or artificial, inspired or trumped up, it took plenty of *culot* (and of course a bit of alcohol) to dash up to the open doorway of a police station and yell at the top of one's lungs: *"Merde à vous tous, espèces de cons!"* Twice I witnessed him do this, myself walking slowly along and him scurrying like mad around the corner. Meeting him at the appointed bar a few minutes later he would still be panting, still apoplectic with feigned rage. Since the evening had begun that way, he would continue in the same vein, insulting any one and every one with or without provocation. In

such moments he seemed possessed by the desire to have his head bashed in. All his efforts proving futile, he would finally stand in the street, baring his chest or thrusting out his jaw, and yell: "*You* take a crack at me, Joey . . . go ahead . . . I want to see how it feels." If I gave him a good crack, as he requested, he would get angry and complain that I had taken advantage of him. But a minute later he would be laughing, perhaps opening his mouth very wide, to say *b-e-a-u*. He would repeat it a dozen times: *beau, beau, beau* . . . "It's so much more beautiful than beautiful," he'd say. "But you have to open your mouth wide, like this," and he would throw his head back to let me look down his gullet while he uttered the magic word. Then, stumbling along, rolling from side to side, he would invent phrase after phrase in which *beau* could be used effectively, always prolonging the O sound, resting on it as a rower rests on his oars. "Qu'il fait *beau* aujourd'hui!" "Qu'il fait *beau*, fait *beau*, fait *beau* . . ." This could go on from La Fourche to the Porte de Clichy and beyond. Everything was *beau*—always with the wide open mouth, as if he were gargling his throat. "That's the way to speak French, Joey. Move the muscles of your mouth. Make grimaces. Look idiotic. Never swallow your words. French is a musical language. You must open your mouth wide. Like this . . . B-E-A-U. Now say *'comédie'!* Not comedy . . . *comédie!* That's it." Here he might branch off into a disquisition on Paul Valéry's use of the French language, expatiating on his flair for that infallible resonance which makes French poetry conspicuously different from all other poetry.

During all these years of intimate association we were always fully conscious of the fact that we were enjoying life to the hilt. We knew there could not be anything better than what we were experiencing every day of our lives. We felicitated one another on it frequently. For the world in general I rather think that the ten years preceding the war were not particularly joyful times. The continuous succession of economic and political crises which characterized the decade proved nerve-racking to most people. But, as we often used to say: "Bad times are good times for us." Why that should be so I don't know, but it was true. Perhaps the artist, in following his own rhythm, is permanently out of step with the world. The threat of war only served to remind us that we had waged war with the world all our lives. "During a war money is plentiful," Fred used to say with a grin. "It's only before and after the war that things are bad. War time is a good time for guys like us. You'll see."

Fred had spent the closing years of the first World War in an insane asylum. Apparently it hadn't done him any great injury. He was out of harm's way, as we say. As soon as they opened the gates he sailed out, free as a bird, his tail set for Paris. He may have lived a while in Berlin and Prague before reaching Paris. I think he had also been in Copenhagen and Amsterdam. By the time we met in Paris his wanderings had become rather dim in his memory. Italy, Jugoslavia, North Africa, even these more recent adventures had lost their edge. What I remember distinctly about all these wanderings is that in every place he was hungry. He never seemed to forget the number of days on end he had gone without food in a certain place. Since my own wanderings had been colored by the same preoccupation, I relished the morbid accounts he gave me now and then. Usually these reminiscences were aroused when we were pulling our belts tight. I remember once at the Villa Seurat, not having had a morsel for forty-eight hours, how I flopped down on the couch, declaring that I would remain there until a miracle happened. "You can't do that," he said, a tone of unusual desperation in his voice. "That's what I did in Rome once. I nearly died. No one came for ten days." That started him off. He talked so much about prolonged and involuntary fasts that it goaded me into action. For some reason we had ceased to think in terms of credit. In the old days it was easy for me, because I was innocent and ignorant of the ways of the French. Somehow, the longer I lived in Paris the less courage I had to ask a restaurant keeper for credit. The war was getting closer and closer; people were getting more and more jittery. Finally, towards the end, knowing the war could not be staved off, they began to splurge. There was that last minute gaiety which means the jig is up.

Our gaiety, which had been constant, was the result of a deep conviction that the world would never be put to rights. Not for us, at least. We were going to live *en marge*, fattening on the crumbs which were dropped from the rich man's table. We tried to accommodate ourselves to doing without those essentials which keep the ordinary citizen ensnared. We wanted no possessions, no titles, no promises of better conditions in the future. "Day by day," that was our motto. To reach bottom we did not have to sink very far. Besides, we were resilient. There could be no very bad news in store for us; we had heard it all over and over, we were used to it. We were always on the alert for a windfall. Miracles did happen, not once or twice, but frequently. We relied on Providence in the way a gangster relies on his gat. In our hearts we honestly did believe that we were right with the world. We acted in good faith, even when to some patriotic souls it seemed like treason. It's curious, now that I mention this, to recall how, soon after war was declared, I wrote to Durrell and to Fred that I was certain they would emerge from it without a scratch. About Edgar I wasn't so certain. But he came out swimmingly too. The unpredictable thing about Edgar was—he enjoyed the war! I don't mean that he enjoyed the horrors of it; he enjoyed forgetting about himself and his neurosis.

Even Reichel, who seemed doomed, came out of it in good shape. All these men, and I say it not because they were my friends, all of them were clean, honest souls, *innocent,* if the word still has meaning. Despite all the buffetings of Fate, they were destined to lead charmed lives. Their problems were never the world's problems. Their problems went deeper, much deeper. With the exception of Durrell, who was decidedly gregarious, they were all lonely men. Reichel more than any of the others, I should say. Reichel was terrifyingly apart and alone. But that is what made him so wonderful when he entered a room full of people, or rather when he entered the company of a few chosen friends. His desire for companionship and communion was so great that sometimes it seemed, when he entered a gathering, that a bomb had gone off.

Never shall I forget one Christmas day we spent together, Reichel, Fred and myself. It was about noon when they turned up, expecting naturally that I would have food and wine on hand. I had nothing. Nothing but a hard crust of bread which I was too disgusted to bother nibbling. Oh yes, there was a drop of wine— about the fifth of a litre bottle. I remember that distinctly because what fascinated me later, after they had left, was the recollection of how long this meagre portion of wine had lasted. I remember too, most distinctly, that for a long time the crust of bread and the almost empty bottle stood untouched in the middle of the table. Perhaps because it *was* Christmas we all exhibited an unusual restraint about the absence of food. Perhaps too it was because our stomachs were light and the cigarettes short that the conversation proved much more exciting than filling our bellies would. The crust of bread lying there in full view all the time had started Reichel off on a story about his prison experiences. It was a long story about his awkwardness and stupidity, how he had been cuffed and cursed for being a hopeless idiot. There was a great to-do about right hand and left hand, his not remembering which was his right hand and which was his left hand. In telling a story Reichel always acted it out. There he was, walking up and down the studio, rehearsing his stupid past, his gestures so grotesque, so pathetic, that we laughed and cried at the same time. In the act of demonstrating a salute which "they" had finally succeeded in teaching him to do with éclat, he suddenly took notice of the crust of bread. Without interrupting his story he gently broke off a corner of it, poured himself a thimbleful of wine and leisurely dipped the bread in the wine. With this Fred and I automatically did the same. We were standing up, each with a tiny glass in one hand and a morsel of bread in the other. I remember that moment vividly: it was like taking communion, I thought to myself. As a matter of fact, it was really the first communion I ever participated in. I think we were all aware of this, though nothing was said about it. Anyhow, as the story progressed we marched back and forth, crossed and recrossed each other's path numerous times, sometimes bumping into one another and making quick apologies, but continuing to pace back and forth, to cross and recross one another's paths.

About five in the afternoon there was still a drop of wine in the bottle, still a tiny morsel of bread lying on the table. The three of us were as lucid, as bright, as gay as could be. We might have continued that way until midnight were it not for an unexpected visit from an Englishwoman and a young poet. The formalities concluded, I immediately inquired if they had any money on them, adding at once that we were in need of food. They were delighted to come to our rescue. We gave them a big basket and told them to gather whatever they could. In about a half hour they returned laden with food and wines. We sat down and fell to like hungry wolves. The cold chicken which they had bought disappeared like magic. The cheeses, the fruit, the bread we washed down with the most excellent wines. It was really criminal to toss those good wines off the way we did. Fred, of course, had become hilarious and uncontrollable during the feast. With each bottle that was opened he poured himself a good tumblerful and emptied it down his gullet in one draught. The veins were standing out at the temples, his eyes were popping, the saliva dribbled from his mouth. Reichel had disappeared, or perhaps we had locked him out. Our English friends took everything with composure and equanimity. Perhaps they looked upon it as the customary scene at the Villa Seurat which they had heard so much about.

That evening was fraught with strange consequences for Fred. Never did he reveal to any one what precisely had occurred that evening to alter him. That he *was* altered, definitely and for good, no one who had known him intimately could deny. It was a conversion. From then on the warring selves seemed to fall apart; little by little his true self asserted itself, gained the ascendancy over the transient personalities which he used to assume like masks. The change-over had occurred in the dark, literally and figuratively. He had closeted himself in another room with the

Englishwoman, for about an hour, I should say. In that time something occurred between them which decided the future course of his life. He predicted as much when we were alone together the next day. But even he did not realize at the time how truthfully he was speaking.

The outbreak of war was the crucial test. He was in England at the time and very much enamored of the English. I think he had already taken steps to become a citizen. To my amazement I received a letter one day saying that he had volunteered in the British Army. Any one who knew him in the past would have thought it impossible of him. He more than any one would have scoffed at the idea—before the conversion. "One war is enough in one's lifetime," he used to say. He used to brag about his inability to become a soldier. "I'm a physical coward," he would say. "Just to touch a gun makes me ill." In the space of a few months he was at home in the British Army. He took to it like a duck takes to water. He found everything enjoyable, even the food. Curiously enough, the thing he dreaded most—to kill some one in cold blood and at a distance—never proved necessary. But I remember him writing me that he was prepared even for that, that he would do it with zest if it were necessary. That was so typical of him. Whatever he did he did with good will, in the spirit of play. It may be a strain to think of a man killing joyously, but the more one thinks about it, the more one wonders if it isn't the best way. In this too his innocence asserted itself. He could not kill out of hatred, or greed or envy, nor because he was commanded to do it. He could kill only out of sheer exuberance. Sometimes I almost regret that he had not killed at least one man. I should like to have shaken hands with him after that, to have said: "Joey, my lad, fine work! I never thought it was in you." I can well imagine his response, can picture how he would have hung his head blushingly, not out of shame but out of embarrassment, grinning all the while and stammering out some absurd remark about it all being in the day's work, or pretending to brag about being an extraordinary marksman.

But let me not stop on this note. Let me go back in retrospect to that rainy day when Durrell, Nancy, Fred and myself were sitting in the little restaurant in the 13th arrondissement, somewhere in the vicinity of the rue de la Glacière. We are in high spirits as usual, Durrell laughing so uproariously over Fred's quips that the proprietor is irritated. (Often we were asked to leave the cinema because of Durrell's infectious laugh.) Suddenly, apropos of nothing at all, with his fork arrested in mid-air, Fred blurts out: *"The mission of man on earth is to remember . . ."* There was a brief pause, as if we had received a slap in the face, followed by peals of laughter. It was just inconceivable that Fred should have uttered this phrase at that particular moment. What was more inconceivable was that this time we could not put him off with our laughter. He began the sentence again, not once but several times . . . *"The mission of man on earth is to remember."* He could get no further with his thought; we simply drowned him in gales of laughter. Some one asked him if he had read it somewhere. No, he had made it up himself. He said this blushing, as if aware that he had given birth to something extremely significant. Whether he had thought it up himself or not, we all agreed that it was marvelous, more than that, memorable, that we would give him credit for it sometime, somewhere, somehow. But he didn't want any credit for it, he tried to let us know. He wanted us to listen. We couldn't listen. The phrase had electrified us. Another word tacked on to it and it would have been ruined. Especially an explanatory word.

It was Edgar who used to chew my ear off about the boon of memory—in Devachan. I used to fight him tooth and nail on this, I remember. I used to insist that memory must be killed off, that if the intervals between births have any purpose it must be to get rid of the baggage of memory. "But you can't do that before you have remembered everything," Edgar would argue. "You must rehearse every tiniest detail of your life over and over, until you have extracted the last significant juices from your experiences." Well, I could see the point of that clearly enough. "But in the end," I kept harping, "is it not true that you do lose all memory of things past?" I would say it to myself, not to Edgar. With Edgar, as you may imagine, it was more expedient to give in quickly. Not too quickly either, because then he would become suspicious.

But Fred's view of it was that it was here on earth man was to remember. That was what was novel and alarming at the same time. Novel because no one thinks of remembrance as "a mission," alarming because what then would one do in Devachan? Was he implying that Nirvana should be attained in *this* lifetime? Had he suddenly realized that, whatever or whoever he was, he now was once and for all, that all the pasts led to this endless present in which being and vision were one? Had he experienced his last death, and was it deathless that he uttered his innocent and sententious phrase? Of course these thoughts did not flit through my mind at the moment of utterance. They have come since, along with countless others, in moments of sudden recollection. But there is always something gratuitous which accompanies the remembrance of the phrase, something beyond his indescribable look and the indescribable shock which all of us experienced simultaneously. That something I cannot put my finger on. I can only give intimations, captured reverberations.

All this happened some seven years ago. One remembers lots of strange, startling, inexplicable events and situations. One of them often stands out more vividly, more hauntingly than the others. Its unguessed significance increases with the passage of time. It seems to gather other phenomenal occurrences into its own magnetic field, to give them focus or a wholly new orientation. If it is remembered over and above everything else there must be a deep reason for it. Our ability to forget certain painful experiences is only matched by our ability to remember others. What is buried and what is kept alive seem to have equal importance. One works subterraneously, the other in etheric realms. But both are eternally operative.

In one of Fred's books (*The Renegade*), in which I notice he has resuscitated the phrase, attributing it to another person, he emphasizes that one has to forget much before one can remember. The passage towards the end of the book in which the subject of "remembrance" is dwelt on at some length is introduced by a most significant phrase. The narrator and the woman called Iris Day are having a farewell dinner. A wine is introduced which he says went to his head almost instantly, filling him with a sensation of great serenity and lucidity. "It's a wine," he is informed, "that was drunk long before Bacchus. It comes from the shores of the Eridanos where the water is purer and more limpid than anywhere else . . . They say (and this is the phrase I consider significant) *it makes the sick forget and the pure remember.*"

Then says the narrator: "It's miraculous! What is it? There is a marvelous light in me, I can't describe it."

"You will see better when you get your eyes used to it . . . Don't think it is the wine, it's you: you've merely found the key to the treasure that belongs to you."

"I don't remember, Iris."

"Don't worry, you will . . . *The mission of man on earth is to remember* . . . There's no science, no wisdom, not even love. In the end, everything boils down to one thing: *remembrance.*"

When Iris Day proceeds to explain the sacrificial nature of renunciation (in which the "present" as a concept of time is eliminated) we learn that the purpose is "to rejoin the Source, which you do not as yet remember" . . . Then she adds: "Not till you have sacrificed everything you have acquired will remembrance come back to you . . . With every successive sacrifice you get nearer the Source."

The narrator here goes on to explain that the meeting with Iris

Day was ordained. Had he not met her precisely when he did his life would have taken the wrong turn. "I've met you at the crossroads," he says.

This meeting, which the author places in London, corresponds with the Villa Seurat episode. Iris Day is unquestionably the woman who arrived that Christmas Day. Now then, though I had read *The Renegade* when it first came out (in 1943), I had completely forgotten that Fred had treated of all this in his book. It was only a few moments ago that I suddenly asked myself if my good friend Fred had not spoken of all this himself somewhere. What amazes me more, after reading the closing pages of the book, is to see how he himself explained his new attitude towards war. I think it is important to add a few excerpts from the discussion which follows upon the foregoing. I give merely the highlights, of course . . .

"Is war very wrong?" I asked.

"Not wrong, childish . . ." After a few remarks about the nature of the coming war (now finished), Iris Day adds: "I am happy to find you on the right side. From the point of view of the individual, it does not matter whether one is, by fate, on the right or the wrong side."

"How do you mean that, Iris?"

"You can still be right if destiny puts you in the wrong camp, but it is much more difficult, of course; it requires greater strength and greater sacrifices . . . It can be taken for granted that the vast majority of people who fight one another are convinced that they are on the right side. What makes their wars so sophomoric is that they believe it to be possible to enforce, by victory, the laws, order, dogmas, or ideas which they consider just; for in reality the only Law by which human beings can live at all has been laid down long before the earth was inhabited . . . Whether we are good or evil, we have to live by Right, Justice and Love; otherwise we perish in the long run. Hence it is unimportant (from the cosmic viewpoint) which side wins the war, for in the end he that stands for Right, Justice and Love is bound to be victorious. Simply because it is the Law."

"I daresay what you say is true, Iris, but it does not quite apply to us. I don't think we have a right to sit back and watch Destiny taking its long-winded course: man has got to fight for what he thinks is right."

"I am glad to hear you say that . . . There is nothing wrong if some one evades the war because he does not believe in its justice. I know you hate war, but I also know that deep down you sense

that there is something great at stake—something that concerns
the whole of humanity, and *ipso facto* yourself . . ."

After some lengthy remarks about England's role in the conflict,
Iris Day returns to the heart of the subject. Her words assume a
prophetic tone.

"Apart from the events that are being shaped in this conflict, in
which you may be called upon to play but a small part, this war
may have much to do in the moulding of your own personality. It
may touch you in the quick. The very basis of your nature may be
affected. *You have not yet begun living your own life, and it is
important to live one's own life.* Your past existence was merely
the manifestation of something that was not essentially you . . .
Not till you are bare and naked and all in ruins will you be able to
clear the ground and start building your real house . . . This war,
which may decide the future of mankind for many clock centuries,
affords you the unique opportunity of atoning for the past. For you
are involved in this war *personally*. It may sound cruel, and I
daresay it is not altogether your own fault, but the fact remains
that you are personally responsible for the war to the extent that
you have not lived your own life: the sum total of innumerable
pasts like yours has to bear the responsibility of the catastrophe.
It is no use pleading that you never hated anybody, that you had
always kept clear of any direct activities that led up to the unavoid-
ability of the war. That was not enough. Your great fault, which
you share with the vast majority of men, was to lead a wrong life.
It is that fault which you now have a chance to redeem. I know
you will do it."

So this is the justification for participating in mass slaughter?
you ask. By simply joining up with the "right" side your good
friend Fred is going to redeem a wasted life? In the name of Peace
and Justice he is going to kill, just like any other misguided
individual, is that it? I know *all* the questions you are ready to hurl
at me. And on top of it you are going to say, "What bilge! What
self-deception! What utter rot! We could have turned to the *Bhagavad Gita* and found it expressed more eloquently and convinc-
ingly."

Let us forget for a moment what justification he gave to his
motives. Let us concentrate for a moment on what happened to
him during the great catastrophe. How was it that he was not only
spared, that he not only grew in stature morally and spiritually,
but that he was never obliged to fire a shot; that moreover, instead
of killing his fellow-man, he was enabled to save a number from
death? Had he not participated directly and openly, in what way
would he have "participated," since we are all involved, like it or

not? Did he participate in slaughter or did he participate in a cause which lies deeper than the war itself? I believe the latter. I know that he had nothing personally to gain, as we say, by joining the British Army. But he had everything to gain, as a human being, by identifying himself with the plight of the world. He was renouncing the false security or immunity he enjoyed as a man living *en marge*. He ceased being the "renegade" in order to be himself. He made war not against his fellow-man, for he never had any hatred of his fellow-man, but against what he considered were the forces of evil. Evil in this instance—and is not this the true meaning of evil?—representing all that prevents one from leading his own true life. He was ready to violate the commandment "Thou Shalt Not Kill!", in which he had taken refuge out of weakness (Don't kill me and I won't kill you!), because something bigger than obedience to the Law seemed at stake. Actually, and I stress this point once again, as events turned out he was never called upon to break the Law. With those who retort that this was a mere accident, or that by serving in the Army he was helping others to kill, I beg to differ. In no way were his services instrumental to the furtherance of slaughter. Or, if they were, then the grocer who supplied the able-bodied citizens of his country with food was also collaborating in wholesale murder. As for its being accidental that he did not kill any one, well, by what accident was it that instead of being sent to the trenches he was employed in the Pioneer Corps? Many of his comrades wanted desperately to go across and wage active warfare; some of them had their wish and were killed. Fred cheerfully accepted the dirty work, which meant dashing into burning buildings on occasion and rescuing helpless men, women and children. Some of his comrades met their death that way. They were spared none of the agonies which attend a heroic death on the battlefield. Fred, as I said earlier, led a charmed life. He was "saved," as we sometimes put it. Saved not *from* something, since he desired no protection, but *for* something. He emerged from the war with a sane, healthy, joyous outlook on life. He would have emerged from it in the same jubilant spirit even had he killed a few men. Besides, he would never have regarded himself as guiltless for those deaths: he would have considered himself thoroughly responsible—to God. He would have said, on the Day of Judgment, with a bit of the old *"culot factice,"* "I did it for *you,* O God. I acted according to the light that was in me."

Here we arrive at the contradiction which so deeply disturbs the ordinary mind. Neither the man who refuses to participate nor the man who does is of necessity guilty. The question of responsibility for mass slaughter cuts deeper than the matter of willingness or unwillingness to shed blood. Both he who kills and he who refrains from killing may be in the right, or they may just as well be in the wrong. The man who did not lift a finger may be more guilty than the man who proved himself responsible for thousands of deaths. Only a pacifist zealot would consider a man like General Eisenhower, for example, as "guilty." Only short-sighted beings can pin the guilt for the war on Hitler or Mussolini. War, like peace, involves us all.

There are always individuals who, though living in the very midst of catastrophe, remain untouched by it. I mean not just physically, but morally and spiritually. They are not only "above the fray," they are beyond the zone of fatality. They are out of all danger because, though they can not and would not remove themselves physically, in their heart of hearts they had elected from the beginning to stay out. *They have no heart in such things,* as the saying goes. The wine which they drank at the Source helps them to remember. It is only the pure who remember, only the pure who can remain aloof, and that not from choice but from necessity. With them the realm of accident is not a quixotic one but a deeply intelligible one. They are always conscious of direction just as they are always conscious of the real identity of those who confront them. They relegate nothing to chance; for them all proceeds according to law and all is therefore in order. They do not busy themselves putting things to right, neither do they occupy themselves with doing good. It is in the service of life that they are enrolled; they *elected* to serve, they were not conscripted. Consequently they are never called upon by fate "to take sides"; they are not crucified upon the horns of a tragic dilemma. The turbulent waves of conflict break before reaching them; they are never engulfed.

With such as my friend Fred, on the other hand, wars and revolutions provide an opportunity for them to "lose themselves." It is important for them to take sides, *not* to aid the right, *not* to become heroic instruments of justice, but to discover the meaning of sacrifice. Often through participation they achieve immunity. Immunity not so much from the hazards and dangers of involvement, but immunity from fear, immunity from the cowardly deceptions of the ego. They discover a deathless reality in which there can never again be the pain of separation. They have reached home, face to face with the Source, as much alive in the spirit world as in the flesh. Some of them, mourned as "lost," find freedom in death. Others, living the anonymous life of the little man, are privileged to manifest their freedom in life. These are the immortal spirits living in accordance with the Law who have discovered that victory and eternity are synonymous. To live one's own life, to lead it to the full, carries with it the reward of immortality. "That which now has life and is forever exempt from death," such is the definition of immortal. But the definition might also be stated thus: "That which has life is forever exempt from death." That is the meaning which the metamorphosis of mortal to immortal conveys. The immortal is the victorious one: he has conquered over time and death. He has triumphed over the "creature" by passing through the fires of sacrifice. Renouncing all claim to personal survival he becomes deathless. Remembering the road back, he "puts outside of himself" (*forgets,* in short) all the obstacles which he himself had put in his path. The snares and delusions of the world no longer exist: like a spider he realizes that he had spun the intricate, entangling web out of his own substance. Free of the world, he is free from Fate. He no longer postpones living. The past has been atoned for and thus obliterated; the future, robbed of its time track, has no meaning. The present dissolves in the all which has neither beginning nor end. *In the beginning was the Word and the Word was with God and the Word was God.* At the Source there is no separation either of God and creature or of spirit and time.

The mission of man on earth is to remember . . .

GREECE

•

(1939–1940)

I would never have gone to Greece had it not been for a girl named Betty Ryan who lived in the same house with me in Paris. One evening, over a glass of white wine, she began to talk of her experiences in roaming about the world. I always listened to her with great attention, not only because her experiences were strange but because when she talked about her wanderings she seemed to paint them: everything she described remained in my head like finished canvases by a master. It was a peculiar conversation that evening: we began by talking about China and the Chinese language which she had begun to study. Soon we were in North Africa, in the desert, among peoples I had never heard of before. And then suddenly she was all alone, walking beside a river, and the light was intense and I was following her as best I could in the blinding sun but she got lost and I found myself wandering about in a strange land listening to a language I had never heard before. She is not exactly a story teller, this girl, but she is an artist of some sort because nobody has ever given me the ambiance of a place so thoroughly as she did Greece. Long afterwards I discovered that it was near Olympia that she had gone astray and I with her, but at the time it was just Greece to me, a world of light such as I had never dreamed of and never hoped to see.

For months prior to this conversation I had been receiving letters from Greece from my friend Lawrence Durrell who had practically made Corfu his home. His letters were marvellous too, and yet a bit unreal to me. Durrell is a poet and his letters were poetic: they caused a certain confusion in me owing to the fact that the dream and the reality, the historical and the mythological, were so artfully blended. Later I was to discover for myself that this confusion is real and not due entirely to the poetic faculty. But at the time I thought he was laying it on, that it was his way of coaxing me to accept his repeated invitations to come and stay with him.

A few months before the war broke out I decided to take a long vacation. I had long wanted to visit the valley of the Dordogne, for one thing. So I packed my valise and took the train for Rocamadour where I arrived early one morning about sun up, the moon still gleaming brightly. It was a stroke of genius on my part to make the tour of the Dordogne region before plunging into the bright and hoary world of Greece. Just to glimpse the black, mysterious river at Dômme from the beautiful bluff at the edge of the town is something to be grateful for all one's life. To me this river, this country, belong to the poet, Rainer Maria Rilke. It is not French, not Austrian, not European even: it is the country of enchantment which the poets have staked out and which they alone may lay claim to. It is the nearest thing to Paradise this side of Greece. Let us call it the Frenchman's paradise, by way of making a concession. Actually it must have been a paradise for many thousands of years. I believe it must have been so for the Cro-Magnon man, despite the fossilized evidences of the great caves which point to a condition of life rather bewildering and terrifying. I believe that the Cro-Magnon man settled here because he was extremely intelligent and had a highly developed sense of beauty. I believe that in him the religious sense was already highly developed and that it flourished here even if he lived like an animal in the depths of the caves. I believe that this great peaceful region of France will always be a sacred spot for man and that when the cities have killed off the poets this will be the refuge and the cradle of the poets to come. I repeat, it was most important for me to have seen the Dordogne: it gives me hope for the future of the race, for the future of the earth itself. France may one day exist no more, but the Dordogne will live on just as dreams live on and nourish the souls of men.

At Marseilles I took the boat for Piraeus. My friend Durrell was to meet me in Athens and take me to Corfu. On the boat there were many people from the Levant. I singled them out immediately, in preference to the Americans, the French, the English. I had a strong desire to talk to Arabs and Turks and Syrians and such like. I was curious to know how they looked at the world. The voyage lasted four or five days, giving me ample time to make acquaintance with those whom I was eager to know more about. Quite by accident the first friend I made was a Greek medical student returning from Paris. We spoke French together. The first evening we talked until three or four in the morning, mostly about Knut Hamsun, whom I discovered the Greeks were passionate about. It seemed strange at first to be talking about this genius of the North whilst sailing into warm waters. But that conversation taught me immediately that the Greeks are an enthusiastic, curious-minded, passionate people. *Passion*—it was something I had long missed in France. Not only passion, but contradictoriness, confusion, chaos—all these sterling human qualities I rediscovered and cherished again in the person of my new-found friend. *And generosity.* I had almost thought it had perished from the earth. There we were, a Greek and an American, with something in common, yet two vastly different beings. It was a splendid introduction to that world which was about to open before my eyes. I was already enamored of Greece, and the Greeks, before catching sight of the country. I could see in advance that they were a friendly, hospitable people, easy to reach, easy to deal with.

The next day I opened conversation with the others—a Turk, a Syrian, some students from Lebanon, an Argentine man of Italian extraction. The Turk aroused my antipathies almost at once. He had a mania for logic which infuriated me. It was bad logic too. And like the others, all of whom I violently disagreed with, I found in him an expression of the American spirit at its worst. Progress was their obsession. More machines, more efficiency, more capital, more comforts—that was their whole talk. I asked them if they had heard of the millions who were unemployed in America. They ignored the question. I asked them if they realized how empty, restless and miserable the American people were with all their machine-made luxuries and comforts. They were impervious to my sarcasm. What they wanted was success—money, power, a place in the sun. None of them wanted to return to their own country; for some reason they had all of them been obliged to return against their will. They said there was no life for them in their own country. *When would life begin?* I wanted to know. When they had all the things which America had, or Germany, or France. Life was made up of things, of machines mainly, from what I could gather. Life without money was an impossibility: one had to have clothes, a good home, a radio, a car, a tennis racquet, and so on. I told them I had none of those things and that I was happy without them, that I had turned my back on America precisely because these things meant nothing to me. They said I was the strangest American they had ever met. But they liked me. They stuck to me throughout the voyage, plying me with all sorts of questions which I answered in vain. Evenings I would get together with the Greek. We understood one another better, much better, despite his adoration for Germany and the German régime. He too, of course, wanted to go to America some day. Every Greek dreams of going to American and making a nest egg. I didn't try to dissuade him; I gave him a picture of America as I knew it, as I had seen it and experienced it. That seemed to frighten him a little: he admitted he had never heard anything like that about America before. "You go," I said, "and see for yourself. I may be wrong. I am only telling you what I know from my own experience." "Remember," I added, "Knut Hamsun didn't have such a wonderful time of it there, nor your beloved Edgar Allan Poe. . . ."

There was a French archaeologist returning to Greece who sat opposite me at the table; he could have told me a lot of things about Greece but I never gave him a chance; I disliked him from the time I first laid eyes on him. The chap I really liked most during the voyage was the Italian from the Argentine. He was about the most ignorant fellow I have ever met and charming at the same time. At Naples we went ashore together to have a good meal and to visit Pompeii which he had never even heard of. Despite the overpowering heat I enjoyed the trip to Pompeii; if I had gone with an archaeologist I would have been bored stiff. At Piraeus he came ashore with me to visit the Acropolis. The heat was even worse than at Pompeii, which was pretty bad. At nine in the morning it must have been 120 degrees in the sun. We had hardly gotten through the gate at the dock when we fell into the hands of a wily Greek guide who spoke a little English and French and who promised to show us everything of interest for a modest sum. We tried to find out what he wanted for his services but in vain. It was too hot to discuss prices; we fell into a taxi and told him to steer us straight to the Acropolis. I had changed my francs into drachmas on the boat; it seemed like a tremendous wad that I had stuffed into my pocket and I felt that I could meet the bill no matter how exorbitant it might be. I knew we were going to be gypped and I looked forward to it with relish. The only thing that was solidly fixed in my mind about the Greeks was that you couldn't trust them; I would have been disappointed if our guide had turned out to be magnanimous and chivalrous. My companion on the other hand was somewhat worried about the situation. He was going on to Beyrout. I could actually hear him making mental calculations as we rode along in the suffocating dust and heat.

The ride from Piraeus to Athens is a good introduction to Greece. There is nothing inviting about it. It makes you wonder why you decided to come to Greece. There is something not only arid and desolate about the scene, but something terrifying too. You feel stripped and plundered, almost annihilated. The driver was like an animal who had been miraculously taught to operate a crazy machine: our guide was constantly directing him to go to the right or the left, as though they had never made the journey before. I felt an enormous sympathy for the driver whom I knew would be gypped also. I had the feeling that he could not count beyond a hundred; I had also the feeling that he would drive into a ditch if he were directed to. When we got to the Acropolis—it was an insane idea to go there immediately—there were several hundred people ahead of us storming the gate. By this time the heat was so terrific that all I thought of was where to sit down and enjoy a bit of shade. I found myself a fairly cool spot and I waited there while the Argentine chap got his money's worth. Our guide had remained at the entrance with the taxi driver after turning us over to one of the official guides. He was going to escort us to the Temple of Jupiter and the Thesion and other places as soon as we had had our fill of the Acropolis. We never went to these places, of course. We told him to drive into town, find a cool spot and order some ice cream. It was about ten thirty when we parked ourselves on the terrace of a cafe. Everybody looked fagged out from the heat, even the Greeks. We ate the ice cream, drank the iced water, then more ice cream and more iced water. After that I called for some hot tea, because I suddenly remembered somebody telling me once that hot tea cools you off.

The taxi was standing at the curb with the motor running. Our guide seemed to be the only one who didn't mind the heat. I suppose he thought we would cool off a bit and then start trotting around again in the sun looking at ruins and monuments. We told him finally that we wanted to dispense with his services. He said there was no hurry, he had nothing special to do, and was happy to keep us company. We told him we had had enough for the day and would like to settle up. He called the waiter and paid the check out of his own pocket. We kept prodding him to tell us how much. He seemed reluctant as hell to tell us. He wanted to know how much we thought his services were worth. We said we didn't know—we would leave it to him to decide. Whereupon, after a long pause, after looking us over from head to foot, scratching himself, tilting his hat back, mopping his brow, and so on, he blandly announced that he thought 2500 drachmas would square the account. I gave my companion a look and told him to open fire. The Greek of course was thoroughly prepared for our reaction. And it's this, I must confess, that I really like about the Greeks, when they are wily and cunning. Almost at once he said, "well, all right, if you don't think my price is fair then you make *me* a price." So we did. We made him one as ridiculously low as his was high. It seemed to make him feel good, this crude bargaining. As a matter of fact, we all felt good about it. It was making service into something tangible and real like a commodity. We weighed it and appraised it, we juggled it like a ripe tomato or an ear of corn. And finally we agreed, not on a fair price, because that would have been an insult to our guide's ability, but we agreed that for this unique occasion, because of the heat, because we had

not seen everything, and so on and so forth, that we would fix on
thus and such a sum and part good friends. One of the little items
we haggled about a long time was the amount paid by our guide to
the official guide at the Acropolis. He swore he had given the man
150 drachmas. I had seen the transaction with my own eyes, and I
knew he had given only fifty drachmas. He maintained that I had
not seen well. We smoothed it out by pretending that he had
inadvertently handed the man a hundred drachmas more than he
intended to, a piece of casuistry so thoroughly un-Greek that had
he then and there decided to rob us of all we possessed he would
have been justified and the courts of Greece would have upheld
him.

An hour later I said good-bye to my companion, found myself a
room in a small hotel at double the usual price, stripped down and
lay on the bed naked in a pool of sweat until nine that evening. I
looked for a restaurant, tried to eat, but after taking a few mouth-
fuls gave it up. I have never been so hot in all my life. To sit near
an electric light was torture. After a few cold drinks I got up from
the terrace where I was sitting and headed for the park. I should
say it was about eleven o'clock. People were swarming in all
directions to the park. It reminded me of New York on a sweltering
night in August. It was the herd again, something I had never felt
in Paris, except during the aborted revolution. I sauntered slowly
through the park towards the Temple of Jupiter. There were little
tables along the dusty paths set out in an absent-minded way:
couples were sitting there quietly in the dark, talking in low voices,
over glasses of water. *The glass of water* . . . everywhere I saw the
glass of water. It became obsessional. I began to think of water as
a new thing, a new vital element of life. Earth, air, fire, water.
Right now water had become the cardinal element. Seeing lovers
sitting there in the dark drinking water, sitting there in peace and
quiet and talking in low tones, gave me a wonderful feeling about
the Greek character. The dust, the heat, the poverty, the bareness,
the containedness of the people, and the water everywhere in little
tumblers standing between the quiet, peaceful couples, gave me
the feeling that there was something holy about the place, something nourishing and sustaining. I walked about enchanted on this
first night in the Zapion. It remains in my memory like no other
park I have known. It is the quintessence of park, the thing one
feels sometimes in looking at a canvas or dreaming of a place
you'd like to be in and never find. It is lovely in the morning, too,
as I was to discover. But at night, coming upon it from nowhere,
feeling the hard dirt under your feet and hearing a buzz of language
which is altogether unfamiliar to you, it is magical—and it is more

magical to me perhaps because I think of it as filled with the poorest people in the world, and the gentlest. I am glad I arrived in Athens during that incredible heat wave, glad I saw it under the worst conditions. I felt the naked strength of the people, their purity, their nobility, their resignation. I saw their children, a sight which warmed me, because coming from France it was as if children were missing from the world, as if they were not being born any more. I saw people in rags, and that was cleansing too. The Greek knows how to live with his rags: they don't utterly degrade and befoul him as in other countries I have visited.

The following day I decided to take the boat to Corfu where my friend Durrell was waiting for me. We pulled out of Piraeus about five in the afternoon, the sun still burning like a furnace. I had made the mistake of buying a second class ticket. When I saw the animals coming aboard, the bedding, all the crazy paraphernalia which the Greeks drag with them on their voyages, I promptly changed to first class, which was only a trifle more expensive than second. I had never travelled first class before on anything, except the Metro in Paris—it seemed like a genuine luxury to me. The waiter was continuously circulating about with a tray filled with glasses of water. It was the first Greek word I learned: *nero* (water) and a beautiful word it is. Night was coming on and the islands were looming up in the distance, always floating above the water, not resting on it. The stars came out with magnificent brilliance and the wind was soft and cooling. I began to get the feel of it at once, what Greece was, what it had been, what it will always be even should it meet with the misfortune of being overrun by American tourists. When the steward asked me what I would like for dinner, when I gathered what it was we were going to have for dinner, I almost broke down and wept. The meals on a Greek boat are staggering. I like a good Greek meal better than a good French meal, even though it be heresy to admit it. There was lots to eat and lots to drink: there was the air outside and the sky full of stars. I had promised myself on leaving Paris not to do a stroke of work for a year. It was my first real vacation in twenty years and I was ready for it. Everything seemed right to me. There was no time any more, just me drifting along in a slow boat ready to meet all comers and take whatever came along. Out of the sea, as if Homer himself had arranged it for me, the islands bobbed up, lonely, deserted, mysterious in the fading light. I couldn't ask for more, nor did I want anything more. I had everything a man could desire, and I knew it. I knew too that I might never have it again. I felt the war coming on—it was getting closer and closer every day. For a little while yet there would be peace and men might still behave like human beings.

We didn't go through the Corinth canal because there had been a landslide: we practically circumnavigated the Peloponnesus. The second night out we pulled into Patras opposite Missolonghi. I have come into this port several times since, always about the same hour, and always I experienced the same fascination. You ride straight into a big headland, like an arrow burying itself in the side of a mountain. The electric lights strung along the waterfront create a Japanese effect; there is something impromptu about the lighting in all Greek ports, something which gives the impression of an impending festival. As you pull into port the little boats come out to meet you: they are filled with passengers and luggage and livestock and bedding and furniture. The men row standing up, pushing instead of pulling. They seem absolutely tireless, moving their heavy burdens about at will with deft and almost impercepti- ble movements of the wrist. As they draw alongside a pandemo- nium sets in. Everybody goes the wrong way, everything is con- fused, chaotic, disorderly. But nobody is ever lost or hurt, nothing is stolen, no blows are exchanged. It is a kind of ferment which is created by reason of the fact that for a Greek every event, no matter how stale, is always unique. He is always doing the same thing for the first time: he is curious, avidly curious, and experi- mental. He experiments for the sake of experimenting, not to establish a better or more efficient way of doing things. He likes to do things with his hands, which his whole body, with his soul, I might as well say. Thus Homer lives on. Though I've never read a line of Homer I believe the Greek of to-day is essentially un- changed. If anything he is more Greek than he ever was. And here I must make a parenthesis to say a word about my friend Mayo, the painter, whom I knew in Paris. Malliarakis was his real name and I think he came originally from Crete. Anyway, pulling into Patras I got to thinking about him violently. I remembered asking him in Paris to tell me something about Greece and suddenly, as we were coming into the port of Patras, I understood everything he had been trying to tell me that night and I felt bad that he was not alongside me to share my enjoyment. I remembered how he had said with quiet, steady conviction, after describing the country for me as best he could—"Miller, you will like Greece, I am sure of it." Somehow those words impressed me more than anything he had said about Greece. *You will like it.* . . . that stuck in my crop. "By God, yes, I like it," I was saying to myself over and over as I stood at the rail taking in the movement and the hubbub.

I leaned back and looked up at the sky. I had never seen a sky like this before. It was magnificent. I felt completley detached from Europe. I had entered a new realm as a free man—everything had conjoined to make the experience unique and fructifying. Christ, I was happy. But for the first time in my life I was happy with the full consciousness of being happy. It's good to be just plain happy; it's a little better to know that you're happy; but to understand that you're happy and to know why and how, in what way, because of what concatenation of events or circumstances, and still be happy, be happy in the being and the knowing, well that is beyond happiness, that is bliss, and if you have any sense you ought to kill yourself on the spot and be done with it. And that's how I was— except that I didn't have the power or the courage to kill myself then and there. It was good, too, that I didn't do myself in because there were even greater moments to come, something beyond bliss even, something which if any one had tried to describe to me I would probably not have believed. I didn't know then that I would one day stand at Mycenae, or at Phaestos, or that I would wake up one morning and looking through a port hole see with my own eyes the place I had written about in a book but which I never knew existed nor that it bore the same name as the one I had given it in my imagination. Marvellous things happen to one in Greece— marvellous *good* things which can happen to one nowhere else on earth. Somehow, almost as if He were nodding, Greece still remains under the protection of the Creator. Men may go about their puny, ineffectual bedevilment, even in Greece, but God's magic is still at work and, no matter what the race of man may do or try to do, Greece is still a sacred precinct—and my belief is it will remain so until the end of time.

It was almost high noon when the boat pulled in at Corfu. Durrell was waiting at the dock with Spiro Americanus, his factotum. It was about an hour's drive to Kalami, the little village towards the north end of the island where Durrell had his home. Before sitting down to lunch we had a swim in front of the house. I hadn't been in the water for almost twenty years. Durrell and Nancy, his wife, were like a couple of dolphins; they practically lived in the water. We took a siesta after lunch and then we rowed to another little cove about a mile away where there was a tiny white shrine. Here we baptized ourselves anew in the raw. In the evening I was presented to Kyrios Karamenaios, the local gendarme, and to Nicola, the village schoolmaster. We immediately became firm friends. With Nicola I spoke a broken-down French; with Kara-

menaios a sort of cluck-cluck language made up largely of good
will and a desire to understand one another.

About once a week we went to town in the caique. I never got to
like the town of Corfu. It has a desultory air which by evening
becomes a quiet, irritating sort of dementia. You are constantly
sitting down drinking something you don't want to drink or else
walking up and down aimlessly feeling desperately like a prisoner.
Usuallly I treated myself to a shave and haircut whenever I went
to town: I did it to while away the time and because it was so
ridiculously cheap. It was the King's barber, I was informed, who
attended me, and the whole job came to about three and a half
cents, including the tip. Corfu is a typical place of exile. The
Kaiser used to make his residence here before he lost his crown. I
went through the palace once to see what it was like. All palaces
strike me as dreary and lugubrious places, but the Kaiser's mad-
house is about the worst piece of gimcrackery I have ever laid eyes
on. It would make an excellent museum for Surrealistic art. At one
end of the island, however, facing the abandoned palace, is the
little spot called Kanoni, whence you look down upon the magical
Toten Insel. In the evening Spiro sits here dreaming of his life in
Rhode Island when the boot-legging traffic was in full swing. It is
a spot which rightfully belongs to my friend Hans Reichel, the
water colorist. The associations are Homeric, I know, but for me
it partakes more of Stuttgart than of ancient Greece. When the
moon is out and there is no sound save the breathing of the earth
it is exactly the atmosphere which Reichel creates when he sits in
a petrified dream and becomes *limitrophe* to birds and snails and
gargoyles, to smoky moons and sweating stones, or to the sorrow-
laden music which is constantly playing in his heart even when he
rears like a crazed kangaroo and begins smashing everything in
sight with his prehensile tail. If he should ever read these lines and
know that I thought of him while looking at the Toten Insel, know
that I was never the enemy he imagined me to be, it would make
me very happy. Perhaps it was on one of these very evenings when
I sat at Kanoni with Spiro looking down upon this place of
enchantment that Reichel, who had nothing but love for the
French, was dragged from his lair in the Impasse Rouet and placed
in a sordid concentration camp.

One day Theodore turned up—Dr. Theodore Stephanides. He
knew all about plants, flowers, trees, rocks, minerals, low forms of
animal life, microbes, diseases, stars, planets, comets and so on.
Theodore is the most learned man I have ever met, and a saint to
boot. Theodore has also translated a number of Greek poems into

English. It was in this way that I heard for the first time the name Seferis, which is George Seferiades' pen name. And then with a mixture of love, admiration and sly humor he pronounced for me the name Katsimbalis which, for some strange reason, immediately made an impression upon me. That evening Theodore gave us hallucinating descriptions of his life in the trenches with Katsimbalis on the Balkan front during the World War. The next day Durrell and I wrote an enthusiastic letter to Katsimbalis, who was in Athens, expressing the hope that we would all meet there shortly. *Katsimbalis*. . . . we employed his name familiarly, as if we had known him all our lives. Soon thereafter Theodore left and then came the Countess X. with Niki and a family of young acrobats. They came upon us unexpectedly in a little boat laden with marvellous victuals and bottles of rare wine from the Countess' estate. With this troupe of linguists, jugglers, acrobats and water nymphs things went whacky right from the start. Niki had Nile green eyes and her hair seemed to be entwined with serpents. Between the first and second visits of this extraordinary troupe, who always came by water in a boat heavily laden with good things, the Durrells and myself went camping for a stretch on a sandy beach facing the sea. Here time was completely blotted out. Mornings we were awakened by a crazy shepherd who insisted on leading his flock of sheep over our prone bodies. On a cliff directly behind us a demented witch would suddenly appear to curse him out. Each morning it was a surprise; we would awake with groans and curses followed by peals of laughter. Then a quick plunge into the sea where we would watch the goats clambering up the precipitous slopes of the cliff: the scene was an almost faithful replica of the Rhodesian rock drawings which one can see at the Musée de l'Homme in Paris. Sometimes in high fettle we would clamber up after the goats, only to descend covered with cuts and bruises. A week passed in which we saw no one except the mayor of a mountain village some miles away who came to look us over. He came on a day when I was dozing alone in the shade of a huge rock. I knew about ten words of Greek and he knew about three words of English. We had a remarkable colloquy, considering the limitations of language. Seeing that he was half-cracked I felt at ease and, since the Durrells were not there to warn me against such antics, I began to do my own cracked song and dance for him, which was to imitate male and female movie stars, a Chinese mandarin, a bronco, a high diver and such like. He seemed to be vastly amused and for some reason was particularly interested in my Chinese performance. I began to talk Chinese to him, not knowing a word of the language, whereupon to my astonishment he answered me in Chinese, his own Chinese, which was just as good as mine. The next day he brought an interpreter with him for the express purpose of telling me a whopping lie, to wit, that some years ago a Chinese junk had been stranded on this very beach and that some four hundred Chinamen had put up on the beach until their boat was repaired. He said he liked the Chinese very much, that they were a fine people, and that their language was very musical, very intelligent. I asked did he mean *intelligible*, but no, he meant intelligent. The Greek language was intelligent too. And the German language. Then I told him I had been in China, which was another lie, and after describing that country I drifted to Africa and told him about the Pygmies with whom I had also lived for a while. He said they had some Pygmies in a neighboring village. It went on like this from one lie to another for several hours, during which we consumed some wine and olives. Then someone produced a flute and we began to dance, a veritable St. Vitus' dance which went on interminably to finish in the sea where we bit one another like crabs and screamed and bellowed in all the tongues of the earth.

We broke up camp early one morning to return to Kalami. It was a strange sultry day and we had a two hour climb ahead of us to reach the mountain village where Spiro awaited us with the car. There was first of all a stretch of sand to be traversed at a gallop, because even with sandals on the sand scorched one's feet. Then came a long trek through a dried-up river bed which, because of the boulders, was a test for even the stoutest ankles. Finally we came to the path that led up the mountain side, a sort of gully rather than path, which taxed even the mountain ponies on which we had loaded our things. As we climbed a weird melody greeted us from above. Like the heavy mist sweeping up from the sea, it enveloped us in its nostalgic folds and then as suddenly died away. When we had risen another few hundred feet we came upon a clearing in the midst of which was a huge vat filled with a poisonous liquid, an insecticide for the olive trees, which the young women were stirring as they sang. It was a song of death which blended singularly with the mist-laden landscape. Here and there, where the vaporish clouds had rolled apart to reveal a clump of trees or a bare, jagged fang-like snag of rocks, the reverberations of their haunting melody sang out like a choir of brass in an orchestra. Now and then a great blue area of sea rose out of the fog, not at the level of the earth but in some middle realm between heaven and earth, as though after a typhoon. The houses too, when their solidity burst through the mirage, seemed to be suspended in space. The whole atmosphere was ridden with a shuddering Biblical splendor punctuated with the tinkling bells of the ponies, the reverberations of the poison song, the faint boom of the surf far below and an undefinable mountain murmuring which was probably nothing more than the hammering of the temples in the high and sultry haze of an Ionian morning. We took spells of resting at the edge of the precipice, too fascinated by the spectacle to continue on through the pass into the clear, bright work-a-day world of the little mountain village beyond. In that operatic realm, where the Tao Teh King and the ancient Vedas fused dramatically in contrapuntal confusion, the taste of the light Greek cigarette was even more like straw. Here the palate itself became metaphysically attuned: the drama was of the airs, of the upper regions, of the eternal conflict between the soul and the spirit.

Then the pass, which I shall always think of as the carrefour of meaningless butcheries. Here the most frightful, vengeful massacres must have been perpetrated again and again throughout the endless bloody past of man. It is a trap devised by Nature herself for man's undoing. Greece is full of such death-traps. It is like a strong cosmic note which gives the diapason to the intoxicating light world wherein the heroic and mythological figures of the resplendent past threaten continually to dominate the consciousness. The ancient Greek was a murderer: he lived amidst brutal clarities which tormented and maddened the spirit. He was at war with every one, including himself. Out of this fiery anarchy came the lucid, healing metaphysical speculations which even to-day enthrall the world. Going through the pass, which demands a sort of swastika manoeuvering in order to debouch free and clear on the high plateau, I had the impression of wading through phantom seas of blood; the earth was not parched and convulsed in the usual Greek way but bleached and twisted as must have been the mangled, death-stilled limbs of the slain who were left to rot and give their blood here in the merciless sun to the roots of the wild olives which cling to the steep mountain slope with vulturous claws. In this mountain pass there must also have been moments of clear vision when men of distant races stood holding hands and looking into one another's eyes with sympathy and understanding. Here too men of the Pythagorean stripe must have stopped to meditate in silence and solitude, gaining fresh clarity, fresh vision, from the dust-strewn place of carnage. All Greece is diademed with such antinomian spots; it is perhaps the explanation for the fact that Greece has emancipated itself as a country, a nation, a people, in order to continue as the luminous carrefour of a changing humanity.

At Kalami the days rolled by like a song. Now and then I wrote a letter or tried to paint a water color. There was plenty to read in the house but I had no desire to look at a book. Durrell tried to get me to read Shakespeare's Sonnets and, after he had laid siege to me for about a week, I did read one, perhaps the most mysterious sonnet that Shakespeare ever wrote. (I believe it was "The Phoenix and the Turtle.") Soon thereafter I received a copy in the mail of *The Secret Doctrine* and this I fell on with a will. I also reread Nijinsky's Diary. I know I shall read it again and again. There are only a few books which I can read over and over—one is *Mysteries* and another is *The Eternal Husband*. Perhaps I should also add *Alice in Wonderland*. At any rate, it was far better to spend the evening talking and singing, or standing on the rocks at the edge of the water with a telescope studying the stars.

When the Countess again appeared on the scene she persuaded us to spend a few days on her estate in another part of the island. We had three wonderful days together and then in the middle of the night the Greek army was mobilized. War had not yet been declared, but the King's hasty return to Athens was interpreted by every one as an ominous sign. Every one who had the means seemed determined to follow the King's example. The town of Corfu was in a veritable panic. Durrell wanted to enlist in the Greek army for service on the Albanian frontier; Spiro, who was past the age limit, also wanted to offer his services. A few days passed this way in hysterical gesturings and then, quite as if it had been arranged by an impresario, we all found ourselves waiting for the boat to take us to Athens. The boat was to arrive at nine in the morning; we didn't get aboard her until four the next morning. By that time the quay was filled with an indescribable litter of baggage on which the feverish owners sat or sprawled themselves out, pretending to look unconcerned but actually quaking with fear. The most disgraceful scene ensued when the tenders finally hove to. As usual, the rich insisted on going aboard first. Having a first-class passage I found myself among the rich. I was thoroughly disgusted and half minded not to take the boat at all but return quietly to Durrell's house and let things take their course. Then, by some miraculous quirk, I discovered that we weren't to go aboard first, that we were to go last. All the fine luggage was being taken out of the tenders and thrown back on the quay. Bravo! My heart went up. The Countess, who had more luggage than any one, was the very last to go aboard. Later I discovered to my surprise that it was she who had arranged matters thus. It was the inefficiency that had annoyed her, not the question of class or privilege. She hadn't the least fear of the Italians apparently—what she minded was the disorder, the shameful scramble. It was four in the morning, as I say, with a bright moon gleaming on a swollen, angry sea, when we pushed off from the quay in the little caiques. I had never expected to leave Corfu under such conditions. I was a bit angry with myself for having consented to go to Athens. I was more concerned about the interruption of my blissful vacation than about the dangers of the impending war. It was still Summer and I had by no means had enough of sun and sea. I thought of the peasant women and the ragged children who would soon be without food, and the look in their eyes as they waved good-bye to us. It seemed cowardly to be running away like this, leaving the weak and innocent to their doom. Money again. Those who have escape; those who have not are massacred. I found myself praying that the Italians would intercept us, that we would not get off scot free in this shameless way.

When I awoke and went up on deck the boat was gliding through a narrow strait; on either side of us were low barren hills, soft, violet-studded hummocks of earth of such intimate human proportions as to make one weep with joy. The sun was almost at zenith and the glare was dazzlingly intense. I was in precisely that little Greek world whose frontiers I had described in my book a few months before leaving Paris. It was like awakening to find oneself alive in a dream. There was something phenomenal about the luminous immediacy of these two violet-colored shores. We were gliding along in precisely the way that Rousseau *le douanier* has described it in his painting. It was more than a Greek atmosphere— it was poetic and of no time or place actually known to man. The boat itself was the only link with reality. The boat was filled to the gunwales with lost souls desperately clinging to their few earthly possessions. Women in rags, their breasts bared, were vainly trying to nurse their howling brats; they sat on the deck floor in a mess of vomit and blood and the dream through which they were passing never brushed their eye-lids. If we had been torpedoed then and there we would have passed like that, in vomit and blood and confusion, to the dark underworld. At that moment I rejoiced that I was free of possessions, free of all ties, free of fear and envy and malice. I could have passed quietly from one dream to another, owning nothing, regretting nothing, wishing nothing. I was never more certain that life and death are one and that neither can be enjoyed or embraced if the other be absent.

At Patras we decided to go ashore and take the train to Athens. The Hotel Cecil, which we stopped at, is the best hotel I've ever been in, and I've been in a good many. It cost about 23 cents a day for a room the likes of which could not be duplicated in America for less than five dollars. I hope everybody who is passing through Greece will stop off at the Hotel Cecil and see for themselves. It is an event in one's life. . . . We breakfasted towards noon on the terrace of the solarium overlooking the sea. Here a terrible wrangle ensued between Durrell and his wife. I felt quite helpless and could only pity them both from the depths of my heart. It was really a private quarrel in which the war was used as a camouflage. The thought of war drives people frantic, makes them quite cuckoo, even when they are intelligent and far-seeing, as both Durrell and Nancy are. War has another bad effect—it makes young people feel guilty and conscience-stricken. In Corfu I had been studying the antics of a superbly healthy young Englishman, a lad of twenty or so, who had intended to be a Greek scholar. He was running around like a chicken with its head off begging someone to put him in the front line where he could have himself blown to smithereens. Now Durrell was talking the same way, the only difference being that he was not so crazy to be killed as to be with the Greek forces in Albania—because he thought more of the Greeks than he did of his own countrymen. I said as little as possible because if I had attempted to dissuade him I would only have succeeded in abetting his suicidal impulse. I didn't want to see him killed; it seemed to me that the war could very well be fought to its fruitless end without the sacrifice of one destined to give so much to the world. He knew what I thought about war and I think in his heart he agrees with me, but being young, being serviceable, being English despite himself, he was in a quandary. It was a bad place in which to discuss a subject of this sort. The atmosphere was charged with memories of Byron. Sitting there, with Missolonghi so near, it was almost impossible to think sanely about war. The British Consul at Patras was far more clear-headed. After a brief talk with him I felt a renewed respect for the British Empire. I also reminded myself that war hadn't actually been declared yet. It had threatened to break out so often—possibly it wouldn't happen after all.

We had a good meal at the public square and towards the late afternoon we took the automotrice for Athens. During the course of a conversation with some fellow travellers a Greek returning from America hailed me in jovial fashion as a brother American and began a long, irritatingly stupid monologue about the glories of Chicago which I doubt he had ever lived in more than a month. The gist of it was that he was eager to get back home—meaning *America*; he found his countrymen ignorant, dirty, backward, inefficient and so on and so forth. Durrell interrupted once to inquire what language the man was speaking—he had never heard a Greek speaking that kind of American. The men I had been

talking with were eager to know what this strange countryman of
theirs was so excited about. We had been talking in French until
this Yahoo came along. I told them in French that the man was an
ignoramus. At this the Greek asked me what language I was
speaking and when I said French he answered—"I don't know
those languages; American's good enough for me . . . I'm from
Chicago." Though I showed him plainly that I wasn't interested in
listening to his stories he insisted on telling me all about himself.
He said he was now on his way to a little mountain village where
his mother lived; he wanted to say good-bye to her before leaving.
"Show you how ignorant these people are," he added, "I brought
a bath tub for my mother all the way from Chicago; I set it up with
my own hands too. Think they appreciated it? They laughed at
me, said I was crazy. They don't want to keep themselves clean.
Now in Chicago . . ." I apologized to my fellow passengers for the
presence of this idiot; I explained to them that that's what America
does to its adopted sons. At this they all laughed heartily, including
the benighted Greek at my side who hadn't understood a word I
had said since it was in French I made the remark. To cap it all the
dolt asked me where I had learned my English. When I told him I
was born in America he replied that he had never heard any one
speak English like me; he said it in a way to imply that the only
decent English worth speaking was his own slaughter-house variety.

In Athens it was actually chilly enough to wear an overcoat when
we arrived. Athens has a temperamental climate, like New York.
It has plenty of dust, too, if you start walking towards the outskirts.
Even in the heart of the city sometimes, where the most fashionable, ultramodern apartment houses are to be seen, the street is
nothing but a dirt road. One can walk to the edge of the city in a
half hour. It is really an enormous city containing almost a million
inhabitants; it has grown a hundred times over since Byron's day.
The color scheme is blue and white, as it is throughout Greece.
Even the newspapers use blue ink, a bright sky-blue, which makes
the papers seem innocent and juvenile. The Athenians practically
devour the newspapers; they have a perpetual hunger for news.
From the balcony of my room at the Grand Hotel I could look
down on Constitution Square which in the evening is black with
people, thousands of them, seated at little tables loaded with drinks
and ices, the waiters scurrying back and forth with trays to the
cafes adjoining the square.

    Here one evening on his way back to Amaroussion I met
Katsimbalis. It was definitely a meeting. As far as encounters with

men go I have only known two others to compare with it in my whole life—when I met Blaise Cendrars and when I met Lawrence Durrell. I didn't have very much to say that first evening; I listened spellbound, enchanted by every phrase he let drop. I saw that he was made for the monologue, like Cendrars, like Moricand the astrologer. I like the monologue even more than the duet, when it is good. It's like watching a man write a book expressly for you: he writes it, reads it aloud, acts it, revises it, savours it, enjoys it, enjoys your enjoyment of it, and then tears it up and throws it to the winds. It's a sublime performance, because while he's going through with it you are God for him—unless you happen to be an insensitive and impatient dolt. But in that case the kind of monologue I refer to never happens.

He was a curious mixture of things to me on that first occasion; he had the general physique of a bull, the tenacity of a vulture, the agility of a leopard, the tenderness of a lamb, and the coyness of a dove. He had a curious overgrown head which fascinated me and which, for some reason, I took to be singularly Athenian. His hands were rather small for his body, and overly delicate. He was a vital, powerful man, capable of brutal gestures and rough words, yet somehow conveying a sense of warmth which was soft and feminine. There was also a great element of the tragic in him which his adroit mimicry only enhanced. He was extremely sympathetic and at the same time ruthless as a boor. He seemed to be talking about himself all the time, but never egotistically. He talked about himself because he himself was the most interesting person he knew. I liked that quality very much—I have a little of it myself.

We met a few days later to have dinner together—he, his wife Aspasia and the Durrells. After dinner we were to meet some friends of his. From the time he met us he was bubbling over. He was always that way, even on bad days when he complained of headache or dizziness or any of the hundred and one ailments which pestered him. He was taking us to a *taverna* in Piraeus, he said, because he wanted us to enjoy Greek cooking in the Greek way. It was one of his favorite hang-outs in the old days. "I made a mistake to get married," he said—his wife listening and smiling indulgently—"I wasn't cut out for marriage—it's ruining me. I can't sleep, I can't smoke, I can't drink any more. . . . I'm finished." He was always talking about himself as of some one who was done for: it was a little motif which he wove into the monologue by way of warming up to a subject. Things which happened only yesterday fell into this same nostalgic done-for past. Sometimes, when he talked this way, he gave me the impression of being an enormous tortoise which had slipped out of its

shell, a creature which was spending itself in a desperate struggle
to get back into the shell which it had outgrown. In this struggle
he always made himself look grotesque and ridiculous—he did it
deliberately. He would laugh at himself, in the tragic way of the
buffoon. We would all laugh, his wife too. No matter how sad or
morbid or pathetic the story might be he would have us laughing
continuously. He saw the humorous aspect of everything, which is
the real test of the tragic sense.

The food . . . food was something he was passionate about. He
had been enjoying good food since childhood and I guess he will
go on enjoying it until he dies. His father had been a great gourmet
and Katsimbalis, though perhaps lacking some of his father's
sensual refinements and accomplishments, was following the family tradition. Between great carnivorous gulps of food he would
pound his chest like a gorilla before washing it down with a
hogshead of *rezina*. He had drunk a lot of *rezina* in his time: he
said it was good for one, good for the kidneys, good for the liver,
good for the lungs, good for the bowels and for the mind, good for
everything. Everything he took into his system was good, whether
it was poison or ambrosia. He didn't believe in moderation nor
good sense nor anything that was inhibitory. He believed in going
the whole hog and then taking your punishment. There were a lot
of things he couldn't do any more—the war had bunged him up a
bit. But despite the bad arm, the dislocated knee, the damaged
eye, the disorganized liver, the rheumatic twinges, the arthritic
disturbances, the migraine, the dizziness and God knows what,
what was left of the catastrophe was alive and flourishing like a
smoking dung-heap. He could galvanize the dead with his talk. It
was a sort of devouring process: when he described a place he ate
into it, like a goat attacking a carpet. If he described a person he
ate him alive from head to toe. If it were an event he would devour
every detail, like an army of white ants descending upon a forest.
He was everywhere at once, in his talk. He attacked from above
and below, from the front, rear and flanks. If he couldn't dispose
of a thing at once, for lack of a phrase or an image, he would spike
it temporarily and move on, coming back to it later and devouring
it piecemeal. Or like a juggler, he would toss it in the air and, just
when you thought he had forgotten it, that it would fall and break,
he would deftly put an arm behind his back and catch it in his palm
without even turning his eye. It wasn't just talk he handed out, but
language—food and beast language. He always talked against a
landscape, like the protagonist of a lost world. The Attic landscape
was best of all for his purpose: it contains the necessary ingredients
for the dramatic monologue. One has only to see the open air

theatres buried in the hillsides to understand the importance of this setting. Even if his talk carried him to Paris, for example, to a place like the Faubourg Montmartre, he spiced and flavored it with his Attic ingredients, with thyme, sage, tufa, asphodel, honey, red clay, blue roofs, acanthus trimmings, violet light, hot rocks, dry winds, dust, *rezina*, arthritis and the electrical crackle that plays over the low hills like a swift serpent with a broken spine. He was a strange contradiction, even in his talk. With his snake-like tongue which struck like lightning, with fingers moving nervously, as though wandering over an imaginary spinet, with pounding, brutal gestures which somehow never smashed anything but simply raised a din, with all the boom of surf and the roar and sizzle and razzle-dazzle, if you suddenly observed him closely you got the impression that he was sitting there immobile, that only the round falcon's eye was alert, that he was a bird which had been hypnotized, or had hypnotized itself, and that his claws were fastened to the wrist of an invisible giant, a giant like the earth. All this flurry and din, all these kaleidoscopic prestidigitations of his, was only a sort of wizardry which he employed to conceal the fact that he was a prisoner—that was the impression he gave me when I studied him, when I could break the spell for a moment and observe him attentively. But to break the spell required a power and a magic almost equal to his own; it made one feel foolish and impotent, as one always does when one succeeds in destroying the power of illusion. Magic is never destroyed—the most we can do is to cut ourselves off, amputate the mysterious antennae which serve to connect us with forces beyond our power of understanding. Many a time, as Katsimbalis talked, I caught that look on the face of a listener which told me that the invisible wires had been connected, that something was being communicated which was over and above language, over and above personality, something magical which we recognize in dream and which makes the face of the sleeper relax and expand with a bloom such as we rarely see in waking life. Often when meditating on this quality of his I thought of his frequent allusions to the incomparable honey which is stored by the bees on the slopes of his beloved Hymettos. Over and over he would try to explain the reasons why this honey from Mount Hymettos was unique. Nobody can explain it satisfactorily. Nobody can explain anything which is unique. One can describe, worship and adore. And that is all I can do with Katsimbalis' talk.

It was later, after I had returned to Corfu and had had a good taste of solitude, that I appreciated the Katsimbalistic monologue even more. Lying nude in the sun on a ledge of rock by the sea I would often close my eyes and try to re-weave the pattern of his talks. It was then that I made the discovery that his talk created reverberations, that the echo took a long time to reach one's ears. I began to compare it with French talk in which I had been enveloped for so long. The latter seemed more like the play of light on an alabaster vase, something reflective, nimble, dancing, liquid, evanescent, whereas the other, the Katsimbalistic language, was opaque, cloudy, pregnant with resonances which could only be understood long afterwards when the reverberations announced the collision with thoughts, people, objects located in distant parts of the earth. The Frenchman puts walls about his talk, as he does about his garden: he puts limits about everything in order to feel at home. At bottom he lacks confidence in his fellow-man; he is skeptical because he doesn't believe in the innate goodness of human beings. He has become a realist because it is safe and practical. The Greek, on the other hand, is an adventurer: he is reckless and adaptable, he makes friends easily. The walls which you see in Greece, when they are not of Turkish or Venetian origin, go back to the Cyclopean age. Of my own experience I would say that there is no more direct, approachable, easy man to deal with than the Greek. He becomes a friend immediately: he goes out to you. With the Frenchman friendship is a long and laborious process: it may take a lifetime to make a friend of him. He is best in acquaintanceship where there is little to risk and where there are no aftermaths. The very word *ami* contains almost nothing of the flavor of friend, as we feel it in English. *C'est mon ami* can not be translated by "this is my friend." There is no counterpart to this English phrase in the French language. It is a gap which has never been filled, like the word "home." These things affect conversation. One can converse all right, but it is difficult to have a heart to heart talk. All France, it has often been said, is a garden, and if you love France, as I do, it can be a very beautiful garden. For myself I found it healing and soothing to the spirit; I recovered from the shocks and bruises which I had received in my own country. But there comes a day, when you are well again and strong, when this atmosphere ceases to be nourishing. You long to break out and test your powers. Then the French spirit seems inadequate. You long to make friends, to create enemies, to look beyond walls and cultivated patches of earth. You want to cease thinking in terms of life insurance, sick benefits, old age pensions and so on.

After the succulent repast at the *taverna* in Piraeus, all of us a bit stinko from the *rezina*, we moved back to the big square in Athens. It was midnight or a little after and the square still crowded with people. Katsimbalis seemed to divine the spot where his friends were seated. We were introduced to his bosom comrades, George Seferiades and Captain Antoniou of the good ship "Acropolis." They soon began plying me with questions about America and American writers. Like most educated Europeans they knew more about American literature than I ever will. Antoniou had been to America several times, had walked about the streets of New York, Boston, New Orleans, San Francisco and other ports. The thought of him walking about the streets of our big cities in bewilderment led me to broach the name of Sherwood Anderson whom I always think of as the one American writer of our time who has walked the streets of our American cities as a genuine poet. Since they scarcely knew his name, and since the conversation was already veering towards more familiar ground, namely Edgar Allan Poe, a subject I am weary of listening to, I suddenly bcame obsessed with the idea of selling them Sherwood Anderson. I began a monologue myself for a change—about writers who walk the streets in America and are not recognized until they are ready for the grave. I was so enthusiastic about the subject that I actually identified myself with Sherwood Anderson. He would probably have been astounded had he heard of the exploits I was crediting him with. I've always had a particular weakness for the author of "Many Marriages." In my worst days in America he was the man who comforted me, by his writings. It was only the other day that I met him for the first time. I found no discrepancy between the man and the writer. I saw in him the born story teller, the man who can make even the egg triumphant.

As I say, I went on talking about Sherwood Anderson like a blue streak. It was to Captain Antoniou that I chiefly addressed myself. I remember the look he gave me when I had finished, the look which said: "Sold. Wrap them up, I'll take the whole set." Many times since I've enjoyed the pleasure of rereading Sherwood Anderson through Antoniou's eyes. Antoniou is constantly sailing from one island to another, writing his poems as he walks about strange cities at night. Once, a few months later, I met him for a few minutes one evening in the strange port of Herakleion in Crete. He was still thinking about Sherwood Anderson, though his talk was of cargoes and weather reports and water supplies. Once out to sea I could picture him going up to his cabin and, taking a little book from the rack, bury himself in the mysterious night of a nameless Ohio town. The night always made me a little envious of him, envious of his peace and solitude at sea. I envied him the islands he was always stopping off at and the lonely walks through silent villages whose names mean nothing to us. To be a pilot was

the first ambition I had ever voiced. I liked the idea of being alone
in the little house above the deck, steering the ship over its perilous
course. To be aware of the weather, to be in it, battling with it,
meant everything to me. In Antoniou's countenance there were
always traces of the weather. And in Sherwood Anderson's writing
there are always traces of the weather. I like men who have the
weather in their blood. . . .

We separated in the early hours of the morning. I went back to
the hotel, opened the window and stood for a while on the balcony
looking down on the square which was now deserted. I had made
two more stalwart Greek friends and I was happy about it. I began
to think of all the friends I had made in the short time that I was
there. I thought of Spiro, the taxi-driver, and of Karemenaios, the
gendarme. There was also Max, the refugee, living like a duke at
the King George Hotel; he seemed to have nothing on his mind but
how to make his friends happy with the drachmas which he
couldn't take out of the country. There was also the proprietor of
my hotel who, unlike any French hotel keeper I have ever met,
used to say to me at intervals—"do you need any money?" If I
told him I was taking a little trip he would say: "Be sure to wire
me if you need any money." Spiro was the same way. When we
said good-bye at the dock the night of the general panic, his last
words were—"Mr. Henry, if you come back to Corfu I want you
to stay with me. I don't want any money, Mr. Henry—I want you
to come and live with us as long as you like." Everywhere I went
in Greece it was the same tune. Even at the prefecture, while
waiting to have my papers put in order, the gendarmé would send
out for a coffee and cigarettes to put me at ease. I liked the way
they begged too. They weren't shamefaced about it. They would
hold you up openly and ask for money or cigarettes as if they were
entitled to it. It's a good sign when people beg that way: it means
that they know how to give. The French, for example, know
neither how to give nor how to ask for favors—either way they feel
uneasy. They make a virtue of not molesting you. It's the wall
again. A Greek has no walls around him: he gives and takes
without stint.

The English in Greece—a sorry lot, by the way—seem to have a
poor opinion of the Greek character. The English are torpid,
unimaginative, lacking in resiliency. They seem to think that the
Greeks should be eternally grateful to them because they have a
powerful fleet. The Englishman in Greece is a farce and an eye-
sore: he isn't worth the dirt between a poor Greek's toes. For
centuries the Greeks have had the cruelest enemy a people could
have—the Turks. After centuries of enslavement they threw off the

yoke and, had the big Powers not interfered, they would probably have driven the Turks into the ground and annihilated them. Today the two peoples, after an exchange of populations which is nothing if not extraordinary, are friends. They respect one another. And yet the English, who would have disappeared from the face of the earth had they been subjected to the same treatment, pretend to look down on the Greeks.

Everywhere you go in Greece the atmosphere is pregnant with heroic deeds. I am speaking of modern Greece, not ancient Greece. And the women, when you look into the history of this little country, were just as heroic as the men. In fact, I have even a greater respect for the Greek woman than for the Greek man. The Greek woman and the Greek Orthodox priest—*they* sustained the fighting spirit. For stubbornness, courage, recklessness, daring, there are no greater examples anywhere. No wonder Durrell wanted to fight with the Greeks. Who wouldn't prefer to fight beside a Bouboulina, for example, than with a gang of sickly, effeminate recruits from Oxford or Cambridge?

I made no English friends in Greece. I felt apologetic towards the Greeks whenever I was found in their company. The friends I made in Greece were Greek and I am proud of them, honored that they consider me a friend. I hope that the few Englishmen I knew in Greece will realize, when they read these lines, what I thought of their behavior. I hope they will consider me an enemy of their kind.

I'd rather talk about something more interesting—about Katsimbalis, for instance, about the visit to his home in Amaroussion one day towards twilight. Another marvellous day, another red letter day in my life! We had been asked to come early in order to watch the sunset. Stephanides had made a translation of some Greek poems—we were going to hear them in English. When we arrived Katsimbalis hadn't quite finished his nap. He was rather ashamed of being caught napping because he was always bragging about how little sleep he required. He came downstairs looking a bit foggy and pasty. He was talking as if to himself, making little futile gestures with his hands as if to get the damned spinet working. He was mumbling something about a word which he had remembered in his dream a few moments ago. He was always rummaging about in his brain for adequate English words and phrases to express some remarkable Greek image which he had just stumbled on in a book. Anyway, as I say, we had roused him from a sound sleep and he was moving about in a drugged way, muttering and gesturing like a man trying to shake off the cob-webs which still enveloped him. His talk began on the fringe of this dream which he had not wholly shaken clear of. To begin you begin anywhere, and since he had just been dreaming he talked dream. The dream was unimportant, forgotten in a moment, but the remembrance of the dream led him back to the word which had been bothering him, which he had been tracking down for days, so he said, and which was now becoming clearer as he himself became clearer, as the cob-webs fell away. The word, whatever it was, led to language and language led to honey and honey was good for one, as were other things, *rezina* for example, especially *rezina*, good for the lungs, good for the liver, good for anything that ailed you, especially too much of it, which one should not do, not take too much of it, but which he did anyway regardless of the doctor's orders, particularly if it were a good *rezina* such as the one we had the other night at the *taverna* in Piraeus. The young lamb was good too, had we noticed? He made the gesture of licking his fingers, wiped his mouth with the back of his hand, sniffed the air as though to breathe again the aromatic smoke from the oven. He paused a moment and looked about him, as if searching for something with which to wet his tongue before going into the monologue full tilt. Nobody said anything. Nobody dared to interrupt now just as he was getting into his stride. The poems were lying on the table; Seferiades was expected any moment and the captain with him. I could feel that he was growing a bit frantic inwardly, that he was making a rapid calculation to see if there were time enough to get it off his chest before his friends arrived. He was fluttering a bit, like a bird whose wing is caught. He kept on mumbling and muttering, just to keep the engine going until he had decided on his direction. And then somehow, without being aware of the transition, we were standing on the aerial verandah overlooking the low hills, on one of which there was a lone windmill, and Katsimbalis was in full flight, a spread eagle performance about the clear atmosphere and the blue-violet hues that descend with the twilight, about ascending and descending varieties of monotony, about individualistic herbs and trees, about exotic fruits and inland voyages, about thyme and honey and the sap of the arbutus which makes one drunk, about islanders and highlanders, about the men of the Peloponnesus, about the crazy Russian woman who got moonstruck one night and threw off her clothes, how she danced about in the moonlight without a stitch on while her lover ran to get a strait-jacket. As he talked I was taking in for the first time with my own eyes the true splendor of the Attic landscape, observing with a growing exhilaration that here and there over the bare brown sward, amidst anomalous and eccentric growths, men and women, single, solitary figures, were strolling about in the clear fading light, and for some reason they appeared to me as being very Greek, walking as no other people walk, making clear-cut patterns in their ethereal meandering, patterns such as I had seen earlier in the day on the vases in the museum. There are so many ways of walking about and the best, in my opinion, is the Greek way, because it is aimless, anarchic, thoroughly and discordantly human. And this walking about on the brown sward amidst the eccentric, inelegant trees, the thick foliage flying like hair stiff-brushed in the well of the distant mountains, blended strangely with the Katsimbalistic monologue which I heard, digested and silently communicated to the Asiatic loungers below who were fading softly now in the dimming light. . . . On the high verandah in Amaroussion, just as the light from the other worlds began to shed its brilliance, I caught the old and the new Greece in their soft translucence and thus they remain in my memory. I realized at that moment that there is no old or new, only Greece, a world conceived and created in perpetuity. The man who was talking had ceased to be of human size or proportions but had become a Colossus whose silhouette swooned backwards and forwards with the deep droning rhythm of his drug-laden phrases. He went on and on and on, unhurried, unruffled, inexhaustible, inextinguishable, a voice that had taken form and shape and substance, a figure that had outgrown its human frame, a silhouette whose reverberations rumbled in the depths of the distant mountain sides.

After about ten days of it in Athens I had a longing to return to Corfu. The war had begun, but since the Italians had announced their intention of remaining neutral I saw no reason why I should not return and make the most of the remaining days of Summer. When I arrived I found the Greeks still mobilized on the Albanian frontier. I had to get a pass from the police every time I went in or out of the town. Karamenaios was still patrolling the beach from his little reed hut at the edge of the water. Nicola would soon be returning to the village up in the mountains to open school. A wonderful period of solitude set in. I had nothing but time on my hands. Spiro sent his son Lillis out to give me some Greek lessons. Then Lillis went back to town and I was left alone. It was the first time in my life that I was truly alone. It was an experience which I enjoyed deeply. Towards evening I would stop by Nicola's house to chat with him a few minutes and hear about the war. After dinner Karamenaios would drop in. We had about fifty words with which to make lingual currency. We didn't even need that many, as I soon discovered. There are a thousand ways of talking and words don't help if the spirit is absent. Karamenaios and I were eager to talk. It made little difference to me whether we talked about the war or about knives and forks. Sometimes we discovered that a word or phrase which we had been using for days, he in English or I in Greek, meant something entirely different than we had thought it to mean. It made no difference. We understood one another even with the wrong words. I could learn five new words in an evening and forget six or eight during my sleep. The important thing was the warm handclasp, the light in the eyes, the grapes which we devoured in common, the glass we raised to our lips in sign of friendship. Now and then I would get excited and, using a melange of English, Greek, German, French, Choctaw, Eskimo, Swahili or any other tongue I felt would serve the purpose, using the chair, the table, the spoon, the lamp, the bread knife, I would enact for him a fragment of my life in New York, Paris, London, Chula Vista, Canarsie, Hackensack or in some place I had never been or some place I had been in a dream or when lying asleep on the operating table. Sometimes I felt so good, so versatile and acrobatic, that I would stand on the table and sing in some unknown language or hop from the table to the commode and from the commode to the staircase or swing from the rafters, anything to entertain him, keep him amused, make him roll from side to side with laughter. I was considered an old man in the village because of my bald pate and fringe of white hair. Nobody had ever seen an old man cut up the way I did. "The old man is going for a swim," they would say. "The old man is taking the boat out." Always "the old man." If a storm came up and they knew I was out in the middle of the pond they would send some one out to see that "the old man" got in safely. If I decided to take a jaunt through the hills Karamenaios would offer to accompany me so that no harm would come to me. If I got stranded somewhere I had only to announce that I was an American and at once a dozen hands were ready to help me. I would set out in the morning and look for new coves and inlets in which to swim. There was never a soul about. I was like Robinson Crusoe on the island of Tobago. For hours at a stretch I would lie in the sun doing nothing, thinking of nothing. To keep the mind empty is a feat, a very healthful feat too. To be silent the whole day long, see no newspaper, hear no radio, listen to no gossip, be thoroughly and completely lazy, thoroughly and completely indifferent to the fate of the world is the finest medicine a man can give himself. The book-learning gradually dribbles away; problems melt and dissolve; ties are gently severed; thinking, when you deign to indulge in it, becomes very primitive; the body becomes a new and wonderful instrument;

you look at plants or stones or fish with different eyes; you wonder what people are struggling to accomplish by their frenzied activities; you know there is a war on but you haven't the faintest idea what it's about or why people should enjoy killing one another; you look at a place like Albania—it was constantly staring me in the eyes—and you say to yourself, yesterday it was Greek, to-day it's Italian, to-morrow it may be German or Japanese, and you let it be anything it chooses to be. When you're right with yourself it doesn't matter what flag is flying over your head or who owns what or whether you speak English or Monongahela. The absence of newspapers, the absence of news about what men are doing in different parts of the world to make life more livable or unlivable is the greatest single boon. If we could just eliminate newspapers a great advance would be made, I am sure of it. Newspapers engender lies, hatred, greed, envy, suspicion, fear, malice. We don't need the truth as it is dished up to us in the daily papers. We need peace and solitude and idleness. If we could all go on strike and honestly disavow all interest in what our neighbor is doing we might get a new lease of life. We might learn to do without telephones and radios and newspapers, without machines of any kind, without factories, without mills, without mines, without explosives, without battleships, without politicians, without lawyers, without canned goods, without gadgets, without razor blades even or cellophane or cigarettes or money. This is a pipe dream, I know. People only go on strike for better working conditions, better wages, better opportunities to become something other than they are.

As the Fall came on the rains set in. It was almost impossible to climb up the steep goat path back of the house which led to the highway. After a severe storm there would be wash-outs and all the roads would be blocked by the debris of rocks and trees caused by the landslides. I was marooned for days on end. One day Nancy arrived unexpectedly to get some household belongings. She was returning to Athens by the same boat, that very afternoon. I decided impulsively to return with her.

It was dry in Athens, and unexpectedly hot. It was as though we were going back to Summer again. Now and then the wind blew down from the encircling mountains and then it was as chill as a knife blade. Mornings I would often walk to the Acropolis. I like the base of the Acropolis better than the Acropolis itself. I like the tumbledown shacks, the confusion, the erosion, the anarchic character of the landscape. The archaeologists have ruined the place; they have laid waste big tracts of land in order to uncover a mess of ancient relics which will be hidden away in museums. The whole base of the Acropolis resembles more and more a volcanic crater in which the loving hands of the archaeologists have laid out cemeteries of art. The tourist comes and looks down at these ruins, these scientifically created lava beds, with a moist eye. The live Greek walks about unnoticed or else is regarded as an interloper. Meanwhile the new city of Athens covers almost the entire valley, is groping its way up the flanks of the surrounding mountains. For a country of only seven million inhabitants it is something of a phenomenon, the city of Athens. It is still in the throes of birth: it is awkward, confused, clumsy, unsure of itself; it has all the diseases of childhood and some of the melancholy and desolation of adolescence. But it has chosen a magnificent site in which to rear itself; in the sunlight it gleams like a jewel; at night it sparkles with a million twinkling lights which seem to be switching on and off with lightning-like speed. It is a city of startling atmospheric effects: it has not dug itself into the earth—it floats in a constantly changing light, beats with a chromatic rhythm. One is impelled to keep walking, to move on towards the mirage which is ever retreating. When one comes to the edge, to the great wall of mountains, the light becomes even more intoxicating; one feels as if he could bound up the side of the mountain in a few giant strides, and then—why then, if one did get to the top, one would race like mad along the smooth spine and jump clear into the sky, one clear headlong flight into the blue and Amen forever. Along the Sacred Way, from Daphni to the sea, I was on the point of madness several times. I actually did start running up the hillside only to stop midway, terror-stricken, wondering what had taken possession of me. On one side are stones and shrubs which stand out with microscopic clarity; on the other are trees such as one sees in Japanese prints, trees flooded with light, intoxicated, coryphantic trees which must have been planted by the gods in moments of drunken exaltation. One should not race along the Sacred Way in a motor car—it is sacrilege. One should walk, walk as the men of old walked, and allow one's whole being to become flooded with light. This is not a Christian highway: it was made by the feet of devout pagans on their way to initiation at Eleusis. There is no suffering, no martyrdom, no flagellation of the flesh connected with this processional artery. Everything here speaks now, as it did centuries ago, of illumination, of blinding, joyous illumination. Light acquires a transcendental quality: it is not the light of the Mediterranean alone, it is something more, something unfathomable, something holy. Here the light penetrates directly to the soul, opens the doors and windows of the heart, makes one naked, exposed, isolated in a metaphysical bliss which makes everything clear without being known. No analysis can go on in this light: here the neurotic is either instantly healed or goes mad. The rocks themselves are quite mad: they have been lying for centuries exposed to this divine illumination: they lie very still and quiet, nestling amid dancing colored shrubs in a blood-stained soil, but they are mad, I say, and to touch them is to risk losing one's grip on everything which once seemed firm, solid and unshakeable. One must glide through this gully with extreme caution, naked, alone, and devoid of all Christian humbug. One must throw off two thousand years of ignorance and superstition, of morbid, sickly subterranean living and lying. One must come to Eleusis stripped of the barnacles which have accumulated from centuries of lying in stagnant waters. At Eleusis one realizes, if never before, that there is no salvation in becoming adapted to a world which is crazy. At Eleusis one becomes adapted to the cosmos. Outwardly Eleusis may seem broken, disintegrated with the crumbled past; actually Eleusis is still intact and it is we who are broken, dispersed, crumbling to dust. Eleusis lives, lives eternally in the midst of a dying world.

The man who has caught this spirit of eternality which is everywhere in Greece and who has embedded it in his poems is George Seferiades, whose pen name is Seferis. I know his work only from translation, but even if I had never read his poetry I would say this is the man who is destined to transmit the flame. Seferiades is more Asiatic than any of the Greeks I met; he is from Smyrna originally but has lived abroad for many years. He is languorous, suave, vital and capable of surprising feats of strength and agility. He is the arbiter and reconciler of conflicting schools of thought and ways of life. He asks innumerable questions in a polyglot language; he is interested in all forms of cultural expression and seeks to abstract and assimilate what is genuine and fecundating in all epochs. He is passionate about his own country, his own people, not in a hidebound chauvinistic way but as a result of patient discovery following upon years of absence abroad. This passion for one's country is a special peculiarity of the intellectual Greek who has lived abroad. In other peoples I have found it distasteful, but in the Greek I find it justifiable, and not only justifiable, but thrilling, inspiring. I remember going with Seferiades one afternoon to look at a piece of land on which he thought he might build himself a bungalow. There was nothing extraordinary about the place—it was even a bit shabby and forlorn, I might say. Or rather it *was*, at first sight. I never had a chance to consolidate my first fleeting impression; it changed right under my eyes as he led me about like an electrified jelly-fish from spot to spot, rhapsodizing on herbs, flowers, shrubs, rocks, clay, slopes, declivities, coves, inlets and so on. Everything he looked at was Greek in a way that he had never known before leaving his country. He could look at a headland and read into it the history of the Medes, the Persians, the Dorians, the Minoans, the Atlanteans. He could also read into it some fragments of the poem which he would write in his head on the way home while plying me with questions about the New World. He was attracted by the Sibylline character of everything which met his eye. He had a way of looking forwards and backwards, of making the object of his contemplation revolve and show forth its multiple aspects. When he talked about a thing or a person or an experience he caressed it with his tongue. Sometimes he gave me the impression of being a wild boar which had broken its tusks in furious onslaughts born of love and ecstasy. In his voice there was a bruised quality as if the object of his love, his beloved Greece, had awkwardly and unwittingly mangled the shrill notes of ululation. The mellifluous Asiatic warbler had more than once been floored by an unexpected thunderbolt; his poems were becoming more and more gem-like, more compact, compressed, scintillating and revelatory. His native flexibility was responding to the cosmic laws of curvature and finitude. He had ceased going out in all directions: his lines were making the encircling movement of embrace. He had begun to ripen into the universal poet—by passionately rooting himself into the soil of his people. Wherever there is life to-day in Greek art it is based on this Antaean gesture, this passion which transmits itself from heart to feet, creating strong roots which transform the body into a tree of potent beauty. This cultural transmutation is also evidenced in a physical way by the vast work of reclamation which is going on throughout the country. The Turks, in their fervid desire to desolate Greece, converted the land into a desert and a graveyard; since their emancipation the Greeks have been struggling to reforest the land. The goat has now become the national enemy. He will be dislodged as the Turk was dislodged, in time. He is the symbol of poverty and helplessness. *Trees, more trees,* that is the cry. The tree brings water, fodder, cattle, produce; the tree brings shade, leisure, song, brings poets, painters, legislators, visionaries. Greece is now, bare and lean as a wolf though she be, the only Paradise in Europe. What a place it will be when it is restored to its pristine verdure exceeds the imagination of man today. Anything may happen when this focal spot blazes forth with new life. A revivified Greece can very conceivably alter the whole destiny of Europe. Greece does not need archaeologists—she needs arboriculturists. A verdant Greece may give hope to a world now eaten away by white-heart rot.

My talks with Seferiades really began on the high verandah at Amaroussion when, taking me by the arm, he walked me back and forth in the gathering dusk. Every time I met him he came to me with his whole being, wrapping it around my arm with warmth and tenderness. If I visited him at his chambers it was the same thing: he would open all the doors and windows leading to his heart. Usually he would put on his hat and accompany me to my hotel; it was not just a polite gesture, it was an act of friendship, a demonstration of an enduring love. I shall remember Seferiades and all my Greek friends for this quality which is now so rare among men. I shall remember his sister Jeanne too, and other Greek women whom I met, because of their queenliness. It is a quality we scarcely ever meet with in the modern woman. Like the warm friendliness of the men this quality which all Greek women share to a greater or less degree is the counterpart, or shall I say the corresponding human virtue, which goes with the supernal light. One would have to be a toad, a snail, or a slug not to be affected by this radiance which emanates from the human heart as well as from the heavens. Wherever you go in Greece the people open up like flowers. Cynical-minded people will say that it is because Greece is a small country, because they are eager to have visitors, and so on. I don't believe it. I have been in a few small countries which left quite the opposite impression upon me. And as I said once before, Greece is *not* a small country—it is impressively vast. No country I have visited has given me such a sense of grandeur. Size is not created by mileage always. In a way which it is beyond the comprehension of my fellow countrymen to grasp Greece is infinitely larger than the United States. Greece could swallow both the United States and Europe. Greece is a little like China or India. It is a world of illusion. And the Greek himself is everywhere, like the Chinaman again. What is Greek in him does not rub off with his ceaseless voyaging. He does not leave little particles of himself distributed all over the lot, as the American does, for example. When the Greek leaves a place he leaves a hole. The American leaves behind him a litter of junk—shoe laces, collar buttons, razor blades, petroleum tins, vaseline jars and so on. The Chinese coolies, as I also said somewhere before, actually feed on the garbage which the Americans throw overboard when they are in port. The poor Greek walks around in the remnants dropped by rich visitors from all parts of the world; he is a true internationalist, disdaining nothing which is made by human hands, not even the leaky tubs discarded by the British mercantile marine. To try to instill in him a sense of national pride, to ask him to become chauvinistic about national industries, fisheries and so forth seems to be a piece of absurdity. What difference does it make to a man whose heart is filled with light whose clothes he is wearing or whether these clothes be of the latest model or pre-war in design? I have seen Greeks walking about in the most ludicrous and abominable garb imaginable—straw hat from the year 1900, billiard cloth vest with pearl buttons, discarded British ulster, pale dungarees, busted umbrella, hair shirt, bare feet, hair matted and twisted—a make-up which even a Kaffir would disdain, and yet, I say it sincerely and deliberately, I would a thousand times rather be that poor Greek than an American millionaire. I remember the old keeper of the ancient fortress at Nauplia. He had done twenty years in that same prison for murder. He was one of the most aristocratic beings I ever met. His face was positively radiant. The pittance on which he was trying to live would not keep a dog, his clothes were in tatters, his prospects were nil. He showed us a tiny patch of earth he had cleared near the rampart where he hoped next year to grow a few stalks of corn. If the government would give him about three cents more a day he would just about be able to pull through. He begged us, if we had any influence, to speak to one of the officials for him. He wasn't bitter, he wasn't melancholy, he wasn't morbid. He had killed a man in anger and he had done twenty years for it; he would do it again, he said, if the same situation arose. He had no remorse, no guilt. He was a marvellous old fellow, stout as an oak, gay, hearty, insouciant. Just three cents more a day and everything would be jake. That was all that was on his mind. I envy him. If I had my choice between being the president of a rubber tire company in America or the prison keeper of the old fortress at Nauplia I would prefer to be the prison keeper, even without the additional three cents. I would take the twenty years in jail too, as part of the bargain. I would prefer to be a murderer with a clear conscience, walking about in tatters and waiting for next year's crop of corn, than the president of the most successful industrial corporation in America. No business magnate ever wore such a benign and radiant expression as this miserable Greek. Of course there is this to remember—the Greek only killed one man, and that in righteous anger, whereas the successful American business man is murdering thousands of innocent men, women and children in his sleep every day of his life. Here nobody can have a clear conscience: we are all part of a vast interlocking murdering machine. There a murderer can look noble and saintly, even though he live like a dog.

Nauplia. . . . Nauplia is a sea port directly south of Corinth on a peninsula where are located Tiryns and Epidaurus. You can look across the water and see Argos. Above Argos, going north towards Corinth, lies Mycenae. Draw a ring about these places and you mark off one of the most hoary, legendary areas in Greece. I had touched the Peleponnesus before, at Patras, but this is the other side, the magical side. How I got to Nauplia is a long story. I must go back a bit. . . .

I am in Athens. Winter is coming on. People are asking me—have you been to Delphi, have you been to San Turini, have you been to Lesbos or Samos or Poros? I have been practically nowhere, except back and forth to Corfu. One day I had been as far as Mandra, which is past Eleusis on the way to Megara. Fortunately the road was blocked and we had to turn back. I say fortunately because on that day, if we had gone another few miles, I would have lost my head completely. In another way I was doing a great deal of traveling; people came to me at the cafes and poured out their journeys to me; the captain was always returning from a new trajectory; Seferiades was always writing a new poem which went back deep into the past and forward as far as the seventh root race; Katsimbalis would take me on his monologues to Mt. Athos, to Pelion and Ossa, to Leonidion and Monemvasia; Durrell would set my mind whirling with Pythagorean adventures; a little Welshman, just back from Persia, would drag me over the high plateaus and deposit me in Samarkand where I would meet the headless horseman called Death. All the Englishmen I met were always coming back from somewhere, some island, some monastery, some ancient ruin, some place of mystery. I was so bewildered by all the opportunities lying before me that I was paralyzed.

Then one day Seferiades and Katsimbalis introduced me to the painter Ghika. I saw a new Greece, the quintessential Greece which the artist had abstracted from the muck and confusion of time, of place, of history. I got a bi-focal slant on this world which was now making me giddy with names, dates, legends. Ghika has placed himself in the center of all time, in that self-perpetuating Greece which has no borders, no limits, no age. Ghika's canvases are as fresh and clean, as pure and naked of all pretense, as the sea and light which bathes the dazzling island. Ghika is a seeker after light and truth: his paintings go beyond the Greek world. It was Ghika's painting which roused me from my bedazzled stupor. A week or so later we all boarded the boat at Piraeus to go to Hydra where Ghika had his ancestral home. Seferiades and Katsimbalis were jubilant: they had not had a holiday in ages. It was late Fall, which means that the weather was beautifully mild. Towards noon we came within sight of the island of Poros. We had been having a bite on deck—one of those impromptu meals which Katsimbalis loves to put away at any hour of the day or night, when he is in good fettle. I suppose I'll never again experience the warmth of affection which surrounded me that morning as we embarked on our journey. Everybody was talking at once, the wine was flowing, the food was being replenished, the sun which had been veiled came out strong, the boat was rocking gently, the war was on but forgotten, the sea was there but the shore too, the goats were clambering about, the lemon groves were in sight and the madness which is in their fragrance had already seized us and drawn us tightly together in a frenzy of self-surrender.

I don't know which affected me more deeply—the story of the lemon groves just opposite us or the sight of Poros itself when suddenly I realized that we were sailing through the streets. If there is one dream which I like above all others it is that of sailing on land. Coming into Poros gives the illusion of the deep dream. Suddenly the land converges on all sides and the boat is squeezed into an arrow strait from which there seems to be no egress. The men and women of Poros are hanging out of the windows, just above your head. You pull in right under their friendly nostrils, as though for a shave and hair cut en route. The loungers on the quay are walking with the same speed as the boat; they can walk faster than the boat if they choose to quicken their pace. The island revolves in cubistic planes, one of walls and windows, one of rocks and goats, one of stiff-blown trees and shrubs, and so on. Yonder, where the mainland curves like a whip, lie the wild lemon groves and there in the Spring young and old go mad from the fragrance of sap and blossom. You enter the harbor of Poros swaying and swirling, a gentle idiot tossed about amidst masts and nets in a world which only the painter knows and which he has made live again because like you, when he first saw this world, he was drunk and happy and care-free. To sail slowly through the streets of Poros is to recapture the joy of passing through the neck of the womb. It is a joy too deep almost to be remembered. It is a kind of numb idiot's delight which produces legends such as that of the birth of an island out of a foundering ship. The ship, the passage, the revolving walls, the gentle undulating tremor under the belly of the boat, the dazzling light, the green snake-like curve of the shore, the beards hanging down over your scalp from the inhabitants suspended above you, all these and the palpitant breath of friendship, sympathy, guidance, envelop and entrance you until you are blown out like a star fulfilled and your heart with its molten smithereens scattered far and wide. It is now, as I write this, just about the same time of day some few months later. The clock and the calendar say so, at any rate. In point of truth it is aeons since I passed through that narrow strait. It will never happen again. Ordinarily I would be sad at the thought, but I am not now. There is every reason to be sad at this moment: all the premonitions which I have had for ten years are coming true. This is one of the lowest moments in the history of the human race. There is no sign of hope on the horizon. The whole world is involved in slaughter and bloodshed. I repeat—*I am not sad*. Let the world have its bath of blood—I will cling to Poros. Millions of years may pass and I may come back again and again on one planet or another, as human, as devil, as archangel (I care not how, which, what or when), but my feet will never leave that boat, my eyes will never close on that scene, my friends will never disappear. That was a moment which endures, which survives world wars, which outlasts the life of the planet Earth itself. If I should ever attain the fulfillment which the Buddhists speak of, if I should ever have the choice of attaining Nirvana or remaining behind to watch over and guide those to come, I say now let me remain behind, let me hover as a gentle spirit above the roofs of Poros and look down upon the voyager with a smile of peace and good cheer. I can see the whole human race straining through the neck of the bottle here, searching for egress into the world of light and beauty. May they come, may they disembark, may they stay and rest awhile in peace. And on a glad day let them push on, let them cross the narrow strait, on, on, a few more miles—to Epidaurus, the very seat of tranquillity, the world center of the healing art.

Some days intervened before I saw with my own eyes the still, healing splendor of Epidaurus. During that interval I almost lost my life, but of that I will speak in a moment. Our destination was Hydra where Ghika and his wife awaited us. Hydra is almost a bare rock of an island and its population, made up almost exclusively of seamen, is rapidly dwindling. The town, which clusters about the harbor in the form of an amphitheatre, is immaculate. There are only two colors, blue and white, and the white is whitewashed every day, down to the cobblestones in the street. The houses are even more cubistically arranged than at Poros. Aesthetically it is perfect, the very epitome of that flawless anarchy which supersedes, because it includes and goes beyond, all the formal arrangements of the imagination. This purity, this wild and naked perfection of Hydra, is in great part due to the spirit of the men who once dominated the island. For centuries the men of Hydra were bold, buccaneering spirits: the island produced nothing but heroes and emancipators. The least of them was an admiral at heart, if not in fact. To recount the exploits of the men of Hydra would be to write a book about a race of madmen; it would mean writing the word DARING across the firmament in letters of fire.

Hydra is a rock which rises out of the sea like a huge loaf of petrified bread. It is the bread turned to stone which the artist receives as reward for his labors when he first catches sight of the promised land. After the uterine illumination comes the ordeal of rock out of which must be born the spark which is to fire the world. I speak in broad, swift images because to move from place to place in Greece is to become aware of the stirring, fateful drama of the race as it circles from paradise to paradise. Each halt is a stepping stone along a path marked out by the gods. They are stations of rest, of prayer, of meditation, of deed, of sacrifice, of transfiguration. At no point along the way is it marked FINIS. The very rocks, and nowhere on earth has God been so lavish with them as in Greece, are symbols of life eternal. In Greece the rocks are eloquent: men may go dead but the rocks never. At a place like Hydra, for example, one knows that when a man dies he becomes part of his native rock. But this rock is a living rock, a divine wave of energy suspended in time and space, creating a pause of long or short duration in the endless melody. Hydra was entered as a pause in the musical score of creation by an expert calligrapher. It is one of those divine pauses which permit the musician, when he resumes the melody, to go forth again in a totally new direction. At this point one may as well throw the compass away. To move towards creation does one need a compass? Having touched this rock I lost all sense of earthly direction. What happened to me from this point on is in the nature of progression, not direction. There was no longer any goal beyond—I became one with the Path. Each station thenceforth marked a progression into a new spiritual latitude and longitude. Mycenae was not greater than Tiryns nor Epidaurus more beautiful than Mycenae: each was different in a degree for which I had lost the circle of comparison. There is only one analogy I can make to explain the nature of this illuminating voyage which began at Poros and ended at Tripolis perhaps two months later. I must refer the reader to the ascension of Seraphita, as it was glimpsed by her devout followers. It was a voyage into the light. The earth became illuminated by her own inner light. At Mycenae I walked over the incandescent dead; at Epidaurus I felt a stillness so intense that for a fraction of a second I heard the great heart of the world beat and I understood the meaning of pain and sorrow; at Tiryns I stood in the shadow of the Cyclopean man and felt the blaze of that inner eye which has now become a sickly gland; at Argos the whole plain was a fiery mist in which I saw the ghosts of our own American Indians and greeted them in silence. I moved about in a detached way, my feet flooded with the earthly glow. I am at Corinth in a rose light, the sun battling the moon, the earth turning slowly with its fat ruins, wheeling in light like a waterwheel reflected in a still pond. I am at Arachova when the eagle soars from its nest and hangs poised above the boiling cauldron of earth, stunned by the brilliant pattern of colors which dress the heaving abyss. I am at Leonidion at sundown and behind the heavy pall of marsh vapor looms the dark portal of the Inferno where the shades of bats and snakes and lizards come to rest, and perhaps to pray. In each place I open a new vein of experience, a miner digging deeper into the earth, approaching the heart of the star which is not yet extinguished. The light is no longer solar or lunar; it is the starry light of the planet to which man has given life. The earth is alive to its innermost depths; at the center it is a sun in the form of a man crucified. The sun bleeds on its cross in the hidden depths. The sun is man struggling to emerge towards another light. From light to light, from calvary to calvary. The earth song. . . .

I stayed at Hydra a few days during which time I ran up and down thousands of steps, visited the home of several admirals, made votive offerings to the saints who protect the island, said prayers for the dead, the halt and the blind in the little chapel attached to Ghika's house, played ping pong, drank champagne, cognac, *ouzo* and *rezina* at the Old Curiosity Shop, sat up with a bottle of whiskey talking to Ghika about the monks in Tibet, began the log of the Immaculate Conception which I finished for Seferiades at Delphi—*and* listened to Katsimbalis, to the Ninth Symphony of his travails and transgressions. Madame Hadji-Kyriakos, Ghika's wife, laid a wonderful table; we rose from the table like wine casks without legs. From the terrace, which was distinctly Oriental in flavor, we could look out on the sea in drunken stupefaction. The house had forty rooms, some of which were buried deep in the earth. The big rooms were like the saloon of an ocean liner; the little rooms were like cool dungeons fitted up by temperamental pirates. The maids were of divine origin and one of them, at least, was descended directly from the Erectheum though she bore the name of a sacred cereal.

One evening, while scaling the broad steps which led to the tip of the island, Katsimbalis began talking of madness. A mist was coming up from the sea and all I could distinguish of him was the huge head which floated above me like the auric egg itself. He was talking of cities, of how he had gotten a mania for Haussmannizing the big cities of the world. He would take the map of London say, or Constantinople, and after the most painstaking study would draw up a new plan of the city, to suit himself. Some cities he rearranged so thoroughly that later he had difficulty finding his way about—I mean in his own imaginative plan. Naturally a great many monuments had to be torn down and new statues, by unheard of men, erected in their place. While working on Constantinople, for example, he would be seized by a desire to alter Shanghai. By day he would be rebuilding Constantinople and in his sleep he would be remodelling Shanghai. It was confusing, to say the least. Having reconstructed one city he would go on to another and then another. There was no let up to it. The walls were papered with the plans for these new cities. Knowing most of these cities by heart he would often revisit them in his dreams; and since he had altered them throughout, even to such a detail as changing the names of the streets, the result was that he would pass sleepless nights trying to extricate himself and, on awakening, had difficulty recovering his own identity. It was a kind of megalomania, he thought, a sort of glorified constructivism which was a pathologic hangover from his Peloponnesian heritage. We developed the subject further at Tiryns when examining the Cyclopean walls, and again at Mycenae, and for the last time at Nauplia, after climbing the 999 steps leading to the top of the fortress. I came to the conclusion that the Peloponnesians were a race of builders whose spiritual development had been arrested at a formative period and who, consequently, had gone on building automatically, like heavy-handed, heavy-footed sleepwalkers. Nobody knows what these people were trying to create in their sleep; we know only that they preferred to work with the most untractable material. Not a single poet emerged from this race of stone builders. They produced some marvellous "assassinators," legislators and military leaders. When the curtain fell on the scene the house was not only dark but empty. The soil was so saturated with blood that even to-day the crops from the rich plains and valleys are superlatively luxuriant.

When we took the boat for Spetsai Katsimbalis was still talking. The two of us were going on alone. Spetsai was only a few hours away. As I say, Katsimbalis was still talking. As we neared our destination it began to sprinkle a bit. We got into the small boat and were rowed ashore, Katsimbalis remarking that the place looked strange, that perhaps we had pulled in to the opposite side of the island. We got out of the small boat and walked along the quay. Suddenly we were standing in front of a war monument and to my surprise Katsimbalis began to laugh. "I'm crazy," he said, "this isn't Spetsai, this is Ermioni—we're on the mainland." A gendarme came over and spoke to us. He recommended us to go to the other side of the island and there catch a small boat for Spetsai. There was a rattle-trap of a Ford which served as a bus waiting for us. It already had six passengers in it but we managed to squeeze in anyway. As we started off it began to rain. We went through the town of Kranidion at lightning-like speed, half of the car on the sidewalk and the other half in the gutter; we made a sharp turn and descended the mountainside with the engine shut off. The car was falling apart and the young pig on which our feet were resting was squealing like a flea-bitten lunatic. When we got to the little port of Portochelli the rain was coming down in torrents. We waded through mud ankle-deep to get to the tavern at the waterfront. A typical Mediterranean storm was raging. When we inquired if we could get a small boat the card-players looked at us as if we were crazy. We said—"after the storm blows over." They shook their heads. "It will last all day," they said, "and maybe all night." We watched the storm for an hour or more, bored stiff by the prospect of remaining here all night. Wasn't there some one, we inquired, who would take a chance when the storm abated a bit? We let it be known that we would pay double or treble the usual tariff. "By the way," I asked Katsimbalis, "what *is* the usual price?" He inquired of the bar-keeper. "A hundred drachmas," he said. If we were to pay three hundred drachmas that would be handsome. Three hundred drachmas is about two dollars. "You mean that some one would be foolish enough to risk his life for two dollars?" I asked. "What about *us?*" he answered, and then suddenly I realized that it might be a foolhardy thing to tempt some one to sail us over that sea. We sat down and talked it over. "Are you sure you want to risk it?" Katsimbalis asked. "What about you?" I parried. "We may never make it," he said, "it's a gamble. Anyway, it would be a romantic death—*for you.*" And then he started to talk about all the English poets who had been drowned in the Mediterranean. "The hell with it," I said, "if you'll come along I'll risk it. Where's that guy who was going to take us?" We asked where the fellow had gone to. "He's gone to take a little nap," they said, "he didn't get any sleep all night." We tried to find another fellow, but there was no one foolish enough to listen to our pleas. "Can you swim?" asked Katsimbalis. The thought of trying to swim in that boiling sea took some of the steam out of me. "Better wait a while," he added. "No use getting drowned immediately." An old tar came up to us and tried to dissuade us from going. "Very treacherous weather," he said. "It may let up for a little while, but not long enough to reach Spetsai. Better stay here overnight. Nobody will take you out in this sea." Katsimbalis looked at me as though to say—"did you hear that? these fellows know what they're talking about."

A few minutes later the sun came out and with it appeared the fellow who had been taking a nap. We ran out to greet him but he motioned us back with his hand. We stood at the doorway and watched him bail out the boat and hoist the sails. It seemed to take a devil of a time; meanwhile the clouds had gathered again and there came a crack of lightning and a splash of rain. The fellow ducked down into the hatch. We stood and watched the sky some more. It was raining pitchforks again. When it seemed as if all were hopeless suddenly the fellow came up on deck and beckoned to us. The rain had thinned out and the clouds back of us were breaking. "Is it all right to take a chance now?" we asked, none too sure of ourselves. The fellow shrugged his shoulders. "What does he mean by that?" I inquired. To this Katsimbalis also shrugged his shoulders, adding with a malicious smile—"that means that if we're crazy enough to risk our lives he is too." We jumped in and stood up forward, holding on to the mast. "Why don't you go down below?" I said. Katsimbalis didn't want to go below, it made him seasick. "Well, you'll get seasick anyway," I said. "We're in for it now." We had already pushed off and were running close to shore. As we got near the open water a violent gust of wind hit us squarely. The Greek left the tiller to pull down the sails. "Look at that," said Katsimbalis, "these fellows are mad." We were skirting dangerously close to the rocks by the time the fellow had pulled in the sails. The sea was running high—ahead of us was a seething mass of white caps. I began to realize just how mad it was when I saw the huge troughs into which we were plunging with terrifying vertigo.

We looked back instinctively at the helmsman to catch a ray of hope from his countenance, but his expression was impassive. "He's probably mad," said Katsimbalis, and with that a wave broke clean over us and drenched us to the skin. The ducking had an exhilarating effect upon us. We were even more exhilarated when we caught sight of a small yacht pulling up on us. It was only a trifle bigger than our own *benzina* and had about the same speed. Side by side, like two sea horses, the little boats tossed and plunged. I would never have believed that a frail boat could weather such a sea. When we slid down to the bottom of a trough the oncoming wave loomed above us like a white-toothed monster waiting to fall on us belly first. The sky was like the back of a mirror, showing a dull molten glow where the sun vainly strove to beat through. Toward the horizon the lightning was zigzagging back and forth. Now the waves began to strike us from all directions. It took all our strength to hold on to the mast with two hands. We could see Spetsai clearly, the buildings looking ghastly, as if they had vomited up their insides. Oddly enough, neither of us had any fear. I didn't know till afterwards that Katsimbalis had a dread of the sea, being a highlander and not an islander. His face was radiant. Now and then he yelled—*"Homeric,* what?" Good old Katsimbalis! Crazy like all the Greeks. Terrified of the sea he was and yet he had never said a word about it. "We'll have a good meal," he yelled, "if we make it." He had hardly gotten the words out of his mouth when a snarling, whistling spout of water gave us such a clout that I thought we were done for. But the boat was like a cork. Nothing could keel her over or push her down. We looked at each other knowingly, as if to say, "well, if she weathered that she'll weather anything." We became exultant and shouted crazy words of encouragement as if it were a horse we were riding. "Are you all right back there?" Katsimbalis shouted over his shoulder, hardly daring to look back for fear he would find the man overboard. *"Malista,"* came the reply. What a beautiful word for yes, I thought to myself. And then I thought of the first Greek phrase I had learned—*"ligo nero, se para kalo"* . . . a little water, please. Water, water . . . it was running out of my eyes and ears, down my neck, into my belly-button, between my toes. "Bad for the rheumatism," shouted Katsimbalis. "Not too bad," I yelled, "you'll have a good appetite."

There was a little crowd at the quay when we landed. The gendarme eyed us suspiciously. What had brought us to a place like Spetsai in such weather . . . why hadn't we come on the big boat? What was our business? The fact that Katsimbalis was a Greek and had gotten off the big boat by mistake made things look even more suspicious. And what was the crazy American doing— there are no tourists coming to Spetsai in the winter. However, after a few grunts he trundled off. We went to a little hotel nearby and wrote our names in the big book. The proprietor, who was slightly goofy but sympathetic, looked at the names and then said to Katsimbalis—"what regiment were you in during the war? Aren't you my captain?" and he gave his name and the name of the regiment. When we had changed our clothes John the proprietor was waiting for us; he had his little boy by the hand a baby in his arm. "My children, captain," he said proudly. Mister John steered us to a *taverna* where we could get some excellent fried fish and some *rezina*. On the way he told us in English about his fruit store in New York, at one of the subway entrances uptown. I knew that subway entrance very well because I had once sold a

fur-lined coat given to me by a Hindu to a taxi-driver for ten cents
one winter's morning at three A.M. just outside Mister John's fruit
store. Mister John, who was a little goofy, as I said, found it hard
to believe that any native-born American would be so crazy as to
do a thing like that. While we were jabbering away in English a fat
fellow who had been listening attentively at the next table suddenly
turned round and said to me with an impeccable up-state accent—
"Where are you from, stranger? I'm from Buffalo." He came over
and joined us. His name was Nick. "How is the good old U.S.A.?"
he said, ordering another pint of *rezina*. "Jesus, what I wouldn't
give to be back there now." I looked at his clothes, obviously
American, obviously expensive. "What did you do there?" I
asked. "I was a bookie," he said. "You like this suit? I've got
seven more of them at the house. Yeah, I brought a supply of
everything along. You can't get anything decent here—you see
what a dump it is. Jesus, did I have a swell time in Buffalo. . . .
When are you going back?" When I told him that I had no intention
of returning he gave me a strange smile. "Funny," he said, "you
like it here and I like it there. I wish we could swap passports. I'd
give a lot to have an American passport right now."

When I awoke the next morning Katsimbalis had already left the
hotel. Mister John said I would find him down the road by the
Anargyros College. I swallowed Mister John's greasy breakfast
and took the road along the waterfront towards the college. The
college, as well as most everything else of importance in Spetsai,
was donated to the community by the cigarette king. I stood at the
entrance admiring the buildings and as I turned to go I saw
Katsimbalis approaching with a great flourish of the cane. He had
in tow a friend of his—Kyrios Ypsilon, I shall call him, to be
discreet. Kyrios Ypsilon was a political exile, I discovered; he had
been transferred to Spetsai from some other island because of his
poor health. I liked Kyrios Ypsilon at once, the moment I shook
hands with him. He spoke French, not knowing any English, but
with a German accent. He was as Greek as Greek can be, but he
had been educated in Germany. What I liked about him was his
keen, buoyant nature, his directness, his passion for flowers and
for metaphysics. He escorted us to his room in a big deserted
house, the very house in which the famous Bouboulina had been
shot. While we chatted he brought out a tin tub and filled it with
warm water for his bath. On a shelf near his bed he had a collection
of books. I glanced at the titles, which were in five or six languages.
There were The Divine Comedy, Faust, Tom Jones, several volumes of Aristotle, The Plumed Serpent, Plato's Dialogues, two or
three volumes of Shakespeare, and so on. A most excellent diet

for a prolonged siege. "So you do know a little English?" I said.
Oh yes, he had studied it in Germany, but he couldn't speak it
very well. "I would like to read Walt Whitman one day," he added
quickly. He was sitting in the tub soaping and scrubbing himself
vigorously. "To keep up the morale," he said, though neither of
us had made any remark about the bath. "One has to have regular
habits," he went on, "or else you go to pieces. I do a lot of
walking, so that I can sleep at night. The nights are long, you
know, when you are not free."

"He's a great fellow," said Katsimbalis, as we were walking
back to the hotel. "The women are crazy about him. He has an
interesting theory about love . . . get him to talk to you about it
some time."

Talking of love Bouboulina's name came up. "How is it we don't
hear more about Bouboulina?" I asked. "She sounds like another
Joan of Arc."

"Huh," he snorted, stopping dead in his tracks, "what do you
know about Joan of Arc? Do you know anything about her love
life?" He ignored my reply to continue about Bouboulina. It was
an extraordinary story he told me and I have no doubt that most
of it was true. "Why don't you write that story yourself?" I asked
him point blank. He pretended that he was not a writer, that his
task was to discover people and present them to the world. "But I
never met a man who could tell a story like you," I persisted.
"Why don't you try telling your stories aloud—let someone take
it down just as you tell it? Couldn't you do that, at least?"

"To tell a good story," he said, "you have to have a good
listener. I can't tell a story to an automaton who writes short-
hand. Besides, the best stories are those which you don't want to
preserve. If you have any arrière-pensée the story is ruined. It
must be a sheer gift . . . you must throw it to the dogs. . . . I'm not
a writer," he added, "I'm an extemporaneous fellow. I like to hear
myself talk. I talk too much—it's a vice." And then he added
reflectively: "what good would it do to be a writer, a Greek writer?
Nobody reads Greek. If a man can have a thousand readers here
he's lucky. The educated Greeks don't read their own writers;
they prefer to read German, English, French books. A writer
hasn't a chance in Greece."

"But your work could be translated into other languages," I
suggested.

"There is no language that can render the flavor and the beauty
of modern Greek," he replied. "French is wooden, inflexible,
logic-ridden, too precise; English is too flat, too prosaic, too
business-like . . . you don't know how to make verbs in English."

He went on like that, flourishing his cane angrily. He began to
recite one of Seferiades' poems, in Greek. "Do you hear that? The
sound of it alone is wonderful, no? What can you give me in
English to match that for sheer beauty of resonance?" And suddenly he began to intone a verse from the Bible. "Now that's a
little more like it," he said. "But you don't use that language any
more—that's a dead language now. The language hasn't any guts
to-day. You're all castrated, you've become business men, engi-
neers, technicians. It sounds like wooden money dropping into a
sewer. *We've got a language* . . . we're still making it. It's a
language for poets, not for shop-keepers. Listen to this—" and he
began reciting another poem, in Greek. "That's from Sekelianos.
I suppose you never even heard the name, what? You never heard
of Yannopoulos either, did you? Yannopoulos was greater than
your Walt Whitman and all the American poets combined. He was
a madman, yes, like all the great Greek fellows. He fell in love
with his own country—that's a funny thing, eh? Yes, he became
so intoxicated with the Greek language, the Greek philosophy, the
Greek sky, the Greek mountains, the Greek sea, the Greek islands,
the Greek vegetables, even, that he killed himself. I'll tell you how
he killed himself some other time—that's another story. Have you
got any writers who would kill themselves because they were too
full of love? Are there any French writers or German writers or
English writers who feel that way about their country, their race,
their soil? *Who are they?* I'll read you some of Yannopoulos when
we get back to Athens. I'll read you what he says about the
rocks—just the rocks, nothing more. You can't know what a rock
is until you've heard what Yannopoulos has written. He talks
about rocks for pages and pages; he *invents* rocks, by God, when
he can't find any to rave about. People say he was crazy, Yannopoulos. He wasn't crazy—he was *mad*. There's a difference. His
voice was too strong for his body: it consumed him. He was like
Icarus—the sun melted his wings. He soared too high. He was an
eagle. These rabbits we call critics can't understand a man like
Yannopoulos. He was out of proportion. He raved about the wrong
things, according to them. He didn't have *le sens de mesure,* as
the French say. There you are—*mesure*. What a mean little word!
They look at the Parthenon and they find the proportions so
harmonious. All rot. The human proportions which the Greek
extolled were superhuman. They weren't *French* proportions.
They were divine, because the true Greek is a god, not a cautious,
precise, calculating being with the soul of an engineer. . . ."

Our stay at Spetsai was prolonged because the boat for Nauplia failed to appear. I began to fear that we would be marooned there indefinitely. However, one fine day along about four in the afternoon the boat finally did show up. It was an unserviceable English ferry-boat which rolled with the slightest ripple. We sat on deck watching the sinking sun. It was one of those Biblical sunsets in which man is completely absent. Nature simply opens her bloody, insatiable maw and swallows everything in sight. Law, order, morality, justice, wisdom, any abstraction seems like a cruel joke perpetrated on a helpless world of idiots. Sunset at sea is for me a dread spectacle: it is hideous, murderous, soulless. The earth may be cruel but the sea is heartless. There is absolutely no place of refuge; there are only the elements and the elements are treacherous.

We were to touch at Leonidion before putting in at Nauplia. I was hoping it would still be light enough to catch a glimpse of the place because it was this grim corner of the Peloponnesus that the Katsimbalis side of the family stemmed from. Unfortunately the sun was rapidly setting just behind the wall of rock under which Leonidion lies. By the time the boat dropped anchor it was night. All I could distinguish in the gloom was a little cove illuminated by four or five feeble electric bulbs. A dank, chill breath descended from the precipitious black wall above us, adding to the desolate and forbidding atmosphere of the place. Straining my eyes to pierce the chill, mist-laden gloom it seemed to me that I perceived a gap in the hills which my imagination peopled with rude, barbaric tribesmen moving stealthily about in search of forage. I would not have been the least surprised to hear the beat of a tom-tom or a blood-curdling war whoop. The setting was unrelievedly sinister—another death-trap. I could well imagine how it must have been centuries ago, when the morning sun pierced the fever-laden mist, disclosing the naked bodies of the slain, their stalwart, handsome figures mutilated by the javelin, the axe, the wheel. Horrible though the image was I could not help but think how much cleaner that than the sight of a shell-torn trench with bits of human flesh strewn about like chicken feed. I can't for the life of me recall by what weird modulation we arrived at the Rue du Faubourg Montmartre, but as the boat pulled out and we installed ourselves at a table in the saloon before a couple of innocent glasses of *ouzo* Katsimbalis was leading me by the hand from cafe to cafe along that thoroughfare which is engraved in my memory as perhaps no other street in Paris. At least five or six times it has happened to me now that on taking leave of a strange city or saying good-bye to an old friend this street, which is certainly not the most extraordinary street in the world, has been the parting theme. There is without doubt something sinister and fascinatingly evil about the Rue du Faubourg Montmartre. The first time I walked through it, of an evening, I was literally frightened stiff. There was something in the air which warned one to be on one's guard. It is by no means the worst street in Paris, as I have hinted, but there is something malignant, foul, menacing, which lingers there like a poisonous gas, corroding even the most innocent face until it resembles the ulcer-bitten physiognomy of the doomed and defeated. It is a street that one comes back to again and again. One gets to know it slowly, foot by foot, like a trench which is taken and retaken so many times that one no longer knows if it is a bad dream or a monomania.

In a few hours we would be at Nauplia, within striking distance of such breath-taking places as Argos, Tiryns, Mycenae, Epidaurus, and here we are talking of dingy holes, lye-bitten side streets, dilapidated whores, dwarfs, gigolos, *clochards* of the Faubourg Montmartre. I am trying to visualize my friend Katsimbalis sitting in a certain *bistro* opposite a threatre at midnight. The last time I stood at that bar my friend Edgar was trying to sell me Rudolf Steiner, rather unsuccessfully I must say, because just as he was getting on to group souls and the exact nature of the difference between a cow and a mineral, from the occult standpoint, a chorus girl from the theatre opposite, who was now on the bum, wedged her way in between us and diverted our minds to things less abstruse. We took a seat in the corner near the doorway where we were joined by a dwarf who ran a string of whorehouses and who seemed to derive an unholy pleasure from using the adverb *"malment."* The story which Katsimbalis was reeling off was one of those stories which begin as a trifling episode and end as an unfinished novel—unfinished because of lack of breath or space or time or because, as happened, he got sleepy and decided to take a nap. This story, which like all his stories I find it impossible to transcribe, lacking the patience and the finesse of a Thomas Mann, haunted me for days. It was not that the subject was so unusual, it was that with a good stretch of sea before us he felt at liberty to make the most extraordinary digressions, to dwell with scrupulous care and attention on the most trivial details. I have always felt that the art of telling a story consists in so stimulating the listener's imagination that he drowns himself in his own reveries long before the end. The best stories I have heard were pointless, the best books those whose plot I can never remember, the best individuals those whom I never get anywhere with. Though it has been practised on me time and again I never cease to marvel how it happens that, with certain individuals whom I know, within a few minutes after greeting them we are embarked on an endless voyage comparable in feeling and trajectory only to the deep middle dream which the practised dreamer slips into like a bone into its socket. Often, after one of these suprasensible seances, endeavoring to recapture the thread which had broken, I would work my way back as far as some trifling detail—but between that bespangled point of repair and the mainland there was always an impassible void, a sort of no man's land which the wizardry of the artist had encumbered with shell holes and quagmires and barbed wire.

In the case of Katsimbalis there was a quality which, as a writer, I feel to be of the utmost importance where the art of story telling is concerned—the complete disregard of the element of time. He never began in the professional way; he began by fumbling about, sparring for an opening, so to speak. The story usually began when he had come to a knot-hole, when, in order to really launch himself, he would take a tremendous step backward, figuratively, to be sure, saying as he tweaked his nose—"look here, did you never notice that. . . ." or "I say, has it ever happened to you that. . . ." and, not waiting for a yes or a no, his eyes becoming glazed by the surge of inward light, he would actually tumble backwards into the deep well in which all his stories had their source and, gripping the slippery walls of his narrative with finger and toe, he would slowly clamber to the surface, puffing, gasping, shaking himself like a dog to free himself of the last remaining particles of wrack and slime and star-dust. Sometimes, in taking the backward plunge, he would hit the bottom with such a thud that he was speechless: one could look into the pupil of his eyes and see him lying there helpless as a star-fish, a great sprawling mass of flesh lying face up and counting the stars, counting and naming them in fat, unbroken stupefaction as if to make a colossally unthinkable pattern on which to weave the story which would come to his lips when he would catch his breath again.

The great star-fish, as I was saying, was sound asleep before ever we got to Nauplia. He had sprawled out on the bench, leaving me to circle about the Parc Monceau where he had dropped me in a taxi. I was dazed. I went up on deck and paced back and forth, purring to myself, laughing aloud now and then, gesticulating, mimicking his gestures in anticipation of recounting the more succulent fragments of his narrative to my friend Durrell or to Seferiades upon my return to Athens. Several times I slipped back to the saloon to take a look at him, to gaze at that tiny mouth of his which was pried open now in a prolonged mute gasp like the mouth of a fish suffocating with air. Once I approached close to him and bending over I explored the silent cavity with a photographic eye. What an astounding thing is the voice! By what miracle is the hot magma of the earth transformed into that which we call speech? If out of clay such an abstract medium as words can be shaped what is to hinder us from leaving our bodies at will and taking up our abode on other planets or between the planets? What is to prevent us from rearranging all life, atomic, molecular, corporeal, stellar, divine? Why should we stop at words, or at planets, or at divinity? Who or what is powerful enough to eradicate this miraculous leaven which we bear within us like a seed and which, after we have embraced in our mind all the universe, is nothing more than a seed—since to say universe is as easy as to say seed, and we have yet to say greater things, things beyond saying, things limitless and inconceivable, things which no trick of language can encompass. *You* lying there, I was saying to myself, where has that voice gone? Into what inky crevices are you crawling with your ganglionic feelers? Who are you, *what* are you now in drugged silence? Are you fish? Are you spongy root? Are you *you?* If I should bash your skull in now would all be lost—the music, the narcotic vapors, the glissandos, the rugged parentheses, the priapic snorts, the law of diminishing returns, the pebbles between stutters, the shutters you pull down over naked crimes? If I bore into you now with an awl, here at the temple, will there come out with the blood a single tangible clue?

In a few minutes we shall be at Nauplia. In a few minutes he will awake with a start, saying "Huh, I must have dozed off." He always wakes up electrified, as if he were caught committing a crime. He is ashamed to go to sleep. At midnight he is only beginning to feel thoroughly awake. At midnight he goes prowling about in strange quarters looking for some one to talk to. People are collapsing with fatigue: he galvanizes them into attentive listeners. When he is through he pulls out the plug and departs with his vocal apparatus tucked safely away in his diaphragm. He will sit in the dark at a table and stuff himself with bread and olives, with hard-boiled eggs, with herring and cheeses of one sort or another, and while washing it down by his lonesome he will talk to himself, tell himself a story, pat himself on the chest, remind himself to remember to remember it the next time; he will even sing himself a little song in the dark or, if the spirit moves him, get up and do a few bearish paces or urinate through his pants, why not, he's alone, he's happy, he's sad, he's all there is, to himself at least, and who else is there and so forth—*can you see him?* I see him very clearly. It's warm now in Athens and he's had a grand night of it with his cronies. The last one he said good-night to is already home and writing it all down in his diary, having no other existence than this auricular attachment, this appendix of a life in the belly of the whale. The whale is tilting back against a wall under a grape arbor near the niche where Socrates passed his last hours. The whale is again looking for food and drink, trying to spirit it out of a man with a 1905 straw hat brought safely back from America together with fine bed linen, rocking chairs, spittoons and a horned phonograph. The phonograph is standing on a chair in the road and in a moment a canned voice will be screeching a poison song from the time of the Turkish occupation. . . .

In a few minutes we shall be at Nauplia. The whale is now electrified and his memory, which had probably been refreshed by the brief nap, is working with diabolical accuracy on the shreds of a detail which he was too lazy to elaborate on before. The passengers are clearing out and we are caught up and carried along like corks to the forward deck. Near the rail, the first to disembark, are two prisoners escorted by gendarmes with rifles. They are chained to one another by handcuffs. The thought occurs to me that he, Katsimbalis, and myself are also chained to one another, he the teller and I the listener, and that we will go to the end of the world this way, not as prisoners but as willing bondsmen.

Nauplia is dismal and deserted at night. It is a place which has lost caste, like Arles or Avignon. In fact, it is in many ways suggestive of a French provincial town, at night more particularly. There is a military garrison, a fortress, a palace, a cathedral—and a few crazy monuments. There is also a mosque which has been converted into a cinema. By day it is all red tape, lawyers and judges everywhere, with all the despair and futility which follows in the train of these blood-sucking parasites. The fortress and the prison dominate the town. Warrior, jailer, priest—the eternal trinity which symbolizes our fear of life. I don't like Nauplia. I don't like provincial towns. I don't like jails, churches, fortresses, palaces, libraries, museums, nor public statues to the dead.

The hotel was a bit of a mad-house. In the lobby there were engravings of famous Greek ruins and of Indians from the Amazon and the Orinoco. The dining room was plastered with letters from American and English tourists, all praising the comforts of the hotel in extravagant language. The silliest letters were signed by professors from our celebrated universities. Katsimbalis had two beds in his room and I had three. There was no heat because we were the only guests.

We awoke early and hired a car to take us to Epidaurus. The day began in sublime peace. It was my first real glimpse of the

Peloponnesus. It was not a glimpse either, but a vista opening upon a hushed still world such as man will one day inherit when he ceases to indulge in murder and thievery. I wonder how it is that no painter has ever given us the magic of this idyllic landscape. Is it too undramatic, too idyllic? Is the light too ethereal to be captured by the brush? This I can say, and perhaps it will discourage the over-enthusiastic artist: there is no trace of ugliness here, either in line, color, form, feature or sentiment. It is sheer perfection, as in Mozart's music. Indeed, I venture to say that there is more of Mozart here than anywhere else in the world. The road to Epidaurus is like the road to creation. One stops searching. One grows silent, stilled by the hush of mysterious beginnings. If one could speak one would become melodious. There is nothing to be seized or treasured or cornered off here: there is only a breaking down of the walls which lock the spirit in. The landscape does not recede, it installs itself in the open places of the heart; it crowds in, accumulates, dispossesses. You are no longer riding through something—call it Nature, if you will—but participating in a rout, a rout of the forces of greed, malevolence, envy, selfishness, spite, intolerance, pride, arrogance, cunning, duplicity and so on.

It is the morning of the first day of the great peace, the peace of the heart, which comes with surrender. I never knew the meaning of peace until I arrived at Epidaurus. Like everybody I had used the word all my life, without once realizing that I was using a counterfeit. Peace is not the opposite of war any more than death is the opposite of life. The poverty of language, which is to say the poverty of man's imagination or the poverty of his inner life, has created an ambivalence which is absolutely false. I am talking of course of the peace which passeth all understanding. There is no other kind. The peace which most of us know is merely a cessation of hostilities, a truce, an interregnum, a lull, a respite, which is negative. The peace of the heart is positive and invincible, demanding no conditions, requiring no protection. It just is. If it is a victory it is a peculiar one because it is based entirely on surrender, a voluntary surrender, to be sure. There is no mystery in my mind as to the nature of the cures which were wrought at this great therapeutic center of the ancient world. Here the healer himself was healed, first and most important step in the development of the art, which is not medical but religious. Second, the patient was healed before ever he received the cure. The great physicians have always spoken of Nature as being the great healer. That is only partially true. Nature alone can do nothing. Nature can cure only when man recognizes his place in the world, which is not in

Nature, as with the animal, but in the human kingdom, the link between the natural and the divine.

To the infra-human specimens of this benighted scientific age the ritual and worship connected with the art of healing as practised at Epidaurus seems like sheer buncombe. In our world the blind lead the blind and the sick go to the sick to be cured. We are making constant progress, but it is a progress which leads to the operating table, to the poor house, to the insane asylum, to the trenches. We have no healers—we have only butchers whose knowledge of anatomy entitles them to a diploma which in turn entitles them to carve out or amputate our illnesses so that we may carry on in crippled fashion until such time as we are fit for the slaughter house. We announce the discovery of this cure and that but make no mention of the new diseases which we have created en route. The medical cult operates very much like the War Office—the triumphs which they broadcast are sops thrown out to conceal death and disaster. The medicos, like the military authorities, are helpless; they are waging a hopeless fight from the start. What man wants is peace in order that he may live. Defeating our neighbor doesn't give peace any more than curing cancer brings health. Man doesn't begin to live through triumphing over his enemy nor does he begin to acquire health through endless cures. The joy of life comes through peace, which is not static but dynamic. No man can really say that he knows what joy is until he has experienced peace. And without joy there is no life, even if you have a dozen cars, six butlers, a castle, a private chapel and a bomb-proof vault. Our diseases are our attachments, be they habits, ideologies, ideals, principles, possessions, phobias, gods, cults, religions, what you please. Good wages can be a disease just as much as bad wages. Leisure can be just as great a disease as work. Whatever we cling to, even if it be hope or faith, can be the disease which carries us off. Surrender is absolute: if you cling to even the tiniest crumb you nourish the germ which will devour you. As for clinging to God, God long ago abandoned us in order that we might realize the joy of attaining godhood through our own efforts. All this whimpering that is going on in the dark, this insistent, piteous plea for peace which will grow bigger as the pain and the misery increase, where is it to be found? *Peace,* do people imagine that it is something to be cornered, like corn or wheat? Is it something which can be pounced upon and devoured, as with wolves fighting over a carcass? I hear people talking about peace and their faces are clouded with anger or with hatred or with scorn and disdain, with pride and arrogance. There are people who want to fight to bring about peace—the most deluded souls of all. There will be no peace until murder is eliminated from the heart and mind. Murder is the apex of the broad pyramid whose base is the self. That which stands will have to fall. Everything which man has fought for will have to be relinquished before he can begin to live as man. Up till now he has been a sick beast and even his divinity stinks. He is master of many worlds and in his own he is a slave. What rules the world is the heart, not the brain. In every realm our conquests bring only death. We have turned our backs on the one realm wherein freedom lies. At Epidaurus, in the stillness, in the great peace that came over me, I heard the heart of the world beat. I know what the cure is: it is to give up, to relinquish, to surrender, so that our little hearts may beat in unison with the great heart of the world.

I think that the great hordes who made the long trek to Epidaurus from every corner of the ancient world were already cured before they arrived there. Sitting in the strangely silent amphitheatre I thought of the long and devious route by which I had at last come to this healing center of peace. No man could have chosen a more circumlocuitous voyage than mine. Over thirty years I had wandered, as if in a labyrinth. I had tasted every joy, every despair, but I had never known the meaning of peace. En route I had vanquished all my enemies one by one, but the greatest enemy of all I had not even recognized—*myself*. As I entered the still bowl, bathed now in a marble light, I came to that spot in the dead center where the faintest whisper rises like a glad bird and vanishes over the shoulder of the low hill, as the light of a clear day recedes before the velvet black of night. Balboa standing upon the peak of Darien could not have known a greater wonder than I at this moment. There was nothing more to conquer: an ocean of peace lay before me. To be free, as I then knew myself to be, is to realize that all conquest is vain, even the conquest of self, which is the last act of egotism. To be joyous is to carry the ego to its last summit and to deliver it triumphantly. To know peace is total: it is the moment after, when the surrender is complete, when there is no longer even the consciousness of surrender. Peace is at the center and when it is attained the voice issues forth in praise and benediction. Then the voice carries far and wide, to the outermost limits of the universe. Then it heals, because it brings light and the warmth of compassion.

Epidaurus is merely a place symbol: the real place is in the heart, in every man's heart, if he will but stop and search it. Every discovery is mysterious in that it reveals what is so unexpectedly immediate, so close, so long and intimately known. The wise man has no need to journey forth; it is the fool who seeks the pot of gold at the rainbow's end. But the two are always fated to meet and unite. They meet at the heart of the world, which is the beginning and the end of the path. They meet in realization and unite in transcendence of their roles.

The world is both young and old: like the individual, it renews itself in death and ages through infinite births. At every stage there is the possibility of fulfillment. Peace lies at any point along the line. It is a continuum and one that is just as undemonstrable by demarcation as a line is undemonstrable by stringing points together. To make a line requires a totality of being, of will and of imagination. What constitutes a line, which is an exercise in metaphysics, one may speculate on for eternity. But even an idiot can draw a line, and in doing so he is the equal of the professor for whom the nature of a line is a mystery beyond all comprehension.

The mastery of great things comes with the doing of trifles; the little voyage is for the timid soul just as formidable as the big voyage for the great one. Voyages are accomplished inwardly, and the most hazardous ones, needless to say, are made without moving from the spot. But the sense of voyage can wither and die. There are adventurers who penetrate to the remotest parts of the earth, dragging to a fruitless goal in animated corpse. The earth pullulates with adventurous spirits who populate it with death: these are the souls who, bent upon conquest, fill the outer corridors of space with strife and bickering. What gives a phantasmal hue to life is this wretched shadow play between ghoul and ghost. The panic and confusion which grips the soul of the wanderer is the reverberation of the pandemonium created by the lost and the damned.

As I was basking on the steps of the amphitheatre the very natural thought came to my head to send a word of cheer to my friends. I thought particularly of my psychoanalyst friends. I wrote out three cards, one to France, one to England, and one to America. I very gently urged these broken-down hacks who called themselves healers to abandon their work and come to Epidaurus for a cure. All three of them were in dire need of the healing art—saviours who were helpless to save themselves. One of them committed suicide before my word of cheer reached him; another died of a broken heart shortly after receiving my card; the third one answered briefly that he envied me and wished he had the courage to quit his work.

The analyst everywhere is fighting a hopeless fight. For every individual whom he restores to the stream of life, "adapted," as they put it, a dozen are incapacitated. There will never be enough analysts to go round, no matter how fast we turn them out. One brief war is enough to undo the work of centuries. Surgery of course will make new advances, though of what use these advances are it is difficult to see. Our whole way of life has to alter. We don't want better surgical appliances, we want a better life. If all the surgeons, all the analysts, all the medicos could be withdrawn from their activity and gathered together for a spell in the great bowl at Epidaurus, if they could discuss in peace and quiet the immediate, drastic need of humanity at large, the answer would be forthcoming speedily, and it would be unanimous: REVOLUTION. A world-wide revolution from top to bottom, in every country, in every class, in every realm of consciousness. The fight is not against disease: disease is a by-product. The enemy of man is not germs, but man himself, his pride, his prejudices, his stupidity, his arrogance. No class is immune, no system holds a panacea. Each one individually must revolt against a way of life which is not his own. The revolt, to be effective, must be continuous and relentless. It is not enough to overthrow governments, masters, tyrants: one must overthrow his own preconceived ideas of right and wrong, good and bad, just and unjust. We must abandon the hard-fought trenches we have dug ourselves into and come out into the open, surrender our arms, our possessions, our rights as individuals, classes, nations, peoples. A billion men seeking peace cannot be enslaved. We have enslaved ourselves, by our own petty, circumscribed view of life. It is glorious to offer one's life for a cause, but dead men accomplish nothing. Life demands that we offer something more—spirit, soul, intelligence, good-will. Nature is ever ready to repair the gaps caused by death, but nature cannot supply the intelligence, the will, the imagination to conquer the forces of death. Nature restores and repairs, that is all. It is man's task to eradicate the homicidal instinct, which is infinite in its ramifications and manifestations. It is useless to call upon God, as it is futile to meet force with force. Every battle is a marriage conceived in blood and anguish, every war is a defeat to the human spirit. War is only a vast manifestation in dramatic style of the sham, hollow, mock conflicts which take place daily everywhere even in so-called times of peace. Every man contributes his bit to keep the carnage going, even those who seem to be staying aloof. We are all involved, all participating, willy-nilly. The earth is our creation and we must accept the fruits of our creation. As long as we refuse to think in terms of world good and world goods, of world order, world peace, we shall murder and betray one another. It can go on till the crack of doom, if we wish it to be thus. Nothing can bring about a new and better world but our own desire for it. Man kills through fear—and fear is hydra-headed. Once we start slaying there is no end to it. An eternity would not suffice to vanquish the demons who torture us. *Who put the demons there?* That is for each one to ask himself. Let every man search his own heart. Neither God nor the Devil is responsible, and certainly not such puny monsters as Hitler, Mussolini, Stalin, et alia. Certainly not such bugaboos as Catholicism, Capitalism, Communism. Who put the demons there in our heart to torture us? A good question, and if the only way to find out is to go to Epidaurus, then I urge you one and all to drop everything and go there—at once.

In Greece one has the conviction that *genius* is the norm, not mediocrity. No country has produced, in proportion to its numbers, as many geniuses as Greece. In one century alone this tiny nation gave to the world almost five hundred men of genius. Her art, which goes back fifty centuries, is eternal and incomparable. The landscape remains the most satisfactory, the most wondrous, that our earth has to offer. The inhabitants of this little world lived in harmony with their natural surroundings, peopling them with gods who were real and with whom they lived in intimate communion. The Greek cosmos is the most eloquent illustration of the unity of thought and deed. It persists even to-day, though its elements have long since been dispersed. The image of Greece, faded though it be, endures as an archetype of the miracle wrought by the human spirit. A whole people, as the relics of their achievements testify, lifted themselves to a point never before and never since attained. It was miraculous. It still is. The task of genius, and man is nothing if not genius, is to keep the miracle alive, to live always in the miracle, to make the miracle more and more miraculous, to swear allegiance to nothing, but live only miraculously, think only miraculously, die miraculously. It matters little how much is destroyed, if only the germ of the miraculous be preserved and nurtured. At Epidaurus you are confronted with and permeated by the intangible residue of the miraculous surge of the human spirit. It inundates you like the spray of a mighty wave which broke at last upon the farther shore. To-day our attention is centered upon the physical inexhaustibility of the universe; we *must* concentrate all our thought upon that solid fact because never before has man plundered and devastated to such a degree as to-day. We are therefore prone to forget that in the realm of the spirit there is also an inexhaustibility, that in this realm no gain is ever lost. When one stands at Epidaurus one *knows* this to be a fact. With malice and spite the world may buckle and crack but here, no matter into what vast hurricane we may whip our evil passions, lies an area of peace and calm, the pure distilled heritage of a past which is not altogether lost.

If Epidaurus spells peace Mycenae, which is outwardly as calm and hushed, awakens wholly different thoughts and emotions. At Tiryns the day before I was introduced to the Cyclopean world. We entered the ruins of the once impregnable citadel through a womb-like aperture made, if not by supermen, certainly by giants. The walls of the womb were as smooth as alabaster; they had been polished by thick coats of fleece, for here during the long period of night which settled over this region the shepherds brought their flocks for shelter. Tiryns is prehistoric in character. Little remains of this once formidable pioneer settlement save a few colossal ramparts. Why it should be so I don't know, but to me it seems to antedate, at least in spirit, the cave shelters of the Dordogne region. One feels that the terrain has undergone profound alterations. Supposedly Tiryns was settled by an off-shoot from Crete during the Minoan period; if so, the spirit underwent profound transformations, like the land itself. Tiryns is no more like Knossus, for example, than New York is like Rome or Paris. Tiryns represents a relapse, just as America represents Europe in its most degenerate aspects. Crete of the Minoan epochs stands for a culture based upon peace: Tiryns smells of cruelty, barbarism, suspicion, isolation. It is like an H. G. Wells setting for a prehistoric drama, for a thousand years' war between one-eyed giants and blunder-footed dinosaurs.

Mycenae, which follows Tiryns in point of time, is quite another scene. The stillness of it to-day resembles the exhaustion of a cruel and intelligent monster which has been bled to death. Mycenae, and again I give only my impressions and intuitions, seems to have experienced a vast cycle of development and degeneration. It seems to stand outside time, in any historical sense. In some mysterious fashion the same Aegean race which brought the seeds of culture from Crete to Tiryns here evolved to a godlike grandeur, threw out a quick spawn of heroes, Titans, demi-gods, and then, as if exhausted and dazzled by the unprecedented and divine-like flowering, relapsed into a dark and bloody intestinal conflict which lasted for centuries, ending at a point so far back as to appear mythological to their successors. At Mycenae the gods once walked the earth, of that there can be no question. And at Mycenae the progeny of these same gods produced a type of man who was artistic to the core and at the same time monstrous in his passions. The architecture was Cyclopean, the ornaments of a delicacy and grace unrivalled in any period of art. Gold was abundant and used unstintingly. Everything about the place is contradictory. It is one of the navels of the human spirit, the place of attachment to the past and of complete severance too. It wears an impenetrable air: it is grim, lovely, seductive and repellent. What happened here is beyond all conjecture. The historians and the archaeologists have woven a slim and altogether unsatisfying fabric to cover the mystery. They piece together fragmentary items which are linked in the customary manner to suit their necessitous logic. Nobody has yet penetrated the secret of this hoary scene. It defies the feeble processes of the intellectual mind. We must await the return of the gods, the restoration of faculties which now lie dormant.

It was a Sunday morning when Katsimbalis and I left Nauplia for Mycenae. It was hardly eight o'clock when we arrived at the little station bearing this legendary name. Passing through Argos the magic of this world suddenly penetrated my bowels. Things long forgotten came back with frightening clarity. I was not sure whether I was recalling things I had read as a child or whether I was tapping the universal memory of the race. The fact that these places still existed, still bore their ancient names, seemed incredible. It was like a resurrection and the day we had chosen for the journey was more like Easter than Thanksgiving Day. From the station to the ruins was a walk of several kilometers. As at Epidaurus there was a sublime stillness all about. We walked leisurely towards the encircling hills which rise up from the gleaming Argive plain. A few birds were wheeling overhead in the unbroken vault of blue. Suddenly we came upon a little boy crying as if his heart would break. He was standing in the field beside the road. His weeping had absolutely no relation to the hushed and tranquil world in which he stood; it was as if he had been set down in the green field by a spirit from the outside world. What could a little boy be crying about at such an hour in such a wondrous world? Katsimbalis went over and spoke to him. He was crying because his sister had stolen his money. How much money? Three drachmas. Money, money. . . . Even here there was such a thing as money. The word money never sounded so preposterous to me before. How could one think such a word in this world of terror and beauty and magic? If he had lost a donkey or a parrot I could have understood. But three drachmas—I just couldn't visualize the meaning of three drachmas. I couldn't believe he was weeping. It was an hallucination. Let him stand there and weep—the spirit would come and fetch him again; he didn't belong, he was an anomaly.

After you pass the little hostelry run by Agamemnon and his wife, which faces a field of Irish green, you become immediately aware that the earth is sown with the bodies and the relics of legendary figures. Even before Katsimbalis opened his mouth I knew they were lying all about us—the earth tells you so. The approach to the place of horror is fantastically inviting. There are smooth green mounds, hummocks, hillocks, tumuli everywhere, and beneath them, not very deep either, lie the warriors, the heroes, the fabulous innovators who without machinery erected the most formidable fortifications. The sleep of the dead is so deep that the earth and all who walk it dream; even the huge carrion birds who wheel above seem drugged and hypnotized. As one rises slowly with the rising terrain the blood thickens, the heart slows down, the mind comes to rest obsessively on the shuddering image of an endless chain of assassinations. There are two distinct worlds impinging on one another—the heroic world of daylight and the claustral world of dagger and poison. Mycenae, like Epidaurus, swims in light. But Epidaurus is all open, exposed, irrevocably devoted to the spirit. Mycenae folds in upon itself, like a fresh-cut navel, dragging its glory down into the bowels of the earth where the bats and the lizards feed upon it gloatingly. Epidaurus is a bowl from which to drink the pure spirit: the blue of the sky is in it and the stars and the winged creatures who fly between, scattering song and melody. Mycenae, after one turns the last bend, suddenly folds up into a menacing crouch, grim, defiant, impenetrable. Mycenae is closed in, huddled up, writhing with muscular contortions like a wrestler. Even the light, which falls on it with merciless clarity, gets sucked in, shunted off, grayed, beribboned. There were never two worlds so closely juxtaposed and yet so antagonistic. It is Greenwich here with respect to everything that concerns the soul of man. Move a hair's breadth either way and you are in a totally different world. This is the great shining bulge of horror, the high slope whence man, having attained his zenith, slipped back and fell into the bottomless pit.

It was still early morning when we slipped through the lion's gate. No sign of a guardian about. Not a soul in sight. The sun is steadily rising and everything is clearly exposed to view. And yet we proceed timidly, cautiously, fearing we know not what. Here and there are open pits looking ominously smooth and slimy. We walk between the huge slabs of stone that form the circular enclosure. My book knowledge is nil. I can look on this mass of rubble with the eyes of a savage. I am amazed at the diminutive proportions of the palace chambers, of the dwelling places up above. What colossal walls to protect a mere handful of people! Was each and every inhabitant a giant? What dread darkness fell upon them in their evil days to make them burrow into the earth, to hide their treasures from the light, to murder incestuously in the deep bowels of the earth? We of the New World, with millions of acres lying waste and millions unfed, unwashed, unsheltered, we who dig into the earth, who work, eat, sleep, love, walk, ride, fight, buy, sell and murder there below ground, are we going the same way? I am a native of New York, the grandest and the emptiest city in the world; I am standing now at Mycenae, trying to understand what happened here over a period of centuries. I feel like a cockroach crawling about amidst dismantled splendors. It is hard to believe that somewhere back in the leaves and branches of the great genealogical tree of life my progenitors knew this spot, asked the same questions, fell back senseless into the void, were swallowed up and left no trace of thought save these ruins, the scattered relics in museums, a sword, an axle, a helmet, a death mask of beaten gold, a bee-hive tomb, an heraldic lion carved in stone, an exquisite drinking vase. I stand at the summit of the walled citadel and in the early morning I feel the approach of the cold breath from the shaggy gray mountain towering above us. Below, from the great Argive plain the mist is rising. It might be Pueblo, Colorado, so dislocated is it from time and boundary. Down there, in that steaming plain where the automotrice crawls like a caterpillar, is it not possible there once stood wigwams? Can I be sure there never were any Indians here? Everything connected with Argos, shimmering now in the distance as in the romantic illustrations for text-books, smacks of the American Indian. I must be crazy to think thus, but I am honest enough to admit the thought. Argos gleams resplendent, a point of light shooting arrows of gold into the blue. Argos belongs to myth and fable: her heroes never took on flesh. But Mycenae, like Tiryns, is peopled with the ghosts of antediluvial men, Cyclopean monsters washed up from the sunken ridges of Atlantis. Mycenae was first heavy-footed, slow, sluggish, ponderous, thought embodied in dinosaurian frames, war reared in anthropophagous luxury, reptilian, ataraxic, stunning and stunned. Mycenae swung full circle, from limbo to limbo. The monsters devoured one another, like crocodiles. The rhinoceros man gored the hippopotamic man. The walls fell on them, crushed them, flattened them into the primeval ooze. A brief night. Lurid lightning flashes, thunder cannonading between the fierce shoulders of the hills. The eagles fly out, the plain is scavengered, the grass shoots forth. (This is a Brooklyn lad talking. Not a word of truth in it, until the gods bring forth the evidence.) The eagles, the hawks, the snot-knobbed vultures, gray with greed like the parched and barren mountain-sides. The air is alive with winged scavengers. Silence—century upon century of silence, during which the earth puts on a coat of soft green. A mysterious race out of nowhere swoops down upon the country of Argolis. Mysterious only because men have forgotten the sight of the gods. The gods are returning, in full panoply, man-like, making use of the horse, the buckler, the javelin, carving precious jewels, smelting ores, blowing fresh vivid images of war and love on bright dagger blades. The gods stride forth over the sun-lit swards, full-statured, fearless, the gaze frighteningly candid and open. A world of light is born. Man looks at man with new eyes. He is awed, smitten by his own gleaming image reflected everywhere. It goes on thus, century upon century swallowed like cough-drops, a poem, an heraldic poem, as my friend Durrell would say. While the magic is on the lesser men, the initiates, the Druids of the Peloponnesus, prepare the tombs of the gods, hide them away in the soft flanks of the hillocks and hummocks. The gods will depart one day, as mysteriously as they came, leaving behind the human-like shell which deceives the unbelieving, the poor in spirit, the timid souls who have turned the earth into a furnace and a factory.

We have just come up from the slippery staircase, Katsimbalis and I. We have not descended it, only peered down with lighted matches. The heavy roof is buckling with the weight of time. To breathe too heavily is enough to pull the world down over our ears. Katsimbalis was for crawling down on all fours, on his belly if needs be. He has been in many a tight spot before; he has played the mole on the Balkan front, has wormed his way through mud and blood, has danced like a madman from fear and frenzy, killed all in sight including his own men, has been blown skyward clinging to a tree, has had his brain concussed, his rear blunderbussed, his arms hanging in shreds, his face blackened with powder, his bones and sinews wrenched and unsocketed. He is telling me it all over again as we stand midway to earth and sky, the lintel sagging more and more, the matches giving out. "We don't want to miss this," he pleads. But I refuse to go back down into that slimy well of horrors. Not if there were a pot of gold to be filched would I make the descent. I want to see the sky, the big birds, the short grass, the waves of blinding light, the swamp mist rising over the plain.

We come out on the far hillside into a panorama of blinding clarity. A shepherd with his flock moves about on a distant mountain side. He is larger than life, his sheep are covered with golden locks. He moves leisurely in the amplitude of forgotten time. He is moving amidst the still bodies of the dead, their fingers clasped in the short grass. He stops to talk with them, to stroke their beards. He was moving thus in Homeric times when the legend was being embroidered with copperish strands. He added a lie here and there, he pointed to the wrong direction, he altered his itinerary. For the shepherd the poet is too facile, too easily satiated. The poet would say "there *was* . . . they *were* . . ." But the shepherd says *he lives, he is, he does*. . . . The poet is always a thousand years too late—and blind to boot. The shepherd is eternal, an earth-bound spirit, a renunciator. On these hillsides forever and ever there will be the shepherd with his flock: he will survive everything, including the tradition of all that ever was.

Now we are passing over the little bridge above the sundered vault of Clytemnestra's resting place. The earth is flamy with spirit as if it were an invisible compass we are treading and only the needle quivering luminously as it catches a flash of solar radiance. We are veering towards Agamemnon's tomb over the vault of which only the thinnest patch of earth now rests like a quilt of down. The nudity of this divine caché is magnificent. Stop before the heart glows through. Stoop to pick a flower. Shards everywhere and sheep droppings. The clock has stopped. The earth sways for a fraction of a second, waiting to resume its eternal beat.

I have not yet crossed the threshold. I am outside, between the Cyclopean blocks which flank the entrance to the shaft. I am still the man I might have become, assuming every benefit of civilization to be showered upon me with regal indulgence. I am gathering all of this potential civilized muck into a hard, tiny knot of understanding. I am blown to the maximum, like a great bowl of molten glass hanging from the stem of a glass-blower. Make me into any fantastic shape, use all your art, exhaust your lung-power—still I shall only be a thing fabricated, at the best a beautiful cultured soul. I know this, I despise it. I stand outside full-blown, the most beautiful, the most cultured, the most marvellously fabricated soul on earth. I am going to put my foot over the threshold—*now*. I do so. I hear nothing. I am not even there to hear myself shattering into a billion splintered smithereens. Only Agamemnon is there. The body fell apart when they lifted the mask from his face. But he is there, he fills the still bee-hive: he spills out into the open, floods the fields, lifts the sky a little higher. The shepherd walks and talks with him by day and by night. Shepherds are crazy folk. So am I. I am done with civilization and its spawn of cultured souls. I gave myself up when I entered the tomb. From now on I am a nomad, a spiritual nobody. Take your fabricated world and put it away in the museums, I don't want it, can't use it. I don't believe any civilized being knows, or ever did know, what took place in this sacred precinct. A civilized man can't possibly know or understand—he is on the other side of that slope whose summit was scaled long before he or his progenitors came into being. They call it Agamemnon's tomb. Well, possibly some one called Agamemnon was here laid to rest. What of it? Am I to stop there, gaping like an idiot? I do not. I refuse to rest on that too-too-solid fact. I take flight here, not as poet, not as recreator, fabulist, mythologist, but as pure spirit. I say the whole world, fanning out in every direction from this spot, was once alive in a way that no man has ever dreamed of. I say there were gods who roamed everywhere, men like us in form and substance, but free, electrically free. When they departed this earth they took with them the one secret which we shall never wrest from them until we too have made ourselves free again. We are to know one day what it is to have life eternal—*when we have ceased to murder*. Here at this spot, now dedicated to the memory of Agamemnon, some foul and hidden crime blasted the hopes of man. Two worlds lie juxtaposed, the one before, the one after the crime. The crime contains the riddle, as deep as salvation itself. Spades and shovels will uncover nothing of any import. The diggers are blind, feeling their way towards something they will never see. Everything that is unmasked crumbles at the touch. Worlds crumble too, in the same way. We can dig in eternally, like moles, but fear will be ever upon us, clawing us, raping us from the rear.

It seems scarcely credible to me now that what I relate was the enchanting work of a brief morning. By noon we were already winding down the road to the little inn. On the way we came across the guardian who, though he had arrived too late, insisted on filling me with facts and dates which are utterly without sense. He spoke first in Greek and then, when he discovered I was an American, in English. When he had finished his learned recital he began talking about Coney Island. He had been a molasses-thrower on the board-walk. He might just as well have said that he had been a wasp glued to the ceiling of an abandoned chateau for all the interest I showed. Why had he come back? The truth is he hadn't come back. Nobody comes back who has once made the transatlantic voyage westward. He is still throwing molasses on the board-walk. He came back to incarnate as a parrot, to talk this senseless parrot-language to other parrots who pay to listen. This is the language in which it is said that the early Greeks believed in gods, the word god no longer having any meaning but used just the same, thrown out like counterfeit money. Men who believe in nothing write learned tomes about gods who never existed. This is part of the cultural rigmarole. If you are very proficient at it you finally get a seat in the academy where you slowly degenerate into a full-fledged chimpanzee.

Here is Agamemnon and his spouse. Would we like something à la carte or a full banquet, a royal gorge, so to speak? Where is the wine list? A good cold wine while we wait would be in order. Katsimbalis is smacking his lips; his palate is dry. We flop down on the lawn and Agamemnon brings us a de luxe edition of a book by an English archaeologist. This is the hors d'oeuvre, apparently, for the bloody English tourist. The book stinks of learning: it is about upper and lower strata, breast-plates, chicken bones and grave relics. I chuck it aside when Agamemnon has turned his back. He is a tender fellow, this Agamemnon, and is almost a diplomat from force of habit. His wife has the air of being a good cook. Katsimbalis is dozing off under a big tree. Some German sauerkrauts, disguised as human beings, are sitting at a table under another tree. They look frightfully learned and repulsive; they are swollen like toads.

I am gazing blankly at the field of Irish green. It is a Lawrence Durrell field, heraldic in every sense of the word. Looking blankly into that field I suddenly realize what Durrell was trying to tell me in those long rambling poems he called letters. I used to think, when these heraldic messages arrived at the Villa Seurat on a cold summer's day in Paris, that he had taken a sniff of coke before oiling his pen. Once a big fulsome sheaf which looked like prose fell out of the envelope—it was called "Zero" and it was dedicated to me by this same Lawrence Durrell who said he lived in Corfu. I had heard of chicken tracks and of liver mantic and I once came near grasping the idea of absolute Zero, even though the thermometer has yet to be made which could register it, but not until I sat gazing into the field of Irish green in front of Agamemnon's Inn did I ever get the idea of Zero in the heraldic sense. There never was a field so fieldishly green as this. When you spot anything true and clear you are at Zero. Zero is Greek for pure vision. It means what Lawrence Durrell says when he writes Ionian. It means, and now for example, I can tell you more precisely because what I am trying to describe is happening right before my very eyes. . . . Two men and a woman are standing in the field. One man has a tape measure in his hand. He is going to measure off the plot of land which he has received for a wedding present. His bride is there to make certain that not a millimetre of land is miscalculated. They are down on all fours. They are arguing about a tiny piece in the southwest corner. Perhaps a twig has diverted the tape measure the fraction of a millimetre. One can't be too careful. Never look a gift horse in the mouth! They are measuring something which heretofore was only a word to me—*land*. The dead heroes, the gold cups, the bucklers, the jewels, the chased daggers—these items have nothing to do with the business in hand. What is vital here is land, just land. I roll it over and over on my tongue—land, land, land. Why yes, *land,* that's it—I had almost forgotten it meant such a simple, eternal thing. One gets twisted, derouted, spavined and indoctrinated shouting "Land of the Free" et cetera. Land is something on which to grow crops, build a home, raise cows and sheep. Land is land, what a grand, simple word! Yes, Lawrence Durrell, zero is what you make it: you take a piece of wet earth and as you squeeze it between your fingers you get two men and a woman standing in a field of Irish green measuring land. The wine has come. I raise my glass. *Salute, Larry me lad, and keep the flag at zero!* In a few more pages we shall revisit Mycenae together and Nancy will lead the way down the bat-slimed stairs to the bottomless well.

Our grand tour of the Peloponnesus was cut short at Mycenae. Katsimbalis had received an urgent call to return to Athens owing to the unexpected discovery of a piece of land which his attorneys had overlooked. The news didn't seem to thrill him. On the contrary he was depressed: more property meant more taxes, more debts—and more headaches. I could have continued my explorations alone, but I preferred to return to Athens with him and digest what I had seen and felt. We took the automotrice at Mycenae, a direct run of five or six hours, if I remember rightly, for the absurd price of a couple of cocktails at the Ritz.

Between the time of my return and my departure for Crete three or four little incidents occurred which I feel impelled to make brief mention of. The first was "Juarez," the American film which ran for several weeks at one of the leading theatres. Despite the fact that Greece is under a dictatorship this film, which was only slightly modified after the first few showings, was shown night and day to an increasingly packed house. The atmosphere was tense, the applause distinctly Republican. For many reasons the film had acute significance for the Greek people. One felt that the spirit of Venizelos was still alive. In that blunt and magnificent speech which Juarez makes to the assembled plenipotentiaries of the foreign powers one felt that the tragic plight of Mexico under Maximilian had curious and throbbing analogies with the present perilous position of Greece. The only true friend which Greece has at this moment, the only relatively disinterested one, is America. Of that I shall have more to say when I come to Crete, the birthplace of Venizelos as well as of El Greco. But to witness the showing of a film in which all forms of dictatorship are dramatically denounced, to witness it in the midst of an audience whose hands are tied, except to applaud, is an impressive event. It was one of those rare moments when I felt that, in a world which is almost entirely gagged, shackled and manacled, to be an American is almost a luxury.

The second event was a visit to the astronomical observatory in Athens, arranged for Durrell and myself by Theodore Stephanides who, as an amateur astronomer, has made admittedly important astronomical discoveries. The officials received us very cordially,

thanks to the generous aid given them by American fellow-workers
in this field. I had never looked through the telescope of a bona
fide observatory before. Nor had Durrell, I presume. The experience was sensational, though probably not altogether in accord
with the expectations of our hosts. Our remarks, which were
juvenile and ecstatic, seemed to bewilder them. We certainly did
not display the orthodox reactions to the wonders that were
unfolded. I shall never forget their utter amazement when Durrell,
who was gazing at the Pleiades, suddenly exclaimed—*"Rosicru-
cian!"* What did he mean by that? they wanted to know. I mounted
the ladder and took a look for myself. I doubt if I can describe the
effect of that first breathless vision of a splintered star world. The
image I shall always retain is that of Chartres, an effulgent rose
window shattered by a hand grenade. I mean it in a double or triple
sense—of awesome, indestructible beauty, of cosmic violation, of
world ruin suspended in the sky like a fatal omen, of the eternality
of beauty even when blasted and desecrated. "As above so below," runs the famous saying of Hermes Trismegistus. To see the
Pleiades through a powerful telescope is to sense the sublime and
awesome truth of these words. In his highest flights, musical and
architectural above all, for they are one, man gives the illusion of
rivalling the order, the majesty and the splendor of the heavens; in
his fits of destruction the evil and the desolation which he spreads
seems incomparable until we reflect on the great stellar shake-ups
brought on by the mental aberrations of the unknown Wizard. Our
hosts seemed impervious to such reflections; they spoke knowingly of weights, distances, substances, etc. They were removed
from the normal activities of their fellow-men in a quite different
way from ourselves. For them beauty was incidental, for us everything. For them the physicomathematical world palped, calibred,
weighed and transmitted by their instruments was reality itself, the
stars and planets mere proof of their excellent and infallible reasoning. For Durrell and myself reality lay wholly beyond the reach of
their puny instruments which in themselves were nothing more
than clumsy reflections of their circumscribed imagination locked
forever in the hypothetical prison of logic. Their astronomical
figures and calculations, intended to impress and overawe us, only
caused us to smile indulgently or to very impolitely laugh outright
at them. Speaking for myself, facts and figures have always left me
unimpressed. A light year is no more impressive to me than a
second, or a split second. This is a game for the feeble-minded
which can go on ad nauseam backwards and forwards without
taking us anywhere. Similarly I am not more convinced of the
reality of a star when I see it through the telescope. It may be

more brilliant, more wondrous, it may be a thousand times or a million times bigger than when seen with the naked eye, but it is not a whit more real. To say that this is what a thing *really* looks like, just because one sees it larger and grander, seems to me quite fatuous. It is just as real to me if I don't see it at all but merely imagine it to be there. And finally, even when to my own eye and the eye of the astronomer it possesses the same dimensions, the same brilliance, it definitely does not look the same to us both— Durrell's very exclamation is sufficient to prove that.

But let us pass on—to Saturn. Saturn, and our moon likewise, when seen through a magnifying lens, are impressive to the layman in a way which the scientist must instinctively deplore and deprecate. No facts or figures about Saturn, no magnification, can explain the unreasonably disquieting sensation which the sight of this planet produces upon the mind of the spectator. Saturn is a living symbol of gloom, morbidity, disaster, fatality. Its milk-white hue inevitably arouses associations with tripe, dead gray matter, vulnerable organs hidden from sight, loathsome diseases, test-tubes, laboratory specimens, catarrh, rheum, ectoplasm, melancholy shades, morbid phenomena, incuba and succuba war, sterility, anaemia, indecision, defeatism, constipation, anti-toxins, feeble novels, hernia, meningitis, dead-letter laws, red tape, working class conditions, sweat shops, Y.M.C.A.'s, Christian Endeavor meetings, spiritist seances, poets like T. S. Eliot, zealots like Alexander Dowie, healers like Mary Baker Eddy, statesmen like Chamberlain, trivial fatalities like slipping on a banana peel and cracking one's skull, dreaming of better days and getting wedged between two motor trucks, drowning in one's own bath-tub, killing one's best friend accidentally, dying of hiccoughs instead of on the battle field, and so on ad infinitum. Saturn is malefic through force of inertia. Its ring, which is only paperweight in thickness, according to the savants, is the wedding ring which signifies death or misfortune devoid of all significance. Saturn, whatever it may be to the astronomer, is the sign of senseless fatality to the man in the street. He carries it in his heart because his whole life, devoid of significance as it is, is wrapped up in this ultimate symbol which, if all else fails to do him in, this he can count upon to finish him off. Saturn is life in suspense, not dead so much as deathless, i.e. incapable of dying. Saturn is like dead bone in the ear—double mastoid for the soul. Saturn is like a roll of wall-paper wrong side out and smeared with that catarrhal paste which wall-paperers find so indispensable in their metier. Saturn is a vast agglomeration of those evil looking shreds which one hawks up the morning after he has smoked several packs of crisp, toasted, coughless, inspiring cigarettes. Saturn is postponement manifesting itself as an accomplishment in itself. Saturn is doubt, perplexity, scepticism, facts for fact's sake and no hokum, no mysticism, understand? Saturn is the diabolical sweat of learning for its own sake, the congealed fog of the monomaniac's ceaseless pursuit of what is always just beyond his nose. Saturn is deliciously melancholic because it knows and recognizes nothing beyond melancholy; it swims in its own fat. Saturn is the symbol of all omens and superstitions, the phony proof of divine entropy, phony because if it were true that the universe is running down Saturn would have melted away long ago. Saturn is as eternal as fear and irresolution, growing more milky, more cloudy, with each compromise, each capitulation. Timid souls cry for Saturn just as children are reputed to cry for Castoria. Saturn gives us only what we ask for, never an ounce extra. Saturn is the white hope of the white race which prattles endlessly about the wonders of nature and spends its time killing off the greatest wonder of all—MAN. Saturn is the stellar imposter setting itself up as the grand cosmocrator of Fate, Monsieur le Paris, the automatic pole-axer of a world smitten with ataraxy. Let the heavens sing its glory—this lymphatic globe of doubt and ennui will never cease to cast its milk-white rays of lifeless gloom.

This is the emotional photograph of a planet whose unorthodox influence still weighs heavily upon the almost extinct consciousness of man. It is the most cheerless spectacle in the heavens. It corresponds to every craven image conceived in the heart of man; it is the single repository of all the despair and defeat to which the human race from time immemorial has succumbed. It will become invisible only when man has purged it from his consciousness.

The third event was of a wholly different order—a jazz seance at the austere bachelor chambers of Seferiades in the Rue Kydathenaion, one of the streets I was instinctively attracted to on my first exploration of Athens. Seferiades, who is a cross between bull and panther by nature, has strong Virgo traits, speaking astrologically. That is to say, he has a passion for collecting, as did Goethe who was one of the best Virgo types the world has ever known. The first shock I had on entering his place on this particular occasion was that of meeting his most gracious and most lovely sister, Jeanne. She impressed me immediately as being of royal descent, perhaps of the Egyptian line—in any case, distinctly trans-Pontine. As I was gazing at her ecstatically I was suddenly startled by the sound of Cab Calloway's baboon-like voice. Seferiades looked at me with that warm Asiatic smile which always spread over his face like nectar and ambrosia. "Do you know that piece?" he said, beaming with pleasure. "I have some others, if you'd care to hear them," and he pointed to a file of albums about a yard long. "What about Louis Armstrong, do you like him?" he continued. "Here's a Fats Waller record. Wait a minute, have you ever heard Count Basie—or Peewee Russell?" He knew every virtuoso of any account; he was a subscriber to "Le Jazz Hot" I soon discovered. In a few moments we were talking about the Café Boudon in Montmartre where the great Negro performers of the night clubs repair before and after work. He wanted to hear about the American Negro, about life behind the scene. What influence did the Negro have upon American life, what did the American people think of Negro literature? Was it true that there was a Negro aristocracy, a cultural aristocracy which was superior to the white American cultural groups? Could a man like Duke Ellington register at the Savoy-Plaza without embarrassment? What about Caldwell and Faulkner—was it a true picture of the South which they gave? And so on. As I've remarked before, Seferiades is an indefatigable questioner. No detail is too trivial for him to overlook. His curiosity is insatiable, his knowledge vast and varied. After entertaining me with a selection of the most up to date jazz numbers he wanted to know if I should like to hear some exotic music of which he had an interesting variety. While searching for a record he would ply me with questions about some recondite English poet or about the circumstances surrounding Ambrose Bierce's disappearance or what did I know about the Greenberg manuscripts which Hart Crane had made use of. Or, having found the record he was looking for he would suddenly switch to a little anecdote about his life in Albania which, in some curiously dissociated way, had to do with a poem by T. S. Eliot or St. Jean Perse. I speak of these divagations of his because they were a refreshing antidote to the sort of obsessive, single-tracked and wholly mirthless order of conversation indulged in by the English literati in Athens. An evening with these buttery-mouthed jakes always left me in a suicidal mood. A Greek is alive to the finger-tips; he oozes vitality, he's effervescent, he's ubiquitous in spirit. The Englishman is lymphatic, made for the arm-chair, the fireside, the dingy tavern, the didactic tread-mill. Durrell used to take a perverse delight in observing my discomfiture in the presence of his countrymen: they were one and all like animated cartoons from his "Black Book," that devastating chronicle of the English death. In the presence of an Englishman Katsimbalis would positively dry up. Nobody really hated them—they were simply insufferable.

Later that evening I had the privilege of meeting some Greek women, friends of Seferiades' sister. Here again I was impressed by the absence of those glaring defects which make even the most beautiful American or English woman seem positively ugly. The Greek woman, even when she is cultured, is first and foremost a woman. She sheds a distinct fragrance; she warms and thrills you. Due to the absorption of Greeks from Asia Minor the new generation of Athenian womanhood has improved in beauty and vigor. The ordinary Greek girl whom one sees on the street is superior in every way to her American counterpart; above all she has character and race, a combination which makes for deathless beauty and which forever distinguishes the descendants of ancient peoples from the bastard off-shoots of the New World. How can I ever forget the young girl whom we passed one day at the foot of the Acropolis? Perhaps she was ten, perhaps she was fourteen years of age; her hair was reddish gold, her features as noble, as grave and austere as those of the caryatids on the Erectheum. She was playing with some comrades in a little clearing before a clump of ramshackle shanties which had somehow escaped the general demolition. Any one who has read "Death in Venice" will appreciate my sincerity when I say that no woman, not even the loveliest woman I have ever seen, is or was capable of arousing in me such a feeling of adoration as this young girl elicited. If Fate were to put her in my path again I know not what folly I might commit. She was child, virgin, angel, seductress, priestess, harlot, prophetess all in one. She was neither ancient Greek nor modern Greek; she was of no race or time or class, but unique, fabulously unique. In that slow, sustained smile which she gave us as we paused a moment to gaze at her there was that enigmatic quality which da Vinci has immortalized, which one finds everywhere in Buddhistic art, which one finds in the great caves of India and on the facades of her temples, which one finds in the dancers of Java and of Bali and in primitive races, especially in Africa; which indeed seems to be the culminating expression of the spiritual achievement of the human race, but which to-day is totally absent in the countenance of the Western woman. Let me add a strange reflection—that the nearest approximation to this enigmatic quality which I ever noted was in the smile of a peasant woman at Corfu, a woman with six toes, decidedly ugly, and considered by every one as something of a monster. She used to come to the well, as is the custom of the peasant women, to fill her jug, to do her washing, and to gossip. The well was situated at the foot of a steep declivity around which there wandered a goat-like path. In every direction there were thick shady olive groves broken here and there by ravines which formed the beds of mountain streams which in Summer were completely dried up. The well had an extraordinary fascination for me; it was a place reserved for the female beast of burden, for the strong, buxom virgin who could carry her jug of water strapped to her back with grace and ease, for the old toothless hag whose curved back was still capable of sustaining a staggering load of firewood, for the widow with her straggling flock of children, for the servant girls who laughed too easily, for wives who took over the work of their lazy husbands, for every species of female, in short, except the grand mistress or the idle English women of the vicinity. When I first saw the women staggering up the steep slopes, like the women of old in the Bible, I felt a pang of distress. The very manner of strapping the heavy jug to the back gave me a feeling of humiliation. The more so because the men who might have performed this humble task were more than likely sitting in the cool of a tavern or lying prone under an olive tree. My first thought was to relieve the young maid at our house of a minor task; I wanted to feel one of those jugs on my own back, to know with my own muscular aches what that repeated journey to the well meant. When I communicated my desire to Durrell he threw up his hands in horror. It wasn't done, he exclaimed, laughing at my ignorance. I told him it didn't matter to me in the least whether it was done or not done, that he was robbing me of a joy which I had never tasted. He begged me not to do it, for *his* sake—he said he would lose caste, that the Greeks would laugh at us. In short, he made such a point of it that I was obliged to abandon the idea. But on my rambles through the hills I usually made a point of stopping at the well to slake my thirst. There one day I espied the monster with six toes. She was standing in her bare feet, ankle deep in mud, washing a bundle of clothes. That she was ugly I could not deny, but there are all kinds of ugliness and hers was the sort which instead of repelling attracts. To begin with she was strong, sinewy, vital, an animal endowed with a human soul and with indisputable sexual powers. When she bent over to wring out a pair of pants the vitality in her limbs rippled and flashed through the tattered and bedraggled skirt which clung to her swarthy flesh. Her eyes glowed like coals, like the eyes of a Bedouin woman. Her lips were blood red and her strong even teeth as white as chalk. The thick black hair hung over her shoulders in rich, oily strands, as though saturated with olive oil. Renoir would have found her beautiful; he would not have noticed the six toes nor the coarseness of her features. He would have followed the rippling flesh, the full globes of her teats, the easy, swaying stance, the superabundant strength of her arms, her legs, her torso; he would have been ravished by the full, generous slit of the mouth, by the dark and burning glance of the eye, by the massive contours of the head and the gleaming black waves which fell in cascades down her sturdy, columnar neck. He would have caught the animal lust, the ardor unquenchable, the fire in the guts, the tenacity of the tigress, the hunger, the rapacity, the all-devouring appetite of the oversexed female who is not wanted because she has an extra toe.

Anyhow, Renoir apart, there was something in this woman's smile which the sight of the young girl at the base of the Acropolis revived. I said it was the nearest approximation to that enigmatic quality engraved in the countenance of the girl with the reddish gold hair. By that, paradoxical though it may sound, I mean that it was wholly antipodal. The monster might well have been the one to give birth to that startling figure of beauty; she might because in her starved dream of love her embrace had spanned a void beyond the imagination of the most desperately love-lorn woman. All her powers of seduction had been driven back into the coffin of sex where, in the darkness of her loins, passion and desire burned to a thick smoke. Disclaiming all hope of seducing man her lust had turned towards forbidden objects of desire—towards the animals of the field, towards inanimate things, towards objects of veneration, towards mythological deities. Her smile had in it something of the intoxication of parched earth after a sudden and furious downpour; it was the smile of the insatiable one to whom a thousand burning kisses are only the incentive to renewed assaults. In some strange and inexplicable fashion she has remained in my memory as the symbol of that hunger for unbounded love which I sensed in a lesser degree in all Greek women. It is almost the symbol of Greece itself, this unappeasable lust for beauty, passion, love.

For twenty years it had been my dream to visit Knossus. I never realized how simple it would be to make the journey. In Greece you have only to announce to some one that you intend to visit a certain place and presto! in a few moments there is a carriage waiting for you at the door. This time it turned out to be an aeroplane. Seferiades had decided that I should ride in pomp. It was a poetic gesture and I accepted it like a poet.

I had never been in a plane before and I probably will never go up again. I felt foolish sitting in the sky with hands folded; the man beside me was reading a newspaper, apparently oblivious of the clouds that brushed the window-panes. We were probably making a hundred miles an hour, but since we passed nothing but clouds I had the impression of not moving. In short, it was unrelievedly dull and pointless. I was sorry that I had not booked passage on the good ship Acropolis which was to touch at Crete shortly. Man is made to walk the earth and sail the seas; the conquest of the air is reserved for a later stage of his evolution, when he will have sprouted real wings and assumed the form of the angel which he is in essence. Mechanical devices have nothing to do with man's real nature—they are merely traps which Death has baited for him.

We came down at the seaport of Herakleion, one of the principal towns of Crete. The main street is almost a ringer for a movie still in a third-rate Western picture. I found a room quickly in one of the two hotels and set out to look for a restaurant. A gendarme, whom I accosted, took me by the arm and graciously escorted me to a modest place near the public fountain. The meal was bad but I was now within reach of Knossus and too excited to be disturbed about such a trifle. After lunch I went across the street to a cafe and had a Turkish coffee. Two Germans who had arrived by the same plane were discussing the lecture on Wagner which they were to give that evening; they seemed to be fatuously unaware that they had come with their musical poison to the birthplace of Venizelos. I left to take a quick stroll through the town. A few doors away, in a converted mosque, a cinema announced the coming of Laurel and Hardy. The children who were clustered about the billboards were evidently as enthusiastic about these clowns as the children of Dubuque or Kenosha might be. I believe the cinema was called "The Minoan." I wondered vaguely if there would be a cinema at Knossus too, announcing perhaps the coming of the Marx Brothers.

Herakleion is a shabby town bearing all the ear-marks of Turkish domination. The principal streets are filled with open shops in which everything for men's needs are made by hand as in medieval times. From the countryside the Cretans come in garbed in handsome black raiment set off by elegant high boots, of red or white leather offtimes. Next to Hindus and Berbers they are the most handsome, noble, dignified males I have ever seen. They are far more striking than the women: they are a race apart.

I walked to the edge of the town where as always in the Balkans everything comes to an end abruptly, as though the monarch who had designed the weird creation had suddenly become demented, leaving the great gate swinging on one hinge. Here the buses collect like broken-down caterpillars waiting for the dust of the plains to smother them in oblivion. I turned back and dove into the labyrinth of narrow, twisting streets which forms the residential quarter and which, though thoroughly Greek, has the atmospheric flavor of some English outpost in the West Indies. I had long tried to imagine what the approach to Crete would be like. In my ignorance I had supposed that the island was sparsely inhabited, that there was no water to be had except what was brought in from the mainland; I thought that one would see a deserted-looking coast dotted with a few scintillating ruins which would be Knossus, and beyond Knossus there would be a wasteland resembling those vast areas of Australia where the dodo bird, shunned by other feathered species of the bush, forlornly buries his head in the sand and whistles out the other end. I remembered that a friend of mine, a French writer, had been stricken with dysentery here and transported on the back of a donkey to a small boat whence by some miracle he was transported to a passing freighter and returned to the mainland in a state of delirium. I wandered about in a daze, stopping now and then to listen to a cracked record from a horned phonograph standing on a chair in the middle of the street. The butchers were draped in blood-red aprons; they stood before primitive chopping blocks in little booths such as one may still see at Pompeii. Every so often the streets opened up into a public square flanked by insane buildings devoted to law, administration, church, education, sickness and insanity; the architecture was of that startling reality which characterizes the work of the popular primitives such as Bombois, Peyronnet, Kane, Sullivan and Vivin. In the dazzling sunlight a detail such as a grilled gate or a defenceless bastion stands out with hair-raising exactitude such as one sees only in the paintings of the very great or the insane. Every inch of Herakleion is paintable; it is a confused, nightmarish town, thoroughly anomalous, thoroughly heterogeneous, a place-dream suspended in a void between Europe and Africa, smelling strongly of raw hides, caraway seeds, tar and sub-tropical fruits. It has been brutalized by the Turk and infected with the harmless rose water vaporings of the back pages of Charles Dickens. It has no relation whatever to Knossus or Phaestos; it is Minoan in the way that Walt Disney's creations are American; it is a carbuncle on the face of time, a sore spot which one rubs like a horse while asleep on four legs.

I had in my pocket a card of introduction to the leading literary figure of Crete, a friend of Katsimbalis. Towards evening I found him in the café where the Germans had been hatching their Wagnerian machinations. I shall call him Mr. Tsoutsou as I have unfortunately forgotten his name. Mr. Tsoutsou spoke French, English, German, Spanish, Italian, Russian, Portuguese, Turkish, Arabic, demotic Greek, newspaper Greek and ancient Greek. He was a composer, poet, scholar and lover of food and drink. He began by asking me about James Joyce, T. S. Eliot, Walt Whitman, André Gide, Breton, Rimbaud, Lautréamont, Lewis Carroll, Monk Lewis, Heinrich Georg and Rainer Maria Rilke. I say he asked me about them, much as you would ask about a relative or a mutual friend. He spoke of them as if they were all alive, which they are, thank God. I rubbed my head. He started off on Aragon—had I read *"Le Paysan de Paris?"* Did I remember the Passage Jouffroy in Paris? What did I think of St. Jean Perse? Or *"Nadja"* of Breton? Had I been to Knossus yet? I ought to stay a few weeks at least—he would take me over the island from one end to another. He was a very hale and hearty fellow and when he understood that I liked to eat and drink he beamed most approvingly. He regretted sincerely that he was not free for the evening, but hoped to see me the following day; he wanted to introduce me to the little circle of literati in Herakleion. He was excited by the fact that I came from America and begged me to tell him something about New York which I found it almost impossible to do because I had long ceased to identify myself with that odious city.

I went back to the hotel for a nap. There were three beds in the room, all of them very comfortable. I read carefully the sign warning the clients to refrain from tipping the employees. The room cost only about seventeen cents a night and I became involved willy-nilly in a fruitless speculation as to how many drachmas one would give as a tip if one could tip. There were only three or four clients in the hotel. Walking through the wide corridors looking for the W. C. I met the maid, an angelic sort of spinster with straw hair and watery blue eyes who reminded me vividly of the Swedenborgian caretaker of the Maison Balzac in Passy. She was bringing me a glass of water on a tray made of lead, zinc and tin. I undressed and as I was pulling in the blinds I observed two men and a stenographer gazing at me from the window of some outlandish commercial house across the way. It seemed unreal, this transaction of abstract business in a place like Herakleion. The typewriter looked surrealistic and the men with sleeves rolled up as in commercial houses everywhere appeared fantastically like the freaks of the Western world who move grain and corn and wheat around in carload lots by means of the telephone, the ticker, the telegraph. Imagine what it would be like to find two business men and a stenographer on Easter Island! Imagine how a typewriter would sound in that Oceanic silence! I fell back on the bed and into a deep, drugged sleep. No tipping allowed—that was the last thought and a very beautiful one to a weary traveller.

When I awoke it was dark. I opened the blinds and looked down the forlorn main street which was now deserted. I heard a telegraph instrument clicking. I got into my things and hurried to the restaurant near the fountain. The waiter seemed to expect me and stood

ready to translate for me into that Iroquois English which the
itinerant Greek has acquired in the course of his wanderings. I
ordered some cold fish with the skin on it and a bottle of dark-red
Cretan wine. While waiting to be served I noticed a man peering
through the large plate-glass window; he walked away and came
back again in a few minutes. Finally he made up his mind to walk
in. He walked directly up to my table and addressed me—in
English. Was I not Mr. Miller who had arrived by plane a few
hours ago? I was. He begged leave to introduce himself. He was
Mr. So-and-So, the British Vice-Consul at Herakleion. He had
noticed that I was an American, a writer. He was always happy to
make the acquaintance of an American. He paused a moment, as
if embarrassed, and then went on to say that his sole motive for
introducing himself was to let me know that as long as I remained
in Crete I was to consider his humble services entirely at my
disposal. He said that he was originally from Smyrna and that
every Greek from Smyrna was eternally indebted to the American
people. He said that there was no favor too great for me to ask of
him.

The natural reply was to ask him to sit down and share a meal
with me, which I did. He explained that he would be unable to
accept the honor as he was obliged to dine in the bosom of his
family, *but*—would I do him the honor of taking a coffee with him
and his wife at their home after dinner? As the representatives of
the great American people (not at all sure of the heroic role we had
played in the great disaster of Smyrna) I most graciously accepted,
rose, bowed, shook his hand and escorted him to the door where
once again we exchanged polite thanks and mutual felicitations. I
went back to the table, unskinned the cold fish and proceeded to
wet my whistle. The meal was even lousier than at noon, but the
service was extraordinary. The whole restaurant was aware that a
distinguished visitor had arrived and was partaking with them of
their humble food. Mr. Tsoutsou and his wife appeared for just a
moment to see how I was faring, commented bravely on the
delicious, appetizing appearance of the skinned fish and disappeared with bows and salaams which sent an electric thrill through
the assembled patrons of Herakleion's most distinguished restaurant. I began to feel as though something of vast import were about
to happen. I ordered the waiter to send the *chasseur* out for a
coffee and cognac. Never before had a vice-consul or any form of
public servant other than a constable or gendarme sought me out
in a public place. The plane was responsible for it. It was like a
letter of credit.

The home of the vice-consul was rather imposing for Herakleion.

In truth, it was more like a museum than a home. I felt somewhat
hysterical, somewhat disoriented. The vice-consul was a good,
kind-hearted man but vain as a peacock. He drummed nervously
on the arm of the chair, waiting impatiently for his wife to leave
off about Paris, Berlin, Prague, Budapest et cetera in order to
confide that he was the author of a book on Crete. He kept telling
his wife that I was a journalist, an insult which normally I find hard
to swallow, but in this case I found it easy not to take offense since
the vice-consul considered all writers to be journalists. He pressed
a button and very sententiously commanded the maid to go to the
library and find him a copy of the book he had written on Crete.
He confessed that he had never written a book before but, owing
to the general state of ignorance and confusion regarding Crete in
the mind of the average tourist, he had deemed it incumbent upon
him to put down what he knew about his adopted land in more or
less eternal fashion. He admitted that Sir Arthur Evans had expressed it all in unimpeachable style but then there were little
things, trifles by comparison of course which a work of that scope
and grandeur could not hope to encompass. He spoke in this
pompous, ornate, highly fatuous way about his masterpiece. He
said that a journalist like myself would be one of the few to really
appreciate what he had done for the cause of Crete et cetera. He
handed me the book to glance at. He handed it over as if it were
the Gutenberg Bible. I took one glance and realized immediately
that I was dealing with one of the "popular masters of reality," a
blood-brother to the man who had painted "A Rendezvous with
the Soul." He inquired in a pseudo-modest way if the English were
all right, because English was not his native tongue. The implication was that if he had done it in Greek it would be beyond
criticism. I asked him politely where I might hope to obtain a copy
of this obviously extraordinary work whereupon he informed me
that if I came to his office in the morning he would bestow one
upon me as a gift, as a memento of this illustrious occasion which
had culminated in the meeting of two minds thoroughly attuned to
the splendors of the past. This was only the beginning of a cataract
of flowerly horse shit which I had to swallow before going through
the motions of saying good-night. Then came the Smyrna disaster
with a harrowing, detailed recital of the horrors which the Turks
perpetrated on the helpless Greeks and the merciful intervention
of the American people which no Greek would ever forget until his
dying day. I tried desperately, while he spun out the horrors and
atrocities, to recall what I had been doing at this black moment in
the history of Greece. Evidently the disaster had occurred during
one of those long intervals when I had ceased to read the newspa-

pers. I hadn't the faintest remembrance of any such catastrophe. To the best of my recollection the event must have taken place during the year when I was looking for a job without the slightest intention of taking one. It reminded me that, desperate as I thought myself then to be, I had not even bothered to look through the columns of the want ads.

Next morning I took the bus in the direction of Knossus. I had to walk a mile or so after leaving the bus to reach the ruins. I was so elated that it seemed as if I were walking on air. At last my dream was about to be realized. The sky was overcast and it sprinkled a bit as I hopped along. Again, as at Mycenae, I felt that I was being drawn to the spot. Finally, as I rounded a bend, I stopped dead in my tracks; I had the feeling that I was there. I looked about for traces of the ruins but there were none in sight. I stood for several minutes gazing intently at the contours of the smooth hills which barely grazed the electric blue sky. This must be the spot, I said to myself, I can't be wrong. I retraced my steps and cut through the fields to the bottom of a gulch. Suddenly, to my left, I discovered a bald pavilion with columns painted in raw, bold colors—the palace of King Minos. I was at the back entrance of the ruins amidst a clump of buildings that looked as if they had been gutted by fire. I went round the hill to the main entrance and followed a little group of Greeks in the wake of a guide who spoke a boustrophedonous language which was sheer Pelasgian to me.

There has been much controversy about the aesthetics of Sir Arthur Evans' work of restoration. I found myself unable to come to any conclusion about it; I accepted it as a fact. However Knossus may have looked in the past, however it may look in the future, this one which Evans has created is the only one I shall ever know. I am grateful to him for what he did, grateful that he had made it possible for me to descend the grand staircase, to sit on that marvellous throne chair the replica of which at the Hague Peace Tribunal is now almost as much of a relic of the past as the original.

Knossus in all its manifestations suggests the splendor and sanity and opulence of a powerful and peaceful people. It is gay— gay, healthful, sanitary, salubrious. The common people played a great role, that is evident. It has been said that throughout its long history every form of government known to man was tested out; in many ways it is far closer in spirit to modern times, to the twentieth century, I might say, than other later epochs of the Hellenic world. One feels the influence of Egypt, the homely human immediacy of the Etruscan world, the wise, communal organizing spirit of Inca days. I do not pretend to know, but I felt, as I have seldom felt before the ruins of the past, that here throughout long centuries there reigned an era of peace. There is something down to earth about Knossus, the sort of atmosphere which is evoked when one says Chinese or French. The religious note seems to be graciously diminished; women played an important, equal role in the affairs of this people; a spirit of play is markedly noticeable. In short, the prevailing note is one of joy. One feels that man lived to live, that he was not plagued by thoughts of a life beyond, that he was not smothered and restricted by undue reverence for the ancestral spirits, that he was religious in the only way which is becoming to man, by making the most of everything that comes to hand, by extracting the utmost of life from every passing minute. Knossus was worldly in the best sense of the word. The civilization which it epitomized went to pieces fifteen hundred years before the coming of the Saviour, having bequeathed to the Western world the greatest single contribution yet known to man—the alphabet. In another part of the Island, at Gortyna, this discovery is immortalized in huge blocks of stone which run over the countryside like a miniature Chinese wall. To-day the magic has gone out of the alphabet; it is a dead form to express dead thoughts.

Walking back to meet the bus I stopped at a little village to get a drink. The contrast between past and present was tremendous, as though the secret of life had been lost. The men who gathered around me took on the appearance of uncouth savages. They were friendly and hospitable, extraordinarily so, but by comparison with the Minoans they were like neglected domesticated animals. I am not thinking of the comforts which they lacked, for in point of comfort I make no great distinction between the life of a Greek peasant, a Chinese coolie and a migratory American jack-of-all-trades. I am thinking now of the lack of those essential elements of life which make possible a real society of human beings. The great fundamental lack, which is apparent everywhere in our civilized world, is the total absence of anything approaching a communal existence. We have become spiritual nomads; whatever pertains to the soul is derelict, tossed about by the winds like flotsam and jetsam. The village of Hagia Triada, looked at from any point in time, stands out like a jewel of consistency, integrity, significance. When a miserable Greek village, such as the one I am speaking of, and the counterpart of which we have by the thousand in America, embellishes its meagre, stultified life by the adoption of telephone, radio, automobile, tractor, et cetera, the meaning of the word communal becomes so fantastically distorted that one begins to wonder what is meant by the phrase "human society." There is nothing human about these sporadic agglomerations of beings; they are beneath any known level of life which this globe has known. They are less in every way than the pygmies who are truly nomadic and who move in filthy freedom with delicious security.

As I sipped my glass of water, which had a strange taste, I listened to one of these glorified baboons reminisce about the glorious days he had spent in Herkimer, New York. He had run a candy store there and seemed grateful to America for having permitted him to save the few thousand dollars which he required to return to his native land and resume the degrading life of toil which he was accustomed to. He ran back to the house to fetch an American book which he had kept as a souvenir of the wonderful money-making days. It was a farmer's almanac, badly thumb-marked, fly-bitten, louse-ridden. Here in the very cradle of our civilization a dirty baboon hands me a precious monstrosity of letters—the almanac.

The owner of the almanac and myself were seated at a table off the road in the center of a group of louts who were visibly impressed. I ordered cognac for the crowd and surrendered myself to the interlocutor. A man came over and put his big hairy finger on the photograph of a farm implement. The interlocutor said: "good machine, he like this." Another one took the book in his hands and went through it with a wet thumb, grunting now and then to signify his pleasure. Interlocutor said: "Very interesting book. He like American books." Suddenly he espied a friend in the background. "Come here," he called. He presented him to me. "Nick! He work in Michigan. Big farm. He like America too." I shook hands with Nick. Said Nick: "You New York? Me go New York once." He made a motion with his hands to indicate the skyscrapers. Nick spoke animatedly to the others. Suddenly there was a silence and the interlocutor spoke up. "They want to know how you like Greece." "It's marvellous," I answered. He laughed. "Greece very poor country, yes? No money. America rich. Everybody got money, yes?" I said yes to satisfy him. He turned to the others and explained that I had agreed—America was a very rich country, everybody rich, lots of money. "How long you stay in Greece?" he asked. "Maybe a year, maybe two years," I answered. He laughed again, as though I were an idiot. "What your business?" I told him I had no business. "You millionaire?" I told him I was very poor. He laughed, more than ever. The others were listening intently. He spoke a few words to them rapidly. "What you have to drink?" he asked. "Cretan people like Americans. Cretan people good people. You like cognac, yes?" I nodded.

Just then the bus came along. I made as if to go. "No hurry,"

said the interlocutor. "He no go yet. He make water here." The
others were smiling at me. What were they thinking? That I was a
queer bird to come to a place like Crete? Again I was asked what
my business was. I made the motion of writing with a pen. "Ah!"
exclaimed the interlocutor. "Newspaper!" He clapped his hands
and spoke excitedly to the innkeeper. A Greek newspaper was
produced. He shoved it into my hands. "You read that?" I shook
my head. He snatched the paper out of my hand. He read the
headline aloud in Greek, the others listening gravely. As he was
reading I noticed the date—the paper was a month old. The
interlocutor translated for me. "He say President Roosevelt no
want fight. Hitler bad man." Then he got up and seizing a cane
from one of the by-standers he put it to his shoulder and imitated
a man firing point-blank. Bang-bang! he went, dancing around and
aiming at one after the other. Bang-bang! Everybody laughed
heartily. "Me," he said, jerking his thumb towards his breast, "me
good soldier. Me kill Turks . . . many Turks. Me kill, kill, kill" and
he made a ferocious, blood-thirsty grimace. "Cretan people good
soldiers. Italians no good." He went up to one of the men and
seized him by the collar. He made as if he were slitting the man's
throat. "Italians, bah!" He spat on the ground. "Me kill Mussolini
. . . like a that! Mussolini bad man. Greek no like Mussolini. We
kill all Italians." He sat down grinning and chuckling. "President
Roosevelt, he help Greeks, yes?" I nodded. "Greek good fighter.
He kill everybody. He no 'fraid of nobody. Look! Me, one
man . . ." He pointed to the others. "Me one Greek." He pointed
to the others, snatching the cane again and brandishing it like a
club. "Me kill everybody—German, Italian, Russian, Turk,
French. Greek no 'fraid." The others laughed and nodded their
heads approvingly. It was convincing, to say the least.

  The bus was getting ready to move. The whole village seemed
to have gathered to see me off. I climbed aboard and waved good-
bye. A little girl stepped forward and handed me a bunch of
flowers. The interlocutor shouted Hooray! A gawky young lad
yelled *All right!* and they all laughed.

  After dinner that evening I took a walk to the edge of the town.
It was like walking through the land of Ur. I was making for a
brilliantly lit café in the distance. About a mile away, it seemed, I
could hear the loud-speaker blasting out the war news—first in
Greek, then in French, then in English. It seemed to be proclaim-
ing the news throughout a wasteland. Europe speaking. Europe
seemed remote, on some other continent. The noise was deafening. Suddenly another one started up from the opposite direction.

I turned back towards the little park facing a cinema where a Western picture was being advertised. I passed what looked like an immense fortress surrounded by a dry moat. The sky seemed very low and filled with tattered clouds through which the moon sailed unsteadily. I felt out of the world, cut off, a total stranger in every sense of the word. The amplifiers increased this feeling of isolation: they seemed to have tuned up to the wildest pitch in order to carry far beyond me—to Abyssinia, Arabia, Persia, Beluchistan, China, Tibet. The waves were passing over my head; they were not intended for Crete, they had been picked up accidentally. I dove into the narrow winding streets which led to the open square. I walked right into a crowd which had gathered outside a tent in which freaks were being exhibited. A man squatting beside the tent was playing a weird melody on the flute. He held the flute up towards the moon which had grown larger and brighter in the interval. A belly-dancer came out of the tent, dragging a cretin by the hand. The crowd giggled. Just then I turned my head and to my astonishment I saw a woman with a vase on her shoulder descending a little bluff in bare feet. She had the poise and grace of a figure on an ancient frieze. Behind her came a donkey laden with jars. The flute was getting more weird, more insistent. Turbaned men with long white boots and black frock coats were pushing towards the open tent. The man beside me held two squawking chickens by the legs; he was rooted to the spot, as if hypnotized. To the right of me was evidently a barracks barred by a sentry box before which a soldier in white skirts paraded back and forth.

There was nothing more to the scene than this, but for me it held the enchantment of a world I was yet to glimpse. Even before I had sailed for Crete I had been thinking of Persia and Arabia and of more distant lands still. Crete is a jumping off place. Once a still, vital, fecund center, a navel of the world, it now resembles a dead crater. The aeroplane comes along, lifts you up by the seat of the pants, and spits you down in Bagdad, Samarkand, Beluchistan, Fez, Timbuctoo, as far as your money will take you. All these once marvellous places whose very names cast a spell over you are now floating islets in the stormy sea of civilization. They mean homely commodities like rubber, tin, pepper, coffee, carborundum and so forth. The natives are derelicts exploited by the octopus whose tentacles stretch from London, Paris, Berlin, Tokio, New York, Chicago to the icy tips of Iceland and the wild reaches of Patagonia. The evidences of this so-called civilization are strewn and dumped higgledy-piggledy wherever the long, slimy tentacles reach out. Nobody is being civilized, nothing is being altered in any real sense. Some are using knives and forks who formerly ate with their fingers; some have electric lights in their hovels instead of the kerosene lamp or the wax taper; some have Sears-Roebuck catalogues and a Holy Bible on the shelf where once a rifle or a musket lay; some have gleaming automatic revolvers instead of clubs; some are using money instead of shells and cowries; some have straw hats which they don't need; some have Jesus Christ and don't know what to do with Him. But all of them, from the top to the bottom, are restless, dissatisfied, envious, and sick at heart. All of them suffer from cancer and leprosy, in their souls. The most ignorant and degenerate of them will be asked to shoulder a gun and fight for a civilization which has brought them nothing but misery and degradation. In a language which they cannot understand the loud-speaker blares out the disastrous news of victory and defeat. It's a mad world and when you become slightly detached it seems even more mad than usual. The aeroplane brings death; the radio brings death; the machine gun brings death; the tinned goods bring death; the tractor brings death; the priest brings death; the schools bring death; the laws bring death, the electricity brings death; the plumbing brings death; the phonograph brings death; the knives and forks bring death; the books bring death; our very breath brings death, our very language, our very thought, our money, our love, our charity, our sanitation, our joy. No matter whether we are friends or enemies, no matter whether we call ourselves Jap, Turk, Russian, French, English, German or American, wherever we go, wherever we cast our shadow, wherever we breathe, we poison and destroy. Hooray! shouted the Greek. I too yell Hooray! Hooray for civilization! *Hooray! We will kill you all, everybody, everywhere. Hooray for Death! Hooray! Hooray!*

Between drizzles and downpours I explored the town more thoroughly. The outskirts of the city fascinated me. In the sun it was too hot, in the rain it was creepily cold. On all sides the town edged off abruptly, like an etching drowned in a plate of black zinc. Now and then I passed a turkey tied to a door knob by a string; the goat was ubiquitous and the donkey. There were wonderful cretins and dwarves too who wandered about with freedom and ease; they belonged to the scene, like the cactus, like the deserted park, like the dead horse in the moat, like the pet turkeys tied to the door knobs.

Along the waterfront there was a fang-like row of houses behind a hastily made clearing, strangely reminiscent of certain old quarters in Paris where the municipality has begun to create light and air for the children of the poor. In Paris one roams from quarter to quarter through imperceptible transitions, as if moving through invisible beaded curtains. In Greece the changes are sharp, almost painful. In some places you can pass through all the changes of fifty centuries in the space of five minutes. Everything is delineated, sculptured, etched. Even the waste lands have an eternal cast about them. You see everything in its uniqueness—*a* man sitting on *a* road under *a* tree: *a* donkey climbing *a* path near *a* mountain: *a* ship in *a* harbor in *a* sea of turquoise: *a* table on a *a* terrace beneath *a* cloud. And so on. Whatever you look at you see as if for the first time; it won't run away, it won't be demolished overnight; it won't disintegrate or dissolve or revolutionize itself. Every individual thing that exists, whether made by God or man, whether fortuitous or planned, stands out like a nut in an aureole of light, of time and of space. The shrub is the equal of the donkey; a wall is as valid as a belfry; a melon is as good as a man. Nothing is continued or perpetuated beyond its natural time; there is no iron will wreaking its hideous path of power. After a half hour's walk you are refreshed and exhausted by the variety of the anomalous and sporadic. By comparison Park Avenue seems insane and no doubt is insane. The oldest building in Herakleion will outlive the newest building in America. Organisms die; the cell lives on. Life is at the roots, embedded in simplicity, asserting itself uniquely.

To-morrow I'll go to Phaestos, I said to myself, picking my way through the fang-bitten streets like a laminated water-moccasin. I had to remind myself that I was in Crete, a quite different Crete than I had pictured to myself in my dreams. Again I had that feeling of the back pages of Dickens' novels, of a quaint, one-legged world illumined by a jaded moon: a land that had survived every catastrophe and was now palpitating with a blood beat, a land of owls and herons and crazy relics such as sailors bring back from foreign shores. In the moonlight, navigating through the silent streets like a foundering ship, I felt that the earth was bearing me through a zone I had never been carried through before. I was a little nearer to the stars and the ether was charged with their nearness; it was not simply that they were more brilliant, or that the moon which had taken on the color of a yam had grown swollen and lop-sided, but that the atmosphere had undergone a subtle, perfumed alteration. There was a residue, an elixir, I might almost say, which had clung to the aura which the earth gives off and which had increased in essence from repeated journeys through this particular corner of the zodiac. It was nostalgic; it awakened those ageless hordes of ancestral men who stand with eyes closed, like trees after the passing of a flood, in the ever-moving stream of the blood. The blood itself went through a change, thickening with the remembrance of man-made dynasties, of animals raised to divination, of instruments poised to thousand year niceties, of floods lapped up, divested of secrets, unburdened of treasures. The earth became again that strange one-legged creature which pegs and wobbles through diamond-pointed fields, passing faithfully through all the habitations of its solar creation; became that which it will be to the end and which in becoming transmogrifies the obscene goat into the stillness of that which always was, since there is no other, not even the possibility of a simulacrum.

Greece is what everybody knows, even *in absentia,* even as a child or as an idiot or as a not-yet-born. It is what you expect the earth to look like given a fair chance. It is the subliminal threshold of innocence. It stands, as it stood from birth, naked and fully revealed. It is not mysterious or impenetrable, not awesome, not defiant, not pretentious. It is made of earth, air, fire and water. It changes seasonally with harmonious undulating rhythms. It breathes, it beckons, it answers.

Crete is something else. Crete is a cradle, an instrument, a vibrating test tube in which a volcanic experiment has been performed. Crete can hush the mind, still the bubble of thought. I wanted so long and so ardently to see Crete, to touch the soil of Knossus, to look at a faded fresco, to walk where "they" had walked. I had let my mind dwell on Knossus without taking in the rest of the land. Beyond Knossus my mind pictured nothing but a great Australian waste. That Homer had sung of the hundred cities of Crete I didn't know because I could never bring myself to read Homer; that relics of the Minoan period had been found in the tomb of Akhenaton I was ignorant of also. I knew, or believed rather, only that here at Knossus on an island which nowadays scarcely anybody ever thinks to visit there had been initiated some twenty-five or thirty centuries before the dawn of that blight called Christianity a way of life which makes everything that has happened since in this Western World seem pallid, sickly, ghost-ridden and doomed. The Western world, we say, never once thinking to include those other great social experiments which were made in South America and Central America, passing them over always in our rapid historical surveys as if they were accidents, jumping from the Middle Ages to the discovery of America, as if this bastard bloom on the North American continent marked the continuation of the line of true development of man's evolution. Seated on King Minos' throne I felt closer to Montezuma than to Homer or Praxiteles or Caesar or Dante. Looking at the Minoan scripts I thought of the Mayan legends which I had once glimpsed in the British Museum and which stand out in my memory as the most wonderful, the most natural, the most artistic specimens of calligraphy in the long history of letters. Knossus, or what happened there almost fifty centuries ago, is like the hub of a wheel on which many spokes have been fitted only to rot away. The *wheel* was the great discovery; men have since lost themselves in a maze of petty inventions which are merely accessory to the great pristine fact of revolution itself.

The island then was once studded with citadels, the gleaming hub of a wheel whose splendor cast its shadow over the whole known world. In China there was another great revolution going on, in India another, in Egypt another, in Persia another; there were reflections from one to another which intensified the piercing gleams; there were echoes and reverberations. The vertical life of man was constantly churned by the revolutions of these great gleaming wheels of light. Now it is dark. Nowhere throughout the greatly enlarged world is there the least sign or evidence of the turning of a wheel. The last wheel has fallen apart, the vertical life is done with; man is spreading over the face of the earth in every direction like a fungus growth, blotting out the last gleams of light, the last hopes.

I went back to my room determined to plunge into that great unknown tract which we call Crete, anciently the kingdom of Minos, son of Zeus, whose birthplace it was. Since the wheel fell apart, before that too no doubt, every foot of the land has been fought over, conquered and reconquered, sold, bartered, pawned, auctioned off, levelled with fire and sword, sacked, plundered, administered over by tyrants and demons, converted by fanatics and zealots, betrayed, ransomed, traduced by the great powers of our day, desolated by civilized and savage hordes alike, desecrated by all and sundry, hounded to death like a wounded animal, reduced to terror and idiocy, left gasping with rage and impotence, shunned by all like a leper and left to expire in its own dung and ashes. Such is the cradle of our civilization as it was when finally relinquished and bequeathed to its miserable, destitute inhabitants. What had been the birthplace of the greatest of the gods, what had been the cradle and the mother and the inspiration of the Hellenic world, was finally annexed and not so long ago made part of Greece. What a cruel travesty! What a malefic destiny! Here the traveller has to hang his head in shame. This is the Ark left high and dry by the receding waters of civilization. This is the necropolis of culture marking the great cross-roads. This is the stone that was finally given Greece to swallow. To be followed up a few years later by another even more terrible gift, the return of a great mutilated member which had been flung with fire and blood into the sea.

I fell into a nightmare. I was being gently and endlessly rocked by the omnipotent Zeus in a burning cradle. I was toasted to a crisp and then gently dumped into a sea of blood. I swam ceaselessly amidst dismembered bodies marked with the cross and the crescent. I came at last to a rock-ribbed shore. It was bare and absolutely deserted of man. I wandered to a cave in the side of a mountain. In the shivery depths I saw a great heart bright as a ruby suspended from the vault by a huge web. It was beating and with each beat there fell to the ground a huge gout of blood. It was too large to be the heart of any living creature. It was larger even than the heart of a god. It is like the heart of agony, I said aloud, and as I spoke it vanished and a great darkness fell over me. Whereupon I sank down, exhausted, and fell into a sob that reverberated from every part of the cave and finally suffocated me.

I awoke and without consulting the sky I ordered a car for the day. Now there were two things I remembered as I set forth in the sumptuous limousine—one, to remember to ask for Kyrios Alexandros at Phaestos and two, to observe whether, as Monsieur Herriot is reported to have said when he climbed to the precincts of the palace, the sky is really closer to the earth than anywhere else on this globe.

We swung through the dilapidated gate in a cloud of dust, scattering chickens, cats, dogs, turkeys, naked children and hoary vendors of sweets to right and left; we burst at full speed into the drab and dun terrain of gutta percha which closes in on the city like mortar filling a huge crack. There were no wolves, buzzards or poisonous reptiles in sight. There was a sun flooded with lemon and orange which hung ominously over the sultry land in that splashing, dripping radiance which intoxicated Van Gogh. We passed imperceptibly from the quick bad lands to a fertile rolling region studded with fields of bright-colored crops; it reminded me of that serene steady smile which our own South gives as you roll through the State of Virginia. It set me dreaming, dreaming of the gentleness and docility of the earth when man caresses it with loving hands. I began to dream more and more in the American idiom. I was crossing the continent again. There were patches of Oklahoma, of the Carolinas, of Tennessee, of Texas and New Mexico. Never a great river, never a railroad, however. But the illusion of vast distances, the reality of great vistas, the sublimity of silence, the revelation of light. On the top of a dizzying crag a tiny shrine in blue and white; in the ravine a cemetery of terrifying boulders. We begin to climb, curving around the edges of precipitous drops; across the gulch the earth bulges up like the knees of a giant covered with corduroy. Here and there *a* man, *a* woman, the sower, the reaper, silhouetted against billowy clouds of suds. We climb up beyond the cultivated lands, twisting back and forth like a snake, rising to the heights of contemplation, to the abode of the stage, the eagle, the storm cloud. Huge, frenzied pillars of stone, scarred by wind and lightning, grayed to the color of fright, trembling, top-heavy, balanced like macrocosmic fiends, abut the road. The earth grows wan and weird, defertilized, dehumanized, neither brown nor gray nor beige nor taupe nor ecru, the no color of death reflecting light, sponging up light with its hard, parched shag and shooting it back at us in blinding, rock-flaked splinters that bore into the tenderest tissues of the brain and set it whimpering like a maniac.

This is where I begin to exult. This is something to put beside the devastation of man, something to overmatch his bloodiest depredations. This is nature in a state of dementia, nature having lost its grip, having become the hopeless prey of its own elements. This is the earth beaten, brutalized and humiliated by its own violent treachery. This is one of the spots wherein God abdicated, where He surrendered to the cosmic law of inertia. This is a piece of the Absolute, bald as an eagle's knob, hideous as the leer of a hyena, impotent as a granite hybrid. Here nature staggered to a halt in a frozen vomit of hate.

We roll down a crisp, crackling mountain side into an immense plain. The uplands are covered with a sheath of stiff shrub like blue and lavender porcupine quills. Here and there bald patches of red clay, streaks of shale, sand dunes, a field of pea green, a lake of waving champagne. We roll through a village which belongs to no time and no place, an accident, a sudden sprout of human activity because some one some time or other had returned to the scene of the massacre to look for an old photograph amidst the tumbled ruins and had stayed there from force of inertia and staying there had attracted flies and other forms of animate and inanimate life.

Farther on . . . A lone rectangular habitation sunk deep into the ground. A lone pueblo in the midst of a vacuum. It has a door and two windows. It is built like a box. The shelter of some human being. What kind of being? Who lives there? Why? The American scene is behind. We are now traversing the Mesopotamian hinterland. We are riding over dead cities, over elephant bones, over grass-covered sea bottoms. It is beginning to rain, a sudden, quick shower that makes the earth steam. I get out and walk through a lake of mud to examine the ruins of Gortyna. I follow the writing on the wall. It tells of laws which nobody obeys any longer. The only laws which last are the unwritten ones. Man is a lawbreaking animal. A timid one, however.

It is high noon. I want to have my lunch in Phaestos. We push on. The rain has stopped, the clouds have broken; the vault of blue spreads out like a fan, the blue decomposing into that ultimate violet light which makes everything Greek seem holy, natural and familiar. In Greece one has the desire to bathe in the sky. You want to rid yourself of your clothes, take a running leap and vault into the blue. You want to float in the air like an angel or lie in the grass rigid and enjoy the cataleptic trance. Stone and sky, they marry here. It is the perpetual dawn of man's awakening.

We glide through a deer run and the car stops at the edge of a wild park. "Up there," says the man, pointing to a steep bluff— "Phaestos." He had said the word. It was like magic. I hesitated. I wanted to prepare myself. "Better take your lunch with you," said the man. "They may not have any food up there." I put the shoe box under my arm and slowly, meditatively, reverently began the pilgrimage.

It was one of the few times in my life that I was fully aware of being on the brink of a great experience. And not only aware but grateful, grateful for being alive, grateful for having eyes, for being sound in wind and limb, for having rolled in the gutter, for having gone hungry, for having been humiliated, for having done everything that I did do since at last it had culminated in this moment of bliss.

I crossed a wooden bridge or two in the depth of the glen and paused again in the rich mud which was over my shoe tops to survey the little stretch I had traversed. At the turn of the road I would begin the laborious ascent. I had the feeling of being surrounded by deer. I had another strong insistent intuition: that Phaestos was the female stronghold of the Minos family. The historian will smile; he knows better. But in that instant and forever afterwards, regardless of proofs, regardless of logic, Phaestos became the abode of the queens. Every step I climbed corroborated the feeling.

When I had climbed to the level of the bluff I saw a narrow path ahead of me leading to the pavilion which has been erected on the site of the ruins for the convenience of the traveler. Suddenly I espied a man standing at the other end of the path. As I approached he began bowing and salaaming. That must be Kyrios Alexandros, I thought.

"God has sent you," he said, pointing heavenward and smiling at me as if in ecstasy. Graciously he relieved me of my coat and lunch box, informing me rapturously as he trotted along in front of me what a joy it was to see a human being again. "This war," he said, wringing his hands and piously raising his eyes in mute imploration, "this war . . . nobody comes here any more. Alexandros is all alone. Phaestos is dead. Phaestos is forgotten." He stopped to pick a flower which he handed me. He looked at the flower sadly as if commiserating it on the miserable fate of being left to bloom unnoticed. I had stopped to look backward towards the encircling mountains. Alexandros stood at my side. He waited silently and reverently for me to speak. I couldn't speak. I put my hand on his shoulder and tried to communicate my feelings with moist eyes. Alexandros gave me the look of a faithful dog; he took the hand which I had placed on his shoulder and bending low he kissed it.

"You are a good man," he said. "God sent you to me, to share my loneliness. Alexandros is very happy, very happy. Come," and he took me by the hand and led me round to the front of the pavilion. He did it as if he were about to confer on me the greatest gift that man can give to man. "I give you the earth and all the blessings it contains," said that mute, eloquent look in his eyes. I looked. I said—"God, it's incredible!" I turned my eyes away. It was too much, too much to try to accept at once.

Alexandros had gone inside for a moment, leaving me to pace slowly back and forth on the piazza of the pavilion surveying the grandeur of the scene. I felt slightly demented, like some of the great monarchs of the past who had devoted their lives to the enhancement of art and culture. I no longer felt the need of enrichment; I had reached the apogee, I wanted to give, to give prodigally and indiscriminately of all I possessed.

Alexandros appeared with a rag, a shoe brush and a big rusty knife; he got down on his knees and began manicuring my shoes. I was not in the least embarrassed. I thought to myself let him do as he likes, it gives him pleasure. I wondered vaguely what I might do myself to make men realize what great happiness lies in store for all of us. I sent out a benediction in every direction—to old and young, to the neglected savages in the forgotten parts of the earth, to wild as well as domesticated animals, to the birds of the air, to creeping things, to trees and plants and flowers, to rocks and lakes and mountains. This is the first day of my life, said I to myself, that I have included everybody and everything on this earth in one thought. I bless the world, every inch of it, every living atom, and it is all alive, breathing like myself, and conscious through and through.

Alexandros brought out a table and spread it. He suggested that I walk about the grounds and inspect the ruins. I listened to him as in a trance. Yes, I suppose I ought to stroll about and take it all in. That's what one usually does. I descended the broad steps of the levelled palace and glanced here and there automatically. I hadn't the faintest desire to snoop about examining lintels, urns, pottery, children's toys, votive cells and such like. Below me, stretching away like an infinite magic carpet, lay the plain of Messara, girdled by a majestic chain of mountain ranges. From this sublime, serene height it has all the appearance of the Garden of Eden. At the very gates of Paradise the descendants of Zeus halted here on their way to eternity to cast a last look earthward and saw with the eyes of innocents that the earth is indeed what they had always dreamed it to be: a place of beauty and joy and peace. In his heart man is angelic; in his heart man is united with the whole world. Phaestos contains all the elements of the heart; it is feminine through and through. Everything that man has achieved would be lost were it not for this final stage of contrition which is here incarnated in the abode of the heavenly queens.

I walked about the grounds, taking in the vista from every angle. I described a circle within the enfolding circle of hills. Above me the great vault, roofless, thrown open to infinity. Monsieur Herriot was right and wrong at the same time. One *is* nearer to the sky, but one is also farther away than ever from that which lies beyond. To reach the sky is nothing—child's play—from this supreme earthly mansion, but to reach beyond, to grasp if only for an instant the radiance and the splendor of that luminous realm in which the light of the heavens is but a faint and sickly gleam is impossible. Here the most sublime thoughts are nullified, stopped in their winged flight by an ever-deepening halo whose effulgence stills the very processes of thought. At its best thought is but speculation, a pastime such as the machine enjoys when it sparks. God has thought everything out in advance. We have nothing to solve: it has all been solved for us. We have but to melt, to dissolve, to swim in the solution. We are soluble fish and the world is an aquarium.

Alexandros was beckoning to me. Lunch was ready. I saw that he had set the table for me alone. I insisted that he set a place for himself. I had difficulty persuading him to do so. I had to put my arm around him, point to the sky, sweep the horizon, include everything in one large gesture before I could induce him to consent to share the meal with me. He opened a bottle of black wine, a heady, molten wine that situated us immediately in the center of the universe with a few olives, some ham and cheese.

Alexandros was begging me to stay a few days. He got out the guest book to show me when the last visitor had arrived. The last visitor was a drunken American apparently who had thought it a good joke to sign the Duke of Windsor's name to the register, adding "Oolala, what a night!" I glanced quickly over the signatures and discovered to my astonishment the name of an old friend of mine. I couldn't believe my eyes. I felt like crossing it out. I asked Alexandros if many Americans came to Phaestos. He said yes and from the glow in his eyes I gathered that they left liberal tips. I gathered that they liked the wine too.

I believe the wine was called *mavrodaphne*. If not it should have been because it is a beautiful black word and describes the wine perfectly. It slips down like molten glass, firing the veins with a heavy red fluid which expands the heart and the mind. One is heavy and light at the same time; one feels as nimble as the antelope and yet powerless to move. The tongue comes unloosed from its mooring, the palate thickens pleasurably, the hands describe thick, loose gestures such as one would love to obtain with a fat, soft pencil. One would like to depict everything in sanguine or Pompeiian red with splashes of charcoal and lamp black. Objects become enlarged and blurred, the colors more true and vivid, as they do for the myopic person when he removes his glasses. But above all it makes the heart glow.

I sat and talked with Alexandros in the deaf and dumb language of the heart. In a few minutes I would have to go. I was not unhappy about it; there are experiences so wonderful, so unique, that the thought of prolonging them seems like the basest form of ingratitude. If I were not to go now then I should stay forever, turn my back on the world, renounce everything.

I took a last stroll about the grounds. The sun had disappeared, the clouds were piling up; the brightly carpeted plain of Messara was streaked with heavy patches of shadow and sulphurous gleams of light under the leaden sky. The mountains drew nearer, became massive and ominous in their changing depths of blue. A moment ago the world had seemed ethereal, dream-like, a shifting, evanescent panorama; suddenly it had gathered substance and weight, the shimmering contours massed themselves in orchestral formation, the eagles swooped out of their eyries and hung in the sky like sultry messengers of the gods.

I said good-bye to Alexandros who was now in tears. I turned hastily and started forward along the narrow path which skirts the edge of the cliff. A few paces and Alexandros was behind me; he had quickly gathered a little bouquet of flowers which he pressed upon me. We saluted again. Alexandros remained there, waving to me as I looked back from time to time. I came to the sharp declivity down which I had to wind and twist to the glen. I took a last look back. Alexandros was still there, a tiny speck now, but still waving his arms. The sky had become more menacing; soon everything would be drowned in one vast downpour. I wondered on the way down when I would see it again, if ever. I felt somewhat saddened to think that no one had been with me to share the stupendous gift; it was almost too much to bestow on one lone mortal. It was for that reason perhaps that I had left with Alexandros a princely gratuity—not out of generosity, as he probably assumed, but out of a feeling of guilt. If no one had been there I should still have left something.

Just as I got into the car it began to rain, lightly at first, then more and more heavily. By the time we reached the bad lands the earth was a swirling sheet of water; what had been sun-baked clay, sand, barren soil, waste land, was now a series of floating terraces criss-crossed by tawny, turbulent cascades, by rivers flowing in every direction, racing towards the huge steaming sink charged with sullen deposits of earth, broken branches, boulders, shale, ore, wild-flowers, dead insects, lizards, wheel-barrows, ponies, dogs, cats, out-houses, yellow ears of corn, birds' nests, everything which had not the mind nor the feet nor the roots to resist. On the other side of the mountain, in the same torrential downpour, we passed men and women with umbrellas over their heads seated on diminutive beasts leisurely picking their way down the mountain-side. Silent, grave figures moving at a snail's pace, like determined pilgrims on their way to a holy shrine. The huge twisted sentinels of rock piled one on top of another like the giddy monuments of match-boxes which Picasso keeps on his mantelpiece had become huge gnarled mushrooms dripping with black pigment. In the furious rain their tilted, toppling forms seemed even more dangerous and menacing than before. Now and then a great mesa rose up, a mass of delicately veined rock supporting a tiny white sanctuary with a blue roof. If it were not Crete I could have imagined myself to be in some weird demonic stretch of Mongolia, some forbidden pass guarded by evil spirits which lay in wait for the unsuspecting traveler and drive him mad with their three-legged mustangs and henna-colored corpses that stand like frozen semaphores in the bleak, moonlit night.

On my return to Athens I found a stack of mail forwarded from Paris, also several notices from the post office inviting me to call at my earliest convenience for money.

About this time I received a letter from the American Consulate requesting me to step in and have my passport validated or invalidated. I went round to the office to make inquiries. Being a native-born I took the matter lightly. Just a bit of red tape, I thought to myself. Had I brought a photograph, I was asked immediately. No, I hadn't thought of that. The porter took me down the street a few blocks to look for a man who usually stood on a certain corner. The apparatus was there but no sign of the man. I had nothing to do so I sat down on the curb and waited patiently. When I got back to the bureau there were several Americanized Greeks waiting to be cross-examined. One sly old peasant who had evidently become prosperous in America amused me. He was talking in Greek to one of the secretaries, a Greek woman. He evidently didn't like her efficient and somewhat superior attitude. He became mulish. He would say neither Yes nor No to the questions put him. He smelled a rat somewhere and he was on his guard. The young woman was almost beside herself. But the more frantic she became the cooler he behaved. She looked at me in despair. I thought to myself it serves you right, what business have you to be tantalizing people with all these stupid questions? Finally it came my turn. What are you doing in Greece? Where is your home? How many dependents have you? Whom do you work for? I was so pleased with the fact that I could answer readily—no home, no dependents, no boss, no aim, et cetera, that when he said "couldn't you just as well do your writing elsewhere?" I said "of course, I'm a free man, I can work anywhere, nobody is paying me to write." Whereupon he said—very clever of him—"well then, I take it you could write in America too, couldn't you?" And I said "of course, why not? Only I don't care to write in America. I'm writing about Greece now." However, the game was up, as I discovered in a few moments. A brief colloquy with a higher-up and my passport was returned to me invalidated. That meant get home at the earliest possible moment. Clear out!

At first I was angry; I felt that I had been tricked. But after I had walked around the block several times I decided that it was probably an act of fate. At least I was free to clear out. Max was only free to stay and spend his remaining drachmas. The war was spreading. Soon the Balkans would be inflamed. Soon there would be no choice.

I went back the next day to see the American Minister and find out how much time they would accord me. The former director of "The Dial," as he turned out to be, received me cordially. I was delighted to learn of his great sympathy and love for the Greeks. Everything went smoothly. No undue hurry. Only please prepare to leave as soon as possible. I sensed that it was best to comply graciously. So I shook our minister, Mr. Lincoln MacVeagh, cordially by the hand and departed. On the way out I made the sign of the cross in Orthodox fashion.

Winter was coming on; the days were short and sunny, the nights cold and long. The stars seemed more brilliant than ever. Owing to the shortage of coal the heat was turned on for an hour only in the morning and an hour in the evening. I quickly developed sciatica and was reminded that I was getting old. Golfo the maid was very solicitous; Socrates, the night porter, came up every evening to rub me with a Greek horse liniment; the proprietor sent up grapes and mineral waters; Niki with the Nile green eyes came and held my hand; the bell-hop brought letters and telegrams. All in all it was a very pleasant illness.

I shall always remember the walks through Athens at night under the autumn stars. Often I would go up to a bluff just under Lykabettos and stand there for an hour or so gazing at the sky. What was wonderful about it was that it was so Greek—not just the sky, but the houses, the color of the houses, the dusty roads, the nakedness, the sounds that came out of the houses. Something immaculate about it. Somewhere beyond the "ammonia" region, in a forlorn district whose streets are named after the philosophers, I would stumble about in a silence so intense and so velvety at the same time that it seemed as if the atmosphere were full of powdered stars whose light made an inaudible noise. Athens and New York are electrically charged cities, unique in my experience. But Athens is permeated with a violet-blue reality which envelops you with a caress; New York has a trip-hammer vitality which drives you insane with restlessness, if you have no inner stabilizer. In both cases the air is like champagne—a tonic, a revivifier. In Athens I experienced the joy of solitude; in New York I have always felt lonely, the loneliness of the caged animal, which brings on crime, sex, alcohol and other madnesses.

At midnight, returning to the hotel, I was frequently intercepted, usually by some wily Greek who knew enough English to strike up a running conversation. Usually he would invite me to join him in taking a coffee, pretending to be overjoyed to meet an American like himself (sic). One evening I ran into a Cretan from Utica, New York. He had come back to do his military service in Greece, so he said. He had a brother in Herakleion who was well off. After much beating about the bush, inquiring after the state of my health and so on, he admitted blushingly that he was short 73 drachmas for the boat fare to Crete. Now seventy-three drachmas is only about a half dollar in American money and a half dollar is nothing to offer a stranger from Utica who desires to do his military service abroad, especially if like the one I am talking about he has already paid for your coffee, pastry and ice cream, has already offered you his cigarettes and already invited you to make use of his brother's car while in Crete. I hadn't told him that I had just been to Crete, of course. I listened to him in sympathetic silence and acted as naif and ignorant as Americans are supposed to be. As a matter of fact I was really itching to be taken in—otherwise I would have felt cheated, disillusioned about the Greek character. Aside from my experience of the first day nobody in Greece, no Greek certainly, had ever tried to gyp me. And perhaps this one would have been successful had he not been so maladroit. In the first place I happened to know Utica fairly well, having spent one of my honeymoons there, and the street which he described to me as being his home I knew did not exist; in the second place he had made the mistake of telling me that he was taking the "Elsie" to Herakleion, whereas I knew, having just come back on the "Elsie," that this boat would not be returning to Crete for several months; in the third place, having inquired of him what he thought about Phaestos, which is pronounced the same in all languages, including Chinese, he asked me what *it* was, and when I told him it was a place he said he had never heard of it, he even doubted its existence; in the fourth place he couldn't remember the name of the hotel which I ought to stop at when going to Herakleion, and for a man born in Herakleion, which has only two hotels to its name, the sudden loss of memory struck me as rather glaring; in the fifth place he no more resembled a Cretan than a man from Canarsie would, and I very much doubted that he had ever seen the place; in the sixth place he was too free with his brother's car, and cars are not plentiful in Crete where the bullock still draws the plough. None of these factors would have deterred me from handing him the seventy-three drachmas since, being a born American, a half dollar has always seemed to me to be just the right sized coin to throw down a sewer if there is nothing better to be done with it. Only I did want him to know that I knew he was lying. And so I told him so. At this he pretended to be aggrieved. When I pointed out why I thought he had been lying to me he rose up solemnly and said that if I should ever go to Crete and there meet his brother I would regret what I had said—and with that he stalked out looking as injured and wounded as possible. I called the waiter over and asked him if he knew the man. He smiled. "Why, yes," he said, "he's an interpreter." I asked if he had been living a long time in Athens. "He's been here all his life," he said.

There was another one called George, George of Cyrpus, who was even less capable. George pretended to be a close friend of the American Minister, our Mr. MacVeagh no less. He had been watching me read a German news weekly at a little kiosk in the same "ammonia" region. He greeted me in German and I answered him in German. He asked me how long I had been in Athens and I told him. He said it was a beautiful night and I agreed, it was indeed. "Where do you go from here?" he asked next and I said "to Persia perhaps." All this in German. "Where do you come from?" he asked. "From New York," I replied. "And you speak nothing but German?" "I can speak English too," I said. "Then why did you speak German to me?" he inquired, with a sly smile. "Because you addressed me in German," I said. "Can you speak Greek?" he asked next. "No," I said, "but I can speak Chinese and Japanese—can you?" He shook his head. "Do you speak Turkish?" I shook my head. "Arabic?" Again I shook my head. "I speak all the languages except Chinese and Japanese," he said, smiling again in his strange way. "You're very intelligent," I said. "Are you an interpreter?" No, he was not an interpreter. He smiled and lowered his eyes. "Have a drink with me?" he said. I nodded.

Seated at the table he began a long roundabout discussion to find out what my occupation was. I told him I had none. "You are a rich man, yes?" he said, his eyes gleaming. "No, I am very poor. I have no money." He laughed in my face, as if the very thought were absurd. "You like women?" he asked suddenly. I said I liked them very much, especially if they were beautiful. "I have a friend—she is very beautiful," he said immediately. "We will go to see her—now, as soon as you have finished your coffee." I told him I didn't care to see her right away because I was going to bed soon. He pretended not to have heard me correctly and went into a long rhapsody about her charms. "She must be very beautiful," I said. "Aren't you jealous of her?" He looked at me as if I were slightly cracked. "You are my friend," he said. "She

will be honored to see you. Let's go now," and he started to rise
from his seat. I sat there as if made of lead and looking up at him I
blandly inquired what day it was. He wasn't sure—he thought it
was Tuesday. "Ask the waiter," I said. He asked the waiter. It
was Tuesday all right. "Well," I said, slowly dragging it out, "I
shall be busy until Thursday a week from now, but if you are free
Thursday evening, Thursday the 17th, I'll call for you here about
ten in the evening and we'll go to see your friend." He laughed.
"Come, we'll go there now," he said, taking me by the arm. I
remained seated, allowing him to hold my arm which had become
as inert as a stove-pipe. "I'm going to bed in a few minutes," I
repeated calmly. "Besides, I have no money—I told you I was
poor, you remember?" He laughed. Then he sat down, drawing
his chair up closer. "Listen," he said, leaning over in confidential
style, "George knows everybody. You don't need any money—
you are my guest. We'll stay just a few minutes—it's right near
here." "But it's late now," I said, "she may be asleep." He
laughed. "Besides," I continued, "I told you I was tired. Thursday
a week will be fine for me—about ten o'clock." George now dove
into his inside pocket and brought a packet of letters and a dirty,
crumpled passport. He opened the passport and showed me his
photograph, his name, where he was born, etc. I nodded my head.
"That's you, George, no?" I said innocently. He tried to pull his
chair still closer. "I am an English citizen, you see? I know all the
consuls, all the ministers. I will speak to Mr. MacVeagh for you.
He will give you the money to go home. He's a very good man."
Here he dropped his voice. "You like boys—young boys?" I said
I did, sometimes, if they behaved themselves. He laughed again.
He knew a place where there were very beautiful boys, very young
too. I thought that was very interesting—were they friends of his,
I wanted to know. He ignored the question and, dropping his
voice, he inquired discreetly if I had enough to pay for the coffee
and pastry. I said I had enough to pay for my own share. "You
pay for George too?" he said, smiling slyly. I said No flatly. He
looked surprised—not injured or aggrieved, but genuinely
astounded. I called the waiter over and paid for my check. I got up
and started to walk out. I went down the stairs. In a moment—he
had been whispering to the waiter—he followed me to the street.
"Well," I said, "it was a pleasant evening. I'll say good-night
now." "Don't go yet," he urged, "just two more minutes. She
lives right across the street." *"Who?"* I asked innocently. "My
friend." "Oh," I said, "that's very convenient. Next Thursday a
week, then, eh?" I began walking off. He came up close and took
me by the arm again. "Give me fifty drachmas, please!" "No," I

said, "I'm not giving you anything." I walked a few paces. He crawled up on me again. "Please, thirty drachmas!" "No," I said, "no drachmas to-night." *"Fifteen drachmas!"* "No," I repeated, walking away. I got about ten yards away from him. He yelled out: *"Five drachmas!"* "No!" I yelled back, "Not one drachma! Good-night!"

It was the first time in my life I had so stubbornly refused anybody. I enjoyed the experience. As I was nearing the hotel an oldish-looking man with long hair and a rather large Bohemian hat darted out of a dark alley and, greeting me in perfect English, held out his hand for alms. I instinctively put my hand in my change pocket and fished out a handful of coins, perhaps fifty or sixty drachmas. He took it, bowed respectfully as he removed his flowing hat and, with a candor and a sincerity that was amazing to behold, he informed me in his impeccable English that grateful as he was for the generous gesture it would not be sufficient for his needs. He asked me if it were possible, and he added that he knew it was a great deal to ask of a stranger, to give him two hundred drachmas more, which was the sum he required to pay his hotel bill. He added that even then he would be obliged to go without food. I immediately pulled out my wallet and handed him two hundred and fifty drachmas. It was now his turn to be astounded. He had asked, but apparently he had never dreamed of getting it. The tears came to his eyes. He began a wonderful speech which I cut short by saying that I had to catch up with my friends who had strolled ahead. I left him in the middle of the street with hat in hand, gazing after me as if I were a phantom.

The incident put me in a good mood. "Ask," said our Lord and Saviour Jesus Christ, "and it shall be given unto you." *Ask,* mind you. Not demand, not beg, not wheedle or cajole. Very simple, I thought to myself. Almost too simple. And yet what better way is there?

Now that my departure had become a certainty Katsimbalis was desperately attempting to organize a few last-minute excursions. It was impossible, with the limited time at my disposal, to even think of visiting Mt. Athos or Lesbos, or even Mykonos or Santorini. Delphi yes, perhaps even Delos. Towards lunch time every day Katsimbalis was at the hotel waiting for me. Lunch lasted usually until five or six in the afternoon after which we would repair to a little wine cellar where we would have a few aperitifs in order to whip up an appetite for dinner. Katsimbalis was now in greater form than ever, though still complaining of arthritis, migraine, bad liver, loss of memory and so on. Wherever we went we were sure to be joined by some of his numerous friends. In this ambiance the discussion developed to fantastic proportions; the newcomer was fitted into the architectural pattern of his talk with the ease and dexterity of a mediaeval joiner or mason. We made sea voyages and inland voyages; we traveled down the Nile, crawled through the pyramids on our bellies, rested awhile in Constantinople, made the rounds of the cafés in Smyrna, gambled at the casino in Loutraki and again at Monte Carlo; we lived through the first and second Balkan wars, got back to Paris in time for the armistice, sat up nights with the monks at Mt. Athos, went back stage at the Folies Bergère, strolled through the bazaars of Fez, went crazy with boredom in Salonika, stopped off at Toulouse and Carcassonne, explored the Orinoco, floated down the Mississippi, crossed the Gobi desert, joined the Royal Opera at Sofia, got typhus in Tiflis, put on a weight-lifting act at the Medrano, got drunk in Thebes and came back on motorcycles to play a game of dominoes opposite the Metro station at "Ammonia."

Finally it was decided that we would go to Delphi, the ancient navel of the world. Pericles Byzantis, who was a friend of Ghika's, had invited us to spend a few days there at the new pavilion for foreign students which the government was opening up. We pulled up at the museum in Thebes in a beautiful Packard—Ghika, Byzantis and myself. Katsimbalis had decided to go by bus for some reason or other. By some unaccountable logic Thebes looked exactly as I had pictured it to look; the inhabitants too corresponded to the loutish image which I had retained since school days. The guide to the museum was a surly brute who seemed suspicious of every move we made; it was all we could do to induce him to unlock the door. Yet I liked Thebes; it was quite unlike the other Greek towns I had visited. It was about ten in the morning and the air was winey; we seemed to be isolated in the midst of a great space which was dancing with a violet light; we were oriented towards another world.

As we rolled out of the town, snaking over the low hills cropped close and kinky like a negro's poll, Ghika who was sitting beside the driver turned round to tell me of a strange dream which he had had during the night. It was an extraordinary dream of death and transfiguration in which he had risen up out of his own body and gone out of the world. As he was describing the wondrous wraiths whom he had encountered in the other world I looked beyond his eye to the undulating vistas which were unrolling before us. Again that impression of a vast, all-englobing space encircling us, which I had noted in Thebes, came over me. There was a terrific synchronization of dream and reality, the two worlds merging in a bowl of pure light, and we the voyagers suspended, as it were, over the earthly life. All thought of destination was annihilated; we were purring smoothly over the undulating ground, advancing towards the void of pure sensation, and the dream, which was hallucinating, had suddenly become vivid and unbearably real. It was just as he was describing the strange sensation he had experienced of suddenly discovering his own body lying prone on the bed, of balancing himself gingerly above it so as to slowly descend and fit himself into it again without the loss of an arm or a toe, that out of the corner of my eye I caught the full devastating beauty of the great plain of Thebes which we were approaching and, unable to control myself, I burst into tears. Why had no one prepared me for this? I cried out. I begged the driver to stop a moment in order to devour the scene with one full sweeping glance. We were not yet in the bed of the plain; we were amidst the low mounds and hummocks which had been stunned motionless by the swift messengers of light. We were in the dead center of that soft silence which absorbs even the breathing of the gods. Man had nothing to do with this, nor even nature. In this realm nothing moves nor stirs nor breathes save the finger of mystery; this is the hush that descends upon the world before the coming of a miraculous event. The event itself is not recorded here, only the passing of it, only the violet glow of its wake. This is an invisible corridor of time, a vast, breathless parenthesis which swells like the uterus and having bowelled forth its anguish relapses like a run-down clock. We glide through the long level plain, the first real oasis I have ever glimpsed. How am I to distinguish it from those other irrigated Paradises known to man? Was it more lush, more fertile, did it groan with a heavier weight of produce? Was it thriving honey-comb of activity? I cannot say that I was made aware of any of these factors. The plain of Thebes was empty, empty of man, empty of visible produce. In the belly of this emptiness there throbbed a rich pulse of blood which was drained off in black furrowed veins. Through the thick pores of the earth the dreams of men long dead still bubbled and burst, their diaphanous filament carried skyward by flocks of startled birds.

To the left of us ran the range leading to Parnassus, grim, silent, hoary with legend. Strange that all the time I was in Paris, all that joy and misery associated with Montparnasse, I never once thought of the place from which the name derives. On the other hand, though no one had ever counselled me to go there, Thebes had been in my mind ever since the day I landed in Athens. By some unaccountable quirk the name Thebes, just as Memphis in Egypt, always brought to life a welter of fantastic memories and when, in the chill morgue of the museum there, I espied that most exquisite stone drawing so like one of Picasso's illustrations, when I saw the rigid Egyptian-like colossi, I felt as if I were back in some familiar past, back in a world which I had known as a child. Thebes, even after one has visited it, remains in the memory very much like the vague, tremulous reveries which attend a long wait in the ante-chamber of a dentist's office. Waiting to have a tooth extracted one often gets involved in the plan of a new book; one fairly seethes with ideas. Then comes the torture, the book is expunged from the consciousness; days pass in which nothing more brilliant is accomplished than sticking the tongue in a little cavity of the gum which seems enormous. Finally that too is forgotten and one is at work again and perhaps the new book is begun, but not as it was feverishly planned back in the cauterized waiting-room. And then, of a night when one tosses fitfully, plagued by swarms of irrelevant thoughts, suddenly the constellation of the lost tooth swims over the horizon and one is in Thebes, the old childhood Thebes from which all the novels have issued, and one sees the plan of the great life's work finely etched on a tablet of stone—and this is the book one always meant to write but it is forgotten in the morning, and thus Thebes is forgotten and God and the whole meaning of life and one's own identity and the identities of the past and so one worships Picasso who stayed awake all night and kept his bad tooth. This you know when you pass through Thebes, and it is disquieting, but it is also inspiring and when you are thoroughly inspired you hang yourself by the ankles and wait for the vultures to devour you alive. Then the real Montparnasse life begins, with Diana the huntress in the background and the Sphinx waiting for you at a bend in the road.

We stopped for lunch at Levadia, a sort of Alpine village nestling against a wall of the mountain range. The air was crisp and exhilarating, balmy in the sun and chill as a knife in the shade. The doors of the restaurant were opened wide to suck in the sun-lit air. It was a colossal refectory lined with tin like the inside of a biscuit box; the cutlery, the plates, the table tops were ice cold; we ate with our hats and overcoats on.

From Levadia to Arachova was like a breathless ride on the scenic railway through a tropical Iceland. Seldom a human being, seldom a vehicle; a world growing more and more rarefied, more and more miraculous. Under lowering clouds the scene became immediately ominous and terrifying: only a god could survive the furious onslaught of the elements in this stark Olympian world.

At Arachova Ghika got out to vomit. I stood at the edge of a deep canyon and as I looked down into its depths I saw the shadow of a great eagle wheeling over the void. We were on the very ridge of the mountains, in the midst of a convulsed land which was seemingly still writhing and twisting. The village itself had the bleak, frostbitten look of a community cut off from the outside world by an avalanche. There was the continuous roar of an icy waterfall which, though hidden from the eye, seemed omnipresent. The proximity of the eagles, their shadows mysteriously darkening the ground, added to the chill, bleak sense of desolation. And yet from Arachova to the outer precincts of Delphi the earth presents one continuously sublime, dramatic spectacle. Imagine a bubbling cauldron into which a fearless band of men descend to spread a magic carpet. Imagine this carpet to be composed of the most ingenious patterns and the most variegated hues. Imagine that men have been at this task for several thousand years and that to relax for but a season is to destroy the work of centuries. Imagine that with every groan, sneeze or hiccough which the earth vents the carpet is grievously ripped and tattered. Imagine that the tints and hues which compose this dancing carpet of earth rival in splendor and subtlety the most beautiful stained glass windows of the mediaeval cathedrals. Imagine all this and you have only a glimmering comprehension of a spectacle which is changing hourly, monthly, yearly, millennially. Finally, in a state of dazed, drunken, battered stupefaction you come upon Delphi. It is four in the afternoon, say, and a mist blowing in from the sea has turned the world completely upside down. You are in Mongolia and the faint tinkle of bells from across the gully tells you that a caravan is approaching. The sea has become a mountain lake poised high above the mountain tops where the sun is sputtering out like a rum-soaked omelette. On the fierce glacial wall where the mist lifts for a moment some one has written with lightning speed in an unknown script. To the other side, as if borne along like a cataract, a sea of grass slips over the precipitous slope of a cliff. It has the brilliance of the vernal equinox, a green which grows between the stars in the twinkling of an eye.

Seeing it in this strange twilight mist Delphi seemed even more sublime and awe-inspiring than I had imagined it to be. I actually felt relieved, upon rolling up to the little bluff above the pavilion where we left the car, to find a group of idle village boys shooting dice: it gave a human touch to the scene. From the towering windows of the pavilion, which was built along the solid, generous lines of a mediaeval fortress, I could look across the gulch and, as the mist lifted, a pocket of the sea became visible—just beyond the hidden port of Itea. As soon as we had installed our things we looked for Katsimbalis whom we found at the Apollo Hotel—I believe he was the only guest since the departure of H. G. Wells under whose name I signed my own in the register though I was not stopping at the hotel. He, Wells, had a very fine, small hand, almost womanly, like that of a very modest, unobtrusive person, but then that is so characteristic of English handwriting that there is nothing unusual about it.

By dinner-time it was raining and we decided to eat in a little restaurant by the roadside. The place was as chill as the grave. We had a scanty meal supplemented by liberal potions of wine and cognac. I enjoyed that meal immensely, perhaps because I was in the mood to talk. As so often happens, when one has come at last to an impressive spot, the conversation had absolutely nothing to do with the scene. I remember vaguely the expression of astonishment on Ghika's and Katsimbalis' face as I unlimbered at length upon the American scene. I believe it was a description of Kansas that I was giving them; at any rate it was a picture of emptiness and monotony such as to stagger them. When we got back to the bluff behind the pavilion, whence we had to pick our way in the dark, a gale was blowing and the rain was coming down in bucketfuls. It was only a short stretch we had to traverse but it was perilous. Being somewhat lit up I had supreme confidence in my ability to find my way unaided. Now and then a flash of lightning lit up the path which was swimming in mud. In these lurid moments the scene was so harrowingly desolate that I felt as if we were enacting a scene from Macbeth. "Blow wind and crack!" I shouted, gay as a mud-lark, and at that moment I slipped to my knees and would have rolled down a gully had not Katsimbalis caught me by the arm. When I saw the spot next morning I almost fainted.

We slept with the windows closed and a great fire roaring in the huge stove. At breakfast we congregated about a long communion table in a hall that would have done credit to a Dominican monastery. The food was excellent and abundant, the view from the window superb. The place was so enormous, the floor so inviting, that I couldn't resist the temptation to do some fancy skating in my shoes. I sailed in and out the corridors, the refectory, the salon, the studios, delivering glad tidings from the ruler of my ninth house, Mercury himself.

It was now time to inspect the ruins, extract the last oracular juices from the extinct navel. We climbed up the hill to the theatre whence we overlooked the splintered treasuries of the gods, the ruined temples, the fallen columns, trying vainly to recreate the splendor of this ancient site. We speculated at length on the exact position of the city itself which is as yet undiscovered. Suddenly, as we stood there silently and reverently, Katsimbalis strode to the center of the bowl and holding his arms aloft delivered the closing lines of the last oracle. It was an impressive moment, to say the least. For a second, so it seemed, the curtain had been lifted on a world which had never really perished but which had rolled away like a cloud and was preserving itself intact, inviolate, until the day when, restored to his senses, man would summon it back to life again. In the few seconds it took him to pronounce the words I had a long glimpse down the broad avenue of man's folly and, seeing no end to the vista, experienced a poignant feeling of distress and of sadness which was in no way connected with my own fate but with that of the species to which by accident I happen to belong. I recalled other oracular utterances I had heard in Paris, in which the present war, horrible as it is, was represented as but an item in the long catalogue of impending disasters and reversals, and I remembered the sceptical way in which these utterances were received. The world which passed away with Delphi passed away as in a sleep. It is the same now. Victory and defeat are meaningless in the light of the wheel which relentlessly revolves. We are moving into a new latitude of the soul, and a thousand years hence men will wonder at our blindness, our torpor, our supine acquiescence to an order which was doomed.

We had a drink at the Castellian Spring where I suddenly remembered my old friend Nick of the Orpheum Dance Palace on Broadway because he had come from a little village called Castellia in the valley beyond the mountains. In a way my friend Nick was largely responsible for my being here, I reflected, for it was through his terpsichorean instrumentations that I met my wife June and if I hadn't met her I should probably never have become a writer, never have left America, never have met Betty Ryan, Lawrence Durrell and finally Stephanides, Katsimbalis and Ghika.

After wandering about amidst the broken columns we ascended the tortuous path to the stadium on high. Katsimbalis took off his overcoat and with giant strides measured it from end to end. The setting is spectacular. Set just below the crest of the mountain one has the impression that when the course was finished the charioteers must have driven their steeds over the ridge and into the blue. The atmosphere is superhuman, intoxicating to the point of madness. Everything that is extraordinary and miraculous about Delphi gathers here in the memory of the games which were held in the clouds. As I turned to go I saw a shepherd leading his flock over the ridge; his figure was so sharply delineated against the sky that he seemed to be bathed in a violet aura; the sheep moved

slowly over the smooth spine in a golden fuzz, as though somno-
lently emerging from the dead pages of a forgotten idyll.

In the museum I came again upon the colossal Theban statues
which have never ceased to haunt me and finally we stood before
the amazing statue of Antinous, last of the gods. I could not help
but contrast in my mind this most wonderful idealization in stone
of the eternal duality of man, so bold and simple, so thoroughly
Greek in the best sense, with that literary creation of Balzac's,
Seraphita, which is altogether vague and mysterious and, humanly
speaking, altogether unconvincing. Nothing could better convey
the transition from light to darkness, from the pagan to the Christian conception of life, than this enigmatic figure of the last god on
earth who flung himself into the Nile. By emphasizing the soulful
qualities of man Christianity succeeded only in disembodying man;
as angel the sexes fuse into the sublime spiritual being which man
essentially is. The Greeks, on the other hand, gave body to
everything, thereby incarnating the spirit and eternalizing it. In
Greece one is ever filled with the sense of eternity which is
expressed in the here and now; the moment one returns to the
Western world, whether in Europe or America, this feeling of
body, of eternality, of incarnated spirit is shattered. We move in
clock time amidst the debris of vanished worlds, inventing the
instruments of our own destruction, oblivious of fate or destiny,
knowing never a moment of peace, possessing not an ounce of
faith, a prey to the blackest superstitions, functioning neither in
the body nor in the spirit, active not as individuals but as microbes
in the organism of the diseased.

That night, at the dinner table in the big hall, while listening to
Pericles Byzantis, I made up my mind to return to Athens the next
day. He had just been urging me to stay, and indeed there was
every reason for me to stay, but I had the feeling that something
awaited me in Athens and I knew I would not stay. Next morning
at breakfast, to his great amazement, I told him of my decision. I
told him very frankly that I could give no good reason for my
departure—except that best of all reasons, imperious desire. I had
had the distinction of being the very first foreigner to enjoy the
privileges of the new pavilion and my abrupt leave-taking was
undoubtedly a poor way of expressing my gratitude, but so it was.
Ghika and Katsimbalis quickly decided to return with me. I hope
that when he reads what happened to me upon my return to Athens
the good Kyrios Byzantis will forgive my rude behavior and not
consider it typically American.

The return at top speed was even more impressive to me than
our coming. We passed through Thebes in the late afternoon,

Katsimbalis regaling me with a story of his mad motorcycle trips from Thebes to Athens after he had had a skinful. It seemed to me that we had just skirted the vicinity of the great battlefield of Platea and were perhaps facing Mount Kithaeron when suddenly I became aware of a curious trap-like formation through which we were whirling like a drunken cork. Again we had come to one of those formidable passes where the invading enemy had been slaughtered like pigs, a spot which must be the solace and the joy of defending generals everywhere. Here, it would not surprise me to discover, that Oedipus had met the Sphinx. I was profoundly disturbed, shaken to the roots. And by what? By associations born of my knowledge of ancient events? Scarcely, since I have but the scantiest knowledge of Greek history and even that is thoroughly confused, as is all history to me. No, as with the sacred places so with the murderous spots—the record of events is written into the earth. The real joy of the historian or the archaeologist when confronted with a discovery must lie in the fact of confirmation, corroboration, not in surprise. Nothing that has happened on this earth, however deeply buried, is hidden from man. Certain spots stand out like semaphores, revealing not only the clue but the event—provided, to be sure, they are approached with utter purity of heart. I am convinced that there are many layers of history and that the final reading will be delayed until the gift of seeing past and future as one is restored to us.

I thought, when I got back to my hotel and found that money had been cabled me for my return to America, that that was what had drawn me back to Athens, but in the morning when I found Katsimbalis waiting for me with a mysterious smile upon his face I discovered that there was another, more important reason. It was a cold wintry day with a stiff wind blowing down from the encircling hills. It was a Sunday. Somehow everything had undergone a radical change. A boat was leaving in about ten days and the knowledge that I would take that boat had already brought the journey to an end.

Katsimbalis had come to propose a visit to an Armenian soothsayer whom he and several of his friends had already consulted. I consented with alacrity, never having been to a soothsayer in my life. Once in Paris I had been on the verge of doing so, having witnessed the hallucinating effect of such an experience upon two of my close friends. I was of the opinion that nothing more could be expected than a good or bad reading of one's own mind.

The abode of this particular soothsayer was in the Armenian refugee quarter of Athens, a section of the city I had not yet seen. I had heard that it was sordid and picturesque but nothing I had heard about it had quite prepared me for the sight which greeted my eyes. By no means the least curious feature of this neighborhood is its duality. Around the rotten yolk of the egg lies the immaculate new shell of the community which is to be. For almost twenty years these miserable refugees have been waiting to move into the new quarters which have been promised them. These new homes which the government has provided and which now stand ready for occupancy (rent free, I believe), are models in every sense of the word. The contrast between these and the hovels in which the refugees have somehow managed to survive for a generation is fantastic, to say the least. From the rubbish heap a whole community provided shelter for itself and for its animals, its pets, its rodents, its lice, its bedbugs, its microbes. With the march of civilization such pustulant, festering agglomerations of humanity are of course no unusual sight. The more staggering the world-cities become in elegance and proportion, in power and influence, the more cataclysmic the upheavals, the vaster the armies of foot-loose, destitute, homeless, penniless individuals who, unlike the miserable Armenians of Athens, are not even privileged to dig in the dung-heaps for the scraps with which to provide themselves with shelter but are forced to keep on the march like phantoms, confronted in their own land with rifles, hand grenades, barbed wire, shunned like lepers, driven out like the pest.

The home of Aram Hourabedian was buried in the heart of the labyrinth and required much questioning and manoeuvering before we could locate it. When at last we found the little sign announcing his residence we discovered that we had come too early. We killed an hour or so strolling about the quarter, marvelling not so much at the squalor but at the pathetically human efforts that had been made to adorn and beautify these miserable shacks. Despite the fact that it had been created out of the rubbish heap there was more charm and character to this little village than one usually finds in a modern city. It evoked books, paintings, dreams, legends: it evoked such names as Lewis Carroll, Hieronymus Bosch, Breughel, Max Ernst, Hans Reichel, Salvador Dali, Goya, Giotto, Paul Klee, to mention but a few. In the midst of the most terrible poverty and suffering there nevertheless emanated a glow which was holy; the surprise of finding a cow or a sheep in the same room with a mother and child gave way instantly to a feeling of reverence. Nor did one have the slightest desire to laugh at seeing a squalid hut surmounted by an improvised solarium made of pieces of tin. What shelter there was was shared alike and this shelter included provision for the birds of the air and the animals of the field. Only in sorrow and suffering does man draw close to his fellow man; only then, it seems, does his life become beautiful. Walking along a sunken planked street I stopped a moment to gaze at the window of a book shop, arrested by the sight of those lurid adventure magazines which one never expects to find in a foreign land but which flourish everywhere in every land, in every tongue almost. Conspicuous among them was a brilliant red-covered volume of Jules Verne, a Greek edition of "Twenty Thousand Leagues Under the Sea." What impressed me at the moment was the thought that the world in which this fantastic yarn lay buried was far more fantastic than anything Jules Verne had imagined. How could any one possibly imagine, coming out of the sky from another planet in the middle of the night, let us say, and finding himself in this weird community, that there existed on this earth other beings who lived in towering skyscrapers the very materials of which would baffle the mind to describe? And if there could be such a gulf between two worlds lying in such proximity what might be the gulf between the present world and the world to come? To see even fifty or a hundred years ahead taxes our imagination to the utmost; we are incapable of seeing beyond the repetitious cycle of war and peace, rich and poor, right and wrong, good and bad. Look twenty thousand years ahead: do you still see battleships, skyscrapers, churches, lunatic asylums, slums, mansions, national frontiers, tractors, sewing machines, canned sardines, little liver pills, etc. etc.? How will these things be eradicated? How will the new world, brave or poor, come about? Looking at the beautiful volume of Jules Verne I seriously asked myself the question—*how will it come about?* I wondered, indeed, if the elimination of these things ever seriously occupy our imagination. For as I stood there day dreaming I had the impression that everything was at a stand still, that I was not a man living in the twentieth century but a visitor from no century seeing what he had seen before and would see again and again, and the thought that that might be possible was utterly depressing.

It was the soothsayer's wife who opened the door for us. She had a serene, dignified countenance which at once impressed me favorably. She pointed to the next room where her husband sat at a table in his shirt sleeves, his head supported by his elbows. He was apparently engaged in reading a huge, Biblical book. As we entered the room he rose and shook hands cordially. There was nothing theatrical or ostentatious about him; indeed he had more the air of a carpenter pursuing his rabbinical studies than any appearance of being a medium. He hastened to explain that he was not possessed of any extraordinary powers, that he had simply been a student of the Kabbala for many years and that he had been instructed in the art of Arabian astrology. He spoke Arabic, Turkish, Greek, Armenian, German, French, Czech and several other languages and had until recently been in the service of the Czechoslovak consulate. The only information he demanded was the date, hour and place of my birth, my first name and my mother's and father's first names. I should say that before he had put these questions to me he remarked to Katsimbalis that I was decidedly a Capricorn of the Jupiterian type. He consulted the books, made his computations slowly and methodically and then, raising his eyes, began to talk. He spoke to me in French, but now and then, when things became too complicated, he addressed himself to Katsimbalis in Greek and the latter translated it back to me in English. Linguistically, to say the least, the situation was rather interesting. I felt unusually calm, steady, sure of myself, aware as he talked of every object in the room and yet never for a moment distracted. It was the living room we were seated in and it was extremely clean and orderly, the atmosphere reminding me strongly of the homes of poor rabbis whom I had visited in other cities of the world.

He began by telling me that I was approaching a new and most important phase of my life, that up to the present I had been wandering in circles, that I had created many enemies (by what I had written) and caused much harm and suffering to others. He said that I had led not only a dual life (I believe he used the word schizophrenic) but a multiple life and that nobody really understood me, not even my closest friends. But soon, he said, all this was to cease. At a certain date, which he gave me, I would find a clear, open path ahead of me; before dying I would bring great joy to the world, to everybody in the world, he emphasized, and my greatest enemy would bow down before me and beg my forgiveness. He said that I would enjoy before my death the greatest honors, the greatest rewards which man can confer upon man. I would make three trips to the Orient where, among other things, I would meet a man who would understand me as no one had and that this meeting was absolutely indispensable for the both of us. That on my last visit to the Orient I would never return, neither would I die, but vanish in the light. I interrupted him here to ask if he meant by that I would be immortal, through my works or my deeds, and he answered solemnly and most significantly that he did not, that he meant simply and literally that I would never die. At this I confess I felt startled and I glanced at Katsimbalis, without saying a word, to make sure that I had heard correctly.

He went on to tell me that there were signs and indications given which he himself could not understand but which he would relate to me exactly as they were given. Not at all surprised by this I begged him to do so, adding that I would understand quite well myself. He was particularly baffled, and impressed, it seemed, by the fact that I had all the signs of divinity and at the same time my feet were chained to the earth. He paused to explain himself to Katsimbalis in Greek, obviously quite moved and obviously fearful to offer an interpretation of which he was not certain. Turning to me again he made it clear, both by his speech and by his words, that he considered it a rare privilege to be in the presence of such a one as myself. He confessed that he had never seen the indications for such a splendid career as now lay before me. He asked me pertinently if I had not escaped death several times. "In fact," he added, hardly waiting for confirmation, "you have always miraculously escaped whenever a situation became desperate or unbearable. You always will. You lead a charmed life. I want you to remember my words, when danger confronts you again—that however perilous the situation you must never give up, you will be saved. You are like a ship with two rudders: when one gives out the other will function. In addition, you are equipped with wings: you can take flight when those about you must perish. You are protected. You have had only one enemy—*yourself*." And with this he rose, came round to me and seizing my hand raised it to his lips.

I give the gist of his words, omitting numerous details concerning my relations with others which would be of no interest to the reader without knowledge of the personalities and relationships involved. Everything he told me about the past was startlingly accurate and for the most part were about things which no one in Greece, not even Durrell or Katsimbalis, could possibly have had any knowledge about. We chatted a few moments before taking leave and during the course of the conversation he begged me, since I was returning to America, to look up his brother in Detroit from whom he hoped to get aid. There was one touch, incidentally, which I forgot and which is worth relating, because it struck me as so Armenian. In telling me of the fame and glory, the honors and rewards I would receive, he remarked in a puzzled way—"but I see no money!" At this I laughed outright. Money has been the one thing I have never had, and yet I have led a rich life and in the main a happy one. Why should I need money now—or later? When I have been desperately in need I have always found a friend. I go on the assumption that I have friends everywhere. I shall have more and more as time goes on. If I were to have money I might become careless and negligent, believing in a security which does not exist, stressing those values which are illusory and empty. I have no misgivings about the future. In the dark days to come money will be less than ever a protection against evil and suffering.

I was of course profoundly impressed by the interview. More than anything I felt chastened. Aside from the enigmatic reference to my not dying nothing he had predicted for my future astounded me. I have always expected everything of the world and have always been ready to give everything. I had also, even before leaving Paris, the conviction that I would eventually break the vicious chain of cycles which, as he said, were usually of seven years' duration. I had left Paris before the war knowing that my life there had come to an end. The decision to take a vacation for one year, to abstain from writing during that time, the very choice of Greece which, as I see it now, was the only country which could have satisfied my inner needs, all this was significant. In the last year or two in Paris I had been hinting to my friends that I would one day give up writing altogether, give it up voluntarily—at the moment when I would feel myself in possession of the greatest power and mastery. The study of Balzac, which was my final work in Paris, had only corroborated a thought which had begun to crystallize in me, namely that the life of the artist, his devotion to art, is the highest and the last phase of egotism in man. There are friends who tell me that I will never stop writing, that I can't. But I did stop, for a good interval while in Greece, and I know that I can in the future, any time I wish, and for good. I feel under no compulsion to do any particular thing. I feel, on the contrary, a growing liberation, supplemented more and more by a desire to serve the world in the highest possible way. What that way is I have not yet determined, but it seems clear to me that I shall pass from art to life, to exemplify whatever I have mastered through art by my living. I said I felt chastened. It is true that I also felt exalted. But above all I felt a sense of responsibility such as I had never known before. A sense of responsibility towards myself, let me hasten to add. Without tasting the rewards which he had spoken of I had nevertheless enjoyed them in advance, enjoyed them imaginatively, I mean. During all the years that I have been writing I have steeled myself to the idea that I would not really be accepted, at least to my own countrymen, until after my death. Many times, in writing, I have looked over my own shoulder from beyond the grave, more alive to the reaction of those to come than to those of my contemporaries. A good part of my life has, in a way, been lived in the future. With regard to all that vitally concerns me I am really a dead man, alive only to a very few who, like myself, could not wait for the world to catch up with them. I do not say this out of pride or vanity, but with humility not untouched with sadness. Sadness is perhaps hardly the right word either, since I neither regret the course I have followed nor desire things to be any different than they are. I know now what the world is like and knowing I accept it, both the good and the evil. To live creatively, I have discovered, means to live more and more unselfishly, to live more and more *into* the world, identifying oneself with it and thus influencing it at the core, so to speak. Art, like religion, it now seems to me, is only a preparation, an initiation into the way of life. The goal is liberation, freedom, which means assuming greater responsibility. To continue writing beyond the point of self-realization seems futile and arresting. The mastery of any form of expression should lead inevitably to the final expression—mastery of life. In this realm one is absolutely alone, face to face with the very elements of creation. It is an experiment whose outcome nobody can predict. If it be successful the whole world is affected and in a way never known before. I do not wish to boast, nor do I wish to say that I am yet ready to make such a grave step, but it is in this direction that my mind is set. It was my belief before meeting the Armenian, and it still is, that when the honors and rewards shall be conferred upon me I shall not be present to receive them, that I shall be living alone and unknown in some remote part of the world carrying on the adventure which began with the effort to realize myself in words. I know that the greatest dangers lie ahead; the real voyage has only begun. As I write these lines it is almost a year since that moment in Athens which I have just described. May I add that since coming to America everything that has happened to me, one fulfillment, one realization after another, has occurred with an almost clock-like precision. Indeed, I am almost terrified for now, contrary to my life in the past, I have but to desire a thing and my wishes are gratified. I am in the delicate position of one who has to be careful not to wish for something he really does not desire. The effect, I must say, has been to make me desire less and less. The one desire which grows more and more is to give. The very real sense of power and wealth which this entails is also somewhat frightening—because the logic of it seems too utterly simple. It is not until I look about me and realize that the vast majority of my fellow-men are desperately trying to hold on to what they possess or to increase their possessions that I begin to understand that the wisdom of giving is not so simple as it seems. Giving and receiving are at bottom one thing, dependent upon whether one lives open or closed. Living openly one becomes a medium, a transmitter; living thus, as a river, one experiences life to the full, flows along with the current of life, and dies in order to live again as an ocean.

The train was due to leave at four o'clock, so we had time for a last meal together. Durrell did his best to persuade me to stay overnight, convinced that the boat would not leave on schedule. "Nothing goes according to schedule in this bloody country," he assured me. In my heart I was hoping that some convenient accident would detain me. If I were to miss the boat I might not get another for a month and in that time Italy might declare war on Greece and thus shut me off in the Mediterranean, a most delightful prospect. Nevertheless I went through the motions of leaving. It was up to Fate now, I thought to myself. Durrell and Nancy were going to Epidaurus and then to Oympia. I would be going back to jail.

The horse and carriage were at the door waiting for me. Durrell and Nancy stood on the steps waving goodbye. The sleigh bells began to ring, the flaps came down over my eyes and we started off in a teeming mist which was made of rain and tears. "Where will we meet again?" I asked myself. Not in America, not in England, not in Greece, thought I. If anywhere it will be in India or Tibet. And we are going to meet haphazardly—on the road—as Durrell and his friend had met on the way to Mystras. The war will not only change the map of the world but it will affect the destiny of every one I care about. Already, even before the war had broken out, we were scattered to the four winds, those of us who had lived and worked together and who had no thought to do anything but what we were doing. My friend X, who used to be terrified at the very mention of war, had volunteered for service in the British Army; my friend Y, who was utterly indifferent and who used to say that he would go right on working at the Bibliothéque Nationale war or no war, joined the Foreign Legion; my friend Z, who was an out and out pacifist, volunteered for ambulance service and has never been heard of since; some are in concentration camps in France and Germany, one is rotting away in Siberia, another is in China, another in Mexico, another in Australia. When we meet again some will be blind, some legless, some old and white-haired, some demented, some bitter and cynical. Maybe the world will be a better place to live in, maybe it'll be just the same, maybe it'll be worse than it is now—who knows? The strangest thing of all is that in a universal crisis of this sort one instinctively knows that certain ones are doomed and that others will be spared. With some, usually the shining, heroic figures, one can see death written in their faces; they glow with the knowledge of their own death. Others, whom one would normally think of as worthless, in the military sense, you feel nevertheless will become hardened veterans, will go through hell's fire unscathed and emerge grinning, perhaps to settle down in the old routine and amount to nothing. I saw the effect of the last war on some of my friends in America; I can see the effect which this one will produce even more clearly. One thing is certain, I thought to myself—the chaos and confusion which this war is engendering will never be remedied in our lifetime. There will be no resuming where we left off. The world we knew is dead and gone. The next time we meet, any of us, it will be on the ashes of all that we once cherished.

The scene at the railway station was one of utter confusion. Word had just been received that the train would be an hour or two late—there had been a washout up the line somewhere, nobody knew exactly where. The rain came down relentlessly and unceasingly, as if all the cocks in the celestial plumbing system had been opened and the monkey wrench thrown away. I sat down on a bench outside and prepared myself for a long siege. In a few minutes a man approached me and said "Hello, what you doing here? You an American?" I nodded and smiled. "Helluva country this, eh?" he said. "Too poor, that's what's the matter. Where you come from—Chicago?"

He sat down beside me and began to chew my ear off about the wonderful efficiency of the American railways. A Greek, naturally, who had lived in Detroit. "Why I come back to this country I don't know," he went on. "Everybody poor here—you can't make no money here. Soon we go to war. I was a damn fool to leave America. What you think of Greece—you like it? How long you stay here? You think America go to war?"

I decided to get out of his clutches as soon as possible. "Try to find out when the train will arrive," I said, dispatching him to the telegraph office. He didn't budge. "What's the use," he said, "nobody knows when the train will come. Maybe to-morrow morning." He began to talk about automobiles, what a wonderful car the Ford was, for instance.

"I don't know anything about cars," I said.

"That's funny," he said, "and you an American."

"I don't like cars."

"But just the same, when you want to get somewhere. . . ."

"I don't want to get anywhere."

"That's funny," he said. "You like the train better maybe, yes?"

"I like the donkey better than the train. I like to walk too."

"My brother just like that," he said. "My brother say, 'why you want a car?' My brother, he never been in a car in his life. He stay here in Greece. He live in the mountains—very poor, but he say he don't care just so long as he have enough to eat."

"He sounds like an intelligent man," I said.

"Who, my brother? No, he know nothing. He can't read or write; he can't even sign his own name."

"That's fine," I said, "then he must be a happy man."

"My brother? No, he's very sad. He lose his wife and three children. I want him to go to America with me, but he say 'what I go to America for?' I tell him he make lots of money there. He say he don't want to make money. He just want to eat every day, that's all. Nobody got ambition here. America everybody want to be a success. Maybe some day your son be President of the United States, yes?"

"Maybe," I said, just to please him.

"In America everybody got a chance—poor man too, yes?"

"Sure."

"Maybe I go back again and make big money, what you think?"

"Nothing like trying," I answered.

"Sure, that's what I tell my brother. You must work. In America you work like a son of a bitch—but you get paid for it. Here you work and work and work and what you got? Nothing. A piece of bread maybe. What kind of life is that? How you going to succeed?"

I groaned.

"You make lots of money in New York, I bet, yes?"

"No," I said, "I never made a cent."

"What you mean?" he said. "You couldn't find job in New York?"

"I had lots of jobs," I answered.

"You don't stay long on one job, that's it, yes?"

"That's right," I said.

"Maybe you don't find the right job. You got to try many jobs— till you find the right one. You got to save your money. Maybe you have bad luck sometimes—then you have something for a rainy day, yes?"

"That's it," I said.

"Sometimes you get sick and you lose all your money. Sometimes a friend he take your money away from you. But you never give up, right? You stick it out. You try again."

"That's the idea," I grunted.

"You got a good job waiting for you in New York?"

"No," I said, "I haven't any job."

"Not so many jobs now as before," he said. "In 1928 lots of jobs. Now everybody poor. I lose ten thousand dollars in stock market. Some people lose more. I say never mind, try again. Then I come to this country to see my brother. I stay too long. No

money here. Only trouble. . . . You think Italy make trouble soon
for Greece?"

"I don't know," I said.

"You think Germany win—or France?"

"I couldn't say."

"I think United States should go in the war. United States clean
up those sons of bitches quick, yes? If United states make war on
Germany I fight for United States."

"That's the stuff," I said.

"Sure, why not?" he continued. "I no like to fight, but United
States good country. Everybody get square deal, rich or poor.
Uncle Sam afraid of nobody. We raise ten million, twenty million
soldiers—like that! We kill those sons of bitches like dogs, yes?"

"You said it, brother."

"I say to myself Uncle Sam he give me gun, he send me over to
fight, I fight for him. Greek people no like Italians. Greek people
like America. Everybody like America. . . ."

"I like you too," I said, getting up and shaking hands with him,
"but now I've got to leave you—I must make pipi."

"That's all right, I'll wait for you," he said.

You'll have a long wait, I thought to myself, as I disappeared
inside the station. I got out on the other side of the station and
walked around in the rain. When I returned I saw that the train
was due to arrive at eight o'clock. A string of cars was standing at
the platform waiting for the other section to arrive. Towards seven
o'clock a bell hop from the hotel arrived and handed me a note. It
was from Durrell, urging me to come back to the hotel and have
dinner with them. The train wouldn't arrive until after ten, he
informed me. I thought it over and decided against it, more
because I hated to say goodbye a second time than for any other
reason.

I got into one of the coaches and sat there in the dark. Towards
nine-thirty a train pulled in from the opposite direction and everybody got excited. But when we tried to climb aboard we found that
it was an excursion train that had been hired by a club. As I stood
on the platform of the special I learned that it was leaving for
Athens in a few minutes. I was wondering if I couldn't persuade
them to take me along when a man came up to me and spoke to
me in Greek. I answered in French that I couldn't speak Greek,
that I was an American and that I was very anxious to get to
Athens as soon as possible. He called a young lady over who
spoke English and when she learned that I was an American tourist
she got excited and told me to wait, saying she thought she could
fix it for me. I stood there a few mintues congratulating myself on

my good luck. The young lady returned accompanied by a grave, melancholy-looking man with an officious air. He asked me very courteously why it was important for me to get back to Athens quickly, why couldn't I wait for the other train which was due now in a little while, he was certain. I answered very courteously that there was no good reason except fear. He assured me there was nothing to be worried about. The other train was due in a few minutes and he had not the slightest doubt that it would leave in good time. He hesitated a moment and then cautiously, as if giving me a straw to grasp at, he inquired politely and with the utmost tact, as if unwilling to wrest the secret from me, whether I did not have a more urgent reason for wishing to leave ahead of time. There was something about his manner which warned me that it would be better not to invent a false reason. Something told me that he suspected me of being more than just a tourist. Beneath that suave, courteous exterior I divined the police inspector. True, I had in my pocket a letter from the Bureau of Tourisme which Seferiades had given me when I went to Crete, but experience has taught me that when a man is suspicious of you the better your credentials are the worse it is for you. I backed quietly down the steps, thanking him for his courtesy and excusing myself for the inconvenience I had caused him. "Your bags?" he said, with a flash of the eye. "I have none," I said, and quickly disappeared in the crowd.

As soon as the train had pulled out I came out on the platform of the station and dove into the buffet where I put away some tender bits of lamb and a few cognacs. I felt as though I had narrowly missed going to jail. Two prisoners who were handcuffed came in escorted by soldiers. I learned later that they had murdered the man who had violated their sister. They were good men, mountaineers, and they had surrendered without resistance. I went outside and got up an appetite watching a tender lamb being rolled on a spit. I had some more cognac. Then I got inside a coach and fell into conversation with a Greek who had lived in Paris. He was even more of a bore than the guy from Detroit. He was an intellectual who liked all the wrong things. I extricated myself as gracefully as possible and paced up and down in the rain again.

When the train did roll in at midnight I could scarcely believe my eyes. Of course it didn't pull out until about two in the morning—I didn't expect it to do any better. I had changed my ticket for a first-class compartment, thinking thereby to gain a little sleep before morning. There was only one man in the compartment with me and he soon began to doze off. I had a whole bench to myself, an upholstered one with white doylies over it. I stretched out full length and closed my eyes. Presently I felt something crawling over my neck. I sat up and brushed off a fat cockroach. As I sat there, gazing stupidly ahead of me, I noticed a file of cockroaches climbing the wall opposite. Then I took a glance at my fellow traveler. To my disgust I saw that they were crawling at a good pace over the lapel of his coat, on to his tie and down inside his vest. I got up and nudged him, pointing to the cockroaches. He made a grimace, brushed them off and with a smile fell back to sleep again. Not me. I was as wide awake as if I had just swallowed a half dozen cups of coffee. I felt itchy all over. I went outside and stood in the corridor. The train was going downhill, not just fast as trains do when they go downhill, but as if the engineer had gone to sleep and left the throttle wide open. I felt anxious. I wondered whether it would be wise to wake my companion up and warn him that something was wrong. Finally I realized that I didn't know how to express the thought in Greek and I gave up the idea. I clung to the open window with two hands and prayed to Christ and all the little angels that we'd hit the bottom without going off the track. Somewhere before Argos I felt the brakes being applied and realized with a sigh of relief that the engineer was at his post. As we came to a stop I felt a gush of warm, fragrant air. Some urchins in bare feet swarmed around the train with baskets of fruit and soda water. They looked as if they had been routed out of bed— little tots, about eight or ten years of age. I could see nothing but mountains about and overhead the moon scudding through the clouds. The warm air seemed to be coming up from the sea, rising slowly and steadily, like incense. A pile of old ties were going up in flames, casting a weird light on the black mountains yonder.

The greatest single impression which Greece made upon me is that it is a man-sized world. Now it is true that France also conveys this impression, and yet there is a difference, a difference which is profound. Greece is the home of the gods; they may have died but their presence still makes itself felt. The gods were of human proportion: they were created out of the human spirit. In France, as elsewhere in the Western world, this link between the human and the divine is broken. The scepticism and paralysis produced by this schism in the very nature of man provides the clue to the inevitable destruction of our present civilization. If men cease to believe that they will one day become gods then they will surely become worms. Much has been said about a new order of life destined to arise on this American continent. It should be borne in mind, however, that not even a beginning has been visioned for at least a thousand years to come. The present way of life, which is America's, is doomed as surely as is that of Europe. No nation on earth can possibly give birth to a new order of life until a world view is established. We have learned through bitter mistakes that all the peoples of the earth *are* vitally connected, but we have not made use of that knowledge in an intelligent way. We have seen two world wars and we shall undoubtedly see a third and a fourth, possibly more. There will be no hope of peace until the old order is shattered. The world must become small again as the old Greek world was—small enough to include everybody. Until the very last man is included there will be no real human society. My intelligence tells me that such a condition of life will be a long time in coming, but my intelligence also tells me that nothing short of that will ever satisfy man. Until he has become fully human, until he learns to conduct himself as a member of the earth, he will continue to create gods who will destroy him. The tragedy of Greece lies not in the destruction of a great culture but in the abortion of a great vision. We say erroneously that the Greeks humanized the gods. It is just the contrary. The gods humanized the Greeks. There was a moment when it seemed as if the real significance of life had been grasped, a breathless moment when the destiny of the whole human race was in jeopardy. The moment was lost in the blaze of power which engulfed the intoxicated Greeks. They made mythology of a reality which was too great for their human comprehension. We forget, in our enchantment with the myth, that it is born of reality and is fundamentally no different from any other form of creation, except that it has to do with the very quick of life. We too are creating myths, though we are perhaps not aware of it. But in our myths there is no place for the gods. We are building an abstract, dehumanized world out of the ashes of an illusory materialism. We are proving to ourselves that the universe is empty, a task which is justified by our own empty logic. We are determined to conquer and conquer we shall, but the conquest is death.

People seem astounded and enthralled when I speak of the effect which this visit to Greece produced upon me. They say they envy me and that they wish they could one day go there themselves. Why don't they? Because nobody can enjoy the experience he desires until he is ready for it. People seldom mean what they say. Any one who says he is burning to do something other than he is doing or to be somewhere else than he is is lying to himself. To desire is not merely to wish. To desire is to become that which one essentially is. Some men, reading this, will inevitably realize that there is nothing to do but act out their desires. A line of Maeterlinck's concerning truth and action altered my whole conception of life. It took me twenty-five years to fully awaken to the meaning of his phrase. Other men are quicker to coordinate vision and action. But the point is that in Greece I finally achieved that coordination. I became deflated, restored to proper human proportions, ready to accept my lot and prepared to give of all that I have received. Standing in Agamemnon's tomb I went through a veritable re-birth. I don't mind in the least what people think or say when they read such a statement. I have no desire to convert any one to my way of thinking. I know now that any influence I may have upon the world will be a result of the example I set and not because of my words. I give this record of my journey not as a contribution to human knowledge, because my knowledge is small and of little account, but as a contribution to human experience. Errors of one sort and another there undoubtedly are in this account but the truth is that something happened to me and *that* I have given as truthfully as I know how.

My friend Katsimbalis for whom I have written this book, by way of showing my gratitude to him and his compatriots, will I hope forgive me for having exaggerated his proportions to that of a Colossus. Those who know Amaroussion will realize that there is nothing grandiose about the place. Neither is there anything grandiose about Katsimbalis. Neither, in the ultimate, is there anything grandiose about the entire history of Greece. But there is something colossal about any human figure when that individual becomes truly and thoroughly human. A more human individual than Katsimbalis I have never met. Walking with him through the streets of Amaroussion I had the feeling that I was walking the earth in a totally new way. The earth became more intimate, more alive, more promising. He spoke frequently of the past, it is true, not as something dead and forgotten however, but rather as something which we carry within us, something which fructifies the present and makes the future inviting. He spoke of little things and of great with equal reverence; he was never too busy to pause and dwell on the things which moved him; he had endless time on his hands, which in itself is the mark of a great soul. How can I ever forget that last impression he made upon me when we said farewell at the bus station in the heart of Athens? There are men who are so full, so rich, who give themselves so completely that each time you take leave of them you feel that it is absolutely of no consequence whether the parting is for a day or forever. They come to you brimming over and they fill you to overflowing. They ask nothing of you except that you participate in their superabundant joy of living. They never inquire which side of the fence you are on because the world they inhabit has no fences. They make themselves invulnerable by habitually exposing themselves to every danger. They grow more heroic in the measure that they reveal their weaknesses. Certainly in those endless and seemingly fabulous stories which Katsimbalis was in the habit of recounting there must have been a good element of fancy and distortion, yet even if truth was occasionally sacrificed to reality the man behind the story only succeeded thereby in revealing more faithfully and thoroughly his human image. As I turned to go, leaving him sitting there in the bus, his alert, round eye already feasting itself upon other sights, Seferiades who was accompanying me home re- marked with deep feeling: "he is a great fellow, Miller, there is no doubt about it: he is something extraordinary . . . a human phenomenon, I should say." He said it almost as if he Seferiades were saying farewell and not me. He knew Katsimbalis as well as one man can know another, I should imagine; he was sometimes impatient with him, sometimes irritated beyond words, sometimes downright furious, but even if he were one day to become his bitterest enemy I could not imagine him saying one word to reduce the stature or the splendor of his friend. How wonderful it was to hear him say, knowing that I had just left Katsimbalis—"did he tell you that story about the coins he found?" or whatever it might be. He asked with the enthusiasm of a music lover who, learning that his friend has just bought a gramophone, wishes to advise him of a record which he knows will bring his friend great joy. Often, when we were all together and Katsimbalis had launched into a long story, I caught that warm smile of recognition on Seferiades' face—that smile which informs the others that they are about to hear something which has been proved and tested and found good. Or he might say afterwards, taking me by the arm and leading me aside: "too bad he didn't give you the whole story to-night; there is a wonderful part which he tells sometimes when he's in very good spirits—it's a pity you had to miss it." It was also taken for granted by everybody, it seemed to me, that Katsimbalis not only had a right to improvise as he went along but that he was expected to do so. He was regarded as a virtuoso, a virtuoso who played only his own compositions and had therefore the right to alter them as he pleased.

There was another interesting aspect of his remarkable gift, one which again bears analogy to the musician's talent. During the time I knew him Katsimbalis' life was relatively quiet and unadven- turous. But the most trivial incident, if it happened to Katsimbalis, had a way of blossoming into a great event. It might be nothing more than that he had picked a flower by the roadside on his way home. But when he had done with the story that flower, humble though it might be, would become the most wonderful flower that ever a man had picked. That flower would remain in the memory of the listener as the flower which Katsimbalis had picked; it would become unique, not because there was anything in the least extraordinary about it, but because Katsimbalis had immortalized it by noticing it, because he had put into that flower all that he thought and felt about flowers, which is like saying—a universe.

I choose this image at random but how appropriate and accurate it is! When I think of Katsimbalis bending over to pick a flower from the bare soil of Attica the whole Greek world, past, present and future, rises before me. I see again the soft, low mounds in which the illustrious dead were hidden away; I see the violet light in which the stiff scrub, the worn rocks, the huge boulders of the dry river beds gleam like mica; I see the miniature islands floating above the surface of the sea, ringed with dazzling white bands; I see the eagles swooping out from the dizzy crags of inaccessible mountain tops, their sombre shadows slowly staining the bright carpet of earth below; I see the figures of solitary men trailing their flocks over the naked spine of the hills and the fleece of their beasts all golden fuzz as in the days of legend; I see the women gathered at the wells amidst the olive groves, their dress, their manners, their talk no different now than in Biblical times; I see the grand patriarchal figure of the priest, the perfect blend of male and female, his countenance serene, frank, full of peace and dignity; I see the geometrical pattern of nature expounded by the earth itself in a silence which is deafening. The Greek earth opens before me like the Book of Revelation. I never knew that the earth contains so much; I had walked blindfolded, with faltering, hesitant steps; I was proud and arrogant, content to live the false, restricted life of the city man. The light of Greece opened my eyes, penetrated my pores, expanded my whole being. I came home to the world, having found the true center and the real meaning of revolution. No warring conflicts between the nations of the earth can disturb this equilibrium. Greece herself may become embroiled, as we ourselves are now becoming embroiled, but I refuse categorically to become anything less than the citizen of the world which I silently declared myself to be when I stood in Agamemnon's tomb. From that day forth my life was dedicated to the recovery of the divinity of man. Peace to all men, I say, and life more abundant!

FINIS

APPENDIX

Just as I had written the last line the postman delivered me a characteristic letter from Lawrence Durrell dated August 10th, 1940. I give it herewith to round off the portrait of Katsimbalis.

"The peasants are lying everywhere on deck eating watermelons; the gutters are running with the juice. A huge crowd bound on a pilgrimage to the Virgin of Tinos. We are just precariously out of the harbour, scouting the skyline for Eyetalian Subs. What I really have to tell you is the story of the Cocks of Attica: it will frame your portrait of Katsimbalis which I have not yet read but which sounds marvellous from all accounts. It is this. We all went up to the Acropolis the other evening very drunk and exalted by wine and poetry; it was a hot black night and our blood was roaring with cognac. We sat on the steps outside the big gate, passing the bottle, Katsimbalis reciting and G—weeping a little, when all of a sudden K. was seized with a kind of fit. Leaping to his feet he yelled out—"Do you want to hear the cocks of Attica, you damned moderns?" His voice had a hysterical edge to it. We didn't answer and he wasn't waiting for one. He took a little run to the edge of the precipice, like a faery queen, a heavy black faery queen, in his black clothes, threw back his head, clapped the crook of his stock into his wounded arm, and sent out the most blood-curdling clarion I have ever heard. Cock-a-doodle-doo. It echoed all over the city—a sort of dark bowl dotted with lights like cherries. It ricochetted from hillock to hillock and wheeled up under the walls of the Parthenon. . . . We were so shocked that we were struck dumb. And while we were still looking at each other in the darkness, lo, from the distance silvery clear in the darkness a cock drowsily answered—then another, then another. This drove K. wild. Squaring himself, like a bird about to fly into space, and flapping his coat tails, he set up a terrific scream—and the echoes multiplied. He screamed until the veins stood out all over him, looking like a battered and ravaged rooster in profile, flapping on his own dunghill. He screamed himself hysterical and his audience in the valley increased until all over Athens like bugles they were calling and calling, answering him. Finally between laughter and hysteria we had to ask him to stop. The whole night was alive with cockcrows—all Athens, all Attica, all Greece, it seemed, until I almost imagined you being woken at your desk late in New York to hear these terrific silver peals: Katsimbaline cockcrow in Attica. This was epic—a great moment and purely Katsimbalis. If you could have heard these cocks, the frantic psaltery of the Attic

cocks! I dreamt about it for two nights afterwards. Well, we are on our way to Mykonos, resigned now that we have heard the cocks of Attica from the Acropolis. I wish you'd write it—it is part of the mosaic. . . ."

LARRY

THE TRIP
ACROSS
AMERICA

•

(1940–1944)

Preface to
The Air-Conditioned Nightmare

The thought of writing a book on America came to me in Paris some years ago. At that time the possibility of realizing my dream seemed rather remote, for in order to write the book I would have to visit America, travel leisurely, have money in my pocket, and so on. I hadn't the slightest notion when such a day would dawn.

Not having the means to undertake the trip, the next best thing was to live it imaginatively, which I proceeded to do at odd moments. This preliminary journey began, I recall, with the inheritance of a huge scrap-book which once belonged to Walter Lowenfels who, on the eve of his departure from France, invited me to assist at the burning of a huge pile of manuscripts which he had spent years in producing.

Often, on returning to my studio at midnight, I would stand at the table and register in this celestial sort of ledger the innumerable little items which constitute a writer's bookkeeping; dreams, plans of attack and defense, remembrances, titles of books I intended to write, names and addresses of potential creditors, obsessive phrases, editors to harry, battlefields, monuments, monastic retreats, and so on. I remember distinctly the thrill I had when putting down such words as Mobile, Suwanee River, Navajos, Painted Desert, the lynching bee, the electric chair.

It seems a pity now that I didn't write an account of that imaginary journey which began in Paris. What a different book it would have been!

There was a reason, however, for making the physical journey, fruitless though it proved to be. I felt the need to effect a reconciliation with my native land. It was an urgent need because, unlike most prodigal sons, I was returning not with the intention of remaining in the bosom of the family but of wandering forth again, perhaps never to return. I wanted to have a last look at my country and leave it with a good taste in my mouth. I didn't want to run away from it, as I had originally. I wanted to embrace it, to feel that the old wounds were really healed, and set out for the unknown with a blessing on my lips.

On leaving Greece I was in a serene mood. If any one on earth were free of hatred, prejudice, bitterness, I thought it was myself. I was confident that for the first time in my life I would look upon New York and what lay beyond it without a trace of loathing or disgust.

It turned out that the boat was stopping at Boston first. That was unfortunate perhaps, but it was an excellent test. I had never been to Boston and I was rather pleased that Fate had played a trick on me. I was prepared to like Boston.

When I came up on deck to catch my first glimpse of the shore line I was immediately disappointed. Not only disappointed, I might say, but actually saddened. The American coast looked bleak and uninviting to me. I didn't like the look of the American house; there is something cold, austere, something barren and chill, about the architecture of the American home. It was *home*, with all the ugly, evil, sinister connotations which the word contains for a restless soul. There was a frigid, moral aspect to it which chilled me to the bone.

It was a wintry day and a gale was blowing. I went ashore with one of the passengers. I can't remember any more who he was or what he looked like, which is significant of the state of mind I was in. For some unknown reason we strolled through the railway station, a lugubrious place which filled me with dread, and which instantly revived the remembrance of similar stations in similar cities, all painful, harrowing recollections. What I remember most vividly about this Boston railway station were the enormous piles of books and magazines, looking just as cheap, vulgar, trashy as of yore. And the womb-like warmth of the place—so American, so unforgettably so.

It was a Sunday and the mob was out, reinforced by groups of rowdy students. The spectacle nauseated me. I wanted to get back to the ship as fast as possible. In an hour or so I had seen all I wanted to see of Boston. It seemed hideous to me.

Returning to the boat we passed bridges, railroad tracks, warehouses, factories, wharves and what not. It was like following in the wake of a demented giant who had sown the earth with crazy dreams. If I could only have seen a horse or a cow, or just a cantankerous goat chewing tin cans, it would have been a tremendous relief. But there was nothing of the animal, vegetable or human kingdom in sight. It was a vast jumbled waste created by pre-human or sub-human monsters in a delirium of greed. It was something negative, some not-ness of some kind or other. It was a bad dream and towards the end I broke into a trot, what with disgust and nausea, what with the howling icy gale which was whipping everything in sight into a frozen pie crust. When I got back to the boat I was praying that by some miracle the captain would decide to alter his course and return to Piraeus.

It was a bad beginning. The sight of New York, of the harbor, the bridges, the skyscrapers, did nothing to eradicate my first impressions. To the image of stark, grim ugliness which Boston had created was added a familiar feeling of terror. Sailing around the Battery from one river to the other, gliding close to shore, night coming on, the streets dotted with scurrying insects, I felt as I had always felt about New York—that it is the most horrible place on God's earth. No matter how many times I escape I am brought back, like a runaway slave, each time detesting it, loathing it, more and more.

Back in the rat trap. I try to hide away from my old friends; I don't want to relive the past with them because the past is full of wretched, sordid memories. My one thought is to get out of New York, to experience something genuinely American. I want to revisit some of the spots I once knew. I want to get out into the open.

To do anything you need money. I had arrived without a cent, exactly as I left the country years ago. At the Gotham Book Mart I found a little sum of money which Miss Steloff had collected for me from her patrons. It was a pleasant surprise. I was touched. Still, it was not enough to live on for any length of time. I would have to find more money. Perhaps I would have to take a job—a most depressing thought.

Meanwhile my father was dying. He had been dying for three years. I hadn't the heart to visit him empty-handed. I was getting desperate. Something would have to happen, something miraculous. It did. By accident I ran across a man who I thought was my enemy. Almost the first words out of his mouth were: "How are you fixed? Can I help you?" Again I was touched, this time to the point of tears.

In a few months I was down South at the home of an old friend. I spent a good part of the Summer there, then returned to New York. My father was still alive. I visited him regularly at his home in Brooklyn, talked about the old days in New York (the '80's and '90's), met the neighbors, listened to the radio (always that damned "Information Please!"), discussed the nature of the prostate gland, the peculiarities of the bladder, the New Deal which was still new to me and rather goofy and meaningless. "*That Roosevelt!*" I can hear the neighbors saying, as if they were saying "*That Hitler!*" A great change had come over America, no doubt about that. There were greater ones coming, I felt certain. We were only witnessing the prelude to something unimaginable. Everything was cock-eyed, and getting more and more so. Maybe we would end up on all fours, gibbering like baboons. Something disastrous was in store—everybody felt it. Yes, America had changed. The lack of resilience, the feeling of hopelessness, the resignation, the skepticism, the defeatism—I could scarcely believe my ears at first. And over it all that same veneer of fatuous optimism—only now decidedly cracked.

I was getting restless. My father didn't seem ready to die yet. God knows how long I might be marooned in New York. I decided to go ahead with my plans. The trip had to be made some time—why wait? Money again, of course. One needs money to travel around the country for a year or so. Real money, I mean. I had no idea what it would require; I knew only that I must start soon or be bogged down forever.

Ever since my return from the South I had been visiting Abe Rattner's studio in my spare moments, trying to improve my skill as a water-colorist. One day I broached the subject of my forthcoming trip. To my surprise Rattner expressed a desire to accompany me. Soon we were discussing the kind of book we would do—a huge affair with color plates and so on. Something de luxe, like the beautiful French books which we were familiar with. Who would publish it for us we didn't know. The principal thing was to do it—then find a publisher. And if nothing came of it we would have had our trip anyway.

Little by little we evolved the idea of getting a car. The only way to see America is by automobile—that's what everybody says. It's not true, of course, but it sounds wonderful. I had never owned a car, didn't know how to drive one even. I wish now we had chosen a canoe instead.

The first car we looked at was the one we selected. Neither of us knew anything about cars; we just took the man's word for it that it was a good, reliable vehicle. It was, too, all things considered, though it had its weak points.

A few days before we were ready to shove off I met a man called John Woodburn of Doubleday, Doran & Co. He seemed unusually interested in our project. To my amazement a few days later I was signing a contract for the book at his office. Theodore Roosevelt was one of the signatories, if that's how you call it. He had never heard of me and was a little dubious about signing his name, it seems. But he signed it just the same.

I had expected a five thousand dollar advance and got five hundred. The money was gone before I ever left the Holland Tunnel. Rattner's contribution to the book was ruled out. It would have been too expensive to print a book such as we had planned. I was embarrassed and chagrined, the more so because Rattner took it with such good grace. He had expected as much, no doubt. I, on the other hand, always expect the angels to pee in my beer. "The principal thing," said Rattner, "is to see America." I agreed. Secretly I nourished the hope that out of my future royalties I would be able to print Rattner's own version of America in line and color. It was a compromise, and I hate compromises, but that's America for you. "Next time you will be able to do as you please"—that's the song. It's a dastardly lie, but to palliate it you are given hush money.

That's how the trip began. We were in good fettle, nevertheless, when we left New York. A little nervous, I must confess, because we had only had about a half dozen lessons in driving at the Automobile School. I knew how to steer, how to shift gears, how to apply the brake—what more was necessary? As I say, by the time we started out for the Holland Tunnel we were in high spirits. It was a Saturday noon when we left. I had never been in the damned hole before, except once in a taxi. It was a nightmare. The beginning of the endless nightmare, I should say.

When we found ourselves aimlessly circling around in Newark I surrendered the wheel to Rattner. I was all in after an hour's driving. To get to Newark is easy, but to get out of it on a Saturday afternoon in the rain, to find the insane sky-way again, is another thing. In another hour, however, we were in open country, the traffic almost nil, the air tangy, the scenery promising. We were on our way! New Hope was to be our first stop.

New Hope! It's rather curious that we should have selected a town by that name as our first stopping place. It was a beautiful spot too, reminding me somewhat of a slumbering European village. And Bill Ney, whom we were visiting, was the very symbol of new hope, new enthusiasms, new deals. It was an excellent start; the air was full of promise.

New Hope is one of America's art colonies. I have a vivid recollection of my state of mind on leaving the place. It framed itself thus: *no hope for the artist!* The only artists who were not leading a dog's life were the commercial artists; they had beautiful homes, beautiful brushes, beautiful models. The others were living like ex-convicts. This impression was confirmed and deepened as

I travelled along. America is no place for an artist: to be an artist is to be a moral leper, an economic misfit, a social liability. A corn-fed hog enjoys a better life than a creative writer, painter or musician. To be a rabbit is better still.

When I first returned from Europe I was frequently reminded of the fact that I was an "expatriate", often in an unpleasant way. The expatriate had come to be looked upon as an escapist. Until the war broke out it was the dream of every American artist to go to Europe—and to stay there as long as possible. Nobody thought of calling a man an escapist in the old days; it was the natural, proper, fitting thing to do, go to Europe, I mean. With the outbreak of the war a sort of childish, petulant chauvinism set in. "Aren't you glad to be back in the good old U.S.A.?" was the usual greeting. "No place like America, *what*?" To this you were expected to say "You betcha!" Behind these remarks there was of course an unacknowledged feeling of disappointment; the American artist who had been obliged to seek refuge again in his native land was angry with his European friends for having deprived him of the privilege of leading the life he most desired. He was annoyed that they had allowed such an ugly, unnecessary thing as war to break out. America is made up, as we all know, of people who ran away from such ugly situations. America is the land par excellence of expatriates and escapists, *renegades*, to use a strong word. A wonderful world we might have made of this new continent if we had really run out on our fellow-men in Europe, Asia and Africa. A brave, new world it might have become, had we had the courage to turn our back on the old, to build afresh, to eradicate the poisons which had accumulated through centuries of bitter rivalry, jealousy and strife.

A new world is not made simply by trying to forget the old. A new world is made with a new spirit, with new values. Our world may have begun that way, but to-day it is caricatural. Our world is a world of *things*. It is made up of comforts and luxuries, or else the desire for them. What we dread most, in facing the impending débâcle, is that we shall be obliged to give up our gew-gaws, our gadgets, all the little comforts which have made us so uncomfortable. There is nothing brave, chivalrous, heroic or magnanimous about our attitude. We are not peaceful souls; we are smug, timid, queasy and quaky.

I speak of the war because coming from Europe I was constantly besieged for an opinion about the European situation. As if the mere fact that I had lived there a few years could give my words pregnant meaning! Who can unravel the enigma embedded in such a wide-spread conflict? Journalists and historians will pretend to, but their hindsight is so disproportionate to their foresight that one is justified in being skeptical about their analyses. What I am getting round to is this—though I am a born American, though I became what is called an expatriate, I look upon the world not as a partisan of this country or that but as an inhabitant of the globe. That I happened to be born here is no reason why the American way of life should seem the best; that I chose to live in Paris is no reason why I should pay with my life for the errors of the French politicians. To be a victim of one's own mistakes is bad enough, but to be a victim of the other fellow's mistakes as well is too much. Moreover, I see no reason why I should lose *my* balance because a madman named Hitler goes on a rampage. Hitler will pass away, as did Napoleon, Tamerlane, Alexander and the others. A great scourge never appears unless there is a reason for it. There were a thousand excellent reasons for the emergence of the European and Asiatic dictators. We have our own dictator, only he is hydra-headed. Those who believe that the only way to eliminate these personifications of evil is to destroy them, let them destroy. Destroy everything in sight, if you think that's the way to get rid of your problems. I don't believe in that kind of destruction. I believe only in the destruction which is natural, incidental to and inherent in creation. As John Marin said in a letter to Stieglitz once: "Some men's singing time is when they are gashing themselves, some when they are gashing others."

Good News! God Is Love!

It was in a hotel in Pittsburgh that I finished the book on Rama-krishna by Romain Rolland. Pittsburgh and Ramakrishna—could any more violent contrast be possible? The one the symbol of brutal power and wealth, the other the very incarnation of love and wisdom.

We begin here then, in the very quick of the nightmare, in the crucible where all values are reduced to slag.

I am in a small, supposedly comfortable room of a modern hotel equipped with all the latest conveniences. The bed is clean and soft, the shower functions perfectly, the toilet seat has been sterilized since the last occupancy, if I am to believe what is printed on the paper band which garlands it; soap, towels, lights, stationery, everything is provided in abundance.

I am depressed, depressed beyond words. If I were to occupy this room for any length of time I would go mad—or commit suicide. The spirit of the place, the spirit of the men who made it the hideous city it is, seeps through the walls. There is murder in the air. It suffocates me.

A few moments ago I went out to get a breath of air. I was back again in Czarist Russia. I saw Ivan the Terrible followed by a cavalcade of snouted brutes. There they were, armed with clubs and revolvers. They had the look of men who obey with zest, who shoot to kill on the slightest provocation.

Never has the status quo seemed more hideous to me. This is not the worst place, I know. But I am here and what I see hits me hard.

It was fortunate perhaps that I didn't begin my tour of America via Pittsburgh, Youngstown, Detroit; fortunate that I didn't start out by visiting Bayonne, Bethlehem, Scranton and such like. I might never have gotten as far as Chicago. I might have turned into a human bomb and exploded. By some canny instinct of self-preservation I turned south first, to explore the so-called "backward" states of the Union. If I was bored for the most part I at least knew peace. Did I not see suffering and misery in the South too? Of course I did. There is suffering and misery everywhere throughout this broad land. But there are kinds and degrees of suffering; the worst, in my opinion, is the sort one encounters in the very heart of progress.

At this moment we are talking about the defense of our country, our institutions, our way of life. It is taken for granted that these *must* be defended, whether we are invaded or not. But there are things which ought not to be defended, which ought to be allowed to die; there are things which we should destroy voluntarily, with our own hands.

Let us make an imaginative recapitulation. Let us try to think back to the days when our forefathers first came to these shores. To begin with, they were running away from something; like the exiles and expatriates whom we are in the habit of denigrating and reviling, they too had abandoned the homeland in search of something nearer to their heart's desire.

One of the curious things about these progenitors of ours is that though avowedly searching for peace and happiness, for political and religious freedom, they began by robbing, poisoning, murdering, almost exterminating the race to whom this vast continent belonged. Later, when the gold rush started, they did the same to the Mexicans as they had to the Indians. And when the Mormons sprang up they practised the same cruelties, the same intolerance and persecution upon their own white brothers.

I think of these ugly facts because as I was riding from Pittsburgh to Youngstown, through an Inferno which exceeds anything that Dante imagined, the idea suddenly came to me that I ought to have an American Indian by my side, that he ought to share this voyage with me, communicate to me silently or otherwise his emotions and reflections. By preference I would like to have had a descendant of one of the admittedly "civilized" Indian tribes, a Seminole, let us say, who had passed his life in the tangled swamps of Florida.

Imagine the two of us then standing in contemplation before the hideous grandeur of one of those steel mills which dot the railway line. I can almost hear him thinking—"So it was for this that you deprived us of our birthright, took away our slaves, burned our homes, massacred our women and children, poisoned our souls, broke every treaty which you made with us and left us to die in the swamps and jungles of the Everglades!"

Do you think it would be easy to get him to change places with one of our steady workers? What sort of persuasion would you use? What now could you promise him that would be truly seductive? A used car that he could drive to work in? A slap-board shack that he could, if he were ignorant enough, call a home? An education for his children which would lift them out of vice, ignorance and superstition but still keep them in slavery? A clean, healthy life in the midst of poverty, crime, filth, disease and fear? Wages that barely keep your head above water and often not? Radio, telephone, cinema, newspaper, pulp magazine, fountain pen, wrist watch, vacuum cleaner or other gadgets ad infinitum? Are these the baubles that make life worthwhile? Are these what make us happy, carefree, generous-hearted, sympathetic, kindly, peaceful and godly? Are we now prosperous and secure, as so many stupidly dream of being? Are any of us, even the richest and most powerful, certain that an adverse wind will not sweep away our possessions, our authority, the fear or the respect in which we are held?

This frenzied activity which has us all, rich and poor, weak and powerful, in its grip—where is it leading us? There are two things in life which it seems to me all men want and very few ever get (because both of them belong to the domain of the spiritual) and they are health and freedom. The druggist, the doctor, the surgeon are all powerless to give health; money, power, security, authority do not give freedom. Education can never provide wisdom, nor churches religion, nor wealth happiness, nor security peace. What is the meaning of our activity then? To what end?

We are not only as ignorant, as superstitious, as vicious in our conduct as the "ignorant, bloodthirsty savages" whom we dispossessed and annihilated upon arriving here—we are worse than they by far. We have degenerated; we have degraded the life which we sought to establish on this continent. The most productive nation in the world, yet unable to properly feed, clothe and shelter over a third of its population. Vast areas of valuable soil turning to waste land because of neglect, indifference, greed and vandalism. Torn some eighty years ago by the bloodiest civil war in the history of man and yet to this day unable to convince the defeated section of our country of the righteousness of our cause nor able, as liberators and emancipators of the slaves, to give them true freedom and equality, but instead enslaving and degrading our own white brothers. Yes, the industrial North defeated the aristocratic South—the fruits of that victory are now apparent. Wherever there is industry there is ugliness, misery, oppression, gloom and despair. The banks which grew rich by piously teaching us to save, in order to swindle us with our own money, now beg us not to bring our savings to them, threatening to wipe out even that ridiculous interest rate they now offer should we disregard their advice. Three-quarters of the world's gold lies buried in Kentucky. Inventions which would throw millions more out of work, since by the queer irony of our system every potential boon to the human race is converted into an evil, lie idle on the shelves of the patent office or are bought up and destroyed by the powers that control our destiny. The land, thinly populated and producing in wasteful, haphazard way enormous surpluses of every kind, is deemed by its owners, a mere handful of men, unable to accommodate not only the starving millions of Europe but our own starving hordes. A country which makes itself ridiculous by sending out missionaries to the most remote parts of the globe, asking for pennies of the poor in order to maintain the Christian work of deluded devils who no more represent Christ than I do the Pope, and yet unable through its churches and missions at home to rescue the weak and defeated, the miserable and the oppressed. The hospitals, the insane asylums, the prisons filled to overflowing. Counties, some of them big as a European country, practically uninhabited, owned by an intangible corporation whose tentacles reach everywhere and whose responsibilities nobody can formulate or clarify. A man seated in a comfortable chair in New York, Chicago or San Francisco, a man surrounded by every luxury and yet paralyzed with fear and anxiety, controls the lives and destinies of thousands of men and women whom he has never seen, whom he never wishes to see and whose fate he is thoroughly uninterested in.

This is what is called progress in the year 1941 in these United States of America. Since I am not of Indian, Negro or Mexican descent I do not derive any vengeful joy in delineating this picture of the white man's civilization. I am a descendant of two men who ran away from their native land because they did not wish to become soldiers. My descendants, ironically enough, will no longer be able to escape that duty: the whole white world has at last been turned into an armed camp.

Well, as I was saying, I was full of Ramakrishna on leaving Pittsburgh. Ramakrishna who never criticized, who never preached, who accepted all religions, who saw God everywhere in everything: the most ecstatic being, I imagine, that ever lived. Then came Coraopolis, Aliquippa, Wampum. Then Niles, the birth-place of President McKinley, and Warren, the birth-place of Kenneth Patchen. Then Youngstown and two girls are descending the bluff beside the railroad tracks in the most fantastic setting I have laid eyes on since I left Crete. Instantly I am back on that ancient Greek island, standing at the edge of a crowd on the outskirts of Heraklion just a few miles from Knossus. There is no railroad on the island, the sanitation is bad, the dust is thick, the flies are everywhere, the food is lousy—but it is a wonderful place, one of the most wonderful places in the whole world. As at Youngstown by the railroad station there is a bluff here and a Greek peasant woman is slowly descending, a basket on her head, her feet bare, her body poised. *Here the resemblance ends. . . .*

As everybody knows, Ohio has given the country more Presidents than any other State in the Union. Presidents like McKinley, Hayes, Garfield, Grant, Harding—weak, characterless men. It has also given us writers like Sherwood Anderson and Kenneth Patchen, the one looking for poetry everywhere and the other driven almost mad by the evil and ugliness everywhere. The one walks the streets at night in solitude and tells us of the imaginary life going on behind closed doors; the other is so stricken with pain and chagrin by what he sees that he re-creates the cosmos in terms of blood and tears, stands it upside down and walks out on it in loathing and disgust. I am glad I had the chance to see these Ohio towns, this Mahoning River which looks as if the poisonous bile of all humanity had poured into it, though in truth it may contain nothing more evil than the chemicals and waste products of the mills and factories. I am glad I had the chance to see the color of the earth here in winter, a color not of age and death but of disease and sorrow. Glad I could take in the rhinoceros-skinned banks that rise from the river's edge and in the pale light of a wintry afternoon reflect the lunacy of a planet given over to rivalry and hatred. Glad I caught a glimpse of those slag heaps which look like the accumulated droppings of sickly prehistoric monsters which passed in the night. It helps me to understand the black and monstrous poetry which the younger man distils in order to preserve his sanity; helps me to understand why the older writer had to pretend madness in order to escape the prison which he found himself in when he was working in the paint factory. It helps me to understand how prosperity built on this plane of life can make Ohio the mother of presidents and the persecutor of men of genius.

The saddest sight of all is the automobiles parked outside the mills and factories. The automobile stands out in my mind as the very symbol of falsity and illusion. There they are, thousands upon thousands of them, in such profusion that it would seem as if no man were too poor to own one. In Europe, Asia, Africa the toiling masses of humanity look with watery eyes towards this Paradise where the worker rides to work in his own car. What a magnificent world of opportunity it must be, they think to themselves. (At least we like to think that they think that way!) They never ask what one must do to have this great boon. They don't realize that when the American worker steps out of his shining tin chariot he delivers himself body and soul to the most stultifying labor a man can perform. They have no idea that it is possible, even when one works under the best possible conditions, to forfeit all rights as a human being. They don't know that the best possible conditions (in American lingo) mean the biggest profits for the boss, the utmost servitude for the worker, the greatest confusion and disillusionment for the public in general. They see a beautiful, shining car which purrs like a cat; they see endless concrete roads so smooth and flawless that the driver has difficulty keeping awake; they see cinemas which look like palaces; they see department stores with mannikins dressed like princesses. They see the glitter and paint, the baubles, the gadgets, the luxuries; they don't see the bitterness in the heart, the skepticism, the cynicism, the emptiness, the sterility, the despair, the hopelessness which is eating up the American worker. They don't want to see this—they are full of misery themselves. They want a way out: they want the lethal comforts, conveniences, luxuries. And they follow in our footsteps—blindly, heedlessly, recklessly.

Of course not all American workers ride to work in automobiles. In Beaufort, S. C., only a few weeks ago I saw a man on a two-wheeled cart driving a bullock through the main street. He was a black man, to be sure, but from the look on his face I take it that he was far better off than the poor devil in the steel mill who drives his own car. In Tennessee I saw white men toiling like beasts of burden; I saw them struggling desperately to scratch a living from the thin soil on the mountainsides. I saw the shacks they live in and wondered if it were possible to put together anything more primitive. But I can't say that I felt sorry for them. No, they are not the sort of people to inspire pity. On the contrary, one has to admire them. If they represent the "backward" people of America then we need more backward people. In the subway in New York you can see the other type, the newspaper addict, who revels in social and political theories and lives the life of a drudge, foolishly flattering himself that because he is not working with his hands (nor with his brain either, for that matter) he is better off than the poor white trash of the South.

Those two girls in Youngstown coming down the slippery bluff— it was like a bad dream, I tell you. But we look at these bad dreams constantly with eyes open and when some one remarks about it we say, "Yes, that's right, that's how it is!" and we go about our business or we take to dope, the dope which is worse by far than opium or hashish—I mean the newspapers, the radio, the movies. Real dope gives you the freedom to dream your own dreams; the American kind forces you to swallow the perverted dreams of men whose only ambition is to hold their job regardless of what they are bidden to do.

The most terrible thing about America is that there is no escape from the treadmill which we have created. There isn't one fearless champion of truth in the publishing world, not one film company devoted to art instead of profits. We have no theatre worth the name, and what we have of theatre is practically concentrated in one city; we have no music worth talking about except what the Negro has given us, and scarcely a handful of writers who might be called creative. We have murals decorating our public buildings which are about on a par with the aesthetic development of high school students, and sometimes below that level in conception and execution. We have art museums that are crammed with lifeless junk for the most part. We have war memorials in our public squares that must make the dead in whose name they were erected squirm in their graves. We have an architectural taste which is about as near the vanishing point as it is possible to achieve. In the ten thousand miles I have travelled thus far I have come across two cities which have each of them a little section worth a second look—I mean Charleston and New Orleans. As for the other cities, towns and villages through which I passed I hope never to see them again. Some of them have such marvelous names, too, which only makes the deception more cruel. Names like Chattanooga, Pensacola, Tallahassee, like Mantua, Phoebus, Bethlehem, Paoli, like Algiers, Mobile, Natchez, Savannah, like Baton Rouge, Saginaw, Poughkeepsie: names that revive glorious memories of the past or awaken dreams of the future. Visit them, I urge you. See for yourself. Try to think of Schubert or Shakespeare when you are in Phoebus, Virginia. Try to think of North Africa when you are in Algiers, Louisiana. Try to think of the life the Indians once led here when you are on a lake, a mountain or river bearing the names we borrowed from them. Try to think of the dreams of the Spaniards when you are motoring over the old Spanish Trail. Walk around in the old French Quarter of New Orleans and try to reconstruct the life that once this city knew. Less than a hundred years has elapsed since this jewel of America faded out. It seems more like a thousand. Everything that was of beauty, significance or promise has been destroyed and buried in the avalanche of false progress. In the thousand years of almost incessant war Europe has not lost what we have lost in a hundred years of "peace and progress". No foreign enemy ruined the South. No barbaric vandals devastated the great tracts of land which are as barren and hideous as the dead surface of the moon. We can't attribute to the Indians the transformation of a peaceful, slumbering island like Manhattan into the most hideous city in the world. Nor can we blame the collapse of our economic system on the hordes of peaceful, industrious immigrants whom we no longer want. No, the European nations may blame one another for their miseries, but we have no such excuse—we have only ourselves to blame.

Less than two hundred years ago a great social experiment was begun on this virgin continent. The Indians whom we dispossessed, decimated and reduced to the status of outcasts, just as the Aryans did with the Dravidians of India, had a reverent attitude towards the land. The forests were intact, the soil rich and fertile. They lived in communion with Nature on what we choose to call a low level of life. Though they possessed no written language they were poetic to the core and deeply religious. Our forefathers came along and, seeking refuge from their oppressors, began by poisoning the Indians with alcohol and venereal disease, by raping their women and murdering their children. The wisdom of life which the Indians possessed they scorned and denigrated. When they had finally completed their work of conquest and extermination they herded the miserable remnants of a great race into concentration camps and proceeded to break what spirit was left in them.

Not long ago I happened to pass through a tiny Indian reservation belonging to the Cherokees in the mountains of North Carolina. The contrast between this world and ours is almost unbelievable. The little Cherokee reservation is a virtual Paradise. A great peace and silence pervades the land, giving one the impression of being at last in the happy hunting grounds to which the brave Indian goes upon his death. In my journey thus far I have struck only one other community which had anything like this atmosphere, and that was in Lancaster County, Pennsylvania, among the Amish people. Here a small religious group, clinging stubbornly to the ways of their ancestors in comportment, dress, beliefs and customs, have converted the land into a veritable garden of peace and plenty. It is said of them that ever since they settled here they have never known a crop failure. They live a life in direct opposition to that of the majority of the American people—and the result is strikingly apparent. Only a few miles away are the hell-holes of America where, as if to prove to the world that no alien ideas, theories or isms will ever get a foothold here, the American flag is brazenly and tauntingly flown from roofs and smokestacks. And what sorry looking flags they are which the arrogant, bigoted owners of these plants display! You would think that such fervid patriotism would be inconsonant with the display of a torn, blackened, weather-beaten emblem. You would think that out of the huge profits which they accumulate enough might be put aside to purchase a bright, new, gleaming emblem of liberty. But no, in the industrial world everything is soiled, degraded, vilified. It has become so to-day that when you see the flag boldly and proudly displayed you smell a rat somewhere. The flag has become a cloak to hide iniquity. We have two American flags always: one for the rich and one for the poor. When the rich fly it it means that things are under control; when the poor fly it it means danger, revolution, anarchy. In less than two hundred years the land of liberty, home of the free, refuge of the oppressed has so altered the meaning of the Stars and Stripes that to-day when a man or woman succeeds in escaping from the horrors of Europe, when he finally stands before the bar under our glorious national emblem, the first question put to him is: *"How much money have you?"* If you have no money but only a love of freedom, only a prayer for mercy on your lips, you are debarred, returned to the slaughter-house, shunned as a leper. This is the bitter caricature which the descendants of our liberty-loving forefathers have made of the national emblem.

Everything is caricatural here. I take a plane to see my father on his death-bed and up there in the clouds, in a raging storm, I overhear two men behind me discussing how to put over a big deal, the big deal involving paper boxes, no less. The stewardess, who has been trained to behave like a mother, a nurse, a mistress, a cook, a drudge, never to look untidy, never to lose her Marcel wave, never to show a sign of fatigue or disappointment or chagrin or loneliness, the stewardess puts her lily-white hand on the brow of one of the paper-box salesmen and in the voice of a ministering angel, says: "Do you feel tired this evening? Have you a headache? Would you like a little aspirin?" We are up in the clouds and she is going through this performance like a trained seal. When the plane lurches suddenly she falls and reveals a tempting pair of thighs. The two salesmen are now talking about buttons, where to get them cheaply, how to sell them dearly. Another man, a weary banker, is reading the war news. There is a great strike going on somewhere—several of them, in fact. We are going to build a fleet of merchant vessels to help England—*next December*. The storm rages. The girl falls down again—she's full of black and blue marks. But she comes up smiling, dispensing coffee and chewing gum, putting her lily-white hand on someone else's forehead, inquiring if he is a little low, a little tired perhaps. I ask her if she likes her job. For answer she says, "It's better than being a trained nurse." The salesmen are going over her points; they talk about her like a commodity. They buy and sell, buy and sell. For that they have to have the best rooms in the best hotels, the fastest, smoothest planes, the thickest, warmest overcoats, the biggest, fattest purses. We need their paper boxes, their buttons, their synthetic furs, their rubber goods, their hosiery, their plastic this and that. We need the banker, his genius for taking our money and making himself rich. The insurance man, his policies, his talk of security, of dividends—we need him too. *Do we*? I don't see that we need any of these vultures. I don't see that we need any of these cities, these hell-holes I've been in. I don't think we need a two-ocean fleet either. I was in Detroit a few nights ago. I saw the Mannerheim Line in the movies. I saw how the Russians pulverized it. I learned the lesson. *Did you*? Tell me what it is that man can build, to protect himself, which other men cannot destroy? What are we trying to defend? Only what is old, useless, dead, indefensible. Every defense is a provocation to assault. Why not surrender? Why not give—give all? It's so damned practical, so thoroughly effective and disarming. Here we are, we the people of the United States: the greatest people on earth, so we think. We have everything—everything it takes to make people happy. We have land, water, sky and all that goes with it. We could become the great shining example of the world; we could radiate peace, joy, power, benevolence. But there are ghosts all about, ghosts whom we can't seem to lay hands on. We are not happy, not contented, not radiant, not fearless.

We bring miracles about and we sit in the sky taking aspirin and talking paper boxes. On the other side of the ocean they sit in the sky and deal out death and destruction indiscriminately. We're not doing that yet, *not yet*, but we are committed to furnishing the said instruments of destruction. Sometimes, in our greed, we furnish them to the wrong side. But that's nothing—everything will come out right in the end. Eventually we will have helped to wipe out or render prostrate a good part of the human race—not savages this time, but civilized "barbarians." Men like ourselves, in short, except that they have different views about the universe, different ideological principles, as we say. Of course, if we don't destroy them they will destroy us. That's logic—nobody can question it. That's political logic, and that's what we live and die by. A flourishing state of affairs. Really exciting, don't you know. "We live in such exciting times." Aren't you happy about it? The world changing so rapidly and all that—isn't it marvelous? Think what it was a hundred years ago. Time marches on. . . .

A man of genius whom I know would like to be spared the ordeal of indiscriminate killing which they are preparing him for. He is not interested in putting the world to rights. He is interested in putting his thoughts down on paper. But then he has a good set of teeth, he is not flat-footed, his heart and lungs are sound, he has no nervous disorders. He is thoroughly healthy and a genius to boot. He never talks about paper boxes or buttons or new-fangled gadgets. He talks poetry, talks about God. But he doesn't belong to some God sect and therefore is disqualified as a conscientious objector. The answer is that he must get ready to be shipped to the front. He must defend our ideological principles. The banker is too old to be of service; the salesmen I was talking about are too clever; so the genius has to serve, though God knows, since we have so few of them, you would think we might be able to spare one now and then.

I hope that Walt Disney is exempted, because he's the man, though I doubt that he realizes it, to illustrate what I have to say. In fact, he's been doing it all along, unconsciously. He's the master of the nightmare. He's the Gustave Doré of the world of Henry Ford & Co., Inc. The Mannerheim Line is just a scratch on the surface. True, the temperature was abnormal—about forty degrees below zero on the average. (Amazing how men can be trained to kill in all kinds of weather. Almost as intelligent as horses.) But as I was saying, Disney has all kinds of temperature—a temperature to suit every fresh horror. He doesn't have to think: the newspapers are always on tap. Of course they're not real men and women. Oh no! They're more real than real men and women: they're dream creatures. They tell us what we look like beneath the covering of flesh. A fascinating world, what? Really, when you think about it, even more fascinating than Dali's cream puffs. Dali thinks too much. Besides, he has only two hands. Disney has a million. And besides hands he has voices—the voice of the hyena, the voice of the donkey, the voice of the dinosaur. The Soviet film, for example, is intimidating enough, but slow, ponderous, cumbersome, unwieldly. It takes time in real life to demolish all those concrete pill-boxes, cut all that barbed wire, kill all those soldiers, burn all those villages. Slow work. Disney works fast—like greased lightning. That's how we'll all operate soon. What we dream we become. We'll get the knack of it soon. We'll learn how to annihilate the whole planet in the wink of an eye—just wait and see.

The capital of the new planet—the one, I mean, which will kill itself off—is of course Detroit. I realized that the moment I arrived. At first I thought I'd go and see Henry Ford, give him my congratulations. But then I thought—what's the use? He wouldn't know what I was talking about. Neither would Mr. Cameron most likely. That lovely Ford evening hour! Every time I hear it announced I think of Céline—Ferdinand, as he so affectionately calls himself. Yes, I think of Céline standing outside the factory gates (pp. 222–225, I think it is: *Journey to the End of the Night*). Will he get the job? Sure he will. He gets it. He goes through the baptism—the baptism of stultification through noise. He sings a wonderful song there for a few pages about the machine, the blessings that it showers upon mankind. Then he meets Molly. Molly is just a whore. You'll find another Molly in *Ulysses*, but Molly the whore of Detroit is much better. Molly has a soul. Molly is the milk of human kindness. Céline pays a tribute to her at the end of the chapter. It's remarkable because all the other characters are paid off in one way or another. Molly is whitewashed. Molly, believe it or not, looms up bigger and holier than Mr. Ford's huge enterprise. Yes, that's the beautiful and surprising thing about Céline's chapter on Detroit—that he makes the body of a whore triumph over the soul of the machine. You wouldn't suspect that there was such a thing as a soul if you went to Detroit. Everything is too new, too slick, too bright, too ruthless. Souls don't grow in factories. Souls are killed in factories—even the niggardly ones. Detroit can do in a week for the white man what the South couldn't do in a hundred years to the Negro. That's why I like the Ford evening hour—it's so soothing, so inspiring.

Of course Detroit isn't the worst place—not by a long shot. That's what I said about Pittsburgh. That's what I'll say about other places too. None of them is the worst. There is no worst or worstest. The worst is in process of becoming. It's inside us now, only we haven't brought it forth. Disney dreams about it—and he gets paid for it, that's the curious thing. People bring their children to look and scream with laughter. (Ten years later it happens now and then that they fail to recognize the little monster who so joyfully clapped his hands and screamed with delight. It's always hard to believe that a Jack-the-Ripper could have sprung out of your own loins.) However. . . . It's cold in Detroit. A gale is blowing. Happily I am not one of those without work, without food, without shelter. I am stopping at the gay Detroiter, the Mecca of the futilitarian salesmen. There is a swanky haberdashery shop in the lobby. Salesmen love silk shirts. Sometimes they buy cute little panties too—for the ministering angels in the aeroplanes. They buy any and everything—just to keep money in circulation. The men of Detroit who are left out in the cold freeze to death in woolen underwear. The temperature in winter is distinctly subtropical. The buildings are straight and cruel. The wind is like a double-bladed knife. If you're lucky you can go inside where it's warm and see the Mannerheim Line. A cheering spectacle. See how ideological principles can triumph in spite of sub-normal temperatures. See men in white cloaks crawling through the snow on their bellies; they have scissors in their hands, big ones, and when they reach the barbed wire they cut, cut, cut. Now and then they get shot doing it—but then they become heroes—and besides there are always others to take their places, all armed with scissors. Very edifying, very instructive. Heartening, I should say. Outside, on the streets of Detroit, the wind is howling and people are running for shelter. But it's warm and cosy in the cinema. After the spectacle a nice warm cup of chocolate in the lobby of the hotel. Men talking buttons and chewing gum there. Not the same men as in the aeroplane—different ones. Always find them where it's warm and comfortable. Always buying and selling. And of course a pocketful of cigars. Things are picking up in Detroit. Defense orders, you know. The taxi driver told me he expected to get his job back soon. In the factory, I mean. What would happen if the war suddenly stopped I can't imagine. There would be a lot of broken hearts. Maybe another crisis. People wouldn't know what to do for themselves if peace were suddenly declared. Everybody would be laid off. The bread lines would start up. Strange, how we can manage to feed the world and not learn how to feed ourselves.

I remember when the wireless came how everybody thought—how wonderful now we will be in communication with the whole world! And television—how marvelous! now we shall be able to see what's going on in China, in Africa, in the remotest parts of the world! I used to think that perhaps one day I'd own a little apparatus which by turning a dial would enable me to see Chinamen walking through the streets of Peking or Shanghai or savages in the heart of Africa performing their rites of initiation. What do we actually see and hear to-day? What the censors permit us to see and hear, nothing more. India is just as remote as it ever was—in fact, I think it is even more so now than it was fifty years ago. In China a great war is going on—a revolution fraught with far greater significance for the human race than this little affair in Europe. Do you see anything of it in the news reels? Even the newspapers have very little to say about it. Five million Chinese can die of flood, famine or pestilence or be driven from their homes by the invader, and the news (a headliner for one day usually) leaves us unruffled. In Paris I saw one news reel of the bombing of Shanghai and that was all. It was too horrible—the French couldn't stomach it. To this day we haven't been shown the real pictures of the first World War. You have to have influence to get a glimpse of those fairly recent horrors. . . . There are the "educational" pictures, to be sure. Have you seen them? Nice, dull, soporific, hygienic, statistical poems fully castrated and sprinkled with lysol. The sort of thing the Baptist or Methodist Church could endorse.

The news reels deal largely with diplomatic funerals, christenings of battleships, fires and explosions, aeroplane wrecks, athletic contests, beauty parades, fashions, cosmetics and political speeches. Educational pictures deal largely with machines, fabrics, commodities and crime. If there's a war on we get a glimpse of foreign scenery. We get about as much information about the other peoples of this globe, through the movies and the radio, as the Martians get about us. And this abysmal separation is reflected in the American physiognomy. In the towns and cities you find the typical American everywhere. His expression is mild, bland, pseudo-serious and definitely fatuous. He is usually neatly dressed in a cheap ready-made suit, his shoes shined, a fountain pen and pencil in his breast pocket, a brief case under his arm—and of course he wears glasses, the model changing with the changing styles. He looks as though he were turned out by a university with the aid of a chain store cloak and suit house. One looks like the other, just as the automobiles, the radios and the telephones do. This is the type between 25 and 40. After that age we get another type—the middle-aged man who is already fitted with a set of false teeth, who puffs and pants, who insists on wearing a belt though he should be wearing a truss. He is a man who eats and drinks too much, smokes too much, sits too much, talks too much and is always on the edge of a break-down. Often he dies of heart failure in the next few years. In a city like Cleveland this type comes to apotheosis. So do the buildings, the restaurants, the parks, the war memorials. The most typical American city I have struck thus far. Thriving, prosperous, active, clean, spacious, sanitary, vitalized by a liberal infusion of foreign blood and by the ozone from the lake, it stands out in my mind as the composite of many American cities. Possessing all the virtues, all the prerequisites for life, growth, blossoming, it remains nevertheless a thoroughly dead place—a deadly, dull, dead place. (In Cleveland to see "The Doctor's Dilemma" is an exciting event.) I would rather die in Richmond somehow, though God knows Richmond has little enough to offer. But in Richmond, or in any southern city for that matter, you do see types now and then which depart from the norm. The South is full of eccentric characters; it still fosters individuality. And the most individualistic are of course from the land, from the out of the way places. When you go through a sparsely settled state like South Carolina you do meet men, interesting men—jovial, cantankerous, disputative, pleasure-loving, independent-thinking creatures who disagree with everything, on principle, but who make life charming and gracious. There can hardly be any greater contrast between two regions in these United States, in my mind, than between a state like Ohio and a state like South Carolina. Nor can there be a greater contrast in these States than between two cities like Cleveland and Charleston, for example. In the latter place you actually have to pin a man to the mat before you can talk business to him. And if he happens to be a good business man, this chap from Charleston, the chances are that he is also a fanatic about something unheard of. His face registers changes of expression, his eyes light up, his hair stands on end, his voice swells with passion, his cravat slips out of place, his suspenders are apt to come undone, he spits and curses, he coos and prances, he pirouettes now and then. And there's one thing he never dangles in front of your nose—his time-piece. He has time, oodles of time. And he accomplishes everything he chooses to accomplish in due time, with the result that the air is not filled with dust and machine oil and cash register clickings. The great time-wasters, I find, are in the North, among the busybodies. Their whole life, one might say, is just so much time wasted. The fat, puffy, wattle-faced man of forty-five who has turned asexual is the greatest monument to futility that America has created. He's a nymphomaniac of energy accomplishing nothing. He's an hallucination of the Paleolithic man. He's a statistical bundle of fat and jangled nerves for the insurance man to convert into a frightening thesis. He sows the land with prosperous, restless, empty-headed, idle-handed widows who gang together in ghoulish sororities where politics and diabetes go hand in hand.

About Detroit, before I forget it—yes, it was here that Swami Vivekananda kicked over the traces. Some of you who read this may be old enough to remember the stir he created when he spoke before the Parliament of Religions in Chicago back in the early Nineties. The story of the pilgrimage of this man who electrified the American people reads like a legend. At first unrecognized, rejected, reduced to starvation and forced to beg in the streets, he was finally hailed as the greatest spiritual leader of our time. Offers of all kinds were showered upon him; the rich took him in and tried to make a monkey of him. In Detroit, after six weeks of it, he rebelled. All contracts were cancelled and from that time on he went alone from town to town at the invitation of such or such a society. Here are the words of Romain Rolland:

"His first feeling of attraction and admiration for the formidable power of the young republic had faded. Vivekananda almost at once fell foul of the brutality, the inhumanity, the littleness of spirit, the narrow fanaticism, the monumental ignorance, the crushing incomprehension, so frank and sure of itself with regard to all who thought, who believed, who regarded life differently from the paragon nation of the human race . . . And so he had no patience. He hid nothing. He stigmatised the vices and crimes of the Western civilisation with its characteristics of violence, pillage and destruction. Once when he was to speak at Boston on a beautiful religious subject particularly dear to him (Ramakrishna), he felt such repulsion at the sight of his audience, the artificial and cruel crowd of men of affairs and of the world, that he refused to yield them the key of his sanctuary, and brusquely changing the subject, he inveighed furiously against a civilisation represented by such foxes and wolves. The scandal was terrific. Hundreds noisily left the hall and the Press was furious. He was especially bitter against false Christianity and religious hypocrisy: 'With all your brag and boasting, where has your Christianity succeeded without the sword? Yours is a religion preached in the name of luxury. It is all hypocrisy that I have heard in this country. All this prosperity, all this from Christ! Those who call upon Christ care nothing but to amass riches! Christ would not find a stone on which to lay his head among you . . . You are not Christians. Return to Christ!' "

Rolland goes on to contrast this reaction with that inspired by England. "He came as an enemy and he was conquered." Vivekananda himself admitted that his ideas about the English had been revolutionized. "No one," he said, "ever landed on English soil with more hatred in his heart for a race than I did for the English . . . There is none among you . . . who loves the English people more than I do now."

A familiar theme—one hears it over and over again. I think of so many eminent men who visited these shores only to return to their native land saddened, disgusted and disillusioned. There is one thing America has to give, and that they are all in agreement about: MONEY. And as I write this there comes to my mind the case of an obscure individual whom I knew in Paris, a painter of Russian birth who during the twenty years that he lived in Paris knew scarcely a day when he was not hungry. He was quite a figure in Montparnasse—every one wondered how he managed to survive so long without money. Finally he met an American who made it possible for him to visit this country which he had always longed to see and which he hoped to make his adopted land. He stayed a year, travelling about, making portraits, received hospitably by rich and poor. For the first time in his whole life he knew what it was to have money in his pocket, to sleep in a clean, comfortable bed, to be warm, to be well nourished—and what is more important, to have his talent recognized. One day, after he had been back a few weeks I ran into him at a bar. I was extremely curious to hear what he might have to say about America. I had heard of his success and I wondered why he had returned.

He began to talk about the cities he had visited, the people he had met, the houses he had put up at, the meals he had been fed, the museums he had visited, the money he had made. "At first it was wonderful," he said. "I thought I was in Paradise. But after six months of it I began to be bored. It was like living with children—but *vicious* children. What good does it do to have money in your pocket if you can't enjoy yourself? What good is fame if nobody understands what you're doing? You know what my life is like here. I'm a man without a country. If there's a war I'll either be put in a concentration camp or asked to fight for the French. I could have escaped that in America. I could have become a citizen and made a good living. But I'd rather take my chances here. Even if there's only a few years left those few years are worth more here than a lifetime in America. There's no real life for an artist in America—only a living death. By the way, have you got a few francs to lend me? I'm broke again. But I'm happy. I've got my old studio back again—I appreciate that lousy place now. Maybe it was good for me to go to America—if only to make me realize how wonderful is this life which I once thought unbearable."

How many letters I received while in Paris from Americans who had returned home—all singing the same song. "If I could only be back there again. I would give my right arm to be able to return. I didn't realize what I was giving up." Et cetera, et cetera. I never received one letter from a repatriated American saying that he was happy to be home again. When this war is over there will be an exodus to Europe such as this country has never seen. We try to pretend now, because France has collapsed, that she was degenerate. There are artists and art critics in this country who, taking advantage of the situation, endeavor with utter shamelessness to convince the American public that we have nothing to learn from Europe, that Europe, France more particularly, is dead. What an abominable lie! France prostrate and defeated is more alive than we have ever been. Art does not die because of a military defeat, or an economic collapse, or a political débâcle. Moribund France produced more art than young and vigorous America, than fanatical Germany or proselytizing Russia. Art is not born of a dead people.

There are evidences of a very great art in Europe as long ago as twenty-five thousand years, and in Egypt as far back as sixty thousand years. Money had nothing to do with the production of these treasures. Money will have nothing to do with the art of the future. Money will pass away. Even now we are able to realize the futility of money. Had we not become the arsenal of the world, and thus staved off the gigantic collapse of our economic system, we might have witnessed the spectacle of the richest nation on earth starving to death in the midst of the accumulated gold of the entire world. The war is only an interruption of the inevitable disaster which impends. We have a few years ahead of us and then the whole structure will come toppling down and engulf us. Putting a few millions back to work making engines of destruction is no solution of the problem. When the destruction brought about by war is complete another sort of destruction will set in. And it will be far more drastic, far more terrible than the destruction which we are now witnessing. The whole planet will be in the throes of revolution. And the fires will rage until the very foundations of this present world crumble. Then we shall see who has life, the life more abundant. Then we shall see whether the ability to make money and the ability to survive are one and the same. Then we shall see the meaning of true wealth.

I had to cover a tremendous stretch of country before I got the inspiration to begin this book. When I think of what I would have seen in Europe, Asia, or Africa, in the space of ten thousand miles, I feel as though I had been cheated. Sometimes I think that the best books on America are the imaginary ones written by those who have never seen the country. Before I get through with my journey I intend to describe some American scenes as I pictured them in my mind's eye when in Paris. Mobile is one of them.

Meanwhile I have good news for you—I'm going to take you to Chicago, to the Mecca Apartments on the South Side. It's a Sunday morning and my cicerone has borrowed a car to take me around. We stop at a flea market on the way. My friend explains to me that he was raised here in the ghetto; he tries to find the spot where his home used to be. It's a vacant lot now. There are acres and acres of vacant lots here on the South Side. It looks like Belgium did after the World War. Worse, if anything. Reminds me of a diseased jawbone, some of it smashed and pulverized, some of it charred and ulcerated. The flea market is more reminiscent of Cracow than of Clignancourt, but the effect is the same. We are at the back door of civilization, amidst the dregs and débris of the disinherited. Thousands, hundreds of thousands, maybe millions of Americans, are still poor enough to rummage through this offal in search of some sorely needed object. Nothing is too dilapidated or rust-bitten or disease-laden to discourage the hungry buyer. You would think the five-and-ten cent store could satisfy the humblest wants, but the five-and-ten cent store is really expensive in the long run, as one soon learns. The congestion is terrific—we have to elbow our way through the throng. It's like the banks of the Ganges except that there is no odor of sanctity about. As we push our way through the crowd my feet are arrested by a strange sight. There in the middle of the street, dressed in full regalia, is an American Indian. He's selling a snake oil. Instantly the thought of the other miserable derelicts stewing around in this filth and vermin is gone. *"A World I Never Made"*, wrote James Farrell. Well, there stands the real author of the book—an outcast, a freak, a hawker of snake oil. On that same spot the buffaloes once roamed; now it is covered with broken pots and pans, with worn-out watches, with dismantled chandeliers, with busted shoes which even an Igorote would spurn. Of course if you walk on a few blocks you can see the other side of the picture—the grand façade of Michigan Avenue where it seems as if the whole world were composed of millionaires. At night you can see the great monument to chewing gum lit up by flood-lights and marvel that such a monstrosity of architecture should be singled out for special attention. If you wander down the steps leading to the rear of the building and squint your eyes and sharpen your imagination a bit you can even imagine yourself back in Paris, on the Rue Broca. No Bubu here, of course, but perhaps you will run into one of Al Capone's ex-comrades. It must be pleasant to be stuck up behind the glitter of the bright lights.

We dig further into the South Side, getting out now and then to stretch our legs. Interesting evolution going on here. Rows of old mansions flanked by vacant lots. A dingy hotel sticking up like a Mayan ruin in the midst of yellow fangs and chalk teeth. Once respectable dwelling places given up now to the dark-skinned people we "liberated." No heat, no gas, no plumbing, no water, no nothing—sometimes not even a window-pane. Who owns these houses? Better not inquire too closely. What do they do with them when the darkies move out? Tear them down, of course. Federal housing projects. Model tenement houses. . . . I think of old Genoa, one of the last ports I stopped at on my way back to America. Very old, this section. Nothing much to brag about in the way of conveniences. But what a difference between the slums of Genoa and the slums of Chicago! Even the Armenian section of

Athens is preferable to this. For twenty years the Armenian refugees of Athens have lived like goats in the little quarter which they made their own. There were no old mansions to take over—not even an abandoned factory. There was just a plot of land on which they erected their homes out of whatever came to hand. Men like Henry Ford and Rockefeller contributed unwittingly to the creation of this paradise which was entirely built of remnants and discarded objects. I think of this Armenian quarter because as we were walking through the slums of Chicago my friend called my attention to a flower-pot on the window-sill of a wretched hovel. "You see," he said, "even the poorest among them have their flowers." But in Athens I saw dove-cotes, solariums, verandahs floating without support, rabbits sunning themselves on the roofs, goats kneeling before ikons, turkeys tied to the door-knobs. Everybody had flowers—not just flower-pots. A door might be made of Ford fenders and look inviting. A chair might be made of gasoline tins and be pleasant to sit on. There were bookshops where you could read about Buffalo Bill or Jules Verne or Hermes Trismegistus. There was a spirit here which a thousand years of misery had not squelched. Chicago's South Side, on the other hand, is like a vast, unorganized lunatic asylum. Nothing can flourish here but vice and disease. I wonder what the great Emancipator would say if he could see the glorious freedom in which the black man moves now. We made them free, yes—free as rats in a dark cellar.

Well, here we are—the Mecca Apartments! A great quadrangular cluster of buildings, once in good taste, I suppose—architecturally. After the whites moved out the colored people took over. Before it reached its present condition it went through a sort of Indian summer. Every other apartment was a dive. The place glowed with prostitution. It must have been a Mecca indeed for the lonely darky in search of work.

It's a queer building now. The locks are dismantled, the doors unhinged, the globes busted. You enter what seems like the corridor of some dismal Catholic institution, or a deaf and dumb asylum, or a Bronx sanatorium for the discreet practice of abortion. You come to a turn and you find yourself in a court surrounded by several tiers of balconies. In the center of the court is an abandoned fountain covered with a huge wire mesh like the old-fashioned cheese covers. You can imagine what a charming spot this was in the days when the ladies of easy virtue held sway here. You can imagine the peals of laughter which once flooded the court. Now there is a strained silence, except for the sound of roller skates, a dry cough, an oath in the dark. A man and woman are leaning over the balcony rail above us. They look down at us without expression. Just looking. *Dreaming?* Hardly. Their bodies are too worn, their souls too stunted, to permit indulgence in that cheapest of all luxuries. They stand there like animals in the field. The man spits. It makes a queer, dull smack as it hits the pavement. Maybe that's his way of signing the Declaration of Independence. Maybe he didn't know he spat. Maybe it was his ghost that spat. I look at the fountain again. It's been dry a long time. And maybe it's covered like a piece of old cheese so that people won't spit in it and bring it back to life. It would be a terrible thing for Chicago if this black fountain of life should suddenly erupt! My friend assures me there's no danger of that. I don't feel so sure about it. Maybe he's right. Maybe the Negro will always be our friend, no matter what we do to him. I remember a conversation with a colored maid in the home of one of my friends. She said, "I do think we have more love for you than you have for us." "You don't hate us ever?" I asked. "Lord no!" she answered, "we just feel sorry for you. You has all the power and the wealth but you ain't happy."

As we were walking back to the car we heard a great voice shouting as if from the roof-tops. We walked another block and still the voice resounded as mighty as before. We were puzzled. We turned round and retraced our steps. The voice grew stronger and stronger. It was the voice of a preacher and he was shouting with the lungs of a bull: "Jesus is the light of the world!" And then other voices joined in. "*Jesus! Jesus! The light of the world!*" We looked about in perplexity. There was nothing in sight but a Jewish synagogue. And from it, from the very walls, it seemed, came this stentorian voice bellowing about the light of the world. Finally we observed some Negroes entering the tabernacle and when we lifted our eyes we saw the amplifiers attached like gargoyles to the cornice of the building. For three blocks, clear as a bell, the voice followed us. It was like a maniac rising up out of No Man's Land and shouting *Peace!* As we stepped into the car I saw a beautiful colored woman hanging out of a window in what looked like a deserted house. What a vista her eyes took in from the fifth floor of that blackened morgue! Even up there she could hear the preacher talking about the light of the world. It was Sunday and she had nothing to do. Downstairs a ragged urchin was putting a number on the door in green chalk—so that the postman would deliver the letters to the right address, no doubt. A few blocks yonder lay the slaughter-house and on a bright day, if the wind were propitious, one could get a whiff from where she was of the blood of the lamb, of thousands of lambs, millions of lambs, in fact. "There were nothing but cribs around here years ago," my friend was saying. Cribs, cribs. I wasn't paying attention. What's he talking about, I thought to myself. I was thinking of the Lamb of God lying in the manger at the Bethlehem Steel Plant. "There, you see?" he said, nudging me and turning his eyes upward towards the Negress on the fifth floor. She was beckoning to us. She had found God, no doubt, up there in Nigger Heaven. If she was thinking of something else I couldn't tell it. She looked positively ecstatic. No heat, no gas, no water; the windows shattered, the mice making merry, the garbage lying in the gutter. She beckoned to us as though to say: "Come! I am the light of the world! I pay no rent, I do no work, I drink nothing but blood."

We got into the car, rode a few blocks and got out to visit another shell crater. The street was deserted except for some chickens grubbing for food between the slats of a crumbling piazza. More vacant lots, more gutted houses; fire escapes clinging to the walls with their iron teeth, like drunken acrobats. A Sunday atmosphere here. Everything serene and peaceful. Like Louvain or Rheims between bombardments. Like Phoebus, Virginia, dreaming of bringing her steeds to water, or like modern Eleusis smothered by a wet sock. Then suddenly I saw it chalked up on the side of a house in letters ten feet high:

GOOD NEWS! GOD IS LOVE!

When I saw these words I got down on my knees in the open sewer which had been conveniently placed there for the purpose and I offered up a short prayer, a silent one, which must have registered as far as Mound City, Illinois, where the colored muskrats have built their igloos. It was time for a good stiff drink of cod liver oil but as the varnish factories were all closed we had to repair to the abattoir and quaff a bucket of blood. Never has blood tasted so wonderful! It was like taking Vitamines A, B, C, D, E in quick succession and then chewing a stick of cold dynamite. Good news! Aye, wonderful news—for Chicago. I ordered the chauffeur to take us immediately to Mundelein so that I could bless the cardinal and all the real estate operations, but we only got as far as the Bahai Temple. A workman who was shovelling sand opened the door of the temple and showed us around. He kept telling us that we all worshipped the same God, that all religions were alike in essence. In the little pamphlet which he handed us to read I learned that the Forerunner of the Faith, the Founder of the Faith, and the

authorized Interpreter and Exemplar of Baha'u'llah's teachings all
suffered persecution and martyrdom for daring to make God's love
all-inclusive. It's a queer world, even in this enlightened period of
civilization. The Bahai temple has been twenty years building and
is not finished yet. The architect was Mr. Bourgeois, believe it or
not. The interior of the temple, in its unfinished state, makes you
think of a stage setting for *Joan of Arc*. The circular meeting place
on the ground floor resembles the hollow of a shell and inspires
peace and meditation as few places of worship do. The movement
has already spread over most of the globe, thanks to its persecutors
and detractors. There is no color line, as in Christian churches,
and one can believe as he pleases. It is for this reason that the
Bahai movement is destined to outlast all the other religious
organizations on this continent. The Christian Church in all its
freakish ramifications and efflorescences is as dead as a doornail;
it will pass away utterly when the political and social systems in
which it is now embedded collapse. The new religion will be based
on deeds, not beliefs. "Religion is not for empty bellies," said
Ramakrishna. Religion is always revolutionary, far more revolutionary than bread-and-butter philosophies. The priest is always in
league with the devil, just as the political leader always leads to
death. People are trying to get together, it seems to me. Their
representatives, in every walk of life, keep them apart by breeding
hatred and fear. The exceptions are so rare that when they occur
the impulse is to set them apart, make supermen of them, or gods,
anything but men and women like ourselves. And in removing
them thus to the ethereal realms the revolution of love which they
came to preach is nipped in the bud. But the good news is always
there, just around the corner, chalked up on the wall of a deserted
house: GOD IS LOVE! I am sure that when the citizens of Chicago
read these lines they will get up en masse and make a pilgrimage
to that house. It is easy to find because it stands in the middle of a
vacant lot on the South Side. You climb down a manhole in La
Salle Street and let yourself drift with the sewer water. You can't
miss it because it's written in white chalk in letters ten feet high.
All you need to do when you find it is to shake yourself like a
sewer-rat and dust yourself off. God will do the rest. . . .

The Alcoholic Veteran with the Washboard Cranium

In Tulsa not long ago I saw a shorty short movie called "The Happiest Man on Earth." It was in the O. Henry style but the implications were devastating. How a picture like that could be shown in the heart of the oil fields is beyond my comprehension. At any rate it reminded me of an actual human figure whom I encountered some weeks previously in New Orleans. He too was trying to pretend that he was the happiest mortal alive.

It was about midnight and my friend Rattner and I were returning to our hotel after a jaunt through the French Quarter. As we were passing the St. Charles Hotel a man without a hat or overcoat fell into step with us and began talking about the eyeglasses he had just lost at the bar.

"It's hell to be without your glasses," he said, "especially when you're just getting over a jag. I envy you fellows. Some fool drunk in there just knocked mine off and stepped on them. Just sent a telegram to my oculist in Denver—suppose I'll have to wait a few days before they arrive. I'm just getting over one hell of a binge: it must have lasted a week or more, I don't know what day it is or what's happened in the world since I fell off the wagon. I just stepped out to get a breath of air—and some food. I never eat when I'm on a bat—the alcohol keeps me going. There's nothing to do about it, of course; I'm a confirmed alcoholic. Incurable. I know all about the subject—studied medicine before I took up law. I've tried all the cures, read all the theories. . . . Why look here—" and he reached into his breast pocket and extricated a mass of papers along with a thick wallet which fell to the ground— "look at this, here's an article on the subject I wrote myself. Funny, what? It was just published recently in. . ." (he mentioned a well-known publication with a huge circulation).

I stooped down to pick up the wallet and the calling cards which

355

had fluttered out and fallen into the gutter. He was holding the loose bundle of letters and documents in one hand and gesticulating eloquently with the other. He seemed to be utterly unconcerned about losing any of his papers or even about the contents of the wallet. He was raving about the ignorance and stupidity of the medical profession. They were a bunch of quacks; they were hijackers; they were criminal-minded. And so on.

It was cold and rainy and we, who were bundled up in overcoats, were urging him to get moving.

"Oh, don't worry about that," he said, with a good-natured grin, "I never catch cold. I must have left my hat and coat in the bar. The air feels good," and he threw his coat open wide as if to let the mean, penetrating night wind percolate through the thin covering in which he was wrapped. He ran his fingers through his shock of curly blond hair and wiped the corners of his mouth with a soiled handkerchief. He was a man of good stature with a rather weather-beaten face, a man who evidently lived an outdoor life. The most distinctive thing about him was his smile—the warmest, frankest, most ingratiating smile I've ever seen on a man's face. His gestures were jerky and trembly, which was only natural considering the state of his nerves. He was all fire and energy, like a man who has just had a shot in the arm. He talked well, too, exceedingly well, as though he might have been a journalist as well as doctor and lawyer. And he was very obviously not trying to make a touch.

When we had walked a block or so he stopped in front of a cheap eating house and invited us to step in with him and have something to eat or drink. We told him we were on our way home, that we were tired and eager to get to bed.

"But only for a few minutes," he said. "I'm just going to have a quick bite."

Again we tried to beg off. But he persisted, taking us by the arm and leading us to the door of the café. I repeated that I was going home but suggested to Rattner that he might stay if he liked. I started to disengage myself from his grasp.

"Look," he said, suddenly putting on a grave air, "you've got to do me this little favor. I've got to talk to you people. I might do something desperate if you don't. I'm asking you as a human kindness—you wouldn't refuse to give a man a little time, would you, when you knew that it meant so much to him?"

With that of course we surrendered without a word. "We're in for it now," I thought to myself, feeling a little disgusted with myself for letting myself be tricked by a sentimental drunkard.

"What are you going to have?" he said, ordering himself a plate of ham and beans which, before he had even brought it to the table, he sprinkled liberally with ketchup and chili sauce. As he was about to remove it from the counter he turned to the server and ordered him to get another plate of ham and beans ready. "I can eat three or four of these in a row," he explained, "when I begin to sober up." We had ordered coffee for ourselves. Rattner was about to take the checks when our friend reached for them and stuck them in his pocket. "This is on me," he said, "I invited you in here."

We tried to protest but he silenced us by saying, between huge gulps which he washed down with black coffee, that money was one of the things that never bothered him.

"I don't know how much I've got on me now," he continued. "Enough for this anyway. I gave my car to a dealer yesterday to sell for me. I drove down here from Idaho with some old cronies from the bench—they were on a jamboree. I used to be in the legislature once," and he mentioned some Western State where he had served. "I can ride back free on the railroad," he added. "I have a pass. I used to be somebody once upon a time. . . ." He interrupted himself to go to the counter and get another helping.

As he sat down again, while dousing the beans with ketchup and chili sauce, he reached with his left hand into his breast pocket and dumped the whole contents of his pocket on the table. "You're an artist, aren't you?" he said to Rattner. "And you're a writer, I can tell that," he said, looking at me. "You don't have to tell me, I sized you both up immediately." He was pushing the papers about as he spoke, still energetically shoveling down his food, and apparently poking about for some articles which he had written and which he wanted to show us. "I write a bit myself," he said, "whenever I need a little extra change. You see, as soon as I get my allowance I go on a bat. Well, when I come out of it I sit down and write some crap for"—and here he mentioned some of the leading magazines, those with the big circulation. "I can always make a few hundred dollars that way, if I want to. There's nothing to it. I don't say it's literature, of course. But who wants literature? Now where in the hell is that story I wrote about a psychopathic case . . . I just wanted to show you that I know what I'm talking about. You see. . . ." He broke off suddenly and gave us a rather wry, twisted smile, as though it were hopeless to try to put it all in words. He had a forkful of beans which he was about to shovel down. He dropped the fork, like an automaton, the beans spilling all over his soiled letters and documents, and leaning over the table he startled me by seizing my arm and placing my hand on his skull, rubbing it roughly back and forth. "Feel that?" he said, with

a queer gleam in his eye. "Just like a washboard, eh?" I pulled my
hand away as quickly as I could. The feel of that corrugated
brainpan gave me the creeps. "That's just one item," he said. And
with that he rolled up his sleeve and showed us a jagged wound
that ran from the wrist to the elbow. Then he pulled up the leg of
his trousers. More horrible wounds. As if that were not enough he
stood up quickly, pulled off his coat and, quite as if there were no
one but just us three in the place, he opened his shirt and displayed
even uglier scars. As he was putting on his coat he looked boldly
around and in clear, ringing tones he sang with terrible bitter
mockery "America, I love you!" Just the opening phrase. Then
he sat down as abruptly as he had gotten up and quietly proceeded
to finish the ham and beans. I thought there would be a commotion
but no, people continued eating and talking just as before, only
now we had become the center of attention. The man at the cash
register seemed rather nervous and thoroughly undecided as to
what to do. I wondered what next.

I half expected our friend to raise his voice and begin a melodramatic scene. Except however for the fact that he had grown a little
more high-strung and more voluble his behavior was not markedly
different from before. But his tone had altered. He spoke now in
jerky phrases punctuated with the most blasphemous oaths and
accompanied by grimaces which were frightening to behold. The
demon in him seemed to be coming out. Or rather, the mutilated
being who had been wounded and humiliated beyond all human
endurance.

"*Mister* Roosevelt!" he said, his voice full of scorn and contempt. "I was just listening to him over the radio. Getting us in
shape to fight England's battles again, what? Conscription. *Not
this bird!*" and he jerked his thumb backwards viciously. "Decorated three times on the field of battle. The Argonne . . . Chateau
Thierry . . . the Somme . . . concussion of the brain . . . fourteen
months in the hospital outside Paris . . . then months on this side
of the water. Making murderers of us and then begging us to settle
down quietly and go to work again. . . . Wait a minute, I want to
read you a poem I wrote about our Fuehrer the other night." He
fished among the papers lying about on the table. He got up to get
himself another cup of coffee and as he stood with cup in hand,
sipping it, he began to read aloud this vituperative, scabrous poem
about the President. Surely now, I thought, somebody will take
umbrage and start a fight. I looked at Rattner who believes in
Roosevelt, who had traveled 1200 miles to vote for him at the last
election. Rattner was silent. He probably thought it useless to
remonstrate with a man who had obviously been shell shocked.

Still, I couldn't help thinking, the situation was a little unusual, to say the least. A phrase I had heard in Georgia came back to my head. It was from the lips of a woman who had just been to see "Lincoln in Illinois." "What are they trying to do—make a *he*-ro of that man Lincoln?" Yes, something distinctly pre-Civil War about the atmosphere. A president re-elected to office by a great popular vote and yet his name was anathema to millions. Another Woodrow Wilson perchance? Our friend wouldn't even accord him that ranking. He had sat down again and in a fairly moderate tone of voice he began making sport of the politicians, the members of the judiciary, the generals and admirals, the quartermaster generals, the Red Cross, the Salvation Army, the Y.M.C.A. A withering play of mockery and cynicism, larded with personal experiences, grotesque encounters, buffoonish pranks which only a battle-scarred veteran would have the audacity to relate.

"And so," he exploded, "they wanted to parade me like a monkey, with my uniform and medals. They had the brass band out and the mayor all set to give us a glorious welcome. The town is yours, boys, and all that hokum. *Our heroes!* God, it makes me vomit to think of it. I ripped the medals off my uniform and threw them away. I burned the damned uniform in the fireplace. Then I got myself a quart of rye and I locked myself in my room. I drank and wept, all by myself. Outside the band was playing and people cheering hysterically. I was all black inside. Everything I had believed in was gone. All my illusions were shattered. They broke my heart, that's what they did. They didn't leave me a god-damned crumb of solace. Except the booze, of course. Sure, they tried to take that away from me too, at first. They tried to shame me into giving it up. *Shame me*, huh! Me who had killed hundreds of men with the bayonet, who lived like an animal and lost all sense of human decency. They can't do anything to shame *me*, or frighten me, or fool me, or bribe me, or trick me. I know them inside out, the dirty bastards. They've starved me and beaten me and put me behind the bars. That stuff doesn't frighten me. I can put up with hunger, cold, thirst, lice, vermin, disease, blows, insults, degradation, fraud, theft, libel, slander, betrayal . . . I've been through the whole works . . . they've tried everything on me . . . and still they can't crush me, can't stop my mouth, can't make me say it's right. I don't want anything to do with these honest, God-fearing people. They sicken me. I'd rather live with animals—or cannibals." He found a piece of sheet music among his papers and documents. "There's a song I wrote three years ago. It's sentimental but it won't do anyone any harm. I can only write music when I'm drunk. The alcohol blots out the pain. I've still got a heart, a big one, too. My world is a world of memories. Do you remember this one?" He began to hum a familiar melody. "You wrote that?" I said, taken by surprise. "Yes, I wrote that—and I wrote others too"—and he began to reel off the titles of his songs.

I was just beginning to wonder about the truth of all these statements—lawyer, doctor, legislator, scrivener, song writer— when he began to talk about his inventions. He had made three fortunes, it seems, before he fell into complete disgrace. It was getting pretty thick even for me, and I'm a credulous individual, when presently a chance remark he made about a friend of his, a famous architect in the Middle West, drew a surprising response from Rattner. "He was my buddy in the army," said Rattner quietly. "Well," said our friend, "he married my sister." With this there began a lively exchange of reminiscences between the two of them, leaving not the slightest doubt in my mind that our friend was telling the truth, at least so far as the architect was concerned.

From the architect to the construction of a great house in the center of Texas somewhere was but a step. With the last fortune he made he had bought himself a ranch, married and built himself a fantastic chateau in the middle of nowhere. The drinking was gradually tailing off. He was deeply in love with his wife and looking forward to raising a family. Well, to make a long story short, a friend of his persuaded him to go to Alaska with him on a mining speculation. He left his wife behind because he feared the climate would be too rigorous for her. He was away about a year. When he returned—he had come back without warning, thinking to surprise her—he found her in bed with his best friend. With a whip he drove the two of them out of the house in the dead of night, in a blinding snowstorm, not even giving them a chance to put their clothes on. Then he got the bottle out, of course, and after he had had a few shots he began to smash things up. But the house was so damned big that he soon grew tired of that sport. There was only one way to make a good job of it and that was to put a match to the works, which he did. Then he got in his car and drove off, not bothering to even pack a valise. A few days later, in a distant State, he picked up the newspaper and learned that his friend had been found dead of exposure. Nothing was said about the wife. In fact, he never learned what happened to her from that day since. Shortly after this incident he got in a brawl with a man at a bar and cracked his skull open with a broken bottle. That meant a stretch at hard labor for eighteen months, during which time he made a study of prison conditions and proposed certain reforms to the Governor of the State which were accepted and put into practice.

"I was very popular," he said. "I have a good voice and I can entertain a bit. I kept them in good spirits while I was there. Later I did another stretch. It doesn't bother me at all. I can adjust myself to most any conditions. Usually there's a piano and a billiard table and books—and if you can't get anything to drink you can always get yourself a little dope. I switch back and forth. What's the difference? All a man wants is to forget the present. . . ."

"Yes, but can you ever really forget?" Rattner interjected.

"*I* can! You just give me a piano, a quart of rye and a sociable little joint and I can be just as happy as a man wants to be. You see, I don't need all the paraphernalia you fellows require. All I carry with me is a toothbrush. If I want a shave I buy one; if I want to change my linen I get new linen; when I'm hungry I eat; when I'm tired I sleep. It doesn't make much difference to me whether I sleep in a bed or on the ground. If I want to write a story I go to a newspaper office and borrow a machine. If I want to go to Boston all I have to do is show my pass. Any place is home sweet home so long as I can find a place to drink and meet a friendly fellow like myself. I don't pay taxes and I don't pay rent. I have no boss, no responsibilities. I don't vote and I don't care who's President or Vice-President. I don't want to make money and I don't look for fame or success. What can you offer me that I haven't got, eh? I'm a free man—*are you?* And happy. I'm happy because I don't care what happens. All I want is my quart of whiskey every day—a bottle of forgetfulness, that's all. My health? I never worry about it. I'm just as strong and healthy as the next man. If there's anything wrong with me I don't know it. I might live to be a hundred whereas you guys are probably worrying whether you'll live to be sixty. There's only one day—*today*. If I feel good I write a poem and throw it away the next day. I'm not trying to win any literary prizes—I'm just expressing myself in my own cantankerous way. . . ."

At this point he began to go off the track about his literary ability. His vanity was getting the best of him. When it got to the point where he insisted that I glance at a story he had written for some popular magazine I thought it best to pull him up short. I much preferred to hear about the desperado and the drunkard than the man of letters.

"Look here," I said, not mincing my words, "you admit that this is all crap, don't you? Well, I never read crap. What's the use of showing me that stuff—I don't doubt that you can write as badly as the next fellow—it doesn't take genius to do that. What I'm interested in is good writing: I admire genius not success. Now if you have anything that you're proud of that's another thing. I'd be glad to read something that you yourself thought well of."

He gave me a long, down-slanting look. For a few long moments he looked at me that way, silently, scrutinizingly. "I'll tell you," he said finally, "there's just one thing I've ever written which I think good—and I've never put it down on paper. But I've got it up here," and he tapped his forehead with his forefinger. "If you'd like to hear it I'll recite it for you. It's a long poem I wrote one time when I was in Manila. You've heard of Morro Castle, haven't you? All right, it was just outside the walls of Morro Castle that I got the inspiration. I think it's a great poem. I know it is! I wouldn't want to see it printed. I wouldn't want to take money for it. Here it is. . . ."

Without pausing to clear his throat or take a drink he launched into this poem about the sun going down in Manila. He recited it at a rapid pace in a clear musical voice. It was like shooting down the rapids in a light canoe. All around us the conversation had died down; some stood up and moved in close the better to hear him. It seemed to have neither beginning nor end. As I say, it had started off at the velocity of a flood, and it went on and on, image upon image, crescendo upon crescendo, rising and falling in musical cadences. I don't remember a single line of it, more's the pity. All I remember is the sensation I had of being borne along on the swollen bosom of a great river through the heart of a tropical zone in which there was a constant fluttering of dazzling plumage, the sheen of wet green leaves, the bending and swaying of lakes of grass, the throbbing midnight blue of sky, the gleam of stars like coruscating jewels, the song of birds intoxicated by God knows what. There was a fever running through the lines, the fever not of a sick man but of an exalted, frenzied creature who had suddenly found his true voice and was trying it out in the dark. It was a voice which issued straight from the heart, a taut, vibrant column of blood which fell upon the ear in rhapsodic, thunderous waves. The end was an abatement rather than a cessation, a diminuendo which brought the pounding rhythm to a whisper that prolonged itself far beyond the actual silence in which it finally merged. The voice had ceased to register, but the poem continued to pulsate in the echoing cells of the brain.

He broke the silence which ensued by alluding modestly to his unusual facility for memorizing whatever caught his eye. "I remember everything I read in school," he said, "from Longfellow and Wordsworth to Ronsard and François Villon. *Villon*, there's a fellow after my own heart," and he launched into a familiar verse in an accent that betrayed he had more than a textbook knowledge of French. "The greatest poets were the Chinese," he said. "They made the little things reveal the greatness of the universe. They were philosophers first and then poets. They *lived* their poetry. We have nothing to make poetry about, except death and desolation. You can't make a poem about an automobile or a telephone booth. To begin with, the heart has to be intact. One must be able to believe in something. The values we were taught to respect when we were children are all smashed. We're not men any more— we're automatons. We don't even get any satisfaction in killing. The last war killed off our impulses. We don't respond; we react. We're the lost legion of the defeated archangels. We're dangling in chaos and our leaders, blinder than bats, bray like jackasses. You wouldn't call Mister Roosevelt a great leader, would you? Not if you know your history. A leader has to be inspired by a great vision; he has to lift his people out of the mire with mighty pinions; he has to rouse them from the stupor in which they vegetate like stoats and slugs. You don't advance the cause of freedom and humanity by leading poor, feeble dreamers to the slaughterhouse. What's he belly-aching about anyway? Did the Creator appoint him the Saviour of Civilization? When I went over there to fight for Democracy I was just a kid. I didn't have any great ambitions, neither did I have any desire to kill anybody. I was brought up to believe that the shedding of blood was a crime against God and man. Well, I did what they asked me to, like a good soldier. I murdered every son of a bitch that was trying to murder me. What else could I do? It wasn't all murder, of course. I had some good times now and then—a different sort of pleasure than I ever figured I would like. In fact, nothing was like what I thought it would be before I went over. You know what those bastards make you into. Why, your own mother wouldn't recognize you if she saw you taking your pleasure—or crawling in the mud and sticking a bayonet in a man who never did you any harm. I'm telling you, it got so filthy and poisonous I didn't know who I was any more. I was just a number that lit up like a switchboard when the order came to do this, do that, do the other thing. You couldn't call me a man—I didn't have a god-damned bit of feeling left. And I wasn't an animal because if I had been an animal I'd have had better sense than to get myself into such a mess. Animals kill one another only when they're hungry. We kill because we're afraid of our own shadow, afraid that if we used a little common sense we'd have to admit that our glorious principles were wrong. Today I haven't got any principles—I'm an outlaw. I have only one ambition left—to get enough booze under my belt every day so as to forget what the world looks like. I never sanctioned this setup. You can't convince me that I murdered all those Germans in order to bring this unholy mess about. No sir, I refuse to take my part in it. I wash my hands of it. I walk out on it. Now if that makes me a bad citizen why then I'm a bad citizen. So what? Do you suppose if I ran around like a mad dog, begging for a club and a rifle to start murdering all over again, do you suppose that would make me into a good citizen, good enough, what I mean, to vote the straight Democratic ticket? I suppose if I did that I could eat right out of their hand, what? Well, I don't want to eat out of anybody's hand. I want to be left alone; I want to dream my dreams, to believe as I once believed, that life is good and beautiful and that men can live with one another in peace and plenty. No son of a bitch on earth can tell me that to make life better you have to first kill a million or ten million men in cold blood. No sir, those bastards haven't got any heart. I know the Germans are no worse than we are, and by Christ, I know from experience that some of them at least are a damned sight better than the French or the English.

"That schoolteacher we made a President of, he thought he had everything fixed just right, didn't he? Can you picture him crawling around on the floor at Versailles like an old billygoat, putting up imaginary fences with a blue pencil? What's the sense of making new boundaries, will you tell me? Why tariffs and taxes and sentry boxes and pillboxes anyway? Why doesn't England part with some of her unlawful possessions? If the poor people in England can't make a living when the government possesses the biggest empire that ever was how are they going to make a living when the empire falls to pieces? Why don't they emigrate to Canada or Africa or Australia?

"There's another thing I don't understand. We always assume that we're in the right, that we have the best government under the sun. How do we know—have we tried the others out? Is everything running so beautifully here that we couldn't bear the thought of a change? Supposing I honestly believed in Fascism or Communism or polygamy or Mohammedanism or pacifism or any of the things that are now tabu in this country? What would happen to me if I started to open my trap, eh? Why you don't even dare to protest against being vaccinated, though there's plenty of evidence to prove that vaccination does more harm than good. Where is this liberty and freedom we boast about? You're only free if you're in good odor with your neighbors, and even then it's not a hell of a lot of rope they give you. If you happen to be broke and out of a job your freedom isn't worth a button. And if you're old besides then it's just plain misery. They're much kinder to animals and flowers and crazy people. Civilization is a blessing to the unfit and the degenerate—the others it breaks or demoralizes. As far as the comforts of life go I'm better off when I'm in jail than when I'm out. In the one case they take your freedom away and in the other they take your manhood. If you play the game you can have automobiles and town houses and mistresses and *pâté de foie gras* and all the folderol that goes with it. But who wants to play the game? Is it worth it? Did you ever see a millionaire who was happy or who had any self-respect? Did you ever go to Washington and see our lawbreakers—excuse me, I mean lawmakers—in session? There's a sight for you! If you dressed them in striped dungarees and put them behind the bars with pick and shovel nobody on earth could tell but what they belonged there. Or take that rogues' gallery of Vice-Presidents. I was standing in front of a drug store not so long ago studying their physiognomies. There never was a meaner, craftier, uglier, more fanatical bunch of human faces ever assembled in one group. And that's the stuff they make presidents of whenever there's an assassination. Yes, assassinations. I was sitting in a restaurant the day after the election—up in Maine it was—and the fellow next to me was trying to lay a bet with another guy that Roosevelt wouldn't last the term out. He was laying five to one—but nobody would take him up. The thing that struck me was that the waitress, whom nobody had paid any attention to, suddenly remarked in a quiet tone that 'we were about due for another assassination.' Assassinations seem ugly when it's the President of the United States but there's plenty of assassinating going on all the time and nobody seems to get very riled up about it. Where I was raised we used to flog a nigger to death just to show a visitor how it's done. It's still being done, but not so publicly, I suppose. We improve things by covering them up.

"You take the food they hand us. . . . Of course I haven't got any taste left, from all the booze I pour down my system. But a man who has any taste buds left must be in a hell of a way eating the slop they hand you in public places. Now they're discovering that the vitamins are missing. So what do they do? Do they change the diet, change the chef? No, they give you the same rotten slop only they add the necessary vitamins. That's civilization—always doing things assways. Well, I'll tell you, I'm so god-damned civilized now that I prefer to take my poison straight. If I had lived what they call a 'normal' life I'd be on the dump heap by fifty anyway. I'm forty-eight now and sound as a whistle, always doing just the opposite of what they recommend. If you were to live the way I do for two weeks you'd be in the hospital. So what does it add up to, will you tell me? If I didn't drink I'd have some other vice—a baby-snatcher, maybe, or a refined Jack-the-Ripper, who knows? And if I didn't have any vices I'd be just a poor sap, a sucker like millions of others, and where would that get me? Do you think I'd get any satisfaction out of dying in harness, as they say? Not me! I'd rather die in the alcoholic ward among the has-beens and no-goods. At least, if it happens that way, I'll have the satisfaction of saying that I had only one master—John Barley-corn. You have a thousand masters, perfidious, insidious ones who torment you even in your sleep. I've only got one, and to tell the truth he's more like a friend than a taskmaster. He gets me into some nasty messes, but he never lies to me. He never says 'freedom, liberty, equality' or any of that rot. He just says, 'I will make you so stinking drunk that you won't know who you are,' and that's all I crave. Now if Mister Roosevelt or any other politician could make me a promise and keep it I'd have a little respect for him. But who ever heard of a diplomat or a politician keeping his word? It's like expecting a millionaire to give his fortune away to the men and women he robbed it from. It just ain't done.''

He went on at this rate without a letup—long monologues about the perfidy, the cruelty and the injustice of man towards man. Really a grand fellow at heart, with good instincts and all the attributes of a citizen of the world, except for the fact that somewhere along the line he had been flung out of the societal orbit and could never get back into it again. I saw from the queries which Rattner interjected now and then that he had hopes for the man. At two in the morning he was optimistic enough to believe that with a little perseverance there might be sown in this rugged heart the seed of hope. To me, much as I liked the fellow, it seemed just as futile as to attempt to reclaim the bad lands of Arizona or Dakota. The only thing society can do with such people, and it never does, is to be kind and indulgent to them. Just as the earth itself, in its endless experiments, comes to a dead end in certain regions, gives up, as it were, so with individuals. The desire to kill the soul, for that's what it amounts to, is a phenomenon which has an extraordinary fascination for me. Sometimes it lends a grandeur to an individual which seems to rival the sublime struggles of those men whom we consider superior types. Because the gesture of negation, when pure and uncompromising, has also in it the qualities of the heroic. Weaklings are incapable of flinging themselves away in this manner. The weakling merely succumbs while the other, more single-minded character works hand and glove with Fate, egging it on, as it were, and mocking it at the same time. To invoke Fate is to expose oneself to the chaos which the blind forces of the universe are ever ready to set in motion once the will of man is broken. The man of destiny is the extreme opposite: in him we have an example of the miraculous nature of man, in that those same blind forces appear to be harnessed and controlled, directed towards the fulfillment of man's own microscopic purpose. But to act either way one has to lift himself completely out of the set, reactionary pattern of the ordinary individual. Even to vote for self-destruction demands something of a cosmic approach. A man has to have some definite view of the nature of the world in order to reject it. It is far easier to commit suicide than to kill the soul. There remains the doubt, which not even the most determined destroyer can annihilate, that the task is impossible. If it could be accomplished by an act of will then there would be no need to summon Fate. But it is precisely because the will no longer functions that the hopeless individual surrenders to the powers that be. In short he is obliged to renounce the one act which would deliver him of his torment. Our friend had delivered himself up to John Barleycorn. But beyond a certain point John Barleycorn is powerless to operate. Could one succeed in summoning all the paralyzing and inhibiting forces of the universe there would still remain a frontier, a barrier which nothing but man himself can surmount and invade. The body can be killed, but the soul is imperishable. A man like our friend could have killed himself a thousand times had he the least hope of solving his problem thereby. But he had chosen to relapse, to lie cold and inert like the moon, to crush every fructifying impulse and, by imitating death, finally achieve it in the very heart of his being.

When he spoke it was the heart which cried out. They had broken his heart, he said, but it was not true. The heart cannot be broken. The heart can be wounded and cause the whole universe to appear as one vast writhing place of anguish. But the heart knows no limits in its ability to endure suffering and torment. Were it otherwise the race would have perished long ago. As long as the heart pumps blood it pumps life. And life can be lived at levels so utterly disparate one from another that in some cases it would appear to be almost extinct. There are just as violent contrasts in the way life is lived by human beings as there are startling contrasts in the fish, the mineral or the vegetable worlds. When we use the term human society we speak of something which defies definition. No one can encompass the thought and behavior of man with a word or phrase. Human beings move in constellations which, unlike the stars, are anything but fixed. A story, such as I am relating, can be of interest or significance to certain clusters of men and totally devoid of any charm or value to others. What would Shakespeare mean to a Patagonian, assuming he could be taught to read the words? What can "The Varieties of Religious Experience" mean to a Hopi Indian? A man goes along thinking the world to be thus and so, simply because he has never been jolted out of the rut in which he crawls like a worm. For the civilized man war is not always the greatest jolt to his smug every day pattern. Some men, and their number is greater I fear than most of us would like to believe, find war an exciting if not altogether agreeable interruption to the toil and drudgery of common life. The presence of death adds spice, quickens their usually torpid brain cells. But there are others, like our friend who, in their revolt against wanton killing, in the bitter realizing that no power of theirs will ever put an end to it, elect to withdraw from society and if possible destroy even the chance of returning to earth again at some distant and more propitious moment in human history. They want nothing more to do with man; they want to nip the experiment in the bud. And of course they are just as powerless here as in their efforts to eliminate war. But they are a fascinating species of man and ultimately of value to the race, if for no other reason than that they act as semaphores in those periods of darkness when we seem to be rushing headlong to destruction. The one who operates the switchboard remains invisible and it is in him we put our trust, but as long as we hug the rails the flashing semaphores offer a fleeting consolation. We hope that the engineer will bring us safely to our destination. We sit with arms folded and surrender our safekeeping to other hands. But even the best engineer can only take us over a charted course. *Our* adventure is in uncharted realms, with courage, intelligence and faith as our only guides. If we have a duty it is to put our trust in our own powers. No man is great enough or wise enough for any of us to surrender our destiny to. The only way in which any one can lead us is to restore to us the belief in our own guidance. The greatest men have always reaffirmed this thought. But the men who dazzle us and lead us astray are the men who promise us those things which no man can honestly promise another—namely safety, security, peace, etc. And the most deceptive of all such promisers are those who bid us kill one another in order to attain the fictive goal.

Like our friend, thousands, perhaps millions of men, awaken to the realization of their error on the battlefield. When it is too late. When the men whom they no longer have a desire to kill are already upon them, ready to cut their throats. Then it is kill or be killed and whether one kills in the knowledge of the truth or without that knowledge makes little difference. The murdering goes on—until the day the sirens scream their announcement of a truce. When peace comes it descends upon a world too exhausted to show any reaction except a dumb feeling of relief. The men at the helm, who were spared the horrors of combat, now play their ignominious role in which greed and hatred rival one another for mastery. The men who bore the brunt of the struggle are too sickened and disgusted to show any desire to participate in the rearrangement of the world. All they ask is to be left alone to enjoy the luxury of the petty, workaday rhythm which once seemed so dull and barren. How different the new order would be if we could consult the veteran instead of the politician! But logic has it that we ordain innocent millions to slaughter one another, and when the sacrifice is completed, we authorize a handful of bigoted, ambitious men who have never known what it is to suffer to rearrange our lives. What chance has a lone individual to dissent when he has nothing to sanction his protest except his wounds? Who cares about wounds when the war is over? Get them out of sight, all these wounded and maimed and mutilated! Resume work! Take up life where you left off, those of you who are still strong and able! The dead will be given monuments; the mutilated will be pensioned off. Let's get on—business as usual and no feeble sentimentality about the horrors of war. When the next war comes we'll be ready for them! *Und so weiter....*

I was reflecting thus while he and Rattner were exchanging anecdotes about their experiences in France. I was dying to get to bed. Our friend, on the other hand, was obviously becoming more awake; I knew that with the least encouragement he would regale us till dawn with his stories. The more he talked about his misfortunes, oddly enough, the more cheerful he seemed to grow. By the time we managed to persuade him to leave the place he was positively radiant. Out in the street he began bragging again about his wonderful condition—liver, kidneys, bowels, lungs all perfect, eyes super-normal. He had forgotten evidently about his broken glasses, or perhaps that was just an invention by way of breaking the ice.

We had a few blocks to walk before reaching our hotel. He said he would accompany us because he was going to turn in soon himself. There were some thirty-five cent lodging houses in the vicinity, he thought, where he'd get a few hours sleep. Every few steps, it seemed, he stopped dead and planted himself in front of us to expatiate on some incident which he evidently thought it important for us to hear. Or was it an unconscious desire to delay us in nestling down to our warm cozy beds? More than once, when we finally neared the hotel, we held out our hands to say good night, only to drop them again and stand patiently with one foot in the gutter and one on the curb hearing him out to the end.

At last I began to wonder if he had the necessary pence to get himself a flop. Just as I was about to inquire Rattner, whose thoughts were evidently running in the same direction, anticipated me. Had he the money for a room? Why, he was pretty certain he did; he had counted his change at the restaurant. Yes, he was quite sure he had enough—and if he hadn't he would ask us to make it up. Anyhow, that wasn't important. What was he saying? Oh yes, about Nevada . . . about the crazy ghost towns he had lived in . . . the saloon made of beer bottles and the mechanical piano from the Klondike which he rolled out to the desert one night just to hear how it would sound in that great empty space. Yes, the only people worth talking to were the bar flies. They were all living in the past, like himself. Some day he'd write the whole thing out. "Why bother to do that?" I interposed. "Maybe you're right," he said, running his tobacco-stained fingers through his thick curly hair. "I'm going to ask you for a cigarette now," he said. "I'm all out of mine." As we lit the cigarette for him he launched into another tale. "Listen," I said, "make it short, will you, I'm dead tired." We moved at a snail-like pace across the street to the door of the hotel. As he was winding up his story I put my hand on the handle of the door in readiness to make a break. We started to shake hands again when suddenly he took it into his head to count his change. "I guess I'll have to borrow three cents from you," he said. "You can have a couple of bucks if you like," we both started to say simultaneously. No, he didn't want that—that might start him drinking all over again. He didn't want to begin that now—he wanted a little rest first.

There was nothing to do but give him the three cents and what cigarettes we had left. It hurt Rattner to hand him three pennies. "Why don't you take a half dollar at least?" he said. "You might use it for breakfast tomorrow."

"If you give me a half dollar," he said, "I'll probably buy some candles and put them at Robert E. Lee's monument up the street. It was his birthday today, you know. People have forgotten about him already. Everybody's snoring now. I sort of like Lee; I revere his memory. He was more than a great general—he was a man of great delicacy and understanding. As a matter of fact, I think I'll wander up there anyway before turning in. It's just the sort of fool thing a fellow like me would do. Sleep isn't so important. I'll go up there to the monument and talk to him a little while. Let the world sleep! You see, I'm free to do as I please. I'm really better off than a millionaire. . . ."

"Then there's nothing more we can do for you?" I said, cutting him short. "You've got everything you need, you've got your health, you're happy. . . ."

I had no more than uttered the word happy when his face suddenly changed and, grasping me by both arms with a steely grip, he wheeled me around and gazing into my eyes with a look I shall never forget, he broke forth: "*Happy?* Listen, you're a writer—you should know better than that. You know I'm lying like hell. *Happy?* Why, brother, you're looking at the most miserable man on earth." He paused a moment to brush away a tear. He was still holding me firmly with both hands, determined apparently that I should hear him out. "I didn't bump into you accidentally tonight," he continued. "I saw you coming along and I sized you both up. I knew you were artists and that's why I collared you. I always pick the people I want to talk to. I didn't lose any glasses at the bar, nor did I give my car to a dealer to sell for me. But everything else I told you is true. I'm just hoofing it from place to place. I've only been out of the pen a few weeks. They've got their eye on me still—somebody's been trailing me around town, I know it. One false move and they'll clap me back in again. I'm giving them the runaround. If I should go up to the circle now and accidentally fall asleep on a bench they'd have the goods on me. But I'm too wary for that. I'll just amble about leisurely and when I'm good and ready I'll turn in. The bartender'll fix me up in the morning. . . . Look, I don't know what kind of stuff you write, but if you'll take a tip from me the thing to do is to learn what it is to suffer. No writer is any good unless he's suffered. . . ."

At this point Rattner was about to say something in my behalf, but I motioned to him to be silent. It was a strange thing for me to be listening to a man urging me to suffer. I had always been of the opinion that I had had more than my share of suffering. Evidently it didn't show on my face. Or else the fellow was so engrossed with his own misfortunes that he was unable or unwilling to recognize the marks in another. So I let him ramble on. I listened to the last drop without once seeking to interrupt him. When he had finished I held out my hand for the last time to say good-bye. He took my hand in both of his and clasped it warmly. "I've talked your head off, haven't I?" he said, that strange ecstatic smile lighting up his face. "Look, my name is So-and-So." It sounded like Allison or Albertson. He began digging for his wallet. "I'd like to give you an address," he said, "where you could drop me a line." He was searching for something to write on, but couldn't seem to find a card or blank piece of paper among the litter of documents he carried in that thick wallet. "Well, you give me yours," he said. "That will do. I'll write *you* some time."

Rattner was writing out his name and address for the fellow. He took the card and put it carefully in his wallet. He waited for me to write mine.

"I have no address," I said. "Besides, we've got nothing more to say to each other. I don't think we'll ever meet again. You're bent on destroying yourself, and I can't stop you, nor can anybody else. What's the good of pretending that we'll write one another? Tomorrow I'll be somewhere else and so will you. All I can say is I wish you luck." With that I pulled the door open and walked into the lobby of the hotel. Rattner was still saying good-bye to him.

As I stood there waiting for the elevator boy he waved his hand cheerily. I waved back. Then he stood a moment, swaying on his heels and apparently undecided whether to go towards the monument or turn round and look for a flop. Just as the elevator boy started the lift going he signalled for us to wait. I signalled back that it was too late. "Go on up," I said to the boy. As we rose up out of sight our friend stood there in front of the hotel door peering up at us with a blank expression. I didn't feel that it was a lousy thing to do, leave him standing there like that. I looked at Rattner to see how he felt about it. He sort of shrugged his shoulders. "What can you do with a guy like that?" he said, "he won't let you help him." As we entered the room and turned on the lights, he added: "You surely did give him a jolt when you told him he was happy. Do you know what I thought he was going to do? I thought he was going to crack you. Did you notice the look that came over him? And when you refused to give him your name and address, well that just about finished him. I couldn't do that. I'm not reproaching you—I just wonder *why* you acted that way. You could just as well have let him down easy, couldn't you?"

I was about to smile, but so many thoughts entered my head at once that I forgot and instead I frowned.

"Don't get me wrong," said Rattner, misinterpreting my expression. "I think you were damned patient with him. You hardly said a word all evening. . . ."

"No, it's not that," I said. "I'm not thinking of myself. I'm thinking of all the fellows like him I've met in one short lifetime. Listen, did I ever tell you about my experience with the telegraph company? Hell, it's late and I know you're fagged out. So am I. But I just want to tell you one or two things. I'm not trying to defend myself, mind you. I'm guilty, if you like. Maybe I could have done something, said something—I don't know what or how.

Sure, I did let him down. And what's more I probably hurt him deeply. But I figured it would do him good, if you can believe that. I never crossed him once, did I, or criticized him, or urged him to change his ways? No, I never do that. If a man is determined to go to the dogs I help him—I give him a little push if needs be. If he wants to get on his feet I help him to do that. Whatever he asks for. I believe in letting a man do as he pleases, for good or bad, because eventually we'll all wind up in the same place. But what I was starting to tell you is this—I've heard so many terrible tales, met so many guys like this Allison or Albertson, that I've hardly got an ounce of sympathy left in me. That's a horrible thing to say, but it's true. Get this—in one day, sometimes, I've had as many as a half-dozen men break down and weep before me, beg me to do something for them, or if not for them, for their wives and children. In four years I hardly ever had more than four or five hours' sleep a night, largely because I was trying to help people who were helpless to help themselves. What money I earned I gave away; when I couldn't give a man a job myself I went to my friends and begged them to give a man the work he needed. I brought them home and fed them; I fixed them up on the floor when the beds were full. I got hell all around for doing too much and neglecting my own wife and child. My boss looked upon me as a fool, and instead of praising me for my efforts bawled hell out of me continually. I was always between two fires, from above and from below. I saw finally that no matter how much I did it was just a drop in the bucket. I'm not saying that I grew indifferent or hardened. No, but I realized that it would take a revolution to make any appreciable change in conditions. And when I say a revolution I mean a real revolution, something far more radical and sweeping than the Russian revolution, for instance. I still think that, but I don't think it can be done politically or economically. Governments can't bring it about. Only individuals, each one working in his own quiet way. It must be a revolution of the heart. Our attitude towards life has to be fundamentally altered. We've got to advance to another level, a level from which we can take in the whole earth with one glance. We have to have a vision of the globe, including all the people who inhabit it—down to the lowest and most primitive man.

"To come back to our friend. . . . I wasn't too unkind to him, was I? You know damned well I've never refused a man help when he asked for it. But he didn't want help. He wanted sympathy. He wanted us to try to dissuade him from accomplishing his own destruction. And when he had melted us with his heartbreaking stories he wanted to have the pleasure of saying no and leaving us high and dry. He gets a kick out of that. A quiet sort of revenge, as it were, for his inability to cure himself of his sorrows. I figure it doesn't help a man any to encourage him in that direction. If a woman gets hysterical you know that the best thing to do is to slap her face good and hard. The same with these poor devils: they've got to be made to understand that they are not the only ones in the world who are suffering. They make a vice of their suffering. An analyst might cure him—and again he might not. And in any case, how would you get him to the analyst? You don't suppose he'd listen to a suggestion of that sort, do you? If I hadn't been so tired, and if I had had more money, I'd have tried another line with him. I'd have bought him some booze—not just a bottle, but a case of whiskey, two cases or three, if I were able to afford it. I tried that once on a friend of mine—another confirmed drunkard. Do you know, he was so damned furious when he saw all that liquor that he never opened a single bottle. He was insulted, so he pretended. It didn't faze me in the least. I had gotten rather fed up with his antics. When he was sober he was a prince, but when he got drunk he was just impossible. Well, thereafter, every time he came to see me, as soon as he suggested a little drink, I poured out a half dozen glasses at once for him. While he was debating whether to touch it or not I would excuse myself and run out to buy more. It worked—in his case, at least. It cost me his friendship, to be sure, but it stopped him from playing the drunkard with me. They've tried similar things in certain prisons I know of. They don't force a man to work, if he doesn't want to. On the contrary, they give him a comfortable cell, plenty to eat, cigars, cigarettes, wine or beer, according to his taste, a servant to wait on him, anything he wants save his freedom. After a few days of it the fellow usually begs to be permitted to work. A man just can't stand having too much of a good thing. Give a man all he wants and more and you'll cure him of his appetites in nine cases out of ten. It's so damned simple—it's strange we don't take advantage of such ideas.''

When I had crawled into bed and turned out the light I found that I was wide awake. Often, when I've listened to a man for a whole evening, turning myself into a receiving station, I lie awake and rehearse the man's story from beginning to end. I like to see how accurately I can retrace the innumerable incidents which a man can relate in the course of several hours, especially if he is given free rein. I almost always think of such talks as a big tree with limbs and branches and leaves and buds. Roots, too, which have their grip in the common soil of human experience and which make any story, no matter how fantastic or incredible, quite plausible, provided you give the man the time and attention he demands. The most wonderful thing, to carry the image further, is the buds: these are the little incidents which like seeds a man will often plant in your mind to blossom later when the memory of him is almost lost. Some men are particularly skillful in handling these buds; they actually seem to possess the power to graft them on to your own story-telling tree so that when they blossom forth you imagine that they were your own, though you never cease marveling that your own little brain could have produced such astonishing fruit.

As I say, I was turning it all over in my mind and chuckling to myself to think how clever I was to have detected certain definite falsifications, certain distortions and omissions which, when one is listening intently, one seldom catches. Presently I recalled how he had admitted some slight fabrications only to emphasize that the rest of his yarn was pure wool. At this point I chuckled aloud. Rattner was tossing about, evidently no more able than I to close his eyes.

"Are you still awake?" I asked quietly.

He gave a grunt.

"Listen," I said, "there's one thing I want to ask you—do you believe he was telling the truth about himself?"

Rattner, too tired I suppose to go into any subtleties of analysis, began to hem and haw. In the main he thought the fellow had been telling us the truth. "*Why*, didn't you believe him?" he asked.

"You remember," I said, "when I touched him to the quick . . . you remember how sincerely he spoke? Well, it was at that moment that I doubted him. At that moment he told us the biggest lie of all—when he said that the rest was all true. I don't believe that any of it was true, not even the story about knowing your friend. You remember how quickly he married him off to his sister? That was sheer spontaneous invention. I was tracing it all back just now. And I remembered very distinctly how, when you were discussing your friend the architect, he always told his part after you had made a few remarks. He was getting his clue from you all the time. He's very agile and he's certainly fertile, I'll say that for him, but I don't believe a damned thing he told us, except perhaps that he was in the army and got badly bunged up. Even that, of course, could have been trumped up. Did you ever feel a head that was trepanned? That seems like solid fact, of course, and yet somehow, I don't know just why, I could doubt even what my fingers told me. When a man has an inventive brain like his he could tell you anything and make it sound convincing. Mind you, it doesn't make his story any less real, as far as I'm concerned. Whether all those things happened or not, they're true just the same. A minute ago, when I was mulling it over to myself, I caught myself deforming certain incidents, certain remarks he made, in order to make the story a better story. Not to make it more truthful, but more true, if you see the difference. I had it all figured out, how I would tell it myself, if I ever got down to it. . . ."

Rattner began to protest that I was too sweeping in my judgment, which only served to remind me of the marvelous poem he had recited for us.

"I say," I began again, "what would you think if I told you that the poem which he got off with such gusto was somebody else's? Would that shock you?"

"You mean you recognized it—you had heard it before?"

"No, I don't mean to say that, but I'm damned sure he was not the author of it. Why did he talk about his unusual memory immediately afterwards—didn't that strike you as rather strange? He could have spoken about a thousand things, but no, he had to speak of that. Besides, he recited it too well. Poets aren't usually so good at reciting their own things. Very few poets remember their verses, particularly if they're long ones such as his was. To recite a poem with such feeling a man has to admire it greatly and a poet, once he's written a poem out, forgets it. In any case, he wouldn't be going around spouting it aloud to every Tom, Dick and Harry he meets. A bad poet might, but then that poem wasn't written by a bad poet. And furthermore, a poem like that couldn't have been written by a man like our friend who boasted so glibly about turning out crap for the magazines whenever he needed to earn an honest or a dishonest penny. No, he memorized that poem because it was just the sort of thing he would like to have written himself and couldn't. I'm sure of it."

"There's something to what you say there," said Rattner sleepily. He sighed and turned over, his face towards the wall. In a jiffy he had turned round again and was sitting bolt upright.

"What's the matter," I asked, "what hit you?"

"Why my friend what's his name . . . you know, the architect who was my buddy. *Who* mentioned his name first—he did, didn't he? Well, how could he be lying then?"

"That's easy," I said. "Your friend's name is known to millions of people. He selected it just because it was a well-known name; he thought it would add tone to his story. That was when he was talking about his inventions, you remember? He just made a stab in the dark—and happened to strike your friend."

"He seemed to know a hell of a lot about him," said Rattner, still unconvinced.

"Well, don't you know lots of things about people whom you've never met? Why, if a man is any kind of celebrity we often know more about him than he does himself. Besides, this bird may have run into him at a bar some time or other. What sounded fishy to me was marrying him off to his sister right away."

"Yep, he was taking a big chance there," said Rattner, "knowing that I had been such an intimate friend."

"But you had already told him you hadn't seen each other since you were buddies together, don't forget that. Why he could have given him not only a wife but a half dozen children besides—you wouldn't be able to disprove it. Anyway, that's one thing we *can* check up on. I do wish you'd write to your friend and see if he knows this guy or not."

"You bet I will," said Rattner, getting out of bed at once and looking for his notebook. "You've got me all worked up about it now. Jesus, what licks me is that you could have entertained such suspicions and listened to him the way you did. You looked at him as though he were handing you the Gospel. I didn't know you were such an actor."

"I'm not," I hastened to put in. "At the time I really believed every word he was telling us. Or, to be more exact, I never stopped to think whether what he was saying was so or not so. When a story is good I listen, and if it develops afterwards that it was a lie why so much the better—I like a good lie just as much as the truth. A story is a story, whether it's based on fact or fancy."

"Now I'd like to ask you a question," Rattner put in. "Why do you suppose he was so sore at Roosevelt?"

"I don't think he was half so sore as he pretended to be," I answered promptly. "I think his sole motive for introducing Roosevelt's name was to get us to listen to that scurrilous poem he had cooked up. You noticed, I hope, that there was no comparison between the two poems. *He* wrote the one on Roosevelt, that I'm positive of. Only a bar-fly could cook up such ingenious nonsense. He probably hasn't anything against Roosevelt. He wanted us to admire the poem and then, failing to get a reaction from us, he got his wires crossed and connected Roosevelt with Woodrow Wilson, the demon who sent him to hell."

"He certainly had a vicious look when he was talking about the war," said Rattner. "I don't doubt him for a minute when he said he had murdered plenty of men. I wouldn't want to run across him in the dark when he was in a bad mood."

"Yes, there I agree with you," I said. "I think the reason he was so bitter about killing was that he was a killer himself . . . I was almost going to say a killer by nature, but I take that back. What I do think, though, is that the experience in the trenches often brings out the killer in a man. We're all killers, only most of us never get a chance to cultivate the germ. The worst killers, of course, are the ones who stay at home. They can't help it, either. The soldier gets a chance to vent his feelings, but the man who stays at home has no outlet for his passions. They ought to kill off the newspaper men right at the start, that's my idea. Those are the men who inspire the killing. Hitler is a pure, clean-hearted idealist compared to those birds. I don't mean the correspondents. I mean the editors and the stuffed shirts who order the editors to write the poison that they hand out."

"You know," said Rattner, in a soft, reflective voice, "there was only one man I felt like killing when I was in the service—and that was the lieutenant, the second-lieutenant, of our company."

"Don't tell me," I said. "I've heard that same story a thousand times. And it's always a lieutenant. Nobody with any self-respect wants to be a lieutenant. They all have inferiority complexes. Many of them get shot in the back, I'm told."

"Worse than that sometimes," said Rattner. "This chap I'm telling you about, why I can't imagine anyone being hated more than he was—not only by us but by his superiors. The officers loathed him. Anyway, let me finish telling you about him. . . . You see, when we were finally demobilized everybody was gunning for him. I knew some fellows who came all the way to New York from Texas and California to look him up and take a poke at him. And when I say a poke I don't mean just a poke—I mean to beat the piss out of him. I don't know whether it's true or not, but the story I heard later on was this, that he was beaten up so often and so badly that finally he changed his name and moved to another state. You can imagine what what's his name would have done to a guy like that, can't you? I don't think he'd have bothered to soil his hands. I think he'd have plugged him or else cracked him over the head with a bottle. And if he'd have had to swing for it I don't think he would have batted an eyelash. Did you notice how smoothly he passed over that story about cracking a friend with a broken bottle? He told it as though it were incidental to something else—it rang true to me. If it had been a lie he would have made more of it. But he told it as though he were neither ashamed nor proud of doing what he did. He was just giving us the facts, that's all."

I lay on my back, when we had ceased talking, with eyes wide open, staring at the ceiling. Certain phrases which our friend had dropped returned obsessively to plague me. The collection of vice-presidents of the United States, which he had so accurately described, was a most persistent image. I was trying my damnedest to recall in what town I too had seen this collection in a drugstore window. Chattanooga, most likely. And yet it couldn't have been Chattanooga either, because in the same window there was a large photograph of Lincoln. I remembered how my eye had flitted back and forth from the rogues' gallery of vice-presidents to the portrait of Lincoln's wife. I had felt terribly sorry for Lincoln at that moment, not because he had been assassinated but because he had been saddled with that crazy bitch of a wife who almost drove him insane. Yes, as the woman from Georgia had said, we *were* trying to make a *he*-ro of him. And yet for all the good he had tried to do he had caused a lot of harm. He almost wrecked the country. As for Lee, on the other hand, there was no division of opinion throughout the country as to the greatness of his soul. As time goes on the North becomes more enamored of him. . . . *The killing*—that's what I couldn't fathom. What had it accomplished? I wondered if our friend had really gone up to the circle and held communion with the spirit of the man he revered. And then what? Then he had gone to a cheap lodging house and fought with the bed bugs until dawn, was that it? And the next day and the day after? Legions of them floating around. And me priding myself on my detective ability, getting all worked up because I uncovered a few flaws in his story. A revolution of the heart! Fine phrase, that, but meanwhile I'm lying comfortably between clean warm sheets. I'm lying here making emendations in his story so that when I come to put it down on paper it will sound more authentic than the authentic one. Trying to kid myself that if I tell the story real well perhaps it will make people more kindly and tolerant towards such poor devils. Rot! All rot! There are the people who give and forgive without stint, without question, and there are the other kind who always know how to muster a thousand reasons for withholding their aid. The latter never graduate into the former class. Never. The gulf between them is as wide as hell. One is born kind, indulgent, forgiving, tolerant, merciful. One isn't made that way through religion or education. Carry it out to the year 56,927 A.D. and still there will be the two classes of men. And between the two there will always be a shadow world, the world of ghostly creatures who toss about in vain, walking the streets in torment while the world sleeps. . . .

It wasn't so long ago that I was walking in that same shadow world myself. I used to walk around in the dead of night begging for coppers so that I could fill my empty belly. And one night in the rain, walking with head down and full of nothing but misery, I run plump into a man with a cape and an opera hat and in a faint, cheerless voice I beg in my customary way for a few pence. And without stopping, without even looking at me, the man from the opera digs in his vest pocket, pulls out a handful of change and flings it at me. The money rolls all over the sidewalk and into the gutter. Suddenly I straightened up, stiff and taut with anger. Suddenly I was completely out of the coma, snorting like a bull and ready to charge. I waved my fist and shouted in the direction the man had taken, but there was no sight or sound of him. He had vanished as mysteriously as he had appeared. I stood there a moment or so undecided what to do, whether to run after him and vent my spleen or quietly set about searching for the shower of coins he had flung at me. Presently I was laughing hysterically. Run after him, bawl him out, challenge him to a duel? Why, he wouldn't even recognize me! I was a nonentity to him, just a voice in the dark asking for alms. I drew myself up still more erect and took a deep breath. I looked around calmly and deliberately. The street was empty, not even a cab rolling along. I felt strong and chastened, as if I had just taken a whipping I deserved. "You bastard," I said aloud, looking in the direction of my invisible benefactor, "I'm going to thank you for this! You don't know what you've done for me. Yes sir, I want to thank you from the bottom of my heart. I'm cured." And laughing quietly, trembling with thanksgiving, I got down on my hands and knees in the rain and began raking in the wet coins. Those which had rolled into the gutter were covered with mud. I washed them carefully in a little pool of rain water near a post of the elevated line. Then I counted them slowly and deliciously. Thirty-six cents altogether. A tidy sum. The cellar where we lived was near by. I brought the bright clean coins home to my wife and showed them to her triumphantly. She looked at me as if I had gone out of my head.

"Why did you wash them?" she said nervously.

"Because they had fallen in the gutter," I answered. "An angel with an opera hat left them there for me. He was in too much of a hurry to pick them up for me. . . ."

"Are you sure you're all right?" said my wife, eyeing me anxiously.

"I never felt better in my life," I said. "I've just been humiliated, beaten, dragged in the mud and washed in the blood of the Lamb. I'm hungry, are you? Let's eat."

And so at 3:10 of an Easter morning we sallied forth from the dungeon arm in arm and ordered two hamburgers and coffee at the greasy spoon cafeteria on Myrtle Avenue corner of Fulton Street. I was never so wide awake in my life, and after I had offered up a short prayer to St. Anthony I made a vow to remain wide awake and if possible to wake up the whole world, saying in conclusion Amen! and wiping my mouth with a paper napkin.

Arkansas and the Great Pyramid

Arkansas is a great State. It *must* be, otherwise De Soto, who discovered about everything there was to be discovered in the Southwest, would have passed it by, ignored it. Ninety years before the Pilgrims landed at Plymouth the Spaniards, who were also white men, it seems, penetrated this land. After De Soto's death a hundred years passed before white men again set foot in the territory which was to be admitted to the Union as a State only as late as 1836. There were about 60,000 people then in the whole State. Today its population numbers 2,000,000. Arkansas fought on the side of the Confederacy, another point in its favor! In Little Rock one can still see the Old State Capitol, built in 1836, one of the most exquisite pieces of architecture in America. To appreciate it fully one has to see the monstrosity in Des Moines. Will Rogers, that great American figure whose stature is now beginning to rival that of Mark Twain or Abe Lincoln, thought well enough of Arkansas to pick a wife from the town which bears his name. There are all sorts of facts and figures about Arkansas to lend it distinction. I will pass over such as the following—that the largest watermelons in the world, some of them weighing 160 pounds, are grown at Hope; that the only diamond mine in the United States is to be found near Murfreesboro in the south-west corner of the State; that the world's largest peach orchard (17,000 acres, with one and a half million trees) is also to be found here; that Mississippi county is the largest cotton producing county in the world; that 99% of the inhabitants of this State are of pure pioneer American stock, most of them having migrated from the Appalachian mountains; that in a log cabin, now a museum, about two miles south of Mt. Gaylor, Albert Pike once taught school. I glide over these interesting items to dwell at some length on two men, now dead, whom many Americans have possibly never heard of:

Brigadier-General Albert Pike, one time Sovereign Grand Com-
mander of the Ancient and Accepted Scottish Rite of Freemasonry
of the Southern Jurisdiction, U.S.A. and "Coin" (William Hope)
Harvey, builder of the Pyramid which was never built at Monte
Ne, Arkansas.

It was at Judge McHaney's home in Little Rock that I first heard
of "Coin" Harvey, the sobriquet "Coin" having been given him
because of his association with William Jennings Bryan when the
latter was advocating "free silver." Harvey by all accounts was
one of those eccentric, independent, free-thinking men who have
the courage of their convictions—a type now fast becoming extinct
in America. He had made quite a fortune, it appears, through the
sale of a book (a little greenback book, illustrated, 224 pages, price
25¢) which he had written and entitled *The Book* (sic). The book
had to do with the effect of usury "on the organism of governments
since the birth of this civilization down to the present time and the
destructive effect of a financial system based on usury (Usury
always in capital letters!) in the United States, and in the world."
In the early 1930's Harvey called a convention in order to organize
a New Political Party, having lost all faith in either of the two old
political parties. In a sheet called "The Bugle Call", which sold
for 25¢ a year, there is an interesting report of The Impromptu
National Committee which suffered a still-birth, if I am not mistaken. Harvey was of the opinion that the spot selected for the
meeting of the National Convention of his new party should be
centrally located *west* of the Mississippi River. Rather significant,
it seems to me, and indicative of the ever-increasing schism between the East and the West in these United States. As to the
credentials of the delegates to the Convention, Harvey had a rather
original idea. "An application to join any fraternity, any organization, or perform duties under the Civil Service rules requires an
examination," he explained in "The Bugle Call". "There will be
no time for the examination of those applying to enter the Convention as delegates; and yet, it is practical to substitute in lieu of an
examination a signed statement showing that the application is
informed and has knowledge of those things which a personal
examination would cover." So Harvey had the brilliant idea that
the said delegates, in lieu of an examination, should read his book,
The Book, and thus make themselves eligible. "It is the only book
to our knowledge," he sets forth, "containing this historical data
(about Usury and the rise and fall of civilizations); if the applicant
has read *The Book* it is convincing proof that he is in possession of
a knowledge that in this respect entitles him to admission in the
Convention."

Needless to say, the Convention was a flop. But I don't in the least think that "Coin" Harvey was a flop even though his name is already forgotten and the great idea of The Pyramid smothered between the musty pages of a 25¢ booklet called "The Pyramid Booklet". As a result of a chance meeting in Rogers with an obliging Arkansas gentleman, I managed after some digging to acquire one of the three or four existent copies of this extraordinary document. I shall draw liberally on the text of this booklet to explain Harvey's project which, I must add, was partially realized, though the Pyramid itself was never erected.

I visited the site of the project early one morning of a balmy Spring day. The feeling I carried away with me was that Harvey was by no means a fool, a crack-pot, or an idle dreamer. With it there came the somewhat saddening thought that perhaps a hundred years from now the purpose and significance of this aborted undertaking will assume its true importance.

What was the purpose of the Pyramid? I quote his own words: "The purpose of the Pyramid is to attract the attention of the people of the world to the fact that civilizations have come and gone attended with untold suffering to hundreds of millions of people, and that this one is now in danger—on the verge of going. This signal warning that the Pyramid heralds to the world, it is hoped, will set the people thinking and arouse them to an unselfish consciousness of the steps to be taken to save and perfect this civilization. If this is not done, quickly, before utter confusion sets in, time will, in the unlettered language of oblivion and savagery, write an epitaph on the tomb of this civilization."

"When the Pyramid is completed," he adds, "the intention is to erect a broadcasting station and to get and keep in touch with the world, having always in view the thought of arousing the practical, thinking people of the world to the making of a perfect civilization."

Harvey had originally intended to finance the Pyramid himself, but after sinking $10,000.00 into the fund he became financially embarrassed and called for volunteer contributions. Sums ranging from one dollar to fifty dollars were received from all parts of the world, totalling, at the time he wrote the booklet, about $1,000.00. The cost of the Pyramid when completed and sealed up was estimated to be about $75,000.00.

The thing which impressed Harvey and which spurred him on was the fact that, as he puts it, "there is no other undiscovered country to which to flee! Truth and Falsehood, Good and Evil, God and Satan are now face to face in all the world in a deadly conflict. It is the same crisis that came to other civilizations that went down! Individual selfishness crystallized into the laws of nations has destroyed democracies and republics and is the mother of monarchies and despotism. Selfishness uncontrolled is a consuming fire that eats like a cancer at the vitals of governments, bringing with it corruption, prejudices, vanity, a runted, ill fed, and an anaemic race. How are we to meet this crisis? How are the people of the world to meet this crisis?"

The Pyramid was to have been 130 feet high, resting on a base 40 feet square. To the north of it was to be a concrete foyer or terrace capable of seating about a thousand people. At its base, in a lake of cold, clear water, a concrete island equipped with cement furniture was actually built. An expert from the Portland Cement Association gave it as his opinion that, when a water proof finish had been applied to the surface, "the Pyramid would last a million years and longer—indefinitely."

Monte Ne, the site of the project, is situated at the edge of a valley at the end of a spur. Harvey, realizing that the Ozarks by the process of erosion had already been lowered from 14,000 to 1,400 feet, took the precaution of choosing his site at a point where the distance to the top of the mountain was only about 240 feet. "If," he writes, "by process of erosion the valley is filled in and the mountains about it lowered in the long time to come, the Pyramid, at the height of 130 feet, will be visible sticking out of the ground. Geologically, it is figured a certainty that there is no danger from earthquake or volcanic action in these mountains. So the Pyramid is safe to endure for all time."

On top of the shaft in the most enduring metal known there was to be placed a plate containing the following inscription: "When this can be read, go below and find a record of and the cause of the death of a former Civilization."

Similar plates were to have been placed on the exterior wall of the two vaults and the room, except that "go below" would be changed to "go within". In the large room at the base of the shaft and in the two vaults there were to be placed copies of "a book giving the rise and growth of this civilization, dangers threatening its overthrow, and a symposium of opinions as to the cause of its threatened impending death. It will be a leather bound book of probably 300 pages or more printed on paper on which a paper expert in New York City will pass, and each page of the book will be covered with transparent paper that is now made for such purpose, through which one can readily read, thus preserving the ink from fading. When the Pyramid is completed, except for the closing of the entrance to the room and two vaults, it will be given a year to dry. And during that year (sic) the book will be written and three volumes printed and prepared to go therein."

The booklet goes on to explain how these books will be placed in air-tight containers, and how the proceeds from the sale of the book will be used to improve the grounds and provide for the expense of a caretaker. Other volumes were also to be sealed up in the Pyramid—books on industry, science, inventions, discoveries, etc. The Bible, too, and encyclopaedias and histories. Also pictures of people and animals at different stages of our civilization. In the large room were to be placed "small articles now used by us in domestic and industrial life, from the size of a needle and safety pin up to a victrola."

A sagacious piece of foresight was the provision for a key book to the English language "which will aid in its translation, no matter what language is spoken at the time the Pyramid is opened." I like particularly this which then follows:

"It is presumed that a new civilization rising from the ashes of this one will rise slowly, as this one has, making discoveries gradually as prompted by human reason, knowing no more of what we have discovered than we know now, of the stages of advancement of prehistoric civilizations, and that it must arrive at a period when steel and dynamite have been discovered by them, before they can break into the Pyramid. Which presupposes an intelligence for appreciation of what they find in the Pyramid. As the room and each vault will contain information of the existence of the other two compartments, if by explosion of dynamite the contents of the first one entered destroys in part its contents they will use more care in entering the other two.

"The record of ancient civilizations which we have unearthed do not tell the merits and demerits of those civilizations, the struggles of those people and why they fell. The Pyramid to be erected here will contain all such records. Upon opening the Pyramid and reading the documents contained therein, mankind thousands of years hence will learn of the railroads, the telegraph, the radio, the phonograph, the telephone, the linotype, the flying machine and of the circulation of the blood through the human body, all discoveries of the last 400 years. Of the 5,000 years that this civilization has been groping forward it is only in the last 500 years that the Earth was discovered to be round. A globular map of the world will be seen by those who enter the Pyramid.

"Wonderful discoveries have been made by this civilization in a knowledge of the universe and in the sciences as applied to the human anatomy and industries, but comparatively few in statesmanship and none in the study of civilization as a science. Upon the mastery of this latter depends the perfection of a civilization. Nothing less than this in the mental and soul structure embraces this all important divine knowledge.

"This purpose of the Pyramid is as stated and the person of no one will be entombed therein. There will be nothing about it that partakes of self or vanity and no one's name will appear on the outside of it. The only inscription will be what appears on the metal plates."

There was, however, one ironic concession to human vanity which Harvey evidently thought wise to make, harassed as he was by lack of funds. It follows closely upon the foregoing:

"The names *and addresses* (sic) of all contributors to the Pyramid Fund will be written on parchment paper and placed in a glass container with the air taken out and placed on the pedestal in the center of the large room. Their names will also be in the book before mentioned that goes to the public. This assistance will be appreciated and it will hasten the finishing and closing of the Pyramid."

In conclusion there is appended a statement by the treasurer, the First National Bank, Rogers, Arkansas:—"We believe historically and archaeologically it is an undertaking of worldwide importance and we gladly give our cooperation to its construction. We are personally acquainted with Mr. Harvey. He is a valued depositor of this bank and is a gentleman of esteemed reputation for honor and reliability." Et cetera, et cetera.

This little statement ought also to have been written on the finest parchment, put under a glass bell, sealed and entombed with the other documents, it seems to me. One is constrained to wonder if, with that miraculous key to the English language, the men of future millennia, having again arrived at the knowledge of the making of steel and dynamite, would also be able to unravel the meaning of the word "gentleman". I can well imagine them racking their brains for a clue to this extinct animal. I feel positive that, with all the photographs and pictures of men, machines, costumes, animals, birds, inventions, and what not which he thought to leave a touching record of, there never entered Harvey's mind the thought that the appellation "gentleman" would be a term completely devoid of significance to the men of the future. I doubt very much that the people opening the Pyramid one day in the distant future would have the least conception of the type of man Mr. Harvey represented. It would be extremely interesting, could we do it, to read the learned thesis of a savant analyzing the contents of this peculiar repository of a civilization supposed to have existed 250,000 years ago. We who have followed the cavortings of our learned 'ologists in all fields of research may indeed be skeptical of the readings of those to come in that hazy, undefinable period which only Portland Cement might hope to witness. Portland Cement, indeed! My first years out of school were spent in the asphyxiating atmosphere of a cement company. All I remember now of that life is the term f.o.b. That meant that I had to get off the high perch on which I sat filling in inquiry blanks and run downstairs two flights to get the freight rate to Pensacola, Nagasaki, Singapore or Oskaloosa. I never saw a sack of cement during the three years I worked with the cement company. I saw pictures of the plants on the walls of the vice-president's office when on rare occasions I was obliged and permitted to enter that sanctum. I used to wonder what cement was made of. And, judging from the letters we received now and then from irate customers, not all Portland cements were of the same high quality. Some apparently wouldn't outlast a good rain. However, that's neither here nor there. What I should like to say, before leaving the subject of the Pyramid, is this—that in my humble opinion young couples about to set forth on their honeymoon, after having properly passed the required Wassermann test, might do well, instead of taking a ticket for Niagara Falls, to go to Monte Ne. If possible, they ought to provide themselves beforehand with a copy of *The Book*. And while staying at Rogers, which is the logical place to stay when visiting Monte Ne, they should put up at the Harris Hotel—it is one of the best and the most reasonable hotels in the whole United States. I recommend it without reservation.

Day in the Park

Hollywood reminds me vividly of Paris by reason of the fact that there are no children in the street. As a matter of fact, now that I think about it, I don't recall seeing children about anywhere except in the Negro quarters of certain Southern cities. Charleston and Richmond particularly. I remember a boy in Charleston, a colored boy about eight years of age, who impressed me by his impudent swagger. He was a sawed-off, hammered-down runt in long pants with an unlit cigarette hanging from the corner of his mouth. He sauntered into the drug store where I was having a drink, looking for all the world like a miniature edition of Sam Langford. At first I thought he was a Lilliputian, but no, he was just a kid, no more than seven or eight years old. His head didn't even reach to the top of the bar, despite the mannish hat he was wearing. And though he was looking up at us, he gave the impression of looking down, surveying us as if we were fresh vegetables or something. He walked round the bar to where the soda water jerker was standing and coolly asked for a match. The man pretended to be angry and tried to shoo him off, as though he were a big horse-fly. But the kid stood his ground and looked up at him with humorous defiance. He had one hand in his pocket and with the other hand he was nonchalantly twirling a bunch of keys attached to a piece of twine. As the man behind the bar began to assume a more menacing attitude, the kid calmly turned his back on him and strolled over to the rack where the magazines were stacked up. There was an endless series of magazines called "Comics" on the lower shelf just above his head. He moved down the line, reading the titles slowly—Planet, Heroic, Thrilling, Speed, Smash, Jungle, Exciting, Fight, Wings, Startling, True, Magic, Wonderful, etc., etc.—a seemingly inexhaustible variation on the same theme. Finally he picked one out and leisurely flipped the pages. When he

388

had satisfied himself that he wanted it, he tucked it under his arm and then, as he came slowly back towards the bar, he bent down to pick up a parlor match which he found lying on the floor. As he got to the bar he flipped a coin high in the air; it bounced on the counter and fell behind the bar. He did it like a showman, with punctilious braggadocio, which enraged the clerk no end. Meanwhile he looked us all over once again in that impudent way of his and, striking the parlor match on the marble slab of the bar, he lit his cigarette. He held his hand out for the change without looking at the clerk, like a business man too abstracted to be conscious of such a trivial thing as change. When he felt the pennies in his hand he turned his head slightly and spat on the floor. With that of course the clerk made a pass for him but missed. The kid had made a running slide to the doorway. There he paused a moment, grinned insolently at all and sundry and suddenly thumbed his nose at us. Then he took to his heels like a frightened rabbit.

Later, strolling about the Negro quarter with Rattner, I encountered him again, this time leaning against a lamp post reading the "Comics" magazine which he had just bought. He seemed thoroughly absorbed, removed from the world. His hat was tilted back on his head and he had a tooth-pick in his mouth. He looked like a broker who has just finished a hard day on the floor of the Exchange. I felt like ordering a Scotch and soda for him and placing it within his reach without disturbing him. I wondered what the devil he could be reading that held him so enthralled. He had picked out an issue called "Jungle" with a lurid cover depicting a half-naked girl in the arms of a sex-crazed gorilla. We stopped a few feet away to watch him. He never once looked up; he was absolutely impervious to the world.

What a contrast to Bruce and Jacquelin, whom I met in Albuquerque! Bruce was six and Jacquelin about four, I should say. They were the children of Lowell and Lona Springer at whose auto court I was staying for a few days. Lowell worked at the Standard Station at the western end of the town; his wife, Lona, ran a fountain at the entrance to the court. Simple, natural people who seemed happy just to be alive. It was a delight to talk to them. They were intelligent and sensitive, and gracious as only the common people of the world can be. Lowell, the young husband, I was especially intrigued with. He seemed to me to be about the most good-natured person I had ever encountered. You didn't care whether he had any other qualities or not—his goodness of heart was like a tonic. His extraordinary patience and gentleness with the children won my admiration. No matter how busy he was, and he seemed to be working all hours of the day and night, he always had time to answer their inumerable questions or to mend their toys or to bring them a drink when they clamored for it.

The children used to play all day in the court. After a little time, seeing that I left my door open, they got friendly and began to visit me. Soon they began to make known to me that there was a park nearby, where there were lions and tigers and skups and sand piles. They were too well-behaved to ask me outright to take them there, but they threw broad hints in their childish way. "Do you have to work all day every day?" they would ask. "No," I said, "one day I'll take a day off and then we'll go to see the lions and tigers, yes?" That made them terribly excited. Ten minutes later little Jacquelin put her head in the doorway to ask if I was going to work much longer today. "Let's go in your car," she said. "It's a beautiful car."

I was afraid to take them in the car so I asked Lona if it would be all right to walk them to the park—could they walk that far? "Oh, heavens, yes," she said, "they can outwalk me."

I went back and told the youngsters to make themselves ready. "We're all ready," said Bruce, "we're waiting for you." And with that the two of them got me by the two hands and started leading me out of the court.

The park seemed like a good mile off, and we had a lot of fun pretending to lose our way and find it again. They were running ahead of me most of the time, taking short cuts through the tall grass. "Hurry up! Hurry up!" they would yell. "It'll soon be time to feed the lions."

There was an extraordinary grove of trees set in a patch of golden light, a setting I had never expected to find in Albuquerque. It reminded me of a Derain landscape, so golden and legendary it was. I threw myself on the grass and the kids tumbled about like acrobats. In the distance I could hear the lions roaring. Jacquelin was thirsty and kept tugging at me to lead her to the fountain. Bruce wanted to help feed the lions. I wanted simply to lie there forever in the golden lake of light and watch the new sap green moving like mercury through the transparent leaves of the trees. The children were working over me like industrious gnomes to rouse me from the trance; they were tickling my ear drums with blades of grass and pushing and pulling as if I were a fat behemoth. I pulled them on top of me and began tumbling them about like young cubs.

"I want a drink of water, Henry," begged Jacquelin.

"He's not Henry, he's Mr. Miller," said Bruce.

"Call me Henry," I said. "That's my real name."

"Do you know what my name is?" said Bruce. "It's Bruce Michael Springer."

"And what's your name?" said Jacquelin.

"My name is Henry Valentine Miller."

"Valentine! That's a pretty name," said Bruce. "My father's name is Lowell—and my mother's name is Lona. We used to live in Oklahoma. That was years ago. Then we moved to Arkansas."

"And then to Albuquerque," said little Jacquelin, pulling me by the sleeve to get me to my feet.

"Are there any camels or elephants here?" I asked.

"Elephants? What are elephants?" asked Bruce.

"I want to see the tigers," said Jacquelin.

"Yes, let's see the elephants," said Bruce. "Are they tame?"

We moved towards the playground, the children running ahead and clapping their hands with joy. Jacquelin wanted to be put on the skups. So did Bruce. I seated them and began swinging them gently. "Higher!" screamed Jacquelin. "Higher! Higher!" I ran from one to the other pushing as hard as I could. I was afraid that Jacquelin might lose her grip. "Push harder!" she yelled. "Push *me!*" yelled Bruce.

I thought I would never get them down from the skups. "I almost touched the sky, didn't I?" said Bruce. "I bet my father could touch the sky. My father used to take us here every day. My father . . ." He went on about his father. My father this, my father that.

"And Lona?" I said, "what about Lona?"

"She's my mother," said Bruce.

"She's *my* mother, too," said Jacquelin.

"Yes," said Bruce, "she comes too sometimes. But she's not as strong as my father."

"She gets tired," said Jacquelin.

We were approaching the birds and the animals. "I want some peanuts," said Jacquelin. "Please buy me some peanuts, Henry," she said, coaxingly.

"Have you any money?" I asked.

"No, you've got money, haven't you?" she said.

"My father has lots of money," said Bruce. "He gave me two pennies yesterday."

"Where are they?" I asked.

"I spent them. He gives me money every day—all I want. My father makes lots of money. More than Lona."

"I want peanuts!" said Jacquelin, stamping her foot.

We got some peanuts and some ice cream cones and some jelly

beans and some chewing gum. They ate everything at once as if they had been starved.

We were standing in front of the dromedaries. "Give him some of your ice cream," I suggested to Jacquelin. She wouldn't do it. She said it would make them sick. Bruce, I noticed, was hastily finishing his ice cream cone.

"Supposing we get them some beer," I said.

"Yes, yes," said Bruce eagerly, "let's get them some beer." Quite as though that were the customary thing to do. Then he paused to reflect. "Won't they get drunk?" he asked.

"Sure," I said. "They'll get very drunk."

"Then what'll they do?" he asked delightedly.

"They'll stand on their hands maybe or . . ."

"Where are their hands?" he said. "Are those his hands?" and he pointed to the front feet.

"He's got his hands in his pocket now," I said. "He's counting his money."

Jacquelin was tickled at the idea. "Where's his pocket?" she asked. "What does he want money for?" asked Bruce.

"What do *you* want money for?" I answered.

"To buy candy."

"Well, don't you think *he* likes to buy candy too, once in a while?"

"But he can't talk!" said Bruce. "He wouldn't know what to ask for."

"He can too talk!" said Jacquelin.

"You see!" I said, turning to Bruce. "And he can whistle."

"Yes, he *can* whistle," said Jacquelin. "I heard him once."

"Make him whistle now," said Bruce.

"He's tired now," I said.

"Yes, he's very tired," said Jacquelin.

"He can't whistle neither," said Bruce.

"He can too whistle," said Jacquelin.

"He can't!" said Bruce.

"He can!" said Jacquelin. "Can't he, Henry?"

We moved on to where the bears and foxes and pumas and llamas were. I had to stop and read every inscription for Bruce.

"Where's India?" he asked, when I read him about the Bengal tiger.

"India's in Asia," I answered.

"Where's Asia?"

"Asia's across the ocean."

"Very far?"

"Yes, very far."

"How long does it take to get there?"

"Oh, about three months," I said.

"By boat or by aeroplane?" he asked.

"Listen, Bruce," I said, "how long do you think it would take to get to the moon?"

"I don't know," he said. "Maybe two weeks. Why, do people go to the moon sometimes?"

"Not very often," I said.

"And do they come back?"

"Not always."

"What's it like on the moon? Have you ever been there? Is it cold? Do they have animals there like here—and grass and trees?"

"They have everything, Bruce, just like here. Peanuts, too."

"And ice cream?" he said.

"Yes, only it tastes differently."

"How does it taste?"

"It tastes more like chewing gum."

"You mean it doesn't melt?"

"No, it never melts," I said.

"That's funny," he said. "Why doesn't it melt?"

"Because it's rubbery."

"I'd rather have this ice cream," he said. "I like it to melt."

We moved on to where the birds were sequestered. I felt sorry for the eagles and condors cooped up in tiny cages. They sat ruefully on their perches as if they knew their wings were atrophying. There were birds of brilliant plumage which hopped around on the ground like chippies; they came from remote parts of the world and were as exotic as the places they came from. There were peacocks too, incredibly vain and, like society women, seemingly of no use to the world except to display their vulgarity. The ostriches were more interesting—tough bimbos, you might say—with strong individualities and plenty of malice. Just to look at their long, muscular necks made me think of thimbles, broken glass and other inedibles. I missed the kangaroo and the giraffe, such forlorn creatures, and so intimately connected with our intrauterine life. There were foxes of course, creatures which somehow never impress me as being very foxy, perhaps because I've only seen them in menageries. And at last we came to the monarchs of the jungle pacing restlessly back and forth like monomaniacs. To see the lion and tiger caged up is to me one of the cruelest sights in the world. The lion always looks inexpressibly sad, bewildered rather than infuriated. One has an irresistible desire to open the cage and let him run amok. A caged lion somehow always makes the human race look mean and petty. Every time I see lions and tigers in the zoo I feel that we ought to have a cage for human beings too, one of each kind and each in his proper setting: the priest with his altar, the lawyer with his fat, silly law books, the doctor with his instruments of torture, the politician with his dough bag and his wild promises, the teacher with his dunce cap, the policeman with his club and revolver, the judge with his female robes and gavel, and so on. There ought to be a separate cage for the married couple, so that we could study conjugal bliss with a certain detachment and impartiality. How ridiculous we would look if we were put on exhibition! The human peacock! And no studded fan to hide his pusillanimous figure! The laughing stock of creation, that's what we would be.

It was time to be getting home. I had to tear the children gently away. Again we walked beneath the fresh green leaves of the trees that stood in the golden light. Near by ran the Rio Grande, her bed littered with gleaming boulders. Around the broad plain of Albuquerque a great circle of hills which towards dusk assume a variety of fascinating hues. Yes, a land of enchantment, not so much because of what is visible as because of what is hidden in the arid wastes. Walking with the two children in this boundless space I suddenly thought of that South American writer, the poet who wrote about kidnapping children, and the weird, fantastic journey over the pampas in an atmosphere of lunar splendor. I wondered what it would be like to make the rest of the trip with Bruce and Jacquelin in tow. How different my experiences would be! What delicious conversations too! The more I thought about it, the more obsessive became my desire to borrow them of their parents.

Presently, I noticed that Jacquelin was getting tired. She sat down on a rock and looked about her wistfully. Bruce was running ahead, blazing the trail, as it were. "Do you want me to carry you?" I asked Jacquelin. "Yes, Henry, please carry me, I'm so tired," she said, putting out her arms. I lifted her up and placed her little arms around my neck. The next moment the tears were in my eyes. I was happy and sad at the same time. Above all I felt the desire to sacrifice myself. To live one's life without children is to deny oneself a great realm of emotion. Once I had carried my own child this way. Like Lowell Springer I had indulged her every whim. How can one say No to a child? How can one be anything but a slave to one's own flesh and blood?

It was a long walk back to the house. I had to put her down now and then to catch my breath. She was very coy now, flirtatious almost. She knew she had me at her mercy.

"Can't you walk the rest of the way, Jacquelin?" I asked, testing her out.

"No, Henry, I'm too tired." And she held out her arms again appealingly.

Her little arms! The feel of them against my neck melted me completely. Of course she wasn't nearly as tired as she pretended to be. She was exercising her female charms on me, that was all. When we reached the house and I set her down, she began to frisk about like a colt. We had found a discarded toy in back of the house. The unexpected discovery of something she had completely forgotten revived her magically. An old toy is so much better than a new one. Even to me who had not played with it the thing possessed a secret charm. The memories of happy hours seemed to be embedded in it. The very fact that it was worn and dilapidated caused it to create a feeling of warmth and tenderness. Yes, Jacquelin was terribly happy now. She forgot me completely. She had found an old love.

I watched her with fascination. It seemed so completely honest and just to pass like that from one thing to another without thought or consideration. That is a gift which children possess in common with very wise people. The gift of forgetting. The gift of detachment. I went back to the cabin and sat there dreaming for a full hour. Presently a messenger boy arrived with money for me. That brought me back to life, to the monkey world of human values. Money! The very word sounded insane to me. The broken toy in the refuse pile seemed infinitely more valuable and meaningful to me. Suddenly I realized that Albuquerque was a town with stores and banks and moving picture shows. A town like any other town. The magic had gone out of it. The mountains began to assume a touristic look. It began to rain. It never rains in Albuquerque at this time of the year. But it did just the same. It poured. In the little clearance where the children used to play there was now an enormous puddle. Everything had changed. I began to think of sanitariums and deflated lungs, of the little cups which the aeroplane corporations place conveniently beside your seat. Between the cabins a continuous sheet of rain fell slantwise. The children were silent and out of sight. The outing was over. There was neither joy nor sorrow left—just a feeling of emptiness.

Automotive Passacaglia

I feel like doing a little passacaglia now about things automotive. Ever since I decided to sell the car she's been running beautifully. The damned thing behaves like a flirtatious woman.

Back in Albuquerque, where I met that automotive expert Hugh Dutter, everything was going wrong with her. Sometimes I think it was all the fault of the tail wind that swept me along through Oklahoma and the Texas panhandle. Did I mention the episode with the drunk who tried to run me into a ditch? He almost had me convinced that I had lost my generator. I was a bit ashamed, of course, to ask people if my generator was gone, as he said, but every time I had a chance to open up a conversation with a garage man I would work him round to the subject of generators, hoping first of all that he would show me where the damned thing was hidden, and second that he would tell me whether or not a car could function without one. I had just a vague idea that the generator had something to do with the battery. Perhaps it hasn't, but that's my notion of it still.

The thing I enjoy about visiting garage men is that one contradicts the other. It's very much as in medicine, or the field of criticism in literature. Just when you believe you have the answer you find that you're mistaken. A little man will tinker with your machinery for an hour and blushingly ask you for a dime, and whether he's done the correct thing or not the car runs, whereas the big service stations will lay her up in dry dock for a few days, break her down into molecules and atoms, and then like as not she'll run a few miles and collapse.

There's one thing I'd like to advise any one thinking of making a trans-continental journey: see that you have a jack, a monkey wrench and a jimmy. You'll probably find that the wrench won't fit the nuts but that doesn't matter; while you're pretending to

396

fiddle around with it some one will stop and lend you a helping hand. I had to get stuck in the middle of a swamp in Louisiana before I realized that I had no tools. It took me a half hour to realize that if there were any they would be hidden under the front seat. And if a man promises you that he will stop at the next town and send some one to haul you don't believe him. Ask the next man and the next man and the next man. Keep a steady relay going or you'll sit by the roadside till doomsday. And never say that you have no tools—it sounds suspicious, as though you had stolen the car. Say you lost them, or that they were stolen from you in Chicago. Another thing—if you've just had your front wheels packed don't take it for granted that the wheels are on tight. Stop at the next station and ask to have the lugs tightened, then you'll be sure your front wheel won't roll off in the middle of the night. Take it for granted that nobody, not even a genius, can guarantee that your car won't fall apart five minutes after he's examined it. A car is even more delicate than a Swiss watch. And a lot more diabolical, if you know what I mean.

If you don't know much about cars it's only natural to want to take it to a big service station when something goes wrong. A great mistake, of course, but it's better to learn by experience than by hearsay. How are you to know that the little man who looks like a putterer may be a wizard?

Anyway, you go to the service station. And immediately you come smack up against a man dressed in a butcher's smock, a man with a pad in his hand and a pencil behind his ear, looking very professional and alert, a man who never fully assures you that the car will be perfect when they get through with it but who intimates that the service will be impeccable, of the very highest calibre, and that sort of thing. They all have something of the surgeon about them, these entrepreneurs of the automobile industry. You see, they seem to imply, you've come to us only at the last ditch; we can't perform miracles, but we've had twenty or thirty years' experience and can furnish the best of references. And, just as with the surgeon, you have the feeling when you entrust the car to his immaculate hands, that he is going to telephone you in the middle of the night, after the engine has been taken apart and the bearings are lying all about, and tell you that there's something even more drastically wrong with the car than he had at first suspected. Something serious, what! It starts with a case of bad lungs and ends up with a removal of the appendix, gall bladder, liver and testicles. The bill is always indisputably correct and of a figure no less than formidable. Everything is itemized, except the quality of the foreman's brains. Instinctively you put it safely away in order to produce it at the next hospital when the car breaks down again; you want to be able to prove that you knew what was wrong with the car all along.

After you've had a few experiences of this sort you get wary, that is if you're slow to catch on, as I am. After you stay in a town a while and get acquainted, feel that you are among friends, you throw out a feeler; you learn that just around the corner from the big service station there's a little fellow (his place is always in the rear of some other place and therefore hard to find) who's a wizard at fixing things and asks some ridiculously low sum for his services. They'll tell you that he treats *everybody* that way, even those with "foreign" license plates.

Well, that's exactly what happened to me in Albuquerque, thanks to the friendship I struck up with Dr. Peters who is a great surgeon and a *bon vivant* as well. One day, not having anything better to do—one of those days when you call up telephone numbers or else go to have your teeth cleaned—one day, as I say, in the midst of a downpour I decided to consult the master mind, the painless Parker of the automotive world: Hugh Dutter. There was nothing very seriously wrong—just a constant high fever. The men at the service station didn't attach much importance to it— they attributed it to the altitude, the age of the car and so on. I suppose there was nothing more that they could repair or replace. But when on a cold, rainy day a car runs a temperature of 170 to 180 there must be something wrong, so I reasoned. If she was running that high at 5,000 feet what would she run at 7,000 or 10,000?

I stood in the doorway of the repair shop for almost an hour waiting for Dutter to return. He had gone to have a bite with some friends, never dreaming that there would be any customers waiting for him in such a downpour. His assistant, who was from Kansas, regaled me with stories about fording flooded streams back in Kansas. He spoke as though people had nothing better to do when it rained than practise these dangerous manoeuvres with their tin Lizzies. Once he said a bus got caught in the head waters of a creek, keeled over, was washed downstream and never found again. He liked rain—it made him homesick.

Presently Dutter arrived. I had to wait until he went to a shelf and arranged some accessories. After I had sheepishly explained my troubles he leisurely scratched his head and without even looking in the direction of the engine he said: "Well, there could be a lot of reasons for her heating up on you that way. Have you had your radiator boiled out?"

I told him I had—back in Johnson City, Tennessee.

"How long ago was that?" he said.

"Just a few months back."

"I see. I thought you were going to say a few years ago."

The car was still standing outside in the rain. "Don't you want to look her over?" I said, fearing that he might lose interest in the case.

"You might bring her in," he said. "No harm in taking a look. Nine times out of ten it's the radiator. Maybe they didn't do a good job for you back in Cleveland."

"Johnson City!" I corrected.

"Well, wherever it was." He ordered his assistant to drive her in.

I could see he wasn't very enthusiastic about the job: it wasn't as though I had brought him a bursting gall bladder or a pair of elephantine legs. I thought to myself—better leave him alone with it for a while; maybe when he begins to putter around he'll work up a little interest. So I excused myself and went off to get a bite.

"I'll be back soon," I said.

"That's all right, don't hurry," he answered. "It may take hours to find out what's wrong with her."

I had a Chop Suey and on the way back I loitered a bit in order to give him time to arrive at a correct diagnosis. To kill a little time I stopped in at the Chamber of Commerce and inquired about the condition of the roads going to Mesa Verde. I learned that in New Mexico you can tell nothing about the condition of the roads by consulting the map. For one thing the road map doesn't say how much you may be obliged to pay if you get stuck in deep clay and have to be hauled fifty or seventy-five miles. And between gravel and graded roads there's a world of difference. At the Automobile Club in New York I remember the fellow taking a greasy red pencil and tracing a route for me backwards while answering two telephones and cashing a check.

"Mesa Verde won't be officially open until about the middle of May," said the fellow. "I wouldn't risk it yet. If we get a warm rain there's no telling what will happen."

I decided to go to Arizona, unless I had an attack of chilblains. I was a little disappointed though to miss seeing Shiprock and Aztec.

When I got back to the garage I found Dutter bending over the engine; he had his ear to the motor, like a doctor examining a weak lung. From the vital parts there dangled an electric bulb attached to a long wire. The electric bulb always reassures me. It means business. Anyway, he was down in the guts of the thing and getting somewhere—so it looked.

"Found out what's wrong yet?" I ventured to inquire timidly.

"No," he said, burying his wrist in a mess of intricate whirring thingamajigs which looked like the authentic automotive part of the automobile. It was the first time I had ever seen what makes a car go. It was rather beautiful, in a mechanical way. Reminded me of a steam calliope playing Chopin in a tub of grease.

"She wasn't timing right," said Dutter, twisting his neck around to look at me but, like the skilful surgeon, still operating with his deft right hand. "I knew that much before I even looked at her. That'll heat a car up quicker'n anything." And he began explaining to me from deep down in the bowels of the car how the timing worked. As I remember it now an eight cylinder car fires 2,3,5,7 with one cam and 3,4,6,8 with the other. I may be wrong on the figures but the word cam is what interested me. It's a beautiful word and when he tried to point it out to me I liked it still better— the cam. It has a down-to-earth quality about it, like piston and gear. Even an ignoramus like myself knows that piston, just from the sound of the word, means something that has to do with the driving force, that it's intimately connected with the locomotion of the vehicle. I still have to see a piston per se, but I believe in pistons even though I should never have the chance to see one cold and isolate.

The timing occupied him for quite a while. He explained what a difference a quarter of a degree could make. He was working on the carburetor, if I am not mistaken. I accepted this explanation, as I had the others, unquestioningly. Meanwhile I was getting acquainted with the fly-wheel and some other more or less essen-tial organs of the mysterious mechanism. Most everything about a car, I should say in passing, is more or less essential. All but the nuts underneath the chassis; they can get loose and fall out, like old teeth, without serious damage. I'm not speaking now of the universal—that's another matter. But all those rusty nuts which you see dropping off when the car's jacked up on the hoist— actually they mean very little. At worst the running board may drop off, but once you know your running board is off there's no great harm done.

Apropos of something or other he suddenly asked me at what temperature the thermostat was set. I couldn't tell him. I had heard a lot about thermostats, and I knew there was one in the car somewhere, but just where, and just what it looked like, I didn't now. I evaded all references to the subject as skilfully as I could. Again I was ashamed not to know where and what this piece of apparatus was. Starting out from New York, after receiving a brief explanation about the functioning or non-functioning of the thermostat, I had expected the shutters of the hood to fly open automatically when the heat gauge read 180 or 190. To me thermostat meant something like a cuckoo in a cuckoo clock. My eye was constantly on the gauge, waiting for it to hit 180. Rattner, my then side-kick, used to get a bit irritated watching me watch the gauge. Several times we went off the road because of this obsession on my part. But I always expected that some time or other an invisible man would release the trap and the cuckoo would fly out and then bango! the shutters would open up, the air circulate between the legs, and the motor begin to purr like a musical cat. Of course the damned shutters never did fly open. And when the gauge did finally hit 190 the next thing I knew was that the radiator was boiling over and the nearest town was forty miles away.

Well, after the timing had been corrected, the points adjusted, the carburetor calibrated, the accelerator exhilarated, all the nuts, bolts and screws carefully restored to their proper positions, Dutter invited me to accompany him on a test flight. He decided to drive her up through Tijeras Canyon where there was a big grade. He set out at fifty miles an hour, which worried me a bit because the mechanic at the big service station had said to drive her slow for the next thousand miles until she loosened up a bit. The gauge moved slowly up to 180 and, once we were properly in the pass, it swung to 190 and kept on rising.

"I don't think she'll boil," he said, lighting himself a cigarette with a parlor match. "Up here the principle is never to worry until she boils over. Cars act temperamental up here, just like people. It could be weather, it could be scales in the engine box . . . it could be a lot of things. And it mightn't be anything more than altitude. The Buicks never did make big enough radiators for the size of the car." I found this sort of talk rather cheering. More like a good French doctor. The American physician always says immediately—"Better have an X-ray taken; better pull out all your back teeth; better get an artificial leg." He's got you all cut up and bleeding before he's even looked at your throat. If you've got a simple case of worms he finds that you've been suffering from hereditary constriction of the corneal phylactery since childhood. You get drunk and decide to keep the worms or whatever ails you.

Dutter went on to talk in his calm, matter of fact way about new and old Buicks, about too much compression and too little space, about buying whole parts instead of a part of a part, as with the Chevrolet or the Dodge. Not that the Buick wasn't a good car—oh no, it was a damned good car, but like every car it had its weak points too. He talked about boiling over several times on his way from Espanola to Santa Fe. I had boiled over there myself, so I listened sympathetically. I remember getting near the top of the hill and then turning round to coast down in order to get a fresh start. And then suddenly it was dark and there were no clear crystal springs anywhere in sight. And then the lizards began whispering to one another and you could hear them whispering for miles around, so still it was and so utterly desolate.

Coming back Dutter got talking about parts and parts of parts, rather intricate for me, especially when he began comparing Pontiac parts with parts of parts belonging to the Plymouth or the Dodge. The Dodge was a fine car, he thought, but speaking for himself he preferred the old Studebaker. "Why don't you get yourself a nice old Studebaker?" I asked. He looked at me peculiarly. I gathered that the Studebaker must have been taken off the market years ago. And then, almost immediately afterwards, I began talking about Lancias and Pierce Arrows. I wasn't sure whether they made them any more either, but I knew they had always enjoyed a good reputation. I wanted to show him that I was willing to talk cars, if that was the game. He glossed over these remarks however in order to launch into a technical explanation of how cores were casted and molded, how you tested them with an ice pick to see if they were too thick or too thin. This over he went into an excursus about the transmission and the differential, a subject so abstruse that I hadn't the faintest notion what he was getting at. The gauge, I observed, was climbing down towards 170. I thought to myself how pleasant it would be to hire a man like Dutter to accompany me the rest of the way. Even if the car broke down utterly it would be instructive and entertaining to hear him talk about the parts. I could understand how people became attached to their cars, knowing all the parts intimately, as they undoubtedly do.

When we got back to the laboratory he went inside for a thermometer. Then he took the cap off the radiator and stuck the thermometer in the boiling radiator. At intervals he made a reading—comparative readings such as a theologian might do with the Bible. There was a seventeen degree difference, it developed, between the reading of the gauge and the thermometer reading. The difference was in my favor, he said. I didn't understand precisely what he meant by this remark, but I made a mental note of it. The car looked pathetically human with the thermometer sticking out of its throat. It looked like it had quinsy or the mumps.

I heard him mumbling to himself about scales and what a delicate operation that was. The word hydrochloric acid popped up. "Never do that till the very last," he said solemnly.

"Do what?" I asked, but he didn't hear me, I guess.

"Can't tell what will happen to her when the acid hits her," he mumbled between his teeth.

"Now I tell you," he went on, when he had satisfied himself that there was nothing seriously wrong, "I'm going to block that thermostat open a little more with a piece of wood—and put in a new fan belt. We'll give her an eight pound pull to begin with and after she's gone about four hundred miles you can test her yourself and see if she's slipping." He scratched his head and ruminated a bit. "If I were you," he continued, "I'd go back to that service station and ask them to loosen the tappets a little. It says .0010 thousandth on the engine but up here you can ride her at .0008 thousandth—until you hear that funny little noise, that clickety-click-click, you know—like little bracelets. I tried to catch that noise before when she was cold but I couldn't get it. I always like to listen for that little noise—then I know she's not too tight. You see, you've got a hot blue flame in there and when your valves are screwed down too tight that flame just burns them up in no time. That can heat a car up too! Just remember—*the tappets!*"

We had a friendly little chat about the slaughter going on in Europe, to wind up the transaction, and then I shook hands with him. "I don't think you'll have any more trouble," he said. "But just to make sure why you come back here after they loosen the tappets and I'll see how she sounds. Got a nice little car there. She ought to last you another twenty thousand miles—*at least.*"

I went back to the big service station and had the tappets attended to. They were most gracious about it, I must say. No charge for their services this time. Rather strange, I thought. Just as I was pulling out the floorwalker in the butcher's smock informed me with diabolical suavity that, no matter what any one may have told me, the pretty little noise I was looking for had nothing to do with the tightness or looseness of the valves. It was something else which caused that. "We don't believe in loosening them too much," he said. "But you wanted it that way, so we obliged you."

I couldn't pretend to contradict him, not having the knowledge of Hugh Dutter to fortify my argument, so I decided to have the car washed and greased and find out in a roundabout way what the devil he meant.

When I came back for the car the manager came over and politely informed me that there was one other very important thing I ought to have done before leaving. "What's that?" I said.

"Grease the clutch."

How much would that be, I wanted to know. He said it was a thirty minute job—not over a dollar.

"O.K.," I said. "Grease the clutch. Grease everything you can lay hands on."

I took a thirty minute stroll around the block, stopping at a tavern, and when I got back the boy informed me that the clutch didn't need greasing.

"What the hell is this?" I said. "What did he tell me to have it greased for?"

"He tells everybody that," said the boy, grinning.

As I was backing out he asked me slyly if she het up much on me.

"A little," I said.

"Well, don't pay any attention to it," he said. "Just wait till she boils. It's a mighty smooth running car, that Buick. Prettiest little ole car I ever did see. See us again sometime."

Well, there it is. If you've ever served in the coast artillery you know what it's like to take the azimuth. First you take a course in higher trigonometry, including differential calculus and all the logarithms. When you put the shell in the breech be sure to remove all your fingers before locking the breech. A car is the same way. It's like a horse, in short. What brings on the heat is fuss and bother. Feed him properly, water him well, coax him along when he's weary and he'll die for you. The automobile was invented in order for us to learn how to be patient and gentle with one another. It doesn't matter about the parts, or even about the parts of parts, nor what model or what year it is, so long as you treat her right. What a car appreciates is responsiveness. A loose differential may or may not cause friction and no car, not even a Rolls Royce, will run without a universal, but everything else being equal it's not the pressure or lack of pressure in the exhaust pipe which matters— it's the way you handle her, the pleasant little word now and then, the spirit of forbearance and forgiveness. Do unto others as you would have them do by you is the basic principle of automotive engineering. Henry Ford understood these things from the very beginning. That's why he paid universal wages. He was calibrating the exchequer in order to make the steep grades. There's just one thing to remember about driving any automotive apparatus and that is this: when the car begins to act as though it had the blind staggers it's time to get out and put a bullet through its head. We American people have always been kind to animals and other creatures of the earth. It's in our blood. Be kind to your Buick or your Studebaker. God gave us these blessings in order to enrich the automobile manufacturers. He did not mean for us to lose our tempers easily. If that's clear we can go on to Gallup and trade her in for a spavined mule. . . .

A Desert Rat

I sized him up for a desert rat the moment he sat down. He was very quiet, modest, self-contained, with watery blue eyes and blenched lips. The whites of the eyes were blood-shot. It was his eyes which gave me the impression that he had been living in the blinding sun. But when, in a moment or two, I questioned him about his eyes he replied, to my astonishment, that their condition was due to an attack of measles. He had almost lost his sight, he said, when it occurred to him to try eating butter, lots of butter, a quarter of a pound at a time. From then on his eyes had improved. He was of the opinion that the natural grease which butter provides did the trick.

The conversation began smoothly and easily and lasted several hours. The waitress was rather surprised to see me talking to him so earnestly. She had been rather hesitant about placing him at my table—because he was rather shabbily attired and looked as though he might be dirty too. Most of the visitors to the Bright Angel Lodge are decked out in the latest knock-about regalia, the men more so than the women. Some of them go Western when they reach the Grand Canyon and come to table with huge sombreros and boots and checker-board shirts. The women seem crazy to don their pants, especially the fat women with diamond rings on their fingers and feet swollen with corns and bunions.

I must preface all this by remarking that the management of the Bright Angel Lodge seemed surprised that I should remain so long, most of the visitors being in the habit of staying just a day or two, many not even that long, some for just a half hour, long enough, as it were, to look down into the big hole and say they had seen it. I stayed about ten days. It was on the ninth day that I struck up a conversation with the prospector from Barstow. Since I left Albuquerque I hadn't spoken to a soul, except to ask for gas and water.

405

It was wonderful to keep the silence for so long a period. Rambling about the rim of the canyon I caught the weirdest fragments of conversation, startling because so unrelated to the nature of the place. For example, coming up behind an insipid young girl who was flirting with a pudgy Hopi Indian I overheard the following:

She: "In the army you won't be able to. . . ."

He: "But I won't be in the army!"

She: "Oh, that's right, you're going to join the navy." And then she added blithely: "Do you like water . . . and boats . . . and that sort of thing?" As though to say, "because if you do, our admirals and rear-admirals will furnish you with all the water you want . . . good salty water with waves and everything. Wait till you see our ocean—it's real water, every drop of it. And of course there are plenty of cannons to shoot with . . . you know, aeroplanes and what not. It will be quite exciting, you'll see. We have a war every now and then just to keep our boys in trim. You'll love it!"

Another evening, as I'm returning to the lodge from Yavapai Point, an old spinster with a plate of ice cream in her hand remarks to her escort, a seedy-looking professor, as she licks the spoon: "Nothing so extraordinary about this, is there?" It was about seven in the evening and she was pointing to the canyon with her dripping spoon. Evidently the sunset hadn't come up to her expectations. It wasn't all flamy gold like an omelette dripping from Heaven. No, it was a quiet, reserved sunset, showing just a thin rim of fire over the far edge of the canyon. But if she had looked at the ground beneath her feet she might have observed that it was flushed with a beautiful lavender and old rose; and if she had raised her eyes to the topmost rim of rock which supports the thin layer of soil that forms the plateau she would have noticed that it was of a rare tint of black, a poetic tinge of black which could only be compared to a river or the wet trunk of a live oak or that most perfect highway which runs from Jacksonville to Pensacola under a sky filled with dramatic clouds.

The best remark, to be sure, was one I overheard the last evening I spent there. A young girl in the company of three hoodlums, in a voice which seemed to reach clear across the canyon, suddenly says: "Did you see the headline tonight?" She was referring to the San Bernardino crime in which a hunchback figured mysteriously. "It's funny," she said, "I no sooner leave home than my friends get bumped off. You remember Violet? I brought her up to the house once." And she went on in a loud, clear voice, as though speaking through a megaphone, about Violet, Raymond and Jesse, I think it was. Everything struck her as funny, even the stretch one of her friends had done in San Quentin. "He musta been nuts!"

she kept repeating over and over. I observed the expression on the face of a society woman in long pants who was sitting nearby, shocked to death by the young girl's casual jocose remarks. "Where do these horrid creatures ever come from?" she seemed to be asking herself. "Really, something ought to be done about this. I must speak to the management." You could just hear her fulminating and bombinating inside, like a choked up engine gasping in the desert at 130 degrees Fahrenheit.

And then there was the son of a curio-shop-keeper who caught me early one morning, thinking I had just arrived, and insisted on pointing things out through a telescope. "That shirt down there, on the pole—it's a rather interesting phenomenon." I couldn't see what was so interesting about it. But to him everything was phenomenal and interesting, including the hotel on the opposite side of the canyon—because you could see it clearly through the telescope. "Have you seen the large painting of the Canyon in my father's shop?" he asked, as I was about to leave him. "It's a phenomenal piece of work." I told him bluntly I had no intention of looking at it, with all due respect to his father and the shop he ran. He looked aggrieved, wounded, utterly amazed that I should not care to see one of the greatest reproductions of Nature by the hand of man. "When you get a little more sense," I said, "maybe it won't seem so wonderful to you. What do I owe you for looking through the telescope?"

He was taken aback. "Owe me?" he repeated. "Why, you don't owe me anything. We're happy to be of service to you. If you need some films just stop in to my father's shop. We carry a complete line. . . ."

"I never use a camera," I said, starting to walk off.

"*What!* You never use a camera? Why, I never heard . . ."

"No, and I never buy post cards or blankets or tiny meteorites. I came here to see the Canyon, that's all. Good morning to you and may you thrive in bliss and agony." With that I turned my back on him and continued on my jaunt.

I was fuming to think that a young boy should have nothing better to do than try to waylay tourists for his father at that hour of the morning. Pretending to be fixing the telescope, polishing it, and so on, and then pulling off that nonsense about "man imitating God's handiwork"—on a piece of canvas, no less, when there before one's eyes was God himself in all his glory, manifesting his grandeur without the aid or intervention of man. All to sell you a fossil or a string of beads or some photographic film. Reminded me of the bazaars at Lourdes. Coney Island, foul as it is, is more honest. Nobody raves about the salt in the ocean. One goes there

to swelter and stew and be honestly gypped by the most expert
gyppers in the world.

Well, to get back to something clean. There was the old desert
rat smiling at me and talking about the curse of the automobile. It
had done one good thing, he admitted, and that was to break up
people's clannishness. But on the other hand it made people
rootless. Everything was too easy—nobody wanted to fight and
struggle any more. Men were getting soft. Nothing could satisfy
them any more. Looking for thrills all the time. Something he
couldn't fathom—how they could be soft and cowardly and yet not
frightened of death. Long as it gave 'em a thrill, didn't care what
happened. He had just left a party of women down the road a
ways. One of them had broken her neck. Came around a curve too
fast. He spoke about it quietly and easily, as though it were just an
incident. He had seen lots of cars turn over in the desert, racing at
a hundred and a hundred and ten miles an hour. "Seems like they
can't go fast enough," he said. "Nobody goes at forty-five miles
an hour, which is the speed limit in California. I don't know why
they make laws for people to break; it seems foolish to me. If they
want people to drive carefully why do they make motors that run
at seventy-five and eighty and a hundred miles an hour? It ain't
logical, is it?"

He went on about the virtue of living alone in the desert, of
living with the stars and rocks, studying the earth, listening to
one's own voice, wondering about Creation and that sort of thing.
"A man gets to do a lot of thinking when he's by himself all the
time. I ain't never been much of a book reader. All I know is what
I learned myself—from experience, from using my eyes and ears."

I wanted to know, rather foolishly, just where he thought the
desert began.

"Why, as far as I can make out," he said, "it's all desert, all
this country. There's always some vegetation—it ain't just sand,
you know. It has brush on it and there's soil if you can bring water
to it and nourish it. People seem to get panicky when they get to
the desert. Think they're going to die of thirst or freeze to death at
night. Of course it happens sometimes, but mostly through frettin'.
If you just take it easy and don't fret yourself it won't never hurt
you. Most people die of sheer panic. A man can go without water
for a day or two—it won't kill him—not if he don't worry about it.
Why, I wouldn't want to live anywhere else. You couldn't get me
back to Iowa if you paid me to live there."

I wanted to know about the bad lands, if they were absolutely
unreclaimable. I had been impressed, on coming to the Painted
Desert, I said, because the earth looked like something which had

already become extinct. Was it really so—could nothing be done about these regions?

Not much, he thought. They might stay that way for millions of years. There were chemicals in the earth, an acid condition, which made it impossible to grow things in such places. "But I'll tell you," he added, "it's my belief that the tendency is in the other direction."

"What do you mean?" I asked.

"I mean that the earth is coming alive faster than it's going dead. It may take millions of years to notice the change, but it's going on steadily. There's something in the air which feeds the earth. You look at a sunbeam . . . you know how you see things floating in the air. Something is always dropping back to earth . . . little particles which nourish the soil. Now the Painted Desert . . . I've been over a good part of it. There's nothing there to hurt you. It isn't all explored yet, of course. Even the Indians don't know it all." He went on to talk about the colors of the desert, how they had been formed through the cooling of the earth; he talked about prehistoric forms of life embedded in the rocks, about a plateau somewhere in the midst of the desert which an aviator had discovered and which was full of tiny horses. "Some say they were the little horses brought in by the Spaniards years ago, but my theory is that there's something lacking in the water or the vegetation which stunts their growth." He spoke of the horses with such vivid imagery that I began to see in my mind's eye the original prehistoric beast, the eohippus, or whatever it's called, which I had always pictured as running wild and free on the plains of Tartary. "It's not so strange," he was saying. "You take in Africa, they've got pygmies and elephants and that sort of thing." Why elephants? I asked myself. Perhaps he had meant something else. He knew what an elephant was like, I know, because in a little while he got to talking about the bones and skeletons of great animals which had once roamed the country—camels, elephants, dinosaurs, sabre-toothed tigers, etc., all dug up in the desert and elsewhere. He spoke about the fresh meat found on the frozen mastodons in Siberia, Alaska and Canada, about the earth moving into strange new zodiacal realms and flopping over on its axis; about the great climatic changes, sudden, catastrophic changes, burying whole epochs alive, making deserts of tropical seas and pushing up mountains where once there was sea, and so on. He spoke fascinatingly, lingeringly, as if he had witnessed it all himself from some high place in some ageless cloak of flesh.

"It's the same with man," he continued. "I figure that when we get too close to the secret Nature has a way of getting rid of us. Of course, we're getting smarter and smarter every day, but we never get to the bottom of things, and we never will. God didn't intend it that way. We think we know a lot, but we think in a rut. Book people ain't more intelligent than other folk. They just learn how to read things a certain way. Put them in a new situation and they lose their heads. They ain't flexible. They only know how to think the way they were taught. That ain't intelligent, to my way of thinkin'."

He went on to speak about a group of scientists he had encountered once off Catalina Island. They were experts, he said, on the subject of Indian burial mounds. They had come to this spot, where he was doing some dredging, to investigate a huge pile of skeletons found near the water's edge. It was their theory that at some time in the distant past the Indians of the vicinity had eaten too many clams, had been poisoned and had died in droves, their bodies piled pell-mell in a grand heap.

"Ain't my idea of it!" he said to one of the professors, after he had listened to their nonsense as long as he could stand it.

They looked at him as though to say—"Who asked you for an opinion? What could you possibly know about the subject?"

Finally one of the professors asked him what his idea might be.

"I'm not tellin' you yet," he said. "I want to see what you can find out for yourself first."

That made them angry, of course. After a time he began plying them with questions—Socratic questions, which irritated them still more. Wanted to know, since they had been studying Indian burial grounds all their lives, had they ever seen skeletons piled up this way before. "Ever find any clam shells around here?" he queried. No, they hadn't seen a single clam, dead or alive. "Neither have I," he said. "There ain't never been any clams around here."

Next day he called their attention to the soot. "Would have to bake a lot of clams to make all that soot, wouldn't they?" he said to one of the professors. Between the ash of wood and volcanic ash there's a considerable difference, he wanted me to know. "Wood," he said, "makes a greasy soot; no matter how old it is the soot remains greasy. This soot in which the skeletons were buried was volcanic." His theory was that there had been an eruption, that the Indians had attempted to flee to the sea, and were caught under the rain of fire.

The savants of course scoffed at his theory. "I didn't argue with them," he said. "I didn't want to make them mad again. I just put two and two together and told them what I thought. A day or two later they came to me and they agreed that my idea was fairly sound. Said they were going to look into it."

He went on to talk about the Indians. He had lived with them and knew their ways a bit. He seemed to have a deep respect for them.

I wanted him to tell me about the Navajos whom I had been hearing so much about ever since reaching the West. Was it true that they were increasing at a phenomenal pace? Some authority on the subject had been quoted as saying that in a hundred years, if nothing untowards occurred to arrest the development, the Navajos would be as populous as we are now. Rumor had it that they practised polygamy, each Navajo being allowed three wives. In any case, their increase was phenomenal. I was hoping he would tell me that the Indians would grow strong and powerful again.

By way of answer he said that there were legends which predicted the downfall of the white man through some great catastrophe—fire, famine, flood, or some such thing.

"Why not simply through greed and ignorance?" I put in.

"Yes," he said, "the Indian believes that when the time comes only those who are strong and enduring will survive. They have never accepted our way of life. They don't look upon us as superior to them in any way. They tolerate us, that's all. No matter how educated they become they always return to the tribe. They're just waiting for us to die off, I guess."

I was delighted to hear it. It would be marvelous, I thought to myself, if one day they would be able to rise up strong in number and drive us into the sea, take back the land which we stole from them, tear our cities down, or use them as carnival grounds. Only the night before, as I was taking my customary promenade along the rim of the Canyon, the sight of a funny sheet (Prince Valiant was what caught my eye) lying on the edge of the abyss awakened curious reflections. What can possibly appear more futile, sterile and insignificant in the presence of such a vast and mysterious spectacle as the Grand Canyon than the Sunday comic sheet? There it lay, carelessly tossed aside by an indifferent reader, the least wind ready to lift it aloft and blow it to extinction. Behind this gaudy-colored sheet, requiring for its creation the energies of countless men, the varied resources of Nature, the feeble desires of over-fed children, lay the whole story of the culmination of our Western civilization. Between the funny sheet, a battleship, a dynamo, a radio broadcasting station it is hard for me to make any distinction of value. They are all on the same plane, all manifestations of restless, uncontrolled energy, of impermanency, of death and dissolution. Looking out into the Canyon at the great amphitheatres, the Coliseums, the temples which nature over an incalculable period of time has carved out of the different orders of rock, I asked myself why indeed could it not have been the work of man, this vast creation? Why is it that in America the great works of art are all Nature's doing? There were the skyscrapers, to be sure, and the dams and bridges and the concrete highways. All utilitarian. Nowhere in America was there anything comparable to the cathedrals of Europe, the temples of Asia and Egypt— enduring monuments created out of faith and love and passion. No exaltation, no fervor, no zeal—except to increase business, facilitate transportation, enlarge the domain of ruthless exploitation. *The result?* A swiftly decaying people, almost a third of them pauperized, the more intelligent and affluent ones practising race suicide, the under-dogs becoming more and more unruly, more criminal-minded, more degenerate and degraded in every way. A handful of reckless, ambitious politicians trying to convince the mob that this is the last refuge of civilization, God save the mark!

My friend from the desert made frequent allusions to "the great secret." I thought of Goethe's great phrase: "*the open secret*"! The scientists are not the men to read it. They have penetrated nowhere in their attempts to solve the riddle. They have only pushed it back farther, made it appear still more inscrutable. The men of the future will look upon the relics of this age as we now look upon the artifacts of the Stone Age. We are mental dinosaurs. We lumber along heavy-footed, dull-witted, unimaginative amidst miracles to which we are impervious. All our inventions and discoveries lead to annihilation.

Meanwhile the Indian lives very much as he has always lived, unconvinced that we have a better way of life to offer him. He waits stoically for the work of self-destruction to complete itself. When we have grown utterly soft and degenerate, when we collapse inwardly and fall apart, he will take over this land which we have desperately striven to lay waste. He will move out of the bad lands which we have turned into Reservations for the Untouchables and reclaim the forests and streams which were once his. It will grow quiet again when we are gone: no more hideous factories and mills, no more blast furnaces, no more chimneys and smoke-stacks. Men will become clairvoyant again and telepathic. Our instruments are but crutches which have paralyzed us. We have not grown more humane, through our discoveries and inventions, but more inhuman. And so we must perish, be superseded by an "inferior" race of men whom we have treated like pariahs. They at least have never lost their touch with the earth. They are rooted and will revive the moment the fungus of civilization is removed. It may be true that this is the great melting pot of the world. But the fusion has not begun to take place yet. Only when the red man and the black man, the brown man and the yellow man unite with the white peoples of the earth in full equality, in full amity and respect for one another, will the melting pot serve its purpose. Then we may see on this continent—thousands of years hence—the beginnings of a new order of life. But the white American will first have to be humiliated and defeated; he will have to humble himself and cry for mercy; he will have to acknowledge his sins and omissions; he will have to beg and pray that he be admitted to the new and greater fraternity of mankind which he himself was incapable of creating.

We were talking about the war. "It wouldn't be so bad," said my friend, "if the people who want war did the fighting, but to make people who have no hatred in them, people who are innocent, do the slaughtering is horrible. Wars accomplish nothing. Two wrongs never made a right. Supposing I lick you and I hold you down—what will you be thinking? You'll be waiting for your chance to get me when my back is turned, won't you? You can't keep peace by holding people down. You've got to give people what they want—more than they want. You've got to be generous and kind. The war could be stopped tomorrow if we really wanted it to be stopped.

"I'm afraid, though, that we're going to be in the war in less than thirty days. Looks like Roosevelt wants to push us in. He's going to be the next dictator. You remember when he said that he would be the last president of the United States? How did the other dictators gain power? First they won over organized labor, didn't they? Well, it looks as though Roosevelt were doing the same thing, doesn't it? Of course, I don't think he will last his term out. Unless he is assassinated—which may happen—Lindbergh will be our next president. The people of America don't want to go to war. They want peace. And when the President of the United States tries to make a man like Lindbergh look like a traitor he's inciting the people to revolution. We people out here don't want any trouble with other countries. We want to just mind our own business and get along in our own humble way. We're not afraid of Hitler invading this country. And as for us invading Europe—how are we going to do it? Hitler is the master of Europe and we have to wait until he cracks up, that's how I see it. Give a man enough rope and he'll hang himself, that's what I always say. There's only one way to stop war and that's to do what Hitler's doing—gobble up all the small nations, take their arms away from them, and police the world. *We* could do it! *If we wanted to be unselfish.* But we'd have to give equality to everybody first. We couldn't do it as conquerors, like Hitler is trying to do. That won't work. We'd have to take the whole world into consideration and see that every man, woman and child got a square deal. We'd have to have something *positive* to offer the world—not just defending ourselves, like England, and pretending that we were defending civilization. If we really set out to do something for the world, *unselfishly*, I believe we could succeed. But I don't think we'll do that. We haven't got the leaders capable of inspiring the people to such an effort. We're out to save big business, international trade, and that sort of thing. What we ought to do is to kill off our own Hitlers and Mussolinis first. We ought to clean our own house before we start in to save the world. Then maybe the people of the world would believe in us."

He apologized for speaking at such length. Said he hadn't ever had any education and so couldn't explain himself very well. Besides, he had got out of the habit of speaking to people, living alone so much. Didn't know why he had talked so much. Anyway, he felt that he had a right to his ideas, whether they were right or wrong, good or bad. Believed in saying what he thought.

"The brain is everything," he said. "If you keep your brain in condition your body will take care of itself. Age is only what you think. I feel just as young now, maybe younger, than I did twenty years ago. I don't worry about things. The people who live the longest are the people who live the simplest. Money won't save you. Money makes you worry and fret. It's good to be alone and be silent. To do your own thinking. I believe in the stars, you know. I watch them all the time. And I never think too long about any one thing. I try not to get into a rut. We've all got to die sometime, so why make things hard for yourself? If you can be content with a little you'll be happy. The main thing is to be able to live with yourself, to like yourself enough to want to be by yourself—not to need other people around you all the time. That's my idea, anyhow. That's why I live in the desert. Maybe I don't know very much, but what I know I learned for myself."

We got up to go. "Olsen is my name," he said. "I was glad to meet you. If you get to Barstow look me up—I'd like to talk to you again. I'll show you a prehistoric fish I've got in a rock—and some sponges and ferns a couple of million years old."

From Grand Canyon to Burbank

I left Grand Canyon about nine o'clock in the morning of a warm day, looking forward to a serene and beautiful toboggan slide from the clouds to sea level. Now, when I look back on it, I have difficulty in remembering whether Barstow came before or after Needles. I remember vaguely getting to Kingman towards sundown. That soothing noise, as of tiny bracelets passing through a wringer, which is the thing I like best about the engine, had changed to a frightening clatter, as if the clutch, the rear end, the differential, the carburetor, the thermostat and all the nuts, bolts and ball bearings would drop out any minute. I had been advancing by slow stages, stopping every twenty or thirty miles to let the car cool off and add fresh water. Everybody was passing me, heavy trucks, dilapidated jalopies, motorcycles, skooters, teams of oxen, tramps, rats, lizards, even tortoises and snails. On leaving Kingman I saw a stretch of inviting-looking desert ahead. I stepped on the gas, determined to reach Needles at least before turning in. When I got to the foot of a mountain pass, near Oatman, the radiator began to boil over. I had another coke—my fifteenth or twentieth for the day—and sat down on the running board to wait for the engine to cool off again. There was a tremendous glare of fire shooting down through the canyon. An old drunk was hanging about the service station. He got to talking. Said it was the worst spot on Highway 66. Only about twelve miles of it, but pretty bad. I wasn't worrying about whether the road was dangerous or not but whether the water would boil over before I could reach the top of the pass. I tried to find out whether it was a long climb or a short, steep one. "There ain't any part of it you can't do in high," he kept repeating. That meant nothing to me because what other cars do in high I have to do in first sometimes. "Of course it's just as bad going down," he said. "It's only about four miles to the

415

top. If you get over it you're all right." He didn't say *when* you get over it, as one would ordinarily. I didn't like that "if". "What do you mean," I asked, "is it so terribly steep?" No, it wasn't so terribly steep—it was tricky, that's all. People got frightened, it seems, when they found themselves hanging over the edge of the cliff. That's how all the collisions occurred. I watched the sun rapidly setting. I felt the hood to see how cool it was. It was still as hot as a furnace. Well, there were eight miles of descent, I figured out. If I could get to the top I might coast down—that would cool her off.

I started off. She was making a terrible racket, a human racket, like some wounded giant screaming with pain. The signs all warned one to go slowly. Instead I stepped it up. I was riding in high and I intended to keep riding in high till I got to the top. Fortunately I passed only two cars. Out of the corner of my eye I was trying to take in the sight below. It was all a blur—just one unending piece of up-ended earth swimming in liquid fire. When I got to the top the gauge read 195 degrees. I had a two gallon can of water with me and no fear of running short. "Now we're going down," I said to myself. "She'll cool off in a jiffy." I guess it was Oatman that lay at the bottom of the pass. It might have been the end of the world. It was a fantastic place and why any one lived there I couldn't understand, but I didn't have time to ruminate on it very long even though I was lowering myself slowly and gingerly. Seemed to me the cogs were slipping. She was in first but she was rolling too fast. I tried working the brakes around the horse shoe curves and down the vertical walls of the town. Nothing held her back properly. The only thing that worked well was the horn. Usually it was faint but now suddenly it had grown strong and lusty. I switched on my one feeble lamp and honked for all I was worth. It was dark. I had descended to some long gentle slope which nevertheless refused to let me race faster than 30 miles an hour. I thought I was flying—when I looked at the roadside—but actually the illusion was that of being under water, of steering some queer kind of open submarine. Despite the drop it was warm, a pleasant evening warmth which invaded the pores and made one relax. I began to feel jovial. It was only the third or fourth time I had driven a car alone at night, my eyesight being rather poor and night driving being an art which I had forgotten to practise when taking my lessons in New York. People seemed to give me a wide berth for some mysterious reason. Sometimes they slowed down almost to a standstill in order to let me pass. I had forgotten about the one light. The moon was out and it seemed to me that it was bright enough to drive without lights. I could only see a few yards ahead, but then that is all I am ever able to see, so everything seemed quite normal.

Nearing Needles it seemed suddenly as if I had come upon a hot house. The air was overpoweringly fragrant and it had become warmer. Just as I came to what looked like a body of water, a lake probably, a man in uniform rushed out to the middle of the road and ordered me to pull over. "Bring her to a halt," he said quietly. I was so groggy that I hadn't noticed that the car was still rolling. "Put your brake on," he said, a little more firmly. It was the California inspection bureau. "So I'm in California?" I said, pleased with myself. For answer he said: "Where did you come from?" For a moment I couldn't think. Come from? Come from? To stall for time I asked him what he meant. "Where did I come from *to-day*—or what?" I asked. He meant this morning, it was evident, by the tone of disgust in which he emphasized the point. Suddenly I remembered—it was the Grand Canyon I had left early that morning. God, I was happy to remember it. These birds can be awfully suspicious when you get a lapse of memory. "You're travelling alone?" he asked. Turning his searchlight on the empty interior of the car he went on to the next question. "Are you an American citizen?" That seemed thoroughly absurd—after all I had been through since morning. I almost laughed in his face, hysterically. "Yes, I'm an American citizen," I said quietly, containing myself, and damned glad that I didn't have to produce a carte d'identité or some other fool evidence of my status. "Born in New York, I suppose?" "Yes," I answered, "born in New York." "In New York City?" "Yes sir, in New York City." Then it seemed to me he asked about insects, cabbage leaves, rhododendrons, stink weeds and formaldehyde, to all of which I instinctively answered No Sir, No Sir, No Sir! It was like a little class in the catechism only it was California and a big lake or something beside the road and the gauge was running up close to 200 again.

"Your light's out, do you know it?" he said.

"Why no," I answered angelically, shutting off the motor and climbing out to have a look at it.

"Where are you bound for now?" he said.

"Needles. Is it very far away?"

"Just a few miles," he said.

"Fine. I'll be hopping along then. Much obliged to you."

I got in and whizzed off with a terrific buzz and clatter. A few yards down the road I was stopped again. A man with a flashlight, a bit drunk, lurching unsteadily, leaned over the side of the car and, holding me by the arm, asked which way it was to such and such a place, a town I had never heard of in my life.

"To the left," I said, without pausing to reflect a sound.

"Are you sure about it?" he said, his head swinging over my steering wheel in an amazingly flexible way.

"Absolutely," I said, starting her up.

"I don't want to go back to Kingman," he said.

"No, you can't miss it," I said, stepping on the gas and threatening to decapitate him. "The first turn to your left—just a few yards down the road."

I left him standing in the middle of the road and muttering to himself. All I prayed for was that he wouldn't try to follow me in his drunken gleefulness and run me into a ditch, like a guy I met in Texas one day, near Vega, who insisted that there was something wrong—my generator was gone, he said—and tried to escort me to the next town but in doing so almost wrecked me. What he really wanted was a drink. Funny to be held up in the middle of the night by a thirsty drunkard! Better, of course, than to be run down by a pregnant mother with five children, as happened to a friend of mine.

At Needles I went to bed immediately after supper, planning to get up about five the next morning. But at three-thirty I heard the cocks crowing and feeling quite refreshed I took a shower and decided to start with the crack of dawn. I had breakfast, tanked up, and was on the road at four-thirty. It was coolish at that hour—about seventy-five or eighty degrees, I guess. The gauge read about 170. I figured that before the real heat commenced I ought to be in Barstow—say by nine o'clock in the morning surely. Now and then a crazy bird seemed to fly through the car, making a strange chirping which I had been hearing ever since leaving the Ozarks. It was the kind of music the lugs make when they're too tight or too loose. I never knew for sure whether it was the car or the creatures of the air, and sometimes I wondered if a bird had become a prisoner in the back of the car and was perhaps dying of thirst or melancholy.

As I was pulling out of town a New York car slowed up alongside of me and a woman cried out ecstatically—"Hello there, New York!" She was one of those panicky ones who get an attack of hysteria in the middle of nowhere. They were going at a leisurely pace, about forty-five miles an hour, and I thought I'd just hang on to their tail. I clung to them for about three miles and then I saw that the gauge was climbing up over 190. I slowed down to a walk and began doing some mental calculations. Back in Albuquerque, when I visited that wizard of automotive repairing, Hugh Dutter, I had learned that there was a difference between the reading of the gauge and the thermometer reading. A difference of fifteen degrees, supposedly in my favor, though it never really worked out that way in practice. Hugh Dutter had done everything possible to overcome the heating problem—except to boil out the radiator. But that was my own fault. I told him I had had that done about four thousand miles back. It was only when I got to Joseph City, Arizona, where I met an old Indian trader, that I realized there was nothing to do but have her cleaned out again. Bushman, that was the man's name, was kind enough to ride into Winslow with me in order to put me in the right hands. There I met his son-in-law, another automotive wizard, and I waited four hours or so while the radiator was boiled out, the timing re-timed, the fan belt changed, the points tickled up, the valves unloosened, the carburetor calibrated, and so on. All to the tune of a modest four dollars. It was wonderful, after that operation, to ride into Flagstaff in the heat of the afternoon with the gauge reading 130! I could scarcely believe my eyes. Of course, about an hour later, pulling up a long slope on my way to Cameron, just when it was getting real chilly, the damned thing boiled over. But once I got out of the forest and into the no-man's land where the mountains are wine-colored, the earth pea green, the mesas pink, blue, black and white, everything was lovely. For about forty miles I don't think I passed a human habitation. But that can happen of course most anywhere west of the big cities. Only here it's terrifying. Three cars passed me and then there was a stretch of silence and emptiness, a steady, sinister ebbing of all human life, of plant and vegetable life, of light itself. Suddenly, out of nowhere, it seemed, three horsemen galloped into the center of the road about fifty yards ahead of me. They just materialized, as it were. For a moment I thought it might be a hold-up. But no, they pranced a moment or two in the middle of the road, waved me a greeting, and then spurred their horses on into the phantasmal emptiness of dusk, disappearing in the space of a few seconds. What was amazing to me was that they seemed to have a sense of direction; they galloped off as if they were going somewhere when obviously there was nowhere to go to. When I got to Cameron I nearly passed it. Luckily there was a gas station, a few shacks, a hotel and some hogans by the side of the road. "Where's Cameron?" I asked, thinking it lay hidden on the other side of the bridge. "You're in it," said the man at the gas station. I was so fascinated by the eeriness of the décor that before inquiring for a room I walked down to the Little Colorado River and took a good look at the canyon there. I didn't know until the next morning that I was camping beside the Painted Desert which I had left the previous morning. I thought only that I had come to some very definite end, some hidden navel of the world where the rivers disappear and the hot magma pushes the granite up into pinkish veins, like geodesic haemorrhoids.

Well, anyway, to get back. Where was I? Somehow, ever since I hit Tucumcari I have become completely disoriented. On the license plates in New Mexico it reads: "The Land of Enchantment". And that it is, by God! There's a huge rectangle which embraces parts of four States—Utah, Colorado, New Mexico and Arizona—and which is nothing but enchantment, sorcery, illusionismus, phantasmagoria. Perhaps the secret of the American continent is contained in this wild, forbidding and partially unexplored territory. It is the land of the Indian par excellence. Everything is hypnagogic, chthonian and super-celestial. Here Nature has gone gaga and dada. Man is just an irruption, like a wart or a pimple. Man is not wanted here. Red men, yes, but then they are so far removed from what we think of as man that they seem like another species. Embedded in the rocks are their glyphs and hieroglyphs. Not to speak of the footprints of dinosaurs and other lumbering antediluvian beasts. When you come to the Grand Canyon it's as though Nature were breaking out into supplication. On an average it's only ten to eighteen miles from rim to rim of the Canyon, but it takes two days to traverse it on foot or horseback. It takes four days for the mail to travel from one side to the other, a fantastic journey in which your letters pass through four States. Animals and birds rarely cross the abyss. The trees and vegetation differ from one plateau to the other. Passing from top to bottom you go through practically all the climatic changes known on this globe, except the Arctic and Antarctic extremes. Between two formations of rock there was, so the scientists say, an interval of 500,000,000 years. It's mad, completely mad, and at the same time so grandiose, so sublime, so illusory, that when you come upon it for the first time you break down and weep with joy. *I* did, at least. For over thirty years I had been aching to see this huge hole in the earth. Like Phaestos, Mycenae, Epidauros, it is one of the few spots on this earth which not only come up to all expectation but surpass it. My friend Bushman, who had been a guide here for a number of years, had told me some fantastic yarns about the Grand Canyon. I can believe anything that any one might tell me about it, whether it has to do with geological eras and formations, freaks of nature in animal or plant life, or Indian legends. If some one were to tell me that the peaks and mesas and amphitheatres which are so fittingly called Tower of Set, Cheop's Pyramid, Shiva Temple, Osiris Temple, Isis Temple, etc. were the creation of fugitive Egyptians, Hindus, Persians, Chaldeans, Babylonians, Ethiopians, Chinese or Tibetans, I would lend a credulous ear.

The Grand Canyon is an enigma and no matter how much we learn we shall never know the ultimate truth about it. . . .

As I was saying, I was just entering the desert that lies between Needles and Barstow. It was six o'clock in the cool of a desert morning and I was sitting on the running board waiting for the engine to cool off. This repeated itself at regular intervals, every twenty or thirty miles, as I said before. When I had covered about fifty miles or so the car slowed down of itself, found its natural rhythm, as it were, and nothing I could do would make it change its pace. I was condemned to crawl along at twenty to twenty-five miles an hour. When I got to a place called Amboy, I believe it was, I had a cool, consoling chat with an old desert rat who was the incarnation of peace, serenity and charity. "Don't fret yourself," he said. "You'll get there in good time. If not to-day why to-morrow. It makes no difference." Some one had stolen his peanut slot machine during the night. It didn't disturb him in the least. He put it down to human nature. "Some folks make you feel like a king," he said, "and others are lower than worms. We learn a lot about human nature watching the cars pass by." He had warned me that there would come a forty mile stretch which would seem like the longest forty miles I had ever covered. "I've done it hundreds of times," he said, "and each time the miles seem to stretch out more and more."

And by God he was right! It must have happened soon after I took leave of him. I had only travelled about five miles when I had to pull up by the side of the road and practice the beatitudes. I got under a shed with a tin roof and patiently twiddled my thumbs. On the wall was a sort of hieroglyphic nomenclature of the engine—the parts that go wrong and make it heat up. There were so many things, according to this graph, which could bring on fever and dysentery that I wondered how any one could ever lay his finger on the trouble without first getting a diploma from Henry Ford's School of Mechanical Diabolism. Moreover, it seemed to me that all the tender, troublesome parts touched on had been treated, in the case of my *charabanc*. Age alone could account for a great deal, it seemed to me. My own organism wasn't functioning any too handsomely, and I'm not exactly an old model, as they say.

Well, inch by inch then. "Don't fret!" that's what I kept telling myself. The new models were whizzing by at seventy-five and eighty miles an hour. Air-conditioned, most likely. For them it was nothing to traverse the desert—a matter of a couple of hours—with the radio bringing them Bing Crosby or Count Basie.

I passed Ludlow upside down. Gold was lying about everywhere in big bright nuggets. There was a lake of pure condensed milk which had frozen in the night. There were yucca palms, or if not yucca date and if not date then cocoanut—and oleanders and striped sea bass from the Everglades. The heat was rippling up slant-wise, like Jacob's Ladder seen through a corrugated mirror. The sun had become a gory omelette frying itself to a crisp. The cicadas were cricketing and that mysterious bird in the back of the car had somehow found its way under my feet between the clutch and the brake. Everything was dragging, including the miniature piano and the steam calliope which had become entangled in the universal during the previous night's underwater passage. It was a grand cacophony of heat and mystification, the engine boiling in oil like an antique instrument, the tires expanding like dead toads, the nuts falling out like old teeth. The first ten miles seemed like a hundred, the second ten miles like a thousand, and the rest of the way just humanly incalculable.

I got to Barstow about one in the afternoon, after passing another examination by the plant, lice and vegetable inspectors at Daggett or some such ungodly place. I hadn't eaten since four in the morning and yet I had no appetite whatever. I ordered a steak, swallowed a sliver of it, and dove into the iced tea. As I was sitting there lucubrating and testifying in all languages I espied two women whom I recognized as guests of the Bright Angel Lodge. They had left the Grand Canyon in the morning and would probably have dinner in Calgary or Ottawa. I felt like an overheated slug. My brain-pan was vaporized. I never thought of Olsen, of course. I was racking my brains to try to remember whether I had started from Flagstaff, Needles or Winslow. Suddenly I recalled an excursion I had made that day—or was it three days ago?—to Meteor Crater. Where the devil *was* Meteor Crater? I felt slightly hallucinated. The bartender was icing a glass. Meanwhile the owner of the restaurant had taken a squirt gun and was killing flies on the screen door outside. It was Mother's Day. That told me it was Sunday. I had hoped to sit quietly in the shade in Barstow and wait for the sun to set. But you can't sit for hours in a restaurant unless you eat and drink. I grew fidgety. I decided to go to the telegraph office and send a ready made Mother's Day greeting from Barstow. It was sizzling outdoors. The street was just a fried banana flaming with rum and creosote. The houses were wilting, sagging to their knees, threatening to melt into glue or glucose. Only the gas stations seemed capable of surviving. They looked cool, efficient, inviting. They were impeccable and full of mockery. They had nothing to do with human life. There was no distress in them.

The telegraph office was in the railway station. I sat on a bench in the shade, after dispatching my telegram, and floated back to the year 1913, the same month and perhaps the same day, when first I saw Barstow through the window of a railway coach. The train was still standing at the station, just as it had been twenty-eight years ago. Nothing had changed except that I had dragged my carcass halfway around the globe and back again in the meantime. The thing that was most vivid in my memory, curiously enough, was the smell and sight of oranges hanging on the trees. The smell mostly. It was like getting close to a woman for the first time—the woman you never dared hope to meet. I remembered other things too, which had more to do with lemons than with oranges. The job I took near Chula Vista, burning brush all day in a broiling sun. The poster on the wall in San Diego, advertising a coming series of lectures by Emma Goldman—something that altered the whole course of my life. Looking for a job on a cattle ranch near San Pedro, thinking that I would become a cowboy because I was fed up with books. Nights, standing on the porch of the bunk house and looking towards Point Loma, wondering if I had understood that queer book in the library at Brooklyn— *Esoteric Buddhism*. Coming back to it in Paris about twenty years later and going quite daffy over it. No, nothing had radically altered. Confirmations, corroborations rather than disillusionment. At eighteen I was as much of a philosopher as I will ever be. An anarchist at heart, a non-partisan spirit, a free lancer and a free-booter. Strong friendships, strong hatreds, detesting everything lukewarm or compromising. Well, I hadn't liked California then and I had a premonition I wouldn't like it now. One enthusiasm completely vanished—the desire to see the Pacific Ocean. The Pacific leaves me indifferent. That part of it, at any rate, which washes the California shore. Venice, Redondo, Long Beach—I haven't visited them yet, though I'm only a few minutes away from them, being at this precise chronological moment of aberration in the celluloid city of Hollywood.

Well, the car had cooled off and so had I a bit. I had grown a little wistful, in fact. On to San Bernardino!

For twenty miles out of Barstow you ride over a washboard amidst sand dunes reminiscent of Bergen Beach or Canarsie. After a while you notice farms and trees, heavy green trees waving in the breeze. Suddenly the world has grown human again—because of the trees. Slowly, gradually, you begin climbing. And the trees and the farms and the houses climb with you. Every thousand feet there is a big sign indicating the altitude. The landscape becomes thermometric. Around you rugged, towering mountain ranges fading almost to extinction in the dancing heat waves of mid-afternoon. Some of them, indeed, have completely vanished, leaving only the pink snow shimmering in the heavens—like an ice cream cone without the cone. Others leave just a cardboard façade exposed—to indicate their substantiality.

Somewhere about a mile up towards God and his winged satellites the whole works comes toppling down on you. All the ranges converge suddenly—like a publicity stunt. Then comes a burst of green, the wildest, greenest green imaginable, as if to prove beyond the shadow of a doubt that California is indeed the Paradise it boasts of being. Everything but the ocean seems jammed into this mile-high circus at sixty miles an hour. It wasn't I who got the thrill—it was a man inside me trying to recapture the imagined thrill of the pioneers who came through this pass on foot and on horseback. Seated in an automobile, hemmed in by a horde of Sunday afternoon maniacs, one can't possibly experience the emotion which such a scene should produce in the human breast. I want to go back through that pass—Cajon Pass—on foot, holding my hat reverently in my hand and saluting the Creator. I would like it to be winter with a light covering of snow on the ground and a little sleigh under me such as Jean Cocteau used when he was a boy. I'd like to coast down into San Bernardino doing a bellywopper. And if there are oranges ripening maybe God would be kind enough to put a few within reach so that I could pluck them at eighty miles an hour and give them to the poor. Of course the oranges are at Riverside, but with a light sleigh and a thin dry blanket of snow what are a few geographical dislocations!

The important thing to remember is that California begins at Cajon Pass a mile up in the air. Anything prior to that is vestigial and vestibulary. Barstow is in Nevada and Ludlow is a fiction or a mirage. As for Needles, it's on the ocean bed in another time, probably Tertiary or Mesozoic.

By the time I got to Burbank it was dark and full of embryonic aeroplanes. A flock of mechanical students were sitting on the curb along the Main Street eating dry sandwiches and washing them down with Coca-Colas. I tried to summon a feeling of devotion in memory of Luther Burbank but the traffic was too thick and there was no parking space. I couldn't see any connection between Luther and the town that was named after him. Or perhaps they had named it after another Burbank, the king of soda water or popcorn or laminated valves. I stopped at a drug store and took a Bromo Seltzer—for "simple headaches". The real California began to make itself felt. I wanted to puke. But you have to get a permit to vomit in public. So I drove into a hotel and took a beautiful room with a radio apparatus that looked like a repository for dirty linen. Bing Crosby was crooning away—the same old song which I had heard in Chattanooga, Boswell's Tavern, Chickamauga and other places. I wanted Connie Boswell but they were all out of her for the moment. I took my socks off and hung them around the knob of the dial to choke it off. It was eight o'clock and I had awakened at dawn about five days ago, it seemed. There were no beetles or bed-bugs—just the steady roar of traffic on the concrete strip. And Bing Crosby, of course, somewhere out in the blue on the invisible ether waves owned by the five-and-ten cent store.

Soirée in Hollywood

My first evening in Hollywood. It was so typical that I almost thought it had been arranged for me. It was by sheer chance, however, that I found myself rolling up to the home of a millionaire in a handsome black Packard. I had been invited to dinner by a perfect stranger. I didn't even know my host's name. Nor do I know it now.

The first thing which struck me, on being introduced all around, was that I was in the presence of wealthy people, people who were bored to death and who were all, including the octogenarians, already three sheets to the wind. The host and hostess seemed to take pleasure in acting as bartenders. It was hard to follow the conversation because everybody was talking at cross purposes. The important thing was to get an edge on before sitting down to the table. One old geezer who had recently recovered from a horrible automobile accident was having his fifth old-fashioned— he was proud of the fact, proud that he could swill it like a youngster even though he was still partially crippled. Every one thought he was a marvel.

There wasn't an attractive woman about, except the one who had brought me to the place. The men looked like business men, except for one or two who looked like aged strike-breakers. There was one fairly young couple, in their thirties, I should say. The husband was a typical go-getter, one of those ex-football players who go in for publicity or insurance or the stock market, some clean all-American pursuit in which you run no risk of soiling your hands. He was a graduate of some Eastern University and had the intelligence of a high-grade chimpanzee.

That was the set-up. When every one had been properly soused dinner was announced. We seated ourselves at a long table, elegantly decorated, with three or four glasses beside each plate. The

426

ice was abundant, of course. The service began, a dozen flunkeys buzzing at your elbow like horse flies. There was a surfeit of everything; a poor man would have had sufficient with the hors-d'oeuvre alone. As they ate, they became more discursive, more argumentative. An elderly thug in a tuxedo who had the complexion of a boiled lobster was railing against labor agitators. He had a religious strain, much to my amazement, but it was more like Torquemada's than Christ's. President Roosevelt's name almost gave him an apoplectic fit. Roosevelt, Bridges, Stalin, Hitler—they were all in the same class to him. That is to say, they were anathema. He had an extraordinary appetite which served, it seemed, to stimulate his adrenal glands. By the time he had reached the meat course he was talking about hanging being too good for some people. The hostess, meanwhile, who was seated at his elbow, was carrying on one of those delightful inconsequential conversations with the person opposite her. She had left some beautiful dachshunds in Biarritz, or was it Sierra Leone, and to believe her, she was greatly worried about them. In times like these, she was saying, people forget about animals. People can be so cruel, especially in time of war. Why, in Peking the servants had run away and left her with forty trunks to pack—it was outrageous. It was so good to be back in California. God's own country, she called it. She hoped the war wouldn't spread to America. Dear me, where was one to go now? You couldn't feel safe anywhere, except in the desert perhaps.

The ex-football player was talking to some one at the far end of the table in a loud voice. It happened to be an Englishwoman and he was insulting her roundly and openly for daring to arouse sympathy for the English in this country. "Why don't you go back to England?" he shouted at the top of his voice. "What are you doing here? You're a menace. We're not fighting to hold the British Empire together. You're a menace. You ought to be expelled from the country."

The woman was trying to say that she was not English but Canadian, but she couldn't make herself heard above the din. The octogenarian, who was now sampling the champagne, was talking about the automobile accident. Nobody was paying any attention to him. Automobile accidents were too common—every one at the table had been in a smash-up at one time or another. One doesn't make a point about such things unless one is feeble-minded.

The hostess was clapping her hands frantically—she wanted to tell us a little story about an experience she had had in Africa once, on one of her safaris.

"Oh, can that!" shouted the football player. "I want to find out why this great country of ours, in the most crucial moment . . ."

"Shut up!" screamed the hostess. "You're drunk."

"That makes no difference," came his booming voice. "I want to know if we're all hundred percent Americans—and if not why not. I suspect that we have some traitors in our midst," and because I hadn't been taking part in any of the conversation he gave me a fixed, drunken look which was intended to make me declare myself. All I could do was smile. That seemed to infuriate him. His eyes roved about the table challengingly and finally, sensing an antagonist worthy of his mettle, rested on the aged, Florida-baked strike-breaker. The latter was at that moment quietly talking to the person beside him about his good friend, Cardinal So-and-so. He, the Cardinal, was always very good to the poor, I heard him say. A very gentle hard-working man, but he would tolerate no nonsense from the dirty labor agitators who were stirring up revolution, fomenting class hatred, preaching anarchy. The more he talked about his holy eminence, the Cardinal, the more he foamed at the mouth. But his rage in no way affected his appetite. He was carnivorous, bibulous, querulous, cantankerous and poisonous as a snake. One could almost see the bile spreading through his varicose veins. He was a man who had spent millions of dollars of the public's money to help the needy, as he put it. What he meant was to prevent the poor from organizing and fighting for their rights. Had he not been dressed like a banker he would have passed for a hod carrier. When he grew angry he not only became flushed but his whole body quivered like guava. He became so intoxicated by his own venom that finally he overstepped the bounds and began denouncing President Roosevelt as a crook and a traitor, among other things. One of the guests, a woman, protested. That brought the football hero to his feet. He said that no man could insult the President of the United States in his presence. The whole table was soon in an uproar. The flunkey at my elbow had just filled the huge liquor glass with some marvelous cognac. I took a sip and sat back with a grin, wondering how it would all end. The louder the altercation the more peaceful I became. *"How do you like your new boarding house, Mr. Smith?"* I heard President McKinley saying to his secretary. Every night Mr. Smith, the president's private secretary, used to visit Mr. McKinley at his home and read aloud to him the amusing letters which he had selected from the daily correspondence. The president, who was overburdened with affairs of state, used to listen silently from his big armchair by the fire: it was his sole recreation. At the end he would always ask *"How do you like your new boarding house, Mr. Smith?*" So worn out by his duties he was that he couldn't think of anything else to say at the close of these séances. Even after Mr. Smith had left his boarding house and taken a room at a hotel President McKinley continued to say "*How do you like your new boarding house, Mr. Smith?*" Then came the Exposition and Csolgosz, who had no idea what a simpleton the president was, assassinated him. There was something wretched and incongruous about murdering a man like McKinley. I remember the incident only because that same day the horse that my aunt was using for a buggy ride got the blind staggers and ran into a lamp post and when I was going to the hospital to see my aunt the extras were out already and young as I was I understood that a great tragedy had befallen the nation. At the same time I felt sorry for Csolgosz—that's the strange thing about the incident. I don't know why I felt sorry for him, except that in some vague way I realized that the punishment meted out to him would be greater than the crime merited. Even at that tender age I felt that punishment was criminal. I couldn't understand why people should be punished—I don't yet. I couldn't even understand why God had the right to punish us for our sins. And of course, as I later realized, God doesn't punish us—we punish ourselves.

Thoughts like these were floating through my head when suddenly I became aware that people were leaving the table. The meal wasn't over yet, but the guests were departing. Something had happened while I was reminiscing. Pre-civil war days, I thought to myself. Infantilism rampant again. And if Roosevelt is assassinated they will make another Lincoln of him. Only this time the slaves will still be slaves. Meanwhile I overhear some one saying what a wonderful president Melvyn Douglas would make. I prick up my ears. I wonder do they mean Melvyn Douglas, the movie star? Yes, that's who they mean. He has a great mind, the woman is saying. And character. And *savoir faire*. Thinks I to myself "and who will the vice-president be, may I ask? Shure and it's not Jimmy Cagney you're thinkin' of?" But the woman is not worried about the vice-presidency. She had been to a palmist the other day and learned some interesting things about herself. Her life line was broken. "Think of it," she said, "all these years and I never knew it was broken. What do you suppose is going to happen? Does it mean war? Or do you think it means an accident?"

The hostess was running about like a wet hen. Trying to rustle up enough hands for a game of bridge. A desperate soul, surrounded by the booty of a thousand battles. "I understand you're a writer," she said, as she tried to carom from my corner of the room to the bar. "Won't you have something to drink—a highball or something? Dear me, I don't know what's come over everybody this evening. I do hate to hear these political discussions. That young man is positively rude. Of course I don't approve of insulting the President of the United States in public but just the same he might have used a little more tact. After all, Mr. So-and-so is an elderly man. He's entitled to some respect, don't you think? Oh, there's So-and-so!" and she dashed off to greet a cinema star who had just dropped in.

The old geezer who was still tottering about handed me a highball. I tried to tell him that I didn't want any but he insisted that I take it anyway. He wanted to have a word with me, he said, winking at me as though he had something very confidential to impart.

"My name is Harrison," he said. "H-a-r-r-i-s-o-n," spelling it out as if it were a difficult name to remember.

"Now what is your name, may I ask?"

"My name is Miller—M-i-l-l-e-r," I answered, spelling it out in Morse for him.

"Miller! Why, that's a very easy name to remember. We had a druggist on our block by that name. Of course. *Miller*. Yes, a very common name."

"So it is," I said.

"And what are you doing out here, Mr. Miller? You're a stranger, I take it?"

"Yes," I said, "I'm just a visitor."

"You're in business, are you?"

"No, hardly. I'm just visiting California."

"I see. Well, where do you come from—the Middle West?"

"No, from New York."

"From New York City? Or from up State?"

"From the city."

"And have you been here very long?"

"No, just a few hours."

"A few hours? My, my . . . well, that's interesting. Very interesting. And will you be staying long, Mr. Miller?"

"I don't know. It depends."

"I see. Depends on how you like it here, is that it?"

"Yes, exactly."

"Well, it's a grand part of the world, I can tell you that. No place like California, I always say. Of course I'm not a native. But I've been out here almost thirty years now. Wonderful climate. And wonderful people, too."

"I suppose so," I said, just to string him along. I was curious to see how long the idiot would keep up his infernal nonsense.

"You're not in business you say?"

"No, I'm not."

"On a vacation, is that it?"

"No, not precisely. I'm an ornithologist, you see."

"A what? Well, that's interesting."

"*Very*," I said, with great solemnity.

"Then you may be staying with us for a while, is that it?"

"That's hard to say. I may stay a week and I may stay a year. It all depends. Depends on what specimens I find."

"I see. Interesting work, no doubt."

"*Very!*"

"Have you ever been to California before, Mr. Miller?"

"Yes, twenty-five years ago."

"Well, well, is that so? *Twenty-five years ago!* And now you're back again."

"Yes, back again."

"Were you doing the same thing when you were here before?"

"You mean ornithology?"

"Yes, that's it."

"No, I was digging ditches then."

"Digging ditches? You mean you were—*digging ditches?*"

"Yes, that's it, Mr. Harrison. It was either dig ditches or starve to death."

"Well, I'm glad you don't have to dig ditches any more. It's not much fun—*digging ditches*, is it?"

"No, especially if the ground is hard. Or if your back is weak. Or vice versa. Or let's say your mother has just been put in the mad house and the alarm goes off too soon."

"I beg your pardon! *What did you say?*"

"If things are not just right, I said. You know what I mean—bunions, lumbago, scrofula. It's different now, of course. I have my birds and other pets. Mornings I used to watch the sun rise. Then I would saddle the jackasses—I had two and the other fellow had three. . . ."

"This was in California, Mr. Miller?"

"Yes, twenty-five years ago. I had just done a stretch in San Quentin. . . ."

"*San Quentin?*"

"Yes, attempted suicide. I was really gaga but that didn't make any difference to them. You see, when my father set the house afire one of the horses kicked me in the temple. I used to get fainting fits and then after a time I got homicidal spells and finally

I became suicidal. Of course I didn't know that the revolver was loaded. I took a pot shot at my sister, just for fun, and luckily I missed her. I tried to explain it to the judge but he wouldn't listen to me. I never carry a revolver any more. If I have to defend myself I use a jack-knife. The best thing, of course, is to use your knee. . . ."

"Excuse me, Mr. Miller, I have to speak to Mrs. So-and-so a moment. Very interesting what you say. *Very interesting indeed.* We must talk some more. Excuse me just a moment. . . ."

I slipped out of the house unnoticed and started to walk towards the foot of the hill. The highballs, the red and the white wines, the champagne, the cognac were gurgling inside me like a sewer. I had no idea where I was, whose house I had been in or whom I had been introduced to. Perhaps the boiled thug was an ex-Governor of the State. Perhaps the hostess was an ex-movie star, a light that had gone out forever. I remembered that some one had whispered in my ear that So-and-so had made a fortune in the opium traffic in China. Lord Haw-Haw probably. The Englishwoman with the horse face may have been a prominent novelist—or just a charity worker. I thought of my friend Fred, now Private Alfred Perlès, No. 13802023 in the 137th Pioneer Corps or something like that. Fred would have sung the Lorelei at the dinner table or asked for a better brand of cognac or made grimaces at the hostess. Or he might have gone to the telephone and called up Gloria Swanson, pretending to be Aldous Huxley or Chatto & Windus of Wimbledon. Fred would never have permitted the dinner to become a fiasco. Everything else failing he would have slipped his silky paw in some one's bosom, saying as he always did—"The left one is better. Fish it out, won't you please?"

I think frequently of Fred in moving about the country. He was always so damned eager to see America. His picture of America was something like Kafka's. It would be a pity to disillusion him. And yet who can say? He might enjoy it hugely. He might not see anything but what he chose to see. I remember my visit to his own Vienna. Certainly it was not the Vienna I had dreamed of. And yet today, when I think of Vienna, I see the Vienna of my dreams and not the one with bed bugs and broken zithers and stinking drains.

I wobble down the canyon road. It's very Californian somehow. I like the scrubby hills, the weeping trees, the desert coolness. I had expected more fragrance in the air.

The stars are out in full strength. Turning a bend in the road I catch a glimpse of the city below. The illumination is more faërique than in other American cities. The red seems to predominate. A few hours ago, towards dusk, I had a glimpse of it from the bedroom window of the woman on the hill. Looking at it through the mirror on her dressing table it seemed even more magical. It was like looking into the future from the narrow window of an oubliette. Imagine the Marquis de Sade looking at the city of Paris through the bars of his cell in the Bastille. Los Angeles gives one the feeling of the future more strongly than any city I know of. A bad future, too, like something out of Fritz Lang's feeble imagination. *Good-bye, Mr. Chips!*

Walking along one of the Neon-lit streets. A shop window with Nylon stockings. Nothing in the window but a glass leg filled with water and a sea horse rising and falling like a feather sailing through heavy air. Thus we see how Surrealism penetrates to every nook and corner of the world. Dali meanwhile is in Bowling Green, Va., thinking up a loaf of bread 30 feet high by 125 feet long, to be removed from the oven stealthily while every one sleeps and placed very circumspectly in the main square of a big city, say Chicago or San Francisco. Just a loaf of bread, enormous of course. No raison d'être. No propaganda. And tomorrow night two loaves of bread, placed simultaneously in two big cities, say New York and New Orleans. Nobody knows who brought them or why they are there. And the next night three loaves of bread—one in Berlin or Bucharest this time. And so on, ad infinitum. Tremendous, no? Would push the war news off the front page. That's what Dali thinks, at any rate. Very interesting. *Very interesting, indeed.* Excuse me now, I have to talk to a lady over in the corner. . . .

Tomorrow I will discover Sunset Boulevard. Eurythmic dancing, ball room dancing, tap dancing, artistic photography, ordinary photography, lousy photography, electro-fever treatment, internal douche treatment, ultra-violet ray treatment, elocution lessons, psychic readings, institutes of religion, astrological demonstrations, hands read, feet manicured, elbows massaged, faces lifted, warts removed, fat reduced, insteps raised, corsets fitted, busts vibrated, corns removed, hair dyed, glasses fitted, soda jerked, hangovers cured, headaches driven away, flatulence dissipated, business improved, limousines rented, the future made clear, the war made comprehensible, octane made higher and butane lower, drive in and get indigestion, flush the kidneys, get a cheap car wash, stay awake pills and go to sleep pills, Chinese herbs are very good for you and without a Coca-cola life is unthinkable. From the car window it's like a strip teaser doing the St. Vitus dance—a corny one.

The Staff of Life

Bread: prime symbol. Try and find a good loaf. You can travel fifty thousand miles in America without once tasting a piece of good bread. Americans don't care about good bread. They are dying of inanition but they go on eating bread without substance, bread without flavor, bread without vitamins, bread without life. Why? Because the very core of life is contaminated. If they knew what good bread was they would not have such wonderful machines on which they lavish all their time, energy and affection. A plate of false teeth means much more to an American than a loaf of good bread. Here is the sequence: poor bread, bad teeth, indigestion, constipation, halitosis, sexual starvation, disease and accidents, the operating table, artificial limbs, spectacles, baldness, kidney and bladder trouble, neurosis, psychosis, schizophrenia, war and famine. Start with the American loaf of bread so beautifully wrapped in cellophane and you end on the scrap heap at forty-five. The only place to find a good loaf of bread is in the ghettos. Wherever there is a foreign quarter there is apt to be good bread. Wherever there is a Jewish grocer or delicatessen you are almost certain to find an excellent loaf of bread. The dark Russian bread, light in weight, found only rarely on this huge continent, is the best bread of all. No vitamins have been injected into it by laboratory specialists in conformance with the latest food regulations. The Russian just naturally likes good bread, because he also likes caviar and vodka and other good things. Americans are whiskey, gin and beer drinkers who long ago lost their taste for food. And losing that they have also lost their taste for life. For enjoyment. For good conversation. For everything worth while, to put it briefly.

What do I find wrong with America? Everything. I begin at the beginning, with the staff of life: bread. If the bread is bad the whole life is bad. Bad? Rotten, I should say. Like that piece of bread only twenty-four hours old which is good for nothing except perhaps to fill up a hole. Good for target practice maybe. Or shuttlecock and duffle board. Even soaked in urine it is unpalatable; even perverts shun it. Yet millions are wasted advertising it. Who are the men engaged in this wasteful pursuit? Drunkards and failures for the most part. Men who have prostituted their talents in order to help further the decay and dissolution of our once glorious Republic.

Here is one of the latest widely advertised products: Hollywood Bread. On the red, white and blue cellophane jacket in which it is wrapped, this last word in bread from the American bakeries, it reads as follows:

BAKED WITH

whole wheat flour, clear wheat flour, water, non-diastatic malt, yeast, salt, honey, caramel, whole rye flour, yeast food, stone ground oatmeal, soya flour, gluten flour, barley flour, sesame seed, and a small quantity of dehydrated (water free) vegetables including celery, lettuce, pumpkin, cabbage, carrots, spinach, parsley, sea kelp, added for flavor only.

The only thing missing from this concoction is powdered diamonds. How does it taste? Much like any other American product. Of course, this is a reducing bread of which one should eat two slices a day three times a day and not ask how it tastes. Grow thin, as in Hollywood, and be thankful it doesn't taste worse. That's the idea. For several days now I have been trying to get a whiff of some of those ingredients—sea kelp especially—which were included "for flavor only." Why they were not added for health too I don't know. Naturally all these delicious-sounding items amount to about one ten-thousandth part of the loaf. And on the second day, stale, flat and unprofitable, this marvelous new bread is no more attractive to the palate or the stomach than any other loaf of American bread. On the second day it is good for replacing a missing tile on the roof. Or to make a scratchboard for the cat.

The second day! If the first is given to creation, to light, let us say, the second (in America) is given up to garbage. Every second day is garbage day in America. I know because I have had lots to do with garbage. I've hauled it, for pay, and I've eaten it upon necessity. I learned to distinguish between one kind of bread and another by salvaging dry crusts from the garbage can. I don't know which is worse—the day of creation, when everything turns to gas and bilge, with its concomitants dandruff, constipation, halitosis, false teeth, artificial limbs, psychic impotency, and so on, or the second day, given up to garbage, when all creation turns out to be nothing but a mirage and a disillusionment. It has been said, and I have no doubt it is true, that the garbage accumulated by one big American city would feed certain of the little countries of Europe handsomely. I know no quicker way to kill off the warring nations of Europe than to feed them our garbage. The pygmies might thrive on it, possibly even the Chinese coolie, who is supposed to thrive on anything, but I cannot see the Danes, the Swiss, the Swedes, the Greeks, the Albanians, or the Austrians thriving on it. No Sir. I would sooner feed them buzzards than the left-overs from the American table. Already, with our canned food products, our cold storage meat, our dehydrated vegetables, we have brought about a tremendous deterioration in these sturdy people of Europe. From these to the machine and thence to war is but a step. Then, famine, plague, pestilence, dung heaps. And monuments, of course. All sorts of monuments. Done by second or third rate artists.

The care and affection which once was bestowed on the human body now goes to the machines. The machines get the best food, the best attention. Machines are expensive; human lives are cheap. Never in the history of the world was life cheaper than it is to-day. (And no pyramids to show for it either.) How natural, then, that the staff of life should be utterly without value. I begin with bread and I shall end with bread. I say we make the foulest breads in all the world. We pass it off like fake diamonds. We advertise it and sterilize it and protect it from all the germs of life. We make a manure which we eat before we have had time to eliminate it. We not only have failed God, tricked Nature, debased Man, but we have cheated the birds of the air with our corrupt staff of life. Everytime I fling the stale bread over the cliff I beg forgiveness of the birds for offering them our American bread. Perhaps that is why they are not singing any more as they used to when I was a child. The birds are pining and drooping. It's not the war, for they have never participated in our carnages. It's the bread. The stale, flat, unprofitable bread of the second day. It shortens their wing-span, weakens their umbrella-ribs, reduces the scope of their swoop, blunts their beaks, deteriorates their vision, and finally—it kills their song! If you don't believe me, ask my ornithologist. It's a known fact. And how Americans love facts!

Another fact. . . . Food, when it is not enjoyed, kills. The best diet in the world is useless if the patient has no appetite, no gusto, no sensuality. On the whole, Americans eat without pleasure. They eat because the bell rings three times a day. (I omit mention of the clay eaters of the South and other poor whites who live on rats, snakes, and cow-dung.) They don't eat because they love food. To prove it you have only to shove a glass of whiskey before them. See which they reach for first! And now, with vitamins and all the other life-savers, food has become even less important. Why bother trying to squeeze a bit of life out of our worn-out products of the soil? Why pretend? Throw anything down the hatch to stop the gnawing and swallow a dozen vitamins. That way you'll make sure you've had your proper dose of the vital essentials. Should the vitamins fail, see a surgeon. From there to the sanitarium. And from there to the nut-house—or the dung heap. Be sure to get a Hollywood funeral. They're the loveliest, the duckiest, the most sanitary, the most inspiring. And no more expensive than ordinary ground burial. You can, if you like, have your dear lost one propped up in a natural reclining position, her cheeks rouged, a cigarette to her lips, and a phonograph record talking to you just as she once talked to you in life. The most wonderful fake imaginable. Jolly, what? O death, where is thy sting? What's more, she can be kept that way for an unspeakably long period; the cigarette is guaranteed not to rot away before the lips or the buttocks. You can come back and have a second, a third, a twenty-fifth look at the beloved. Still smoking a cigarette. Or you can have her reading a book, the *Iliad*, say, or the *Bhagavad Gita*—something uplifting like that.

I remember when I used to be served a slice of home-made bread with butter and sugar smeared over it. Glorious days! That bread really had a taste. *Schmecht gut, nichtwahr? Yah! Sehr gut. Wunderbar. Ausgezeichnet.* With a piece of bread like that I used to sit and read *Pinocchio* or *Alice Through the Looking Glass* or Hans Christian Andersen or *The Heart of a Boy*. Mothers had time in those days to make good bread with their own hands, and still do the thousand and one things which motherhood demands of a woman. To-day they haven't time to do anything, and hardly a bloody mother in the bloody land knows how to bake a loaf of bread. Mother gets up early now to work in an office or a factory. She's busy doing nothing all day, which is to say—earning a living. Earning a living has nothing to do with living. It's the belt line to the grave, without a transfer or a stopover. A one-way passage via the frying pan and the cookerless cooker. A child is an accident— bad rubber goods or else too much drink and recklessness. Any way, it's there and it has to be fed. You don't bake bread for accidents, do you? And why bother to produce milk from the breast when the cows are working over-time for the dairy companies of America?

Day by day the morons, epileptics and schizoids multiply. By accident, like everything else. Nothing is planned in America except improvements. And all improvements are for the machine. When a plenum is reached war is declared. Then the machine really gets going. War is a Roman Holiday for the machine. Man becomes even less than nothing then. The machine is well fed. The food products become plastics and plastics are what make the world go round. Better to have a good steering wheel than a good stomach. In the old days an army advanced on its stomach; now it advances in tanks or spitfires or super-fortresses. Civilians never advance. Civilians always rot and help make insurance companies richer.

But bread. . . . Let's not forget, it's bread we want—and children that are not accidents brought about by defective rubber or bathtub gin. How to get it? Bread, I mean. By putting a monkey wrench in the machine. By going backwards on all fours, like giraffes with broken necks. By praying for life now and not hereafter. By exercising freedom and not inventing four, five or six freedoms won by the slaughter and starvation of twenty or thirty millions. Begin today by baking your own bread. First of all you need a stove. A wood or a coal stove. Not a gas range. Not an electric apparatus. Then let the flies in. Then roll your sleeves up and get your hands in the dough. Lick your fingers. Never mind if you lose your job. Eat your bread first, then maybe you won't want to work in an office or a factory. Life begins with bread. And a prayer. Not a begging prayer, but a prayer of thanks. Don't bless the block-busters. Bless God for his favors—air, water, sun, moon. God wants you to enjoy the bread of life. He never meant you to go out all day working at a job you loathe so that you can buy a loaf of store bread wrapped in cellophane. God gave us germs as well as air and water and sun. Germs attack only what is already rotting. Man is rotting in every fibre of his being: that is why he is a prey to germs. And that is why he is allergic to everything that is for his own good.

Before Communism was there was Communion and before that there was God and God said let there be light and there was light. And what a glorious light it was. It lasted for aeons, and then came the scientific age and darkness fell upon the land everywhere. Now everything can be proved backwards and out of existence and instead of soaring with our own wings or on the backs of our giant birds we make things of metal and plastics which spread havoc and destruction in their wake. We throw bones to the dogs and eat the dogs instead of the bones. Not one step has been taken towards improving the flow of milk from the mammary glands. Only mothers and wet nurses give milk, whereas with time and experimentation every one could give milk and the food problem would be solved for eternity. We wouldn't even need to sit down to eat: now and then a step-ladder might be necessary, but nothing more. Why hasn't any one thought of that? Is it so improbable? Ants have their milk cows—how did that happen? Anyway, with human milk the universal food, with manna falling from heaven, and nectar and ambrosia for dessert, think what a lot of work would be eliminated. Think too of the gratitude the animals would show, once they got on to the new scheme of things. All we would need, men and animals, would be one huge grass plot. No more dairy companies, no more containers, no more bottles, plates, knives and forks, spoons, pots, pans, stoves. The solution of the food problem would throw a monkey wrench into the entire economic and social system; our mores would change, our religions would disappear, our money become valueless. One can hardly imagine what the cause of war would then be, though doubtless a good excuse will always be found.

Outside of the foreign quarters, then, take it for granted that there is no good bread to be had. Every foreign group has introduced into our life some good substantial bread, even the Scandinavians. (Excepting the English, I should add, but then we hardly think of them as foreign, though why we shouldn't I don't know, for when you think of it the English are even less like us than the Poles or Latvians.) In a Jewish restaurant you usually have a basket filled with all kinds of bread from which to choose. In a typical American restaurant, should you ask for rye, whole wheat or any other kind of bread but the insidious, unwholesome, and unpalatable white, you get white bread. If you insist on rye bread you get whole wheat. If you insist on whole wheat you get graham bread. Once in a great while you come upon nut bread; this is always a sheer accident. Raisin bread is a sort of decoy to lure you into eating unpalatable, perfidious and debilitating white bread. When in doubt go to a Jewish restaurant or delicatessen; if necessary, stand up and eat a sandwich made of sour rye, sweet butter, pastrami and pickle. A Jewish sandwich contains more food value than an eighty-five cent meal in the ordinary American restaurant. With a glass of water to wash it down you can walk away feeling fit. Don't sit down and eat a Jewish meal, because the Jews are bad cooks despite their great concern about food, which amounts to a neurosis. It is curious, though, how the desire to survive has made the Jews keen about preserving the staff of life. It is even more curious that they are just as much riddled with disease as the other members of the community—more so, in fact, judging purely from personal observation. They not only have all the physical ailments which other white peoples are heir to but they have all the mental and nervous ailments. Often they have everything at once, and then they concentrate upon food with even greater acuity and despair. It is only when they become revolutionary that they begin to lose interest in food. The real American, on the other hand, though totally unrevolutionary at heart, seems born with an indifference to food. One can serve a white American food which would make an Igorote turn up his nose. Americans can eat garbage, provided you sprinkle it liberally with ketchup, mustard, chili sauce, tabasco sauce, cayenne pepper, or any other condiment which destroys the original flavor of the dish. On the other hand, olive oil which the French eschew when preparing salads because it has too strong a flavor, Americans hardly ever use in their salads. Nothing on God's earth is more uninviting, more anaemic, than the American salad. At its best it is like refined puke. The lettuce is a joke: even a canary would refuse to touch it. This concoction, mind you, is usually served before the meal, together with the coffee which is cold by the time you are ready to drink it. The moment you sit down at a table in the ordinary American restaurant, the moment you begin scanning the menu, the waitress asks you what you wish to drink. (If by chance you should say "cocoa," the whole kitchen would be thrown out of gear.) To this question I usually counter with another: "Do you have anything but white bread?" If the answer is not a flat No, it is: "We have whole wheat," or "We have graham bread." Whereupon I usually mumble under my breath: "You can stick that up your ass!" When she says, "What did you say?" I reply, "Do you have rye bread by any chance?" Then, before she can say no, I launch into an elaborate explanation of the fact that I don't mean by rye bread the ordinary rye bread, which is no better than white, graham, or whole wheat, but a succulent, tasty, dark, sour rye such as the Russians and the Jews serve. At the mention of these two suspect nationalities a scowl spreads over her face. While she is saying in her most sarcastic voice that she is sorry but they do not have that kind of rye bread or any rye bread, for that matter, I begin asking about the fruit, what kinds of fruit, fresh fruit, they have on hand, knowing damned well that they haven't any. Nine times out of ten her answer will be: "We have apple pie, and peach pie." ("Stick it up your ass!") "I beg your pardon?" she says. "Yes, fruit . . . you know, the kind that grows on trees . . . apples, pears, bananas, plums, oranges . . . something with skin on it that you peel." Whereupon a light dawns and she hastens to interpolate: "Oh, but we have apple sauce!" ("Fuck your apple sauce!") "I beg pardon?" Here I look leisurely round the room, surveying the shelves, the counter, the pie plates. Finally, resting my gaze upon a bowl of artificial fruit, I exclaim with glee: "Like that over there, *only real!*"

Sometimes, upon scanning the menu and knowing that it will only give me a belly-ache, I ask immediately if they can serve me a large bowl of fresh fruit. Here, incidentally, let me call attention to the dishes of mixed fruit prepared early in the morning which stand rotting in disgusting sweet canned juices until lunch or dinner hour. In the Automat type of restaurant one sees the counter piled with these vile stews. These, like the salads mentioned a moment ago, and like the pies fabricated by the wholesale bakers (who are probably responsible for more deaths than all our wars put together), are peculiar to the American temperament. There is not the least food value in any of them. The salad is at its worst when served in one of those delightful little inns run by spinsters in villages of imaginary charm, such as one is supposed to find in Vermont, Maryland, or Connecticut. Here everything looks immaculate and is immaculate, and therefore without value, without flavor, without joy. One suddenly feels like a canary which has been castrated and can no longer warble or differentiate between seed and salad. Beginning with this obscene salad one just knows that the meal is going to end with a charming little dessert such as prune whip or vanilla ice cream. To ask for a grape or a herring in one of these places is like committing sacrilege. There are certain things you must never ask for in an American restaurant. Never. One is good sour rye such as the Russians and the Jews make. Another is a cup of strong coffee. (Exceptions: French and Italian restaurants, and Louisiana. In Louisiana you can get a cup of coffee that is like liquid dynamite. But it tastes good; it has chicory in it. And chicory is excellent, despite all opinion to the contrary.) A third is cheese. A fourth is grapes. A fifth is nuts. Never have I seen a bowl of assorted and uncracked nuts put on the table in an American restaurant. Now and then, rarely, very rarely, one sees nuts in an American home. Usually, however, they are there as decoration. The fruit likewise. Fruit and nuts belong on the sideboard for the children, when there are any, to nibble at. The mixed fruit, or fruit salad, as they have the impudence to call it in America, reaches the height of abomination in the arm-chair Automat type of restaurant. Have you ever noticed the derelicts who frequent these eating places, sitting in the show window munching their lunch or dinner? Is there any more lugubrious sight on earth? (The corollary to it is the cheap traveling salesman type of hotel where all day long the weary commercial traveler sits in an enormous leather armchair staring vacantly out on the street. This is the type who gets orders for useless commodities which the American slave toils his ass off to accumulate, which he sells to his own kind and pretends thereby that he is earning an honest living. This is the type that votes the Democratic or Republican ticket year in and year out, in lean years and fat years, in war and in peace, and is always complaining that business is bad. This is the most traveled man in the world, and yet he knows nothing, absolutely nothing, and brags about it. This is the type who when you mention China says immediately—"coolies." If there is any more ignominious coolie than the traveling salesman I have yet to know him. The fact that he reads the "Digest" or some other compilation of facts gives him the illusion that he is informed and a useful member of society.)

But it's the pie that takes the cake. The pie is at its worst in the Greek restaurant, often called "New York Café," and encountered in every village and hamlet throughout the length and breadth of the land. In fact, everything is at its worst in this type of eating place. But it's here that the pie becomes positively obsessive. Often there is nothing to offer the weary traveler but pie. There they stand, row upon row of pie plates, all filled with gangrene and arsenic. The crust looks like scurf and is scurf, usually of the finest rancid grease made by the Criscomaniacs of America. Here and there one can detect in a whole pie a piece of fruit, such as apple or peach; it is surrounded by a clot of phlegm swimming in a mess of undefinable paste. The piece of apple or peach is sourish, bilious, gaseous, having no more resemblance to the apple or peach in its native state than corn whiskey has to corn on the cob. The Greek proprietor delights in serving white Americans this unholy dish; he despises them for eating it, but, canny business man that he is, he believes in giving them what they ask for. He himself has a totally different cuisine, a damned good one, too, I must say, if you ever make a friend of him and get invited to his home. On his table you will see olives, real olives, okra, olive oil, fruits of all kinds, nuts, rice, vine leaves, the tenderest lamb imaginable, wines of all kind, including retsina, and cognac, Greek cognac, and other delicacies.

Let us digress here a moment. . . . How is it that Americans, composed of nothing but foreign nationalities, living amongst people accustomed to the most varied cuisines, people who have made an art of cooking from time immemorial, continue to be the worst cooks in the world, continue to open one foul restaurant after another? Explain it, if you can. To me it's an enigma. The more mixed becomes the blood in our veins, the more American we become. And by American I mean the more set, crass, conservative, prejudiced, stupid, narrow-minded, unexperimental and unrevolutionary. In every big city we have Chinese, Italian, French, Hungarian, Russian, German, Swedish restaurants. Do we learn anything from these skilled restaurateurs? No, not a thing. We go our way, serving pies, mixed fruit salads, hamburgers, baked beans, steak and onions, vicious veal cutlets, whether breaded or unbreaded, and so on. Has any one ever had a good stew in an American restaurant? The peasants of Europe have thrived on stews for centuries. Here a stew means a couple of spoonfuls of superannuated meat swimming in a tiny pool of grease and bilge with bloated potatoes as a garniture. One hasn't begun to eat when the meal is over. It's an imaginary stew at the best. And the most imaginary part of it is the vegetables without which no stew is complete: leeks, carrots, turnips, onions, celery, parsley, and so on. If you find a tiny piece of any other vegetable than the potato you are indeed a lucky individual.

All right, steak then! Steak is the great American dish. Steak and onions. Fine. Nothing better, I say. Where can you get it? I mean without paying $2.50 per person! The first and only time I got the real flavor of steak was when I passed through Denver. Up till then I never knew what a real steak tasted like. The meat companies are for convincing us that meat from the refrigerator, meat that has been on ice several years, is the best meat of all. The whole world is being shipped and fed this cold storage meat, thanks to Armour & Co. and their subsidiary hog-butchers. In France I used to eat *filet de boeuf* practically every other day. It cost, for one person, a good portion, mind you, from twelve to eighteen cents, at the rate of exchange prevailing in the late thirties. It was delicious meat, and I knew how to prepare it. (Americans as a rule know only how to spoil a good piece of meat in cooking it.) When I came to America, in 1940, I went to the butcher one day and asked for my customary *filet de boeuf*. A piece for two people came to $1.10, so help me God. I couldn't believe my ears. And this was in a cheap butcher shop on Third Avenue, New York. Christ only knows what it would have cost in the Park Avenue neighborhood. I took it home and I fried it. I did everything just as I used to at the Villa Seurat. I had wine with it too, the best I could buy for $1.25 the bottle. I also had grapes and nuts, and a salad prepared with the best olive oil. I had several kinds of cheese, including roquefort and camembert. Despite all precautions the meal didn't taste the same. There was something lacking. As a matter of fact, all the essentials were lacking. A piece of lettuce grown in America is like a piece of lettuce grown in France only in looks and name. American fruit, the most sensational looking fruit in the world (barring the tropics), is practically tasteless compared to the sicklier looking European fruits. American cheeses look delicious, and God knows the Kraft Brothers have tickled them up inordinately, but they do not have the flavor of the cheeses they are made to imitate. A stale piece of Camembert in a dirty French restaurant is worth a whole box of beautiful looking fresh Camembert put out by the crafty cheese-makers of Wisconsin. The flat Dutch cheeses are of course still more flat and tasteless when you eat them in America, being as they are the product of the most pampered cows in all the world. Wines, even when they are good, and in the realm of ordinary table wines America makes some of the best, do not taste as good as in Europe, perhaps because the atmosphere, the violence, the tempo of American life destroys whatever blessings wine confers.

Wine with the meal, in America, produces the wrong result. What is required, when attempting to digest American food, is strong spirits—whiskey, gin, cocktails. The correct procedure is to get soused beforehand; this enables one to eat without noticing how vile the food is. It gets one flushed and excited, and the food is forgotten. It makes one argumentative, which aids in bringing on indigestion and dyspepsia, flatulence, constipation, hemorrhoids, and finally the operating table. Whichever road you take, in America, you always wind up at the surgeon's door. If you buy an automobile it's the surgeon you have to reckon with eventually. If you take a good-paying job, it's the surgeon who will bleed you to death. If you economize and eat in arm-chair restaurants, or the Greek restaurants (where American food is served—not the real Greek restaurant!), you meet the surgeon sooner or later, generally sooner. If you take to the soil and live the outdoor life, you first must have all your teeth pulled out and plates inserted. Farmers have about the worst teeth of all, even worse than factory workers. They have all the physical ailments, too, and are often as not undernourished. Farmers die of inanition in the midst of plenty. There isn't anything you can do, in America, by way of earning a living whereby you can escape dire taxation, disease, accident, misery and humiliation. At the end of every road stands the surgeon, who is for Americans what Nemesis was for the Greeks. The whole culture of America springs from two lunatics: the Marquis de Sade and Sacher Masoch. Justice, always retributive, is apotheosized by the surgeon. His henchmen are the dentists. If you have an ache or pain never mention it to the dentist, or he will immediately extract all your teeth. Nowadays even cowboys are proud of their false teeth. Scarcely any hard-working American, however splendid his physique, is without plates or bridges after forty. Hardly any normal American has a full head of hair after forty. Hardly any American over twenty-one, whether he works hard or takes it easy, is without eye-glasses. Almost every American suffers from hemorrhoids. Practically every American over forty has a bad heart. Cancer, syphilis, arthritis, tuberculosis, schizophrenia are so prevalent that we accept them as part of the bargain—i.e., the American way of life. Nearly every family boasts of one moron among its members, one lunatic, one drunkard, one pervert. All the food advertisements boast of the vitamin contents of their products. All the medicaments advertised boast of their cure for every thing under the sun. It is obvious that our foods lack the proper vitamins, just as it is obvious that in employing these health foods so rich in vitamins we nevertheless are afflicted with all the diseases known to man. We die young, mortgaged to the hilt, insolvent, despite all the insurance policies issued by all the insurance companies whose tentacles reach into every avenue of commercial and industrial life. It is also evident that, despite the fact that this is the land of opportunity where freedom reigns, where every one has the right to worship and the right to vote for the wrong candidate, that the zest for life is so low that less than one child per family is now produced, except among certain Indian tribes, certain religious communities, certain strata of poor whites, and among the Negroes as a whole. Even the Jews, known for their big families as well as their good bread, are beginning to have less children—in America. And when the Jew loses his desire to perpetuate his own kind there must indeed be something seriously wrong with the national life. In the poorest countries of Europe the Jew still remained fertile; here, with everything in his grasp, except recognition by the Gentiles, he withers away. Only among the American Indians, and there only in certain tribes, is the population on the increase. It is said that this is due in part to the practice of polygamy. And here we touch another tender subject, one almost as potent as bread. I mean the fear among native white Americans of indulging in any other form of marriage but that sponsored by the Christian churches. Why not polygamy? Why not polyandry? Why not any kind of marriage, including love marriages? With polygamy the Mormons were fast on the way to building an empire. Nobody can say that the Mormons are, or ever were, an undesirable element in the great American community. They were and still are one of the few communities in this country where poverty is relatively unknown. They produce less criminals than other parts of the country—and less morons, and less idiots, and less trouble of any nature. And God knows they were never, never more immoral than the other members of the community.

On the contrary, they were not only more law-abiding, more peaceful, more prosperous, more social-minded and far-visioned than the other communities of America, but they were absolutely more moral in the strictest sense of the word, that is, in the sense that they actually practised what they preached.

But to get back to bread . . . Today the mailman brought three kinds of bread: Italian bread, a milk loaf, and pumpernickel. (No sour rye, of course, no corn bread.) The bread comes from Monterey, the nearest town, which is fifty miles away. In Monterey there is no Jewish grocer or delicatessen, worse luck. In Monterey there are Mexicans, Portuguese and Filipinos, but who gives a damn what these poor devils eat? The Mexicans have their tortillas, the Portuguese their garlic, and the Filipinos . . . well, among other things they have all our bad habits. Nobody in Monterey has a good slice of bread to eat. Nor in Carmel either, unless it's Robinson Jeffers, and that would be a sacramental bread. Just outside of carmel lives Edward Weston, the photographer. And that leads me to speak of another kind of bread: photographic bread. Have you ever noticed that even the photographic bread tastes poorly? Have you ever seen a piece of bread photographed by our advertising maniacs which you would like to bite into? I haven't. Edward Weston could undoubtedly make you the most wonderful photographic bread conceivable—*but could you eat it?* The bread you hang on your wall is not the bread you want to eat at table. Even a piece of bread by Man Ray would prove unpalatable, particularly if he just happened to be reading his favorite author, the Marquis de Sade. Sacher Masoch might have made a good bread, if he had lived long enough. It has a Kosher sound, *Sacher Masoch*. But in the long run I have a feeling it would make one morbid and introspective, this Sacher Masoch bread.

I have now found that the only way to eat our most unwholesome, unpalatable and unappetizing American bread, the staff of our unsavory and monotonous life, is to adopt the following procedure. This is a recipe, so please follow instructions to the letter.

To begin with, accept any loaf that is offered you without question, even if it is not wrapped in cellophane, even if it contains no kelp. Throw it in the back of the car with the oil can and the grease rags; if possible, bury it under a sack of coal, *bituminous coal*. As you climb up the road to your home, drop it in the mud a few times and dig your heels into it. If you have a dog with you, let him pee on it now and then. When you get to the house, and after you have prepared the other dishes, take a huge carving knife and rip the loaf from stem to stern. Then take one whole onion, peeled or unpeeled, one carrot, one stalk of celery, one huge piece of garlic, one sliced apple, a herring, a handful of anchovies, a sprig of parsley, and an old toothbrush and shove them into the disembowelled guts of the bread. Over these pour first a thimbleful of kerosene, a dash of Lavoris and just a wee bit of Clorox; then sprinkle guts liberally with the following—molasses, honey, orange marmalade, vanilla, soy bean sauce, tabasco sauce, ketchup and arnica. Over this add a layer of chopped nuts, assorted nuts, of course, a few bay leaves (whole), some marjoram, and a stick of licorice cut into fine pieces. Put the loaf in the oven for ten minutes and serve. If it is still lacking in taste whip up a chili con carne piping hot and mix bread with it until it becomes a thick gruel. If this fails, piss on it and throw it to the dog. But under no circumstances feed it to the birds. The birds of North America are already on the decline, as I pointed out earlier. Their beaks have become dull, their wing-span shortened; they are pining and drooping, moulting in season and out. Above all, they no longer sing as they used to; they make sour notes, they bleat instead of tweeting, and sometimes, when the fogs set in, they have even been heard to cackle and wheeze.

Astrological Fricassee

I met Gerald in the lobby of a theatre during the intermission. I had hardly been presented to him when he asked me what my birth date was.

"December 26th, 1891 . . . 12.30 noon . . . New York City . . . Conjunction of Mars, Uranus and the Moon in the 8th house. Does that help?"

He was delighted. "Then you know something about astrology," he said, beaming at me as if I were a devoted disciple.

Just then a dashing young woman came up and greeted Gerald warmly. Gerald quickly presented us to one another. "December 26th, meet April 4th . . . Capricorn—Aries . . . You should get along beautifully together."

I never got the dashing young woman's name nor she mine. That was utterly unimportant to Gerald. People existed merely to corroborate his celestial theorems. He knew in advance what every one was like—quintessentially, that is. In a way, he was like an X-ray specialist. He looked immediately at your astral skeleton. Where the unobserving saw only a Milky Way, Gerald saw constellations, planets, asteroids, shooting stars, nebulae and so on.

"Don't make any important plans the next few days," he would say. "Just lay low for a while. Your Mars is squared with your Mercury. It won't do any good to make decisions now. Wait till the moon is full . . . You're inclined to be rather impulsive, aren't you?" And he'd give his victim a sly, inquisitive look, as though to say: "You can't fool me, you know. I see right through you."

There was a lot of handshaking going on in the lobby during that intermission. Every one was introduced by his celestial monniker. There seemed to be a preponderance of Pisces individuals about—tepid, kindly, milk-and-water creatures who were inclined to be pop-eyed and lymphatic. I kept a weather eye open for Scorpios

448

and Leos, especially of the female variety. The Aquarians I gave a wide berth.

In the restaurant later that evening Gerald and I got down to brass tacks. I don't remember what he said he was—perhaps Gemini or Virgo—but in any case he was damned slippery. There was something androgynous about him too. He seemed to be wound up about Libra, Leo and Sagittarius. Now and then he made some periphrastic remarks about Capricorn—cautiously, guardedly, as if he were sprinkling salt on a bird's tail.

He talked a lot about the various bodily organs, as well as the joints, muscles, mucous membranes and other parts of the body. He advised his host, who had recently been run over by a truck, to be careful of his knee-caps next month. The young lady on my left was to watch her kidneys—some nefarious influence was just entering one of the houses which had to do with the kidneys and the ductless glands. I wondered to myself just what sort of astral set-up it was which had given him such a liverish complexion, and why he hadn't done anything about it, perhaps with the aid of the local pharmacist.

By the time I had had three champagne cocktails I was thoroughly confused. I couldn't remember whether he had said the coming week was to be a good one financially or full of broken bones. What's more I didn't give a damn. Any Saturnian influences revealed by my horoscope are more than offset by a benevolent and beneficent Jupiter. Never once did he mention Venus, I noticed. It was as though he didn't give a shit about one's love life. His forte was accidents, raises in salary, and voyages. The conversation was beginning to taste like a dish of cold scrambled eggs at the Hospital for Joint Diseases. I tried to draw him out about Pluto, because Pluto and her mysterious ways intrigued me more than the other planets, but the subject seemed unpalatable to him; he grew glum, almost morose. What he liked were more mundane queries, such as—"Do you think spaghetti agrees with one of my temperament?" or, "Is exercise good for me at this time?" Or, "What about that job in San Francisco—is this the moment to make a move?" To such questions he always had a ready answer. It was amazing what confidence he possessed. Sometimes, just to make his reply more dramatic, he would close his eyes for a moment to make a rapid survey of the celestial map. He could read the future backwards, yet, in some strange way, like everybody else in this world, he had to buy the morning paper to find out what had happened (during our conversation) on the Russian front. Had the stock market crashed during the night I am certain he would have been none the wiser. When the moon went into eclipse a few weeks later he was on the look-out for quakes and tremblors; fortunately, in some forlorn outpost it was recorded seismographically that there had been a disturbance some five or six thousand miles out in the Pacific. No one suffered, except the monsters of the deep . . .

A week or so later Gerald called me up to invite me to a housewarming. He had promised that I would meet a beautiful Sagittarian with red apple breasts and lips like crushed raspberries. "You're going to be very active soon," said Gerald, as a parting shot. The way he confided this bit of news to me sounded very promising—over the telephone. On reflection, however, I realized that activity in and by itself is meaningless. Ants and bees are active, perpetually active, but where does it get them? Besides, I resented the idea of activity. I was at peace with myself and I wanted to remain that way, at least a little while longer.

It was late afternoon when we drove up to Gerald's house. I had brought two friends along, a Libra and a Sagittarius. Both sides of the street, for the entire length of the block, were filled with cars, mostly limousines, all sleek and shiny, and guarded over by liveried chauffeurs who had already begun to fraternize. Seeing us step out of our Ford coupe they looked us up and down with a critical eye.

It was a rather pleasant little house Gerald had chosen for his new abode. Pleasantly neutral, I should say. It could have been the home of a successful palmist or a 'cellist. The living room was crowded with people—standing, talking, sitting, sipping tea, munching biscuits. As we entered, Gerald dashed forward and began presenting us: Libra—Gemini . . . Sagittarius—Aquarius . . . Leo—Capricorn, and so on. It was all a bit like Alice in Wonderland and Gerald, now that I saw him at close range, was a ringer for the Red Queen.

When the introductions were finished I stood apart, at the bay window, and surveyed the scene. I was wondering who would fasten on me first. I didn't have long to wait.

"Are you interested in astrology?" said a pale, sunken individual who had with difficulty extricated himself from the sofa where he had been crushed between two dowdy females with oatmeal complexions.

"Only mildly," I said, smiling and shaking his limp hand.

"We're all so fond of Gerald. He's really a wizard, you know. I don't know what we'd do without him."

An awkward pause, since I had made no response. He continued: "You're living in Hollywood, I suppose, Mr. . . . What was your name again? Mine is Helblinger . . . Julius Helblinger."

I put out my hand again and said, "Glad to know you, Mr. Helblinger. No I'm not living here, I'm just visiting."

"You're a lawyer, aren't you?"

"No, I'm a writer."

"A writer—how interesting! Indeed, and what sort of books do you write, may I ask?"

At this point I was rescued by Gerald, who had been eavesdropping, and who now joined us all a-flutter.

"You mustn't look at this man's books," said Gerald, holding his arm up with wrist loose and fingers dangling like broken splinters. "He's got a very naughty mind, haven't you December 26th?"

Just then one of the monsters on the sofa tried to rise to her feet with the aid of a thin, gold-knobbed cane. I saw her fall back like a dead fish and hastened to her side to offer my support. As I did so I noticed her legs which were like two splints. Obviously she had never walked any farther than from her car to the door-step. Her eyes, set in a pasty white face, were like two bird seeds. There wasn't a spark of light in them, unless it was the glint of greed and rapacity. She might have been the twin sister of Carrie Nation done by Grant Wood in a moment of satanic illumination. I could see her on the lawn at Pasadena, where she lived, watering the chrysanthemums with a leaky flower pot. She probably went from the hair-dresser to the numerologist and from the numerologist to the palmist and from the palmist to the tea room where, after the second cup of tea, she probably felt a slight stirring in her bowels and congratulated herself that she no longer needed a laxative every day. For her the supreme joy in life was to be able to have a clean stool, no doubt about it. As I gently yanked her to her feet I could hear her dirty heart ticking away like a rusty Ingersoll.

"You're so kind," she said, trying to wreathe her cast-iron face into a beatific smile. "Dear me, my poor legs seem to be giving way on me. Gerald says it's my Mars in opposition with Saturn. That's my cross, I suppose. What are you—an Aries? No, let me think a minute . . . you're a Gemini, aren't you?"

"Yes," I said, "I'm a Gemini . . . and so is my mother, my sister, too. Curious, isn't it?"

"I should think so," she said, wheezing now from the effort of controlling her giddiness. The blood was running through her veins like mucilage soaking through blotting paper.

"Gerald says I worry too much . . . but what are you going to do when the government eats up all your income? Of course I believe we've got to win the war, but dear me, what will be left for us when it's all over? I'm not getting any younger, that's a certainty. We've only got one car now, and God only knows when they'll take that from us. What do *you* think about the war, young man? Isn't it terrible, all this slaughter that's going on? Heavens only knows if we're safe here. I wouldn't be surprised at all if the Japs invaded California and took the coast right under our nose. What do *you* think? You're a very patient listener, I see. You must forgive me if I prattle on like this. I'm not a young woman any more. *Well?*"

I didn't say a word. I just smiled at her—perhaps a bit sadly.

"You're not an alien, are you?" she said, suddenly looking a bit panic-stricken.

"No," I said, "just an American."

"Where are you from—the Middle West?"

"No, New York. That is, I was born there."

"But you don't live there, is that it? I don't blame you. I think it's a horrid place to live . . . all those foreigners. I've been out here thirty years. I'd never go back . . . *Oh*, Lady Astenbroke! . . . well, it's *so* good to see you again. When did you arrive? I didn't know that you were here in California."

I was left holding the crutch, as it were. The old bitch seemed to have forgotten me completely, though I was still at her side ready to give support to her tottering frame the moment she should reel or crumple up. Finally, observing Lady Astenbroke's somewhat embarrassed glances in my direction, she moved her rusty hinges and wheeled about an eighth of an inch, just sufficient to make me aware that she was cognizant of my presence.

"Lady Astenbroke, allow me to present Mr. . . . I'm so sorry, what did you tell me your name was again?"

"I never told you," I said flatly. I allowed a due pause and added: "Himmelweiss . . . August Himmelweiss."

Lady Astenbroke winced visibly at the mention of this horrendous Teutonic name. She held up two icy fingers which I crunched gleefully with a most unseemly hale and hearty handshake. What annoyed Lady Astenbroke more than the disgustingly effusive handshake was the insolent way in which I allowed my eyes to fasten on the three cherries which were dangling over the brim of her incredible hat. Only a madwoman of the British upper class could have discovered such a creation. She stood there like a tipsy Gainsborough to which Marc Chagall had put the finishing touches. All that was needed to consolidate the feeling of Empire was a bunch of asparagus stuck between her deflated leathery breasts. Her breasts! Automatically my eyes roved to the place where the breasts should have been. I had a suspicion that she had stuffed some excelsior there at the last moment, perhaps when squeezing the last drop of perfume out of her atomizer. I'm sure she never looked at her private parts, as they say. So disgusting! Always had been . . . If only one didn't have to make water now and then one could forget about it entirely . . .

"Lady Astenbroke is the author of the Winnie Wimple books," the old Pasadena derelict hastened to inform me. I knew I was supposed to look *au courant* at this juncture but somehow I just didn't give a damn whether Lady Astenbroke was a celebrated writer or a champion croquet player. So I said quite calmly and cold-bloodedly:

"I'm sorry to say I never heard of the Winnie Wimple books."

That fell like a bomb.

"Now please, Mr. . . ."

"Mr. Himmelweiss," I mumbled.

"Please, Mr. Himmelweiss, don't tell us you've never heard of Winnie Wimple. Why, everybody's read the Winnie Wimple books. Where have you been all these years? Dear me, I never heard anything like it."

Said Lady Astenbroke condescendingly: "Mr. Himmelweiss probably reads Thomas Mann and Croce and Unamuno. I don't blame him. I write because I'm bored. I can scarcely read them myself, you know. They're really shockingly simple."

"My dear Lady Astenbroke—how can you say such a thing! Why they're fascinating, your books! Last winter, when I had the gout, I read them all over again . . . every one of them. Such whimsy as you have! Such fantasy! I don't know what we'd do without your Winnie Wimples, really I don't . . . *Oh*, there's Baron Hufnagel. I *must* say a word to him. You'll excuse me, won't you, Lady Astenbroke?" She hobbled off towards the other end of the room, screaming hysterically: "Baron Hufnagel! Baron Hufnagel!"

Lady Astenbroke lowered herself onto the sofa—as if she had a glass ass. I offered to bring her some tea and biscuits but apparently she didn't hear me. She was staring with glassy eyes at a photograph of a lascivious blonde, rather scantily clad, which stood on a little table near her elbow. I edged away from her to find myself rubbing bottoms with a faded actress. I was about to excuse myself when I heard a shrill little laugh, like mica cracking.

"It's only me . . . don't bother," she gurgled. "The Eskimos rub noses . . ." Another little peal of laughter, à la Galli Curci falling downstairs. And then: "I'm November 12th, what are you?"

"December 26th," I said, "all goat and a pair of horns."

"How darling! I don't know what I am—a snake or a centipede.

A little of the devil in me and a lot of sex." She gave a lascivious wink with her pale china blue eyes. "I say," and she snuggled up closer, "you don't think you could find me a drink, do you? I've been waiting for that bird" (indicating Gerald) "to offer me something, but I don't think he ever will, do you? Listen, what's going on here? Is some one going to throw a fit, or what? My name's Peggy, by the way. And yours?"

I gave her my real name. "Officially," I said, "I'm known as Himmelweiss." I gave her the horsewink.

"*Officially!*" she echoed. "I don't get it. Officially *what?*"

"Gaga," I said. "You know," and I tapped my head.

"Oh, that's it? You mean they're all screw-balls? I thought as much. Listen, who *is* this guy . . . the guy that runs the joint? What's his game?"

"Horoscopes."

"You mean astrology? Listen, I'm not such a dumb cluck. But what's the racket? What did he round them up for? Is he getting ready to shake 'em down? If he tries to rustle me he's going to get a big surprise."

"I don't think he'll bother you any," I said. "Not that way anyway." I gave her another slippery horsewink.

"I get you. So that's his game!" She made a cool survey of the guests. "Not much competition that way, I'll say. Maybe they're just a blind." She gave a supercilious nod intended to embrace the old hags who surrounded us.

"What's *your* game?" she asked suddenly.

"*My game?* Oh, I write."

"Go on . . . do you mean it? What sort of stuff? History, biology . . . ?"

"Naughty books," I said, trying to blush deeply.

"What kind of naughty books? Naughty-naughty—or just dirt?"

"Just dirt, I guess."

"You mean—Lady Chatterby, or Chattersley, or whatever the hell it is? Not that swill you don't mean, do you?"

I laughed. "No, not that sort . . . just straight obscenity. You know—duck, chit, kiss, trick, punt, . . ."

"*Not so loud!* Where do you think you are?" She gave a quick look over her shoulder. "Say, listen, why don't we sit down somewhere and talk this over? What else do you know? This sounds promising. What did you say you were—a goat? What's that—Sagittarius?"

"Capricorn."

"*Capricorn!* Well, now we're getting somewhere. What did you say your date was? I want to remember that . . . Are all Capricorns like that? Jesus, I thought I was sexy, but maybe I'm going to learn things. Listen, come over here, where nobody can hear you. Now, what did you say you wrote again? Straight what?"

"Straight duck, chit, kiss, trick, punt, . . ."

She looked up at me as though she were going to bless me. She held out her mitt. "*Shake*, partner! You're talking my language. I say, can you embroider that a little—from where you left off? Those were good clean words, the coin of the realm. Can't you reel off a few fancy ones? Go on, try it. I'm beginning to wet my pants. Cripes, imagine finding *you* here. And what's about a little drink, eh? Don't bring me any stale horse-piss. Some Bourbon, if you can find it . . . Wait a minute, don't run just yet. Tell me some more before you go. Begin with duck, you know—like you did before. Only ring some fancy ones in. Maybe you and I'll go places before the night's over. You don't just say the words, do you? That'd be cruel. Come here, I want to whisper something in your ear."

As I bent over I saw Gerald heading straight towards us.

"Shoo this guy away, will you," she whispered. "He looks like a dose of crabs to me."

"What are you two whispering about?" said Gerald, beaming like the heavenly twins.

"Brother, you'd never guess . . . would he?" She gave a dirty laugh—just a little too loud, I gathered from the expression on Gerald's face.

Gerald bent over, using a *sotto voce*: "It wasn't about sex, was it?"

The woman looked up at him in amazement, almost frightened. "Say, you *are* a mind-reader, aren't you? How the hell did *you* know? You don't read lips, do you?"

"I could read *your* lips even in the dark," said Gerald, giving her a withering glance.

"You're not trying to insult me, I hope? Listen, I know a few tricks myself. Maybe I don't know nothing about astrology, but I've got *your* number."

"Shhhhh!" Gerald put is fingers to his lips. "Not here, my dear. You wouldn't give me away before all these people, would you?"

"Not if you can dig up a drink, I won't. Where do you keep it? I'll get it myself. Just tell me. You weren't brought up on lemonade."

Gerald was just about to whisper in her ear when a ravishing beauty who had just made her entrance pulled him by the coat tails.

"Diana! *You* here? How lovely! I never dreamed that you'd

come." He waltzed her off to another corner of the room without bothering to introduce her. Probably congratulating himself on a lucky escape.

"He's a dirty cheap skate," muttered the blonde between her teeth. "He could have told us where he kept it, couldn't he? Pretending to be all wrapped up in Diana. Huh! He'd faint if any one showed him a—you know!—with hair on it."

It was the sort of place you couldn't sit long in without being molested. While Peggy went to the pantry to search for liquor, a Norwegian spinster who was serving tea in the next room advanced on me, leading by the hand a celebrated analyst. He was an Aquarian whose Venus was unaspected. He looked like a dentist who had degenerated into a desert rat. His false teeth shone with a blue flame beneath a ridge of rubber gums. He wore a perpetual smile which by turns indicated satisfaction, dubiety, ecstasy and disgust. The Norwegian woman, who was psychic, watched him reverently, giving significance even to his sighs and grunts. She was a Piscean, it developed, and her veins were filled with the milk of compassion. She wanted all who were suffering to come unto Dr. Blunderbuss. He was really unique, she informed me, after he had taken leave. She compared him first to Paracelsus, then to Pythagoras, and finally to Hermes Trismegistus. That brought us round to the subject of reincarnation. She said she could remember three previous incarnations—in one of them she had been a man. That was during the time of the Pharaohs, before the temple priests had corrupted the ancient wisdom. She was working out her Karma slowly, confident that in another million years or so she would escape from the wheel of birth and death.

"Time is nothing," she murmured, with eyes half-closed. "There is so much to be done . . . so much. Won't you try one of our delicious cookies? I made them myself."

She took me by the hand and led me into the adjoining room where an aged Daughter of the Revolution was pouring tea.

"Mrs. Farquahar," she said, still holding me by the hand, "this gentleman would like to try one of the cookies. We've just had a grand talk with Dr. Blunderbuss, haven't we?" She looked into my eyes with the touching humility of a trained poodle.

"Mrs. Farquahar is terribly psychic," she continued, handing me a delicious cookie and a cup of tea. "She was a great friend of Madame Blavatsky. You've read *The Secret Doctrine*, of course? Of course you have . . . you're one of us, I know."

I noticed that Mrs. Farquahar was looking at me strangely. She wasn't looking into my eyes, either, but sort of slant-wise from the roots of my hair upward. I thought perhaps Lady Astenbroke might be standing behind me—and the three cherries dangling above my head.

Suddenly Mrs. Farquahar opened her mouth. "What a beautiful aura! *Violet* . . . with a touch of magenta. *Look!*" and she pulled the Norwegian woman to her, made her bend her knees and look at a spot on the wall about three inches above my thinning locks. "Do you see it, Norma? Just squint one eye. Now . . . *there!*"

Norma bent her knees a little more, squinted for all she was worth, but had to confess she could see nothing.

"Why it's as plain as can be. Any one can see it! Keep looking. It'll come . . ."

By now several old hens were crooking their knees and trying for all they were worth to see the halo which enveloped my cranium. One of them swore she saw it very distinctly—but it turned out that she saw green and black instead of violet and magenta. That irritated Mrs. Farquahar. She began to pour tea furiously, finally spilling a cupful over her lavender dress. Norma was terribly upset by this. She fussed over Mrs. Farquahar like a wet hen.

When Mrs. Farquahar stood up there was a tremendous stain visible. It looked as if she had become excited beyond control. I stood there looking at the stain and instinctively put one hand above my head to bathe it in the violet light of my aura.

Just then a clean-shaven, portly, interior decorator type of homosexual gave me a knowing smile and remarked in a suave, silken tone of voice that my aura was perfectly stunning. "I haven't seen one like it for years," he exclaimed, reaching nonchalantly for a handful of home-made cookies. "Mine is just too disgusting for words . . . at least so they tell me. You must have a beautiful character. My only distinction is that I'm clairaudient. I would so love to be clairvoyant too, wouldn't you—or *are* you? I suppose you *are* . . . it's silly of me to ask. Any one with *your* aura . . . " He made a charming little moue and wagged his hips. I thought he was going to wave his hand and shout Yoo-hoo! But he didn't.

"You're an artist, I suppose," I ventured, after this flirtatious exchange.

"I suppose I am," he replied, dropping his eyelashes coyly. "I love to handle beautiful things. And I just loathe figures and all that sort of thing. Of course I've lived abroad most of my life— that helps, don't you think? Have you ever lived in Florence—or Ravenna? Isn't Florence just a darling of a place? I don't know why we had to have a war, do you? It's *so* messy. I do hope the English will spare Ravenna. Those horrible bombs! Ugh! It makes me shudder to think of it . . . "

A woman who had been standing beside us now spoke up. She said luck had been against her the last seven years, ever since she had had her palm read in Majorca. Fortunately she had put aside a little nest egg for a rainy day—a cool million, it was—she said it without batting an eyelash. Now that she had become an agent things were going a little better. She had just made a place for some one at three thousand a week. A few more like that and she wouldn't have to starve to death. Yes, it was rather pleasant work. After all, one had to have something to do, something to occupy one's mind. It was lots better than sitting home and worrying about what the government would do with your money.

I asked if she were a Seventh Day Adventist by any chance. She smiled with her gold teeth. "No, not any more. I guess I'm just a believer."

"And how did you meet Gerald?" I asked.

"Oh, *Gerald* . . ." and she gave a thrilly-dilly little laugh. "I met him at a boxing match one night. He was sitting with a Hindu nabob or something and I asked him for a light. He asked me if I wasn't a Libra and I told him I didn't know what he was talking about. Then he said—'Weren't you born between the first and the fifth of October?' I told him I was born October first. 'That makes you a Libra,' he said. I was so dumbfounded that I had him do my horoscope. Since then things have been looking up. It seems I was under an eclipse or something. I don't understand it all yet . . . do you? Anyway, it's fascinating, don't you think? Imagine asking some one for a light and being told when you were born! He's terribly brilliant, Gerald. I wouldn't make a move without consulting him first."

"I wonder if you could get me a job in the movies," I said. "This is a good period for me, so Gerald says."

"Are you an actor?" She looked rather surprised.

"No, I'm just a writer. I'd make a good hack if I were given a fair break."

"Are you good at dialogue?"

"That's my middle name. Do you want a sample? Look . . . two men are walking down the street. They're walking away from an accident. It's dark and they've lost their way. One of them is over-excited. Dialogue . . .

Excited man: Where do you suppose I could have put those papers?

Calm man: Suppositions are often like random shots on a billiard table without cloth.

Excited man: What? Anyway, if they fall into the wrong hands I'm done for.

Calm man: You're done for anyway . . . I thought we covered all that ages ago.

Excited man: Do you suppose some one could have picked my pockets while we were standing there? Why didn't they take my watch and chain also? How do you explain it?

Calm man: I don't. I neither suppose nor explain. I merely observe.

Excited man: Do you think I ought to phone the police? God, man, we've got to do something.

Calm man: You mean *you* have to do something. I have only to go home and go to sleep. Well, here's where we part. Good-night!

Excited man: You're not going to leave me now, are you? You mean you're going to walk out on me . . . Just like that?

Calm man: I always say exactly what I mean. Good-night and sleep tight!

"I could carry on like that for a half hour. How was it? Pretty bad? All impromptu, of course. If I were putting it down on paper it would sound quite different. I'll give you another sample, if you like . . . Two women, this time. They're waiting for a bus. It's raining and they have no umbrellas . . ."

"Excuse me," said La Libra, "but I've got to go. It was so nice meeting you. I'm sure you'll have no trouble finding a place for yourself in Hollywood."

I was left standing there like a wet umbrella. I wondered if my aura was still showing or if it had become extinguished. Nobody seemed to take a bit of notice any more.

Now that the old ones had bathed their intestines with lukewarm tea they were thinking about getting home for dinner. One by one they gingerly raised themselves from their seats and hobbled slowly towards the door, availing themselves of canes, crutches, umbrellas and golf clubs. Lady Astenbroke was remaining, it appeared. She had fallen into a fascinating conversation with a fat Cuban woman who was dressed in a Butterick pattern of the mutton chop epoch. They were speaking several languages at once, Lady Astenbroke being an accomplished linguist. I was standing behind a rubber plant about two feet away from them, trying to decode this amazing lingo. As the departing ones approached to bid her good-bye, Lady Astenbroke bent forward like a broken hinge and extended her clammy paw which scintillated with jeweled rings. The chauffeurs were crowded round the doorway, ready to proffer an arm to their aged charges. Gerald escorted his patrons in turn to their respective cars. He looked like a distinguished bone-setter who had just pocketed a handsome fee. When the last of the derelicts had vanished he stood on the door-step mopping his brow, took a silver cigarette case from his hip pocket, lit a cork-tipped cigarette and exhaled a thin cloud of smoke through his nostrils. A thin crescent moon was visible low above the horizon. Gerald gazed at it a few moments, took another puff or two, then flung the cigarette away. As he re-entered the house he looked about searchingly. A shade of disappointment was visible in his countenance; apparently the one he was looking for had not arrived. He chewed his lips absent-mindedly. "Oh, foodle!" he seemed to say, and then he made a dash for the kitchen where he probably took a quiet nip all by himself.

Lady Astenbroke was now talking French to the Cuban woman. She was gushing about Juan les Pins, Cannes, Pau and other famous resorts. Evidently she had spent considerable time in the south of France, as well as in Italy, Turkey, Jugoslavia and North Africa. The Cuban woman listened imperturbably, fanning herself the while with a diminutive, ivory-studded fan which could only have been stolen from a museum. The perspiration fell in little drops onto her bosom. Now and then she swabbed the huge crack between her tightly squashed teats with a tiny silk handkerchief. She did it quite casually, never once lowering her eyes. Lady Astenbroke pretended not to notice these unseemly gestures. If she had paused to reflect she would have been horrified. Lady Astenbroke had probably never touched her own breasts since the day they shriveled up.

The Cuban woman was very fat and the chair she was sitting on was very uncomfortable. For one thing, her ass was hanging over the seat of the chair like a piece of limp liver. Occasionally, when Lady Astenbroke's eyes roved wildly about the room, she discreetly scratched her ass with the handle of her little fan. Once she put it down her back, not realizing my proximity, and vigorously poked it up and down. It was obvious that she had lost interest in Lady Astenbroke's disconnected remarks. Her one desire was to get home as soon as possible, rip off her corset, and scratch herself like a mangy dog.

I was amazed, when a dapper little man approached, to hear her present him as her husband. Somehow I had not expected her to own a husband, but there he was in flesh and blood, a monocle in one eye and a pair of butter-colored gloves in his hand. He was an Italian count, so I gathered from the introductions, and his profession was architecture. There was something tremendously alert and pertinacious about him, something of the bird of prey and something of the dandy. Something of the poet also, the kind that walks upside down on the ceiling or swings from the chandelier while pondering a phrase or a cadence. He would have looked more natural in doublet and hose with a big heart pasted over his chest.

With infinite patience, not untinged with malice, he stood behind his wife's chair and waited for her to conclude her séance with Lady Astenbroke. An undefinable asperity gave him the air of a Neapolitan barber waiting for an opportune moment to quietly slit his wife's throat. There was no doubt about it, once they were seated in the car he would pinch her until she was black and blue.

Only about a dozen people were left in the big room now. Mostly Virgos and Geminis, it seemed to me. A torpor had come over them, a gentle torpor induced by the sultry heat and the drone of insects. Gerald was in the bedroom, where the photos of his favorite stars—his clients undoubtedly—were conspicuously displayed. A rather attractive young woman was seated beside him at the writing table. They were going over a horoscope together. I recalled that she had arrived with a handsome young man, who was either her lover or her husband, and that they had separated almost immediately.

The young man, who turned out to be an actor—he was doing Western parts at Universal—had the attractiveness of a man who is just about to go insane. He roved about nervously, flitting from group to group, always hovering on the fringe, listening a few moments, then breaking away like a colt. He was dying to speak to some one, I could see that. But no one gave him a chance. Finally he flung himself on the sofa beside an ugly little woman whom he completely ignored. He looked about disconsolately, ready to explode at the slightest provocation.

Presently a woman with flaming red hair and violet eyes made her entrance; in her wake came a towering young aviator with shoulders like Atlas and the sharp, beak-like features of the airman. "Hello everybody!" she said, assuming that everybody knew at once who she was. "I'm here, you see . . . Couldn't believe it possible, could you? Well, get busy, hand out the compliments . . . I'm all ears," she seemed to say, meanwhile perching herself on the edge of a rickety chair, her back straight as a ramrod, her eyes flashing, her toes quivering with impatience. She had an impeccable English accent which belied the mobility of her features. She might have been Conchita Montenegro—or Loulou Hegoroboru. Anything but a flower of the British Empire. I inquired discreetly who she was. A Brazilian dancer, I was told, who had just burst into the pictures.

A Brazilian peacock would have been more accurate. Vanity, vanity! It was written all over her. She had moved her chair into the very center of the room—to make certain that no one else should monopolize the attention of the torpid assemblage.

"Yes, we took a plane from Rio," she was saying. "I always travel by plane. I suppose it's extravagant, but I'm too impatient. I had to leave the dog with the maid. I think it's stupid, all these silly regulations. I . . ."

I . . . I . . . I . . . I . . . She never seemed to use the second or third person. Even when she referred to the weather she used the first person. She was like a glittering iceberg, the Id completely submerged and about as useful to her as Jonah was to the whale. Her toes twinkled as she spoke. Elegant, polished toes, capable of executing the most intricate figures. The sort of toes that would make one swoon to lick.

What surprised me was the rigidity of her body. Only her head and toes were alive—the rest of her was anaesthetized. It was from the diaphragm of this immobile torso that she threw her voice, a voice which was at once seductive and grating. She said nothing which she had not already said a hundred or a thousand times. She sat there like a rat-catcher, always whistling the same tune, looking bright, gay and alert, but secretly bored to tears, suffocated with ennui. She saw nothing and heard nothing, her mind blank and flawless as stainless steel.

"Yes, I'm a Gemini too," I heard her say, implying by the tone of her voice that the gods had indeed blessed her. "Yes, I'm very dual." I . . . I . . . I . . . I . . . Even in her duality she was just a capital I.

Suddenly Gerald came from the bedroom. "Lolita!" he exclaimed, putting an extra rapturous thrill into his falsetto voice. "How sweet of you! How *gorgeous* you look!" He held her with outstretched arms by the tips of his fingers, as in the ballet, and with fluttering orbs he ravished her from head to foot.

As he was going through this little farce my eye happened to rove and alight upon the woman at the writing table in the bedroom. She had taken a handkerchief from her bag and was drying her eyes. I saw her clasp her hands feverishly and glance imploringly at the ceiling. She seemed utterly distraught.

"My dear Lolita, it was so good of you to come. You came by plane, I suppose? How ducky! You extravagant creature, you! And that lovely hat . . . where *did* you buy it? In Rio, I suppose? You're not running away yet, I hope? I've such wonderful things to tell you. Your Venus is magnificent now."

Lolita didn't seem to be at all surprised by this announcement. She probably knew more about the position of her Venus than Gerald and all the psychopomps of the underworld. Her Venus was right between her legs—and what's more, it was always under control. The only time her love life ever suffered an eclipse was when she had the curse. Even then there were a lot of things one could do without opening or closing the legs.

Now that she was on her feet her body had more animation. There was an effulgence about the hips which was unnoticeable when she was sitting. She used them very much like a flirt uses her eyebrows. She arched them coyly, first one then the other. It was a sort of veiled masturbation, such as boarding-school girls resort to when their hands are otherwise occupied.

She made a few steps towards the bedroom with the sprightliness of an icicle just beginning to thaw. Her voice had a different resonance now. It seemed to come from the girdle of Venus; it was lush and curdled, like radishes floating in sour cream.

"When you're through," she said, glancing over his shoulder at the figure in the bedroom, "I'd like to have a word with you."

What it sounded like was: "Get rid of that weepy wretch in there and I'll tell you about my oojie-woojie love life."

"Oh we'll be through in no time," said Gerald, turning his head stiffly in the direction of the bedroom.

"You'd better make it snappy," said Lolita. "I'm going soon." She gave her left hip an imperceptible jerk, as though to say—"I'm warning you. Make it snappy!"

Just then the Brazilian flyer appeared, laden with a tray of sandwiches and some sherry. Lolita pounced on the food rapaciously. The cowboy with the maniacal look in his eye had jumped to his feet and was helping himself manfully. Lady Astenbroke sat in her corner, waiting disdainfully for some one to pass her the platter. Suddenly it seemed as though every one were on the qui vive. The insects stopped buzzing, the heat abated. The general torpor seemed to be evaporating.

It was the moment the cowboy had been waiting for. He had a chance to spout now and he did, in a deep, booming voice which, despite the note of hysteria, had something ingratiating about it. He was one of those neurotic he-men created by the movie studios who loathe their false masculinity. He wanted to tell us about his fears, of which he had a good skinful. He didn't know quite how to begin, that was obvious, but he was determined to make us listen somehow. So, quite as if that had been the subject of conversation all afternoon, he began talking about shrapnel wounds. He wanted to let us know how it felt to be all cut up and bleeding, particularly under a foreign sky, and no hope of being rescued. He was sick of riding wild horses in the chaparral at a hundred and fifty dollars a week. He had been an actor once, back

East, and though he hadn't become a celebrity he had at least done without a horse. One felt that he was trying to precipitate a dramatic situation in which he could display his true histrionic powers. One also felt that he was hungry, that perhaps the reason why his wife was closeted with Gerald in the bedroom was to find out when they would eat again. One had the suspicion that the hundred and fifty dollars a week meant every fifth or sixth week, and that between times they chewed horse-leather. Perhaps too his wife had closeted herself with Gerald to learn what had become of her husband's missing virility. A lot of things were dangling in the air, above and beyond those brutal, hair-raising descriptions of shrapnel wounds.

He was a most determined, wild-eyed young man—positively Scorpionic. He seemed to be begging our permission to writhe on the carpet, to gnaw Lolita's ankles, to hurl the sherry glass through the window-pane. Something only remotely connected with his profession was eating him up. Probably his status in the draft. Probably the fact that his wife had become pregnant too soon. Probably a lot of things connected with the general catastrophe. Anyway, he was in the dead center of it, whatever it was, and the more he thrashed about the more obfuscated he became. If only some one would gainsay him! If only some one would take exception to his wild, random remarks! But no, no one opened his lips. They sat there, quiet as sheep, and watched him go through his contortions.

At first it was rather difficult to know just where he had oriented himself—amidst the flying shrapnel. He had already mentioned nine different countries without pausing to catch his breath. He had been routed out of Warsaw, bombed out of Rotterdam, driven to the sea at Dunkirk, fallen at Thermopylae, flown to Crete and been rescued by a fishing boat, and now, finally, he was somewhere in the wilds of Australia, grubbing a bite of food from the cannibals of the high plateaus. One couldn't say whether he had actually participated in these bloody disasters or whether he was rehearsing a part for a new radio program. He used all the pronouns, personal, reflexive, possessive, indiscriminately. Sometimes he was piloting a plane, sometimes he was merely a straggler and free-booter in the wake of a defeated army. At one moment he was living on mice and herrings, at another he was swilling champagne like Eric von Stroheim. Under all circumstances, no matter what the time or place, he was miserable. Words can't describe how miserable he wanted us to believe he felt.

It was in the midst of this fever and agony that I decided to get up and take a stroll about the grounds. In the driveway leading to the garden I met my Sagittarian friend, Humberto, who had just sneaked away from the clutches of a hunch-backed woman with eczema. We walked back to the garden, where we found a ping-pong table. A young couple, who introduced themselves as brother and sister, invited us to join them in a game of doubles. We had hardly begun to play when the cow-boy made his appearance on the back porch; he watched us in glum silence for a few minutes, then disappeared inside. Presently a very sun-tanned woman, full of vim and bounce, came out and watched us hungrily. She was like a bull in female clothes, her nostrils breathing fire, her breasts heaving like ripe cantaloupes. The first ball she took a swat at broke in two; the second went over the fence; the third ball caught my friend Humberto square in the eye. With this she retired in disgust, saying that she preferred Badminton.

In a few moments Gerald came out to ask us to stay for dinner. The interior decorator friend had promised to make spaghetti for us, he informed us. "Now don't you run away," he said, pointing his finger at us mockingly.

We of course said we wouldn't think of staying. (Couldn't he see that we were bored stiff?)

"Oh, so you don't like spaghetti? It's not good enough for you, is that it?" said Gerald, putting on the pouting hussy act.

"Can we get some wine?" I asked, hoping that he would take the hint and tell us that cocktails were being prepared.

"Now don't go worrying about those things," said Gerald. "You Capricorns are so damned practical. Yes, we'll have something to drink for you."

"What sort of drink?" said Humberto, whose lips had been parched all afternoon.

"Oh, shush!" said Gerald. "Concentrate on the ping-pong. Haven't you any manners?"

"I'm thirsty," Humberto persisted.

"Then come inside and I'll give you a glass of cold water. That'll do you good. You're getting too excited. Besides, you should watch your liver. Wine is poison for you."

"Offer me something else then," said Humberto, determined to wheedle something alcoholic out of him.

"Now listen, Sagittarius . . . you've got to behave like a gentleman. This isn't John Barrymore's tenement house. Run along now and play your ping-pong. I'm going to send a charming little girl out to play with you." He turned his back on us and slid inside.

"Can you beat that?" said Humberto, throwing his racket aside and pulling on his jacket. "I'm going to get myself a drink." He looked around, waiting for some one to join him. The brother of the beautiful-looking Leo agreed to go along.

"Don't stay too long!" said Humberto's wife.

Humberto suddenly remembered he had forgotten something. He went up to his wife and asked her where her bag was. "I need some change," he said. He fished around in the bag and extracted a couple of bills.

"That means we won't see Humberto for a few hours," said his wife.

They had hardly left when the "charming" young girl came out. She was about sixteen, gawky, with carroty red hair and pimples. Gerald stuck his head out to give an approving nod. Suddenly no one wanted to play any more. The girl was almost on the verge of tears. At this moment, however, the bull-dyker reappeared, rushed to the table and grabbed a racket. "I'll play with you," she said to the gawky one, and with that she whizzed a fast one just over the girl's head. "I've got too much energy," she muttered. She slapped her thighs with the racket while the young gawk crawled on hands and knees among the rose-bushes in search of the ball.

We sat on the stoop and watched them a few minutes. Sister Leo, with the golden spots in her eyes, was talking about the dunes of Indiana. She confided that she had come to California to be near her brother, who was in an army camp nearby. She had found herself a job in a department store, selling candies. "I hope Rodney doesn't get drunk," she murmured. "He can't stand very much. You don't think Humberto will get him drunk do you?"

We assured her that her brother was in good hands.

"I don't want him to get into trouble," she continued. "When he drinks he's apt to pick up with any one. There's so much disease around here . . . you know what I mean. That's why I like to be near him. I don't mind if he finds a nice, clean girl . . . but these other women . . . I understand all the boys get infected some time or other. Rodney never did run around very much at home. We were always good pals together . . ." She looked at me suddenly and exclaimed: "You're smiling. Did I say something foolish?"

"Oh no," I said, "on the contrary, I thought it was very touching."

"Touching? What do you mean? You don't think Rodney's a sissy, do you?"

"I wasn't thinking of Rodney."

"You think there's something wrong with *me*?"

"No, I don't think there's anything wrong . . ."

"You think I'm in love with him?" She laughed gaily. "Well, if you want to know the truth, I *am* in love with him. If he weren't my brother I'd marry him. Wouldn't you?''

"I don't know," I said, "I never was a sister."

A woman came out on the back porch to put some garbage in the can. She didn't look like a charwoman—there was something "spiritual" about her.

"Don't catch cold sitting out here," said the old lady. "The nights are treacherous, you know. We'll be having dinner for you shortly." She gave us a motherly smile, stood a moment with hands clasped over her fallen womb, and disappeared inside.

"Who is she?" I asked.

"That's my mother," said Miss Leo. "Isn't she sweet?"

"Why yes," I said, somewhat surprised that her mother should be doing Gerald's dirty work.

"She's a Quaker," said the girl. "By the way, you can call me Carol if you like. That's my name. Mother doesn't believe in astrology, but she likes Gerald. She thinks he's helpless."

"Are you a Quaker too?"

"Oh no, I haven't any religion. I'm just a plain country girl. I guess I'm sort of dumb."

"I don't think you're so very dumb," I said.

"Maybe not so very . . . but dumb just the same," she responded.

"How do you know? What gives you that idea?"

"By listening to other people talk. I can tell what I sound like when I open my mouth. You see, I just have simple, ordinary thoughts. Most people are too complicated for me. I listen, but I don't know what they're talking about."

"That sounds most intelligent to me," I confessed. "Tell me, do you dream much?"

She seemed startled by this. "What makes you ask that? How do you know I dream?"

"Why, everybody dreams, don't you know that?"

"Yes, I've heard say they do . . . but you didn't mean it that way. Most people forget their dreams, don't they?"

I nodded.

"Well, I don't," said Carol, brightening suddenly. "I remember everything, every detail. I have wonderful dreams. Maybe that's why I don't use my mind more. I dream all day long, as well as at night. It's easier, I suppose. Anyway, I'd rather dream than think . . . you know what I mean?"

I pretended to look puzzled.

"Oh, you know what I mean," she continued. "You can think and think and not get anywhere. But when you dream it's always there—whatever you want, just as you want it. It's like a short cut. Maybe that makes your brain soft, but I don't care. I wouldn't change even if I could . . ."

"Listen, Carol," I interrupted, "could you give me an idea what your dreams are like? Can you remember the one you had last night—or the night before, for instance?"

Carol smiled benignly. "Of course I can tell you," she said. "I'll tell you one I dream over and over . . . Of course, putting it into words spoils it. I can't describe the gorgeous colors I see, or the music I hear. Even if I were a writer, I don't think I could capture it. At least I've never read in a book anything like what I experience. Of course, writers don't go in much for dreams, do they? They're always describing life—or what goes on in people's heads. Maybe they don't dream the way I do. I dream about things that never happen . . . things that *couldn't* happen, I suppose . . . though I don't see why, either. Things happen the way we want them to happen, don't you think? I live so much in my imagination, that's why nothing ever happens to me, I guess. There's nothing I want very much—except to live . . . to go on living forever. That sounds a little foolish, maybe, but I mean it. I don't see any reason why we should die. People die because they want to die—that's what I think. I read somewhere once that life was just a dream. That stuck in my head, because that's exactly what I thought myself. And the more I see of life the more I believe it's true. We're all living the life we dream . . ." She paused a moment to look at me earnestly. "You don't think I'm talking nonsense now, do you? I wouldn't talk to you this way unless I felt that you understood."

I assured her that I was listening most attentively, most sympathetically. Incidentally, she seemed to have grown a hundred times more beautiful. The irises of her eyes had become like veils studded with gold. She was anything but dumb, I reflected, as I waited for her to continue.

"I didn't tell you this, about my dreams, but maybe you've guessed it yourself . . . I often know what's going to happen to those around me. Last night, for instance, I dreamed that I was going to a party, a moonlight party, where I would meet a man who would tell me strange things about myself. There seemed to be a light around his head. He came from a foreign country, but he wasn't a foreigner. He spoke with a soft voice which was very soothing; he had a kind of drawl too—like you."

"What sort of things did you expect to hear about yourself, Carol?" I interrupted again. "What sort of strange things?"

She paused a moment, as if pondering her words. Then she said very frankly and innocently: "I'll tell you what I mean. It isn't about my love for my brother—that's very natural, I believe. Only people with dirty minds think that it's queer to love your own kith and kin . . . No, it wasn't that. It's about the music I hear and the colors I see. There is no earthly music like what I hear in my dreams, nor are the colors like those we see in the sky or in the fields. There is a music out of which all our music comes—and colors come from the same source. They were once one, that's what the man was telling me in my dream. But that was millions of years ago, he said. And when he said that, I knew that he must have understood too. I felt that we had known each other in some other world. But I also knew, from the way he spoke, that it was dangerous to admit such things in public. I had a sudden fear that if I were not careful people would consider me insane and then I would be put away and I would never dream again. I didn't fear that I would go insane—only that by putting me away they would murder this dream life. Then the man said something to me which frightened me. He said: '*But you are insane already, my dear girl. You have nothing to worry about.*' And then he disappeared. The next moment I saw everything in natural colors, only the colors were misplaced. The grass was violet instead of green; horses were blue; men and women were gray, ashen gray, like evil spirits; the sun was black, the moon was green. I knew then that I was out of my mind. I looked for my brother and when I found him he was staring at himself in a mirror. I looked over his shoulder, into the mirror, and I could no longer recognize him. He was a complete stranger. I called him by name, I shook him, but he continued to stare at his image in the mirror. At last I understood that he didn't recognize himself either. My God, I thought, we've both gone insane. The worst of it was, I didn't love him any more. I wanted to run away, but I couldn't. I was paralyzed with fear . . . Then I woke up."

"That's hardly what you'd call a beautiful dream, is it?" I said.

"No," said Carol, "yet it's beautiful to see things upside down some times. I'll never forget how wonderful the grass looked, nor how astonished I was to see the sun so black . . . Now that I think of it, the stars were shining. They were much closer to the earth than they usually are. Everything stood out brilliantly—much more clearly than in yellow sunlight. Did you ever notice how wonderful things look after a rain . . . especially in the late afternoon when the sun is setting? Supposing the stars were out—and twenty times bigger than we generally see them? Do you see what I mean? Maybe some day, when the earth wanders from its orbit, everything will look like that. Who knows? A million years ago the earth must have had a far different appearance, don't you think? The green was probably greener, and the red redder. Everything must have been magnified a thousand times—at least, that's what I imagine. Some people say that we don't see the real sun—only the lens of the sun, so to speak. The real sun is probably so bright that our poor human eyes can't see it. Our eyes are made to see very little really. It's funny but when you close your two eyes and start to dream, you see things so much better, so much clearer, so much lovelier. What eyes are those we see with then? *Where are they?* If one vision is real, why isn't the other also? Are we crazy when we dream? And if we're not crazy when we dream, why shouldn't we dream all the time? Or do you think that's crazy? You see, I told you I was a very simple person. I try to figure things out as best I can myself. But I don't get anywhere trying to think things out. I don't think anybody does."

At this point Humberto and Rodney returned, looking vague and roseate. Gerald was running about frantically, urging his guests to tackle the spaghetti. "It's vile," he whispered in my ear, "but the meat balls are good." We took our plates and sidled up to the Norwegian woman who was dishing it out. It was just like a canteen. The interior decorator went from one to another with a can of grated cheese and sprinkled the cheese over the fresh puke which passed for tomato sauce. He was infinitely pleased with himself, so much so that he forgot to eat. (Or perhaps he had eaten first.) Gerald was hopping about like a cherub, exclaiming: "Isn't it delicious? Did you get a meat ball?" As he passed behind me he nudged me gently and murmured under his breath: "I loathe spaghetti . . . it's vile."

Some newcomers had arrived during the interlude in the garden, youngsters mostly—probably starlets. The one called Claude, with blonde, wavy hair, had a lot of cheek. He seemed to know most every one present, especially the women, who treated him like a pet.

"I thought the party would be over by this time," he said, excusing himself for coming in his pajamas. Then, with a shrill bleat, he yelled across the room: "Gerald! Gerald! I say, Gerald! (Gerald had just ducked into the kitchen to hide his mortification.) "Oh Gerald! When am I going to get a job? Do you hear me, Gerald? When am I going to work?"

Gerald came out with a frying pan in his hand. "If you don't shut your mouth," he said, going up to the dear brazen little Claude and swinging the frying pan over his head, "I'll crown you with this!"

"But you promised me that I'd have something before the month was up!" shrieked Claude, obviously enjoying Gerald's discomfiture.

"I promised no such thing," Gerald retorted. "I said the chances were good—*if you worked hard*. You're lazy . . . you expect things to come to you. Now be quiet and eat some spaghetti. You're making too much noise." He retreated to the kitchen once more.

Claude jumped to his feet and pursued him into the kitchen. I heard him say—"Oh Geraldine, did I say the wrong thing?" and then his voice was smothered, as if some one had laid a hand over his mouth.

Meanwhile the table in the dining room had been pushed back against the wall and a cute young couple began doing the jitterbug. They had the floor to themselves; every one stood and watched, gasping with admiration. The girl, who was tiny, cute, muscular, energetic, had a sort of Nell Brinkley face à la Clara Bow. Her legs twitched like a frog's under the scalpel. The young man, who couldn't have been more than nineteen, was just too beautiful for words. He was like a faun made of Dresden china, a typical California product destined to become either a crooner or an epicene Tarzan. Claude looked on with veiled contempt. Now and then he ran his fingers through his unruly locks and tossed his head back derisively.

To my astonishment Gerald now came forth and requested Humberto's wife to do a fling with him. He went at it with complete assurance, kicking his heels as if he were cock of the walk. What he lacked in finesse he made up for by his gymnastics. He had his own ideas about the jitterbug capers.

When he got a bit winded he stopped in front of Humberto and said: "Why don't you dance with your wife? She's a marvelous dancer." Now Humberto rarely ever danced with his wife—that was something which belonged to the past. But Gerald was insistent. "You *must* dance with her!" he exclaimed, making Humberto the center of all eyes.

Humberto wheeled off in desultory fashion, barely raising his feet from the ground. He was cursing Gerald for being such an idiot.

Lolita, whom nobody had asked for a dance, was furious. She sailed through the room, stomping her heels, and went straight up to the Brazilian flyer. "It's time to go," she hissed. "Will you take me home?" Not waiting for his assent, she took him by the hand and dragged him out of the room, saying in a loud, cheery voice which was full of ashes, "Good-night everybody! Good-night! Good-night!" (See, this is how I leave you, I, Lolita. I despise

you. I'm bored to death. I, the dancer, I am leaving. I will dance
only in public. When I dance I leave everybody gasping. I am
Lolita. I am wasting time here . . .)

At the door, where Gerald was bidding her adieu, she paused to
survey us, to observe if we were sufficiently impressed by her
abrupt departure. Nobody was paying any attention to her. She
had to do something, something dramatic, to call attention to
herself. So she yelled, in her high, stagy, British voice: "Lady
Astenbroke! Would you come here a moment, please? I have
something to tell you . . ."

Lady Astenbroke, who seemed to be nailed to the armchair, had
difficulty in getting to her feet. She had probably never been
summoned like that before, but the thrill of hearing her name, the
consciousness that all eyes were focused on her, overcame any
resentment she may have felt. She moved like a ship in distress,
her hat tilted at an absurd angle, her vigorous nose thrust forward
like a vulture's beak.

"My dear Lady Astenbroke," Lolita was saying in a voice which
seemed to be moderated but which she had thrown to the farthest
corner of the house with the skill of a ventriloquist . . . "I do hope
you will forgive me for running away so soon. You *will* come to the
dress rehearsal, won't you? It's been such a pleasure seeing you
again. You *will* come to see me in Rio, won't you? I'm flying back
in a few days. Well, good-bye, then . . . good-bye! Good-bye
everybody!" She gave a little toss of the head for our benefit, as
though to say—"Now that you know who I am perhaps you'll
behave more gallantly next time. You saw how Lady Astenbroke
came trotting to my side. I have only to crook my little finger and
the world comes running to me."

Her escort, whose chest was covered with medals, had come
and gone without notice. His only chance for fame was to get
killed in action. That would increase Lolita's publicity. One could
easily visualize the item on the front page. "Daring Brazilian Flyer
Killed on the Libyan Front!" A few lines devoted to his exploits
as an ace and then a long sob story about his "rumored" fiancée
Lolita, the well-known dancer now starring in the big Mitso-Violet-
Lufthansa film, "The Rose of the Desert." With photographs, to
be sure, revealing Lolita's world-famous thighs. Perhaps in another
part of the paper it would also be not too discreetly rumored that
Lolita, heart-broken though she was at the news of the Brazilian's
tragic death, had her eyes set on another dashing young officer, an
artillery man this time. They had been seen together at this place
and that during the Brazilian's absence. Lolita seemed to be
attracted to tall, broad-shouldered young men who distinguished

themselves in the gallant fight for freedom . . . And so on and so forth, until the publicity department of Mitso-Violet-Lufthansa thought the Brazilian's death had been properly exploited. For the next film there would of course be plenty to gossip about. If luck was with them, the artillery officer might also be killed in action. That would provide the opportunity for a double spread . . .

Absentmindedly I had taken a seat on the sofa, alongside a squat, garrulous creature whom I had been avoiding the whole afternoon.

"My name is Rubiol," she said, turning to me with disgustingly liquescent eyes. "*Mrs.* Rubiol . . ."

Instead of responding with "My name is Miller . . . *Henry* Miller," I said: "Rubiol . . . Rubiol . . . where have I heard that name before?"

Though it was obvious that there could only be one such name, one such monster in the whole United States, Mrs. Rubiol beamed with suffocating pleasure.

"Have you ever lived in Venice—or Carlsbad?" she cooed. "My husband and I always lived abroad—until the war. You probably heard of *him* . . . he's an inventor. You know, the triple-toothed bit for drilling . . . petroleum drills, of course . . ."

I smiled. "The only drills I know of are the ones that dentists use."

"You're not mechanical-minded, then, are you? Of course we love everything mechanical. This is the mechanical age."

"Yes," I replied, "I've heard it said before."

"You mean you don't believe it?"

"Oh yes, I believe it. Only I find it rather deplorable. I *loathe* everything mechanical."

"Not if you were living with us, you wouldn't. We never talk of anything else. You should have dinner with us some evening . . . our dinner parties are always a great success."

I let her rattle on.

"Everybody has to contribute something . . . some new idea, some fact of general interest . . ."

"How is the food?" I inquired. "Do you have a good cook? I don't care about the conversation as long as the food is good."

"What a funny man!" she giggled. "Of course the food is good."

"That's fine. That's all I ever worry about. What do you usually serve—fowl, steaks, roasts? I like a good roast beef, not too well done, and plenty of blood. And I like fresh fruit . . . not that canned stuff they give you in the restaurants. Can you make a good compôte? *Plums*—that's what I like . . . What did you say your husband was—an engineer?"

"No, an inventor."

"Oh yes, an inventor. That's a little better. What does he look like? Is he friendly?"

"You'd love him . . . he looks just like you . . . he even talks like you." She rattled on. "He's the most fascinating man when he begins talking about his inventions . . ."

"Do you ever have roast duckling—or pheasant?" I interrupted.

"Of course we do . . . What was I saying? Oh yes, about my husband. When we were in London Churchill invited him to . . ."

"*Churchill?*" I looked dumb, as though I had never heard the name.

"Yes, Winston Churchill . . . the premier."

"Oh! Yes, I've heard of him."

"This war is going to be won in the air, that's what my husband says. We've got to build more planes. That's why Church . . ."

"I don't know a thing about planes . . . never use them," I interpolated.

"That doesn't matter," said Mrs. Rubiol. "I've only been up in the air three or four times myself. But if . . ."

"Now you take balloons . . . I like them ever so much better. Do you remember Santos Dumont? He took off in a balloon for Nova Scotia from the top of the Eiffel Tower. That must have been very exciting, don't you think? What were you saying about Churchill? Excuse me for interrupting you."

Mrs. Rubiol composed her mouth to make a long, impressive speech about her husband's tête-à-tête with Churchill.

"I'll tell you something," I said, just as she was about to open her mouth, "the dinners I like best are the ones where there's plenty to drink. You know, everybody gets a little drunk, and then there's an argument and somebody gets a crack in the jaw. It isn't good for the digestion to discuss serious things at the dinner table. By the way, do you have to wear a tuxedo at your dinner parties? I haven't got any . . . I just wanted to let you know."

"You can dress as you please . . . *naturally*," said Mrs. Rubiol, still impervious to my interruptions.

"Good! I have only one suit . . . the one I'm wearing. It doesn't look so bad, do you think?"

Mrs. Rubiol gave a gracious, approving smile. "You remind me of Somerset Maugham sometimes," she rattled on. "I met him on the boat coming back from Italy. Such a charming, modest person! Nobody knew that he was Somerset Maugham except myself. He was traveling incognito . . ."

"Did you notice whether he had a club foot?" I asked.

"A club foot?" echoed Mrs. Rubiol, looking stupefactiously gaga.

"Yes, a club foot," I repeated. "Haven't you ever read his famous novel . . . *Of Human* . . ."

"*Of Human Passions!*" exclaimed Mrs. Rubiol, delighted to have guessed the wrong title. "No, but I saw the film. It was terribly morbid, don't you think?"

"Gruesome perhaps, but not morbid," I ventured. "Jolly gruesome."

"I didn't like Annabella so much in that film," said Mrs. Rubiol.

"Neither did I. But Bette Davis wasn't so bad, was she?"

"I don't remember," said Mrs. Rubiol. "What part did she play?"

"She was the switchman's daughter, don't you remember?"

"Why yes, of course I do!" exclaimed Mrs. Rubiol, trying desperately to remember something she had never seen.

"You remember when she fell headlong down the stairs with a tray full of dishes?"

"Yes, yes, of course I do! Yes, now I remember. She *was* wonderful, wasn't she? What a fall that was!"

"You were telling me about Churchill . . ."

"Yes, so I was . . . Now let me think . . . What was it I wanted to tell you . . .?"

"Tell me first of all," I put in, "does he always have a cigar in his mouth? Some people say he goes to sleep with a cigar in his mouth. Anyway, that doesn't matter. I just wondered if he was as stupid in life as he is on the screen."

"*What!*" shrieked Mrs. Rubiol. "*Churchill stupid?* Whoever heard of such a thing? He's probably the most brilliant man in England."

"Next to Whitehead, you mean."

"*Whitehead?*"

"Yes, the man who rang the gong for Gertrude Stein. You know Gertrude Stein, of course? No? Well, then you must have heard of Ernest Hemingway?"

"Oh yes, now I know. She was his first wife, wasn't she?"

"Exactly," I said. "They were married in Pont-Aven and divorced in Avignon. Whitehead doesn't come into the picture yet. He was the guy who invented the phrase 'divine entropy' . . . or was it Eddington? I'm not sure now. Anyway, when Gertrude Stein wrote *Tender Buttons* around 1919, I should think—Hemingway was still sowing his wild oats. You probably recall the Staviski trial—when Loewenstein jumped out of the aeroplane and fell into the North Sea? A lot of water has passed under the bridge since then . . .''

"I must have been in Florence then," said Mrs. Rubiol.

"And I was in Luxembourg. I suppose you've been in Luxembourg, Mrs. Rubiol? No? A charming place. I'll never forget the luncheon I had with the Grand Duchess. Not exactly what you'd call a beauty, the Grand Duchess. A cross between Eleanor Roosevelt and Queen Wilhelmina—you know what I mean? She had the gout at the time . . . But I'm forgetting about Whitehead. Now what was it you were telling me about Churchill again?''

"I'm sure I don't remember any more," said Mrs. Rubiol. "We seem to flit from one thing to another. You're really a very strange conversationalist." She tried to compose her mouth again. "Now tell me a little more about yourself," she continued. "You haven't told me anything about yourself yet."

"Oh, that's easy," I replied. "What would you like to know? I've been married five times, I have three children, two of them normal, I earn about $375.00 a year, I travel a great deal, I never go fishing or hunting, I'm kind to animals, I believe in astrology, magic, telepathy, I take no exercise, I chew my food slowly, I like dirt and flies and disease, I hate aeroplanes and automobiles, I believe in long hours, and so on. Incidentally, I was born Dec. 26th, 1891. That makes me a Capricorn with a double hernia. I wore a truss until three years ago. You've heard of Lourdes, the city of miracles, haven't you? Well, it was in Lourdes that I threw away the truss. Not that any miracle happened . . . the damned thing just fell apart and I was too broke to buy another. You see, I was born a Lutheran and Lutherans don't believe in miracles. I saw a lot of crutches at the grotto of St. Bernadette—but no trusses. To tell you the truth, Mrs. Rubiol, hernia is not nearly as bad as people pretend. Especially a *double* hernia. The law of compensation, I suppose. I remember a friend of mine who suffered from hay fever. That's something to worry about. Of course you don't go to Lourdes to cure hay fever. As a matter of fact, there is no known cure for hay fever, did you know that?''

Mrs. Rubiol wagged her head in dismay and astonishment.

"It's much easier," I continued, rippling on like a brook, "to combat leprosy. I suppose you've never been to a leper colony, have you? I spent a day once with the lepers . . . somewhere off the island of Crete it was. I was going to Knossus to see the ruins when I happened to fall in with a doctor from Madagascar. He talked so interestingly about the leper colony that I decided to go along with him. We had a wonderful lunch there—with the lepers. Broiled octopus, if I remember rightly, with okra and onions. A marvelous wine they served there. Looked blue as ink. 'The Leper's Tears,' they called it. I discovered afterwards that there was a lot of cobalt in the soil. Magnesium and mica too. Some of the lepers were very wealthy . . . like the Indians of Oklahoma. Rather cheerful people, too, on the whole, though you could never tell whether they were smiling or weeping, they were so disfigured. There was one American among them, a young fellow from Kalamazoo. His father owned a biscuit factory in Racine. He was a Phi Beta Kappa man—from Princeton. Interested in archaeology, I believe. His hands had rotted away rather quickly, it seems. But he managed pretty well with the stumps. Of course he had a good income and could make himself fairly comfortable. He had married a peasant girl . . . a leper like himself, or a *lepress* . . . I don't know how they call them. She was from Turkey, and didn't understand a word of English. But they were madly in love with one another just the same. They used a deaf and dumb language. All in all, it was a very pleasant day I spent there. The wine was excellent. I don't know whether you've ever tasted octopus. It seems a little rubbery at first, but you soon get used to it. Much better food there than at Atlanta, for instance. I had a meal once in the Penitentiary there . . . it nearly turned my stomach. Naturally the prisoners don't eat as well as the visitors . . . but just the same. No, Atlanta was foul. I think it was fried hominy they gave us—and pork drippings. Just to look at the stuff is enough to make you . . . I mean to turn your stomach. And the coffee! Simply incredible. I don't know how you feel about it, but *I* think that coffee, to be any good, must be black. It ought to look a little greasy too . . . oily like. Everything depends on the roasting, they say . . ."

At this point Mrs. Rubiol thought she would like to smoke another cigarette. It seemed to me that she was looking frantically about in search of some one else to talk to.

"My dear Mrs. Rubiol," I continued, lighting a cigarette for her and almost singeing her lips, "this has been a most delightful conversation. Have you any idea what time it is? I pawned my wrist watch just last week."

"I think it's time for me to go," said Mrs. Rubiol, glancing at her watch.

"Please don't go yet," I begged. "You have no idea how much I've enjoyed talking to you. What was it you were starting to tell me about Churchill when I so rudely interrupted you?"

Again Mrs. Rubiol, easily mollified, began composing her mouth.

"Before you begin," I said, agreeably surprised to see her

twitch, "I must tell you one more thing. It's about Whitehead. You remember I mentioned his name a while ago. Well, it's about the theory of divine entropy. Entropy means running down . . . like a clock. The idea is that with time, or *in* time, as the physicists say, everything tends to run down. The question is—will the universe run down . . . and stop? I wonder if you've ever thought of that? Not such an impossible idea, is it? Of course, Spinoza had long ago formulated his own cosmological clock-work, so to speak. Given pantheism, it follows logically that one day everything must come to an end, God included. The Greeks had come to the same conclusion, circa 500 B.C. They had even formulated the idea of eternal recurrence, which is a step beyond Whitehead's theory. You undoubtedly must have run across the idea before. I think it appears in *The Case Against Wagner*. Or perhaps it's in another book. Anyway, Whitehead, being an Englishman of the ruling class, naturally looked with skepticism upon the romantic ideas current in the Nineteenth Century. His tenets, developed in the laboratory, followed *sui generis* upon those of Darwin and Huxley. Some say that, despite the rigorous traditions which hedged him in, there is traceable in his metaphysics the influence of Haeckel— not Hegel, mind you—who was at that time regarded as the Cromwell of morphology. I'm recapitulating all this rather briefly, you understand, merely to refresh your memory . . ." I gave Mrs. Rubiol a penetrating glance which had the effect of making her twitch anew. In fact, I almost feared that she would go into a spasm. I didn't dare to think what I would say next, because I hadn't a thought in my head. I just opened my mouth and continued without a moment's reflection . . .

"There have always been two schools of thought, as you know, about the physical nature of the universe. I could take you back to the atomic theory of Empedocles, by way of corroboration, but that would only lead us afield. What I'm trying to tell you, Mrs. Rubiol, is just this: when Gertrude Stein heard the gong ring and declared Professor Albert Whitehead a genius, she inaugurated a controversy the consequences of which may not be fully felt until another thousand years have elapsed. To repeat, the question which Professor Whitehead posed was this: is the universe a machine which is running down, like an eight day clock, thus involving the inevitable extinction of life everywhere, and not only life but movement, even the movement of electrons—*or*, is this same universe imbued with the principle of regeneration? If the latter, then death has no meaning. And if death has no meaning, then all our metaphysical doctrines are eucharistic and eschatological. And by that I don't mean to embroil you in epistemological subtleties. The trend of the last thirty years is increasingly in the direction indicated by St. Thomas Aquinas. There are no more *pons asinorum* to be traversed, dialectically speaking. We have come out on firm ground . . . *terra firma*, according to Longinus. Hence the increasing interest in cyclical theories . . . witness the battles raging now over the Pluto-Neptune-Uranus transits. I don't wish to give you the impression that I am thoroughly conversant with all these developments . . . not at all! I merely point out that, by a curious spatial parallelism, theories developed in one field, such as astrophysics, for example, produce amazing reverbera-tions in other fields, fields seemingly unrelated, as for example— geomancy and hydrodynamics. You were speaking of the aero-plane a little while ago, of its decisive importance in the ultimate phases of the present war. Quite so. And yet, without a more advanced knowledge of meteorological factors the Flying Fortress, to use a concrete illustration, will only become an impediment in the development of an efficient aerial armada. The Flying Fortress, to make it more clear, Mrs. Rubiol, stands in the same relation to the mechanical bird of the future as the dinosaur stands with regard to the human helicopter. The conquest of the stratosphere is only a step in the development of human aviation. We are merely imitating the birds at present. The birds of prey, to be more precise. We build aerial dinosaurs thinking to frighten the field mice. But one has only to think of the hoary ancestry of the cockroach, to give you an absurd example, to see how utterly ineffective was the dinosaur's maniacal development of the skeletal structure. The ant was never frightened out of existence—nor the grasshopper. They are with us to-day as they were with the *pithecanthropus erectus*. And where are the dinosaurs which once roamed the primeval veldt? Frozen deep in the Arctic tundras, as you know . . ."

Mrs. Rubiol, having heard me out to this point, suddenly began to twitch in earnest. Looking past her nose, which had become as blue as a cobra's belly. I saw in the dim light of the dining room what seemed like a bad dream. Dear precious Claude was sitting in Gerald's lap, pouring thimblefuls of some precious elixir down Gerald's parched throat. Gerald was running his fingers through Claude's golden locks. Mrs. Rubiol pretended not to be aware of this dénouement. She had taken out her little mirror and was sedulously powdering her nose.

From the adjoining room Humberto suddenly made his appear-ance. He had a whiskey bottle in one hand and an empty tumbler in the other. Rocking back and forth on his heels, he looked at us benignly, as if we had requested the benediction.

"Who is that?" asked Mrs. Rubiol, at a loss to remember where she had seen him before.

"Why, don't you remember," I said, "we met at Professor Schoenberg's house last autumn. Humberto is the assistant gynaecologist at the Schizophrenic Sanitarium in New Caledonia."

"Would you like a drink?" said Humberto, staring at Mrs. Rubiol in utter bewilderment.

"Of course she would like a drink. Hand her the bottle!" With this I rose and, seizing the bottle, I pressed it to Mrs. Rubiol's lips. Too fluttered to know what to do, she swallowed a few spoonsful and began to gurgle. Then I put the bottle to my own lips and swallowed a good draught.

"It's getting interesting, don't you think?" I blurted out. "Now we can settle down to a real cosy intimate little chat, can't we?"

Humberto was listening with both ears cocked, the empty tumbler in one hand and the other grasping vainly for the missing bottle. He seemed unconscious of the fact that we had taken the bottle from him. He acted as though his fingers had grown numb; with his free hand he turned his coat collar up.

Spying a cute little vase on the table beside Mrs. Rubiol, I quickly disposed of the wilted flowers and poured a generous portion of whiskey into it. "We'll drink from this," I suggested, "it's much simpler."

"You're a Pisccan, aren't you?" said Humberto, lurching violently towards Mrs. Rubiol. "I can tell by your eyes. You don't need to tell me when you were born, just give me the date."

"He means the *place* . . . latitude and longitude. Give him the azimuth too while you're at it; that makes it less complicated."

"Wait a minute," said Humberto, "you're making it embarrassing for her."

"*Embarrassing?* Nothing could embarrass Mrs. Rubiol. Isn't that so, Mrs. Rubiol?"

"Yes," she said meekly.

I lifted the vase to her lips and decanted a half cup of whiskey. In the dining room Gerald and Claude were still playing chick-a-dee. They seemed oblivious of the world. In that eerie light, joined together like the Siamese twins, they reminded me vividly of a water color I had made recently—the one called The Honeymooners.

"You were about to say . . .?" I chirped, looking fixedly at Humberto who had wheeled round and was staring with ice-cold fascination at the Honeymooners.

"Y-e-es," said Humberto, pivoting slowly around, but without taking his eyes from the forbidden sight, "I wanted to ask you if I might have a drink."

"I just poured you one," I said.

"Where?" he asked, looking in the far corner of the room (as if there were a nice clean spittoon there with a cool drink hidden away in it).

"I was just wondering," he continued, "where my wife disappeared to. I hope she didn't take the car." He held out his free hand expectantly, as though certain the bottle would return to its original position without effort on his part. Like a slow motion picture of a man juggling Indian clubs.

"Your wife left long ago," I said. "She went off with the aviator."

"*To South America?* She must be crazy." By now he had made a few steps forward in the direction of the bottle.

"Don't you think you ought to ask Mrs. Rubiol to have a drink, too?" I said.

He stopped dead. "*A drink?*" he shouted. "She's had half a gallon already. Or am I seeing things again?"

"My dear fellow, she hasn't had as much as a thimbleful yet. She's been sniffing it, that's all. Here, give me your glass. Let her taste it, at least."

Mechanically he proffered the glass. Just as I was about to grasp it he dropped it and, turning on his heel, staggered towards the kitchen. "There must be more glasses in this house," he muttered thickly, weaving through the dining room as if it were enveloped in a thick fog.

"Naughty, naughty!" came Gerald's voice. "Sagittarius has a perpetual thirst." Pause. Then sharply, like a weary, demented old cluck: "Don't you make a mess in that kitchen, you cute little blunderbuss! The glasses are on the top shelf, left-hand side, towards the back. *Silly archer.* These Sagittarians are always stirring up trouble . . ." Another moment of silence. "In case you want to know, it's now 2.30. The party was over at midnight. Cinderella isn't going to appear to-night."

"What's that?" said Humberto, making his appearance in the doorway with a tray full of glasses.

"I said the party ended hours ago. But you're such an exclusive package we're making an exception for you—and your friends in the next room. That dirty writer friend of yours particularly. He's the queerest Capricorn I've ever met. If he wasn't human I'd say he was a leech."

Mrs. Rubiol looked at me in consternation. "Do you suppose he's going to throw us out?" said her eyes.

"My dear Mrs. Rubiol," I said, putting a judicious tincture of benzoin into my voice, "he doesn't dare to throw us out—it would jeopardize the reputation of the establishment." Then, putting a little edge to the words, "You don't mean to tell me you've finished off that vase?"

I could feel her flustering as she staggered to her feet. "Sit down," said Humberto, pushing her none too gently back onto the couch. He reached for the bottle, or where he thought the bottle was, and began to pour as if it were really in his hand. "You must have a little drink first," he said, almost with a purr.

There were five glasses on the tray, all empty.

"Where are the others?" I said.

"How many do you want? Isn't that enough?" He was groping blindly under the couch for the bottle.

"How many what?" I said. "I'm talking about people."

"And I'm trying to find the bottle," said Humberto. "The other glasses are on the shelf."

"Don't mind us!" shouted Claude from the dining room.

"Why don't you go home?" shouted Gerald.

"I think," said Mrs. Rubiol, "that we really ought to be going, don't you?" She made no effort to rise.

Humberto was now half-way under the couch. The bottle was standing on the floor beside Mrs. Rubiol.

"What do you suppose he's looking for?" she said. Absentmindedly she took another sip from the vase.

"Turn out the lights when you go," shouted Gerald. "And be sure to take Sagittarius with you. I won't be responsible for him."

Humberto was now trying to raise himself to a standing position—with the couch on his back and Mrs. Rubiol on the couch. In the commotion Mrs. Rubiol spilled some whiskey on the seat of Humberto's trousers.

"Who's peeing on me?" he yelled, making still more frantic gestures to free himself of the couch.

"If anybody's peeing," shouted Gerald, "it must be that Capricorn goat."

Mrs. Rubiol was now holding on to the back of the couch like a shipwrecked mariner.

"Lie flat, Humberto," I urged, "and I'll drag you out."

"What fell on me?" he mumbled forlornly. "This is a hell of a mess." He put his hand on his rear end, wondering, I suppose, if he had dreamed that it was wet. "As long as I didn't make caca . . . Haha! Caca! Wonderful!" he chuckled.

Mrs. Rubiol, who had now righted herself, thought this last was quite funny. She gave a few cackles and then began to choke.

"If you would go to sleep, the lot of you, I wouldn't mind," shouted Gerald. "Don't you have any sense of privacy?"

Humberto had disengaged himself; he was resting on hands and knees and blowing like a whale. Suddenly he spied the bottle. He flattened out like magic and reached for it with two arms, exactly as if he were struggling for a life-saving belt. In doing so he brushed Mrs. Rubiol's shins. "*Please!*" she murmured, her eyes twittering like two desynchronized song birds.

"Please *shit!*" said Humberto. "This is *my* turn."

"Be careful of that rug!" shouted Gerald. "I hope it's not the goat who's in trouble. The toilet is upstairs."

"Really," said Mrs. Rubiol, "this has gone far enough. I'm not accustomed to this language." She paused, as if quite distraught. Looking straight at me, she said: "Won't some one take me home, please?"

"Of course," I responded, "Humberto will drive you home."

"But can he drive—in his condition?"

"He can drive in any condition, as long as there's a steering wheel."

"I wonder," said Mrs. Rubiol, "if it wouldn't be safer if you drove me?"

"I don't drive. I could learn, though," I added quickly, "if you'd show me how the damned thing works."

"Why don't you drive yourself home?" said Humberto, pouring himself another tumblerful.

"I'd have done that long ago," said Mrs. Rubiol, "if I didn't have an artificial leg."

"*What?*" shouted Humberto. "You mean . . .?"

Mrs. Rubiol didn't have a chance to explain what she meant. "Call the police!" boomed Gerald's voice. "They'll drive you for nothing."

"Fine. Call the police!" echoed Humberto.

"That's an idea," I thought to myself. I was just about to ask where the telephone was when Gerald forestalled me.

"It's in the bedroom, dearies . . . See that you don't knock the lamp over." His voice sounded weary.

"You don't think they'll arrest us?" I heard Mrs. Rubiol saying as I stepped into the next room.

As I lifted the receiver off the hook I suddenly wondered how you ask for the police. "How do you call the police?" I shouted.

"Just yell POLICE!" said Humberto. "They'll hear you."

I called the operator and asked for the police station.

"Is anything wrong?" she asked.

"No, I just want to talk to the lieutenant at the desk."

In a moment I heard a gruff, sleepy voice yelling—*Well?*

"Hello," I said.

There was no answer.

"Hello, hello . . . do you hear me?" I shouted.

After a long silence the same gruff voice replied: "Well, what's on your mind? Anybody dead?"

"No, nobody's dead."

"Speak up! What's the matter, are you frightened stiff?"

"No, I'm all right."

"Well, come on then, get it off your chest. What is it, an accident?"

"No, everything's fine. It's just that . . ."

"What do you mean, everything's fine. What are you calling *me* for? What is this?"

"Just a minute. If you'll let me explain . . ."

"All right, all right. Go ahead and explain. But make it snappy. We can't sit on the telephone all night."

"It's like this," I began.

"Listen, cut the preliminaries! What is it? Who's hurt? Did somebody break in?"

"No, no. Nothing like that. Listen, we just wanted to know . . ."

"Oh, I see . . . Wise guy, eh? Just wanted to know what time it is, is that it?"

"No, honest, nothing like that. I'm not kidding you. I'm serious."

"Well, spit it out, then. If you can't talk I'll send the wagon down."

"The wagon? No, don't send the wagon, please. Couldn't you send a car . . . you know, a regular police car . . . with a radio and all that?"

"And soft seats, I suppose? I get you. Sure we can send a nice little car along. What would you like—a Packard or a Rolls Royce?"

"Listen, Chief . . ."

"Don't chief me! Now *you* listen for a change. Shut your trap, do you hear me? Now listen! How many of you are there?"

"There's just three of us, Chief. We thought . . ."

"Three of you, eh? Now ain't that nice? And I suppose one of you's a lady too. She sprained her ankle, ain't that it? Now listen to me! You want to sleep to-night, don't you? And you don't want any bracelets on your wrists, do you? Well listen! Just go to the bathroom . . . put a nice soft pillow in the bath tub . . . and don't forget the blankets! Then get in the bath tub, the three of you—do you hear me?—and don't let me hear another squawk out of you!

Hello! And listen to this . . . when you get nicely settled in the tub, open the cold water faucet and drown yourselves!" Bang!

"Well," yelled Gerald, when I had hung up, "are they coming?"

"I don't think so. They want us to sleep in the bath tub and then fill it with water."

"Have you ever thought of *walking* home? I think a brisk walk would be just the thing for you. Capricorns are usually very nimble on their feet." With this he advanced out of the darkness.

"But Mrs. Rubiol has an artificial leg," I pleaded.

"Let her hop home then."

Mrs. Rubiol was now deeply insulted. She rose to her feet with a surprising alacrity and made straight for the door.

"Don't let her go," said Humberto. "I'll see her home."

"That's right," shouted Gerald, "you see her home like a good boy and then fry yourself a kidney steak. Take the goat along with you." He glared at me in really menacing fashion. Claude now sidled up in his pajama top. Mrs. Rubiol turned her head away.

I had the presentiment then and there that we were going to get the bum's rush.

"Just a minute," said Humberto, still holding the bottle. He glanced towards Mrs. Rubiol disconsolately.

"Well, what now?" snapped Gerald, drawing still closer.

"But Mrs. Rubiol . . ." stammered Humberto, and he looked with pain and bewilderment at her lower limbs.

"I was just thinking," he continued, not knowing just how to phrase it, "I was wondering, since we're going to walk, if she shouldn't take off . . . well, I mean we could sort of carry her along." He made a helpless gesture with his two hands. The bottle slipped to the floor.

Being on the floor, and not knowing how to express his solicitude in words, Humberto impulsively began to crawl towards Mrs. Rubiol. Suddenly, when within reach of her, he grasped both her legs by the ankles.

"Excuse me," he mumbled, "I just wanted to know which one . . ."

Mrs. Rubiol raised her good leg and shoved him off. Humberto rolled against the leg of a rickety stand, dislodging a marble statuette. Fortunately it fell on the rug; only an arm was broken, at the elbow.

"Get him out of here before the house tumbles down!" hissed Gerald. With this he bent over Humberto's prostrate figure and with the aid of Claude raised him to a semi-standing position. "My God, he's made of rubber." He was almost whimpering with rage now.

Humberto slipped to the floor.

"He needs a drink," I said quietly.

"Give him his bottle then and bundle him out of here. This isn't a distillery."

Now the three of us struggled to raise Humberto to his feet. Mrs. Rubiol graciously rescued the bottle and raised it to Humberto's lips.

"I'm hungry," he murmured faintly.

"He wants a sandwich, I guess," I said in a gentle voice.

"And a cigarette," whispered Humberto. "Just a little puff."

"Oh, dragon's britches!" said Claude. "I'll warm the spaghetti."

"No, no spaghetti!" Humberto protested. "Just a meat ball."

"You'll take spaghetti," said Gerald. "I said it wasn't a distillery. It's not a cafeteria either. It *could be* a menagerie, though."

"It must be getting late," said Humberto. "If only Mrs. Rubiol . . ."

"Just forget about Mrs. Rubiol," snapped Gerald. "I'll take Mrs. Rubiol home."

"That's good of you," muttered Humberto. He reflected a moment. "Why the hell didn't you say so in the first place?"

"O, shush! Button your lips! You Sagittarians are just little children."

Suddenly the door-bell rang. The police, undoubtedly.

Gerald suddenly became an electric eel. In a jiffy he had hoisted Humberto to a sitting position on the couch. The bottle he kicked under the couch. "Now listen, Capricorn," he said, grabbing me by the lapels, "think fast! This is *your* house and *your* party. You're me, understand? Everything's under control. Some one did telephone, but he left. I'll take care of Claude. Now answer the bell," and he whisked off like a flash.

I opened the door to find a plain clothes man standing there. He seemed in no hurry to rush in and fingerprint us.

"Come in," I said, trying to act as if it were my home and only four in the afternoon.

"Where's the body?" That was the first question out of him.

"There ain't any body," I answered. "We're all alive."

"So I see," he said.

"Let me explain . . ." I stammered feebly.

"Don't bother," he said quietly. "Everything's O.K. I'll sit down, if you don't mind."

As he bent over I suddenly got a whiff of his breath.

"Is that your brother?" he asked, nodding in Humberto's direction.

"No, he's just a roomer."

"A rumor? That's a good name for it. Well, don't I get a drink? I saw the lights and I thought . . ."

"Give him a drink," said Humberto. "And give me one too. I don't want any spaghetti."

"*Spaghetti?*" said the man. "I just want a drink."

"Did you bring a car?" asked Humberto.

"No," said the man. After a pause, in a respectful tone: "Is the body upstairs?"

"There is no body."

"That's funny," said the man. "I was told to fetch the body." He seemed to be in dead earnest.

"Who are you?" I asked. "Who sent you?"

"Didn't you phone for us?" said the man.

"Nobody phoned for you," I said.

"I must have the wrong house. Are you sure nobody died— about an hour ago?"

"Give him a drink," said Humberto, stumbling to his feet. "I want to hear what he has to say."

"*Who* asked you to come here?" I put in. "Who are you?"

"Give me a drink, like he says, and I'll tell you. We always get a drink first."

"What's this 'we' business?" said Humberto, growing more and more lucid. "Listen, somebody give him a drink, please. And don't forget me."

"Well," said the man, "you're an astrologer, aren't you?"

"Y-e-s," I said, wondering what next.

"People tell you when they were born, don't they? But nobody can tell you when you're going to die, *right?*"

"Nobody's dying here," said Humberto, his hands twitching for a glass.

"All right," said the man, "I believe you. Anyway, we don't come till they're cold."

"There's that 'we' again. Why don't you tell us? What's your game?" Humberto was almost shouting now.

"I dress 'em," said the man, throwing a bland smile.

"And the others, what do they do?"

"They just sit around and look cheerful."

"Doing what?" I asked.

"Waiting for trade, what do you think?"

Mrs. Rubiol had at last unearthed the bottle. I thought I might as well introduce her. "This is Mrs. Rubiol," I said. "Another body . . . still warm."

"Are you a detective?" said Mrs. Rubiol, extending her hand.

"A detective? What ever gave you that idea?"

Pause.

"Lady, I'm just a plain mortician," said the man. "Somebody phoned and said you wanted us. So I put on my hat and came over. We're just two blocks away, you know." He got out his wallet and handed her a card. "McAllister & Co. That's us. No frills, no fuss."

"Jesus!" said Humberto. "A mortician, no less. Now I must have a meat ball." He stumbled a few feet towards the dining room. "Hey!" he yelled, "what became of the soubrettes?"

I went to the kitchen. No sign of either of them. I opened the back door and looked out. Everything quiet.

"They've vamoosed," I said. "Now let's see what's left in the larder. I could go some ham and eggs."

"So could I," said Humberto. "Ham and eggs. That's more like it." He paused a moment, as if puzzling something out. "You don't suppose," he whispered, "that we might find another bottle somewhere?"

"Sure, we might," said I. "Turn the place upside down. There must be a gold mine here. Ask the undertaker to help you."

Obscenity and the Law of Reflection

To discuss the nature and meaning of obscenity is almost as difficult as to talk about God. Until I began delving into the literature which has grown up about the subject I never realized what a morass I was wading into. If one begins with etymology one is immediately aware that lexicographers are bamboozlers every bit as much as jurists, moralists and politicians. To begin with, those who have seriously attempted to track down the meaning of the term are obliged to confess that they have arrived nowhere. In their book, *To the Pure*, Ernst and Seagle state that "no two persons agree on the definitions of the six deadly adjectives: obscene, lewd, lascivious, filthy, indecent, disgusting." The League of Nations was also stumped when it attempted to define what constituted obscenity. D. H. Lawrence was probably right when he said that "nobody knows what the word obscene means." As for Theodore Schroeder, who has devoted his whole life to fighting for freedom of speech[1] his opinion is that "obscenity does not exist in any book or picture, but is wholly a quality of the reading or viewing mind." "No argument for the suppression of obscene literature," he states, "has ever been offered which by unavoidable implications will not justify, and which has not already justified, every other limitation that has ever been put upon mental freedom."

As someone has well said, to name all the masterpieces which have been labeled obscene would make a tedious catalogue. Most of our choice writers, from Plato to Havelock Ellis, from Aristophanes to Shaw, from Catullus and Ovid to Shakespeare, Shelley and Swinburne, together with the Bible, to be sure, have been the target of those who are forever in search of what is impure,

[1] See his *A Challenge to Sex Censors* and other works.

489

indecent and immoral. In an article called *"Freedom of Expression in Literature,"*[1] Huntington Cairns, one of the most broadminded and clear-sighted of all the censors, stresses the need for the re-education of officials charged with law enforcement. "In general," he states, "such men have had little or no contact with science or art, have had no knowledge of the liberty of expression tacitly granted to men of letters since the beginnings of English literature, and have been, from the point of view of expert opinion, altogether incompetent to handle the subject. Administrative officials, not the populace who in the main have only a negligible contact with art, stand first in need of re-education."

Perhaps it should be noted here, in passing, that though our Federal government exercises no censorship over works of art originating in the country, it does permit the Treasury Department to pass judgments upon importations from abroad. In 1930, the Tariff Act was revised to permit the Secretary of the Treasury, in his discretion, to admit the classics or books of recognized and established literary or scientific merit, even if obscene. What is meant by "books of recognized and established literary merit?" Mr. Cairns gives us the following interpretation: "books which have behind them a substantial and reputable body of American critical opinion indicating that the works are of meritorious quality." This would seem to represent a fairly liberal attitude, but when it comes to a test, when a book or other work of art is capable of creating a furore, this seeming liberality collapses. It has been said with regard to the Sonnets of Aretino that they were condemned for four hundred years. How long we shall have to wait for the ban to be lifted on certain famous contemporary works no one can predict. In the article alluded to above, Mr. Cairns admits that "there is no likelihood whatever that the present obscenity statutes will be repealed." "None of the statutes," he goes on to say, "defines the word 'obscenity' and there is thus a wide latitude of discretion in the meaning to be attributed to the term." Those who imagine that the *Ulysses* decision established a precedent should realize by now that they were over-optimistic. Nothing has been established where books of a disturbing nature are concerned. After years of wrestling with prudes, bigots and other psychopaths who determine what we may or may not read, Theodore Schroeder is of the opinion that "it is not the inherent quality of the book which counts, but its hypothetical influence

[1] From the *Annals of the American Academy of Political and Social Science*, Philadelphia, November, 1938.

upon some hypothetical person, who at some problematical time in the future may hypothetically read the book."

In his book called *A Challenge to the Sex Censors*, Mr. Schroeder quotes an anonymous clergyman of a century ago to the effect that "obscenity exists only in the minds that discover it and charge others with it." This obscure work contains most illuminating passages; in it the author attempts to show that, by a law of reflection in nature, everyone is the performer of acts similar to those he attributes to others; that self-preservation is self-destruction, etc. This wholesome and enlightened viewpoint, attainable, it would seem, only by the rare few, comes nearer to dissipating the fogs which envelop the subject than all the learned treatises of educators, moralists, scholars and jurists combined. In Romans XIV: 14 we have it presented to us axiomatically for all time: "I know and am persuaded by the Lord Jesus that there is nothing unclean of itself, but to him that esteemeth anything to be unclean, to him it is unclean." How far one would get in the courts with this attitude, or what the postal authorities would make of it, surely no sane individual has any doubts about.

A totally different point of view, and one which deserves attention, since it is not only honest and forthright but expressive of the innate conviction of many, is that voiced by Havelock Ellis, that obscenity is a "permanent element of human social life and corresponds to a deep need of the human mind."[1] Ellis indeed goes so far as to say that "adults need obscene literature, as much as children need fairy tales, as a relief from the oppressive force of convention." This is the attitude of a cultured individual whose purity and wisdom has been acknowledged by eminent critics everywhere. It is the worldly view which we profess to admire in the Mediterranean peoples. Ellis, being an Englishman, was of course persecuted for his opinions and ideas upon the subject of sex. From the nineteenth century on all English authors who dared to treat the subject honestly and realistically have been persecuted and humiliated. The prevalent attitude of the English people is, I believe, fairly well presented in such a piece of polished inanity as Viscount Brentford's righteous self-defense—"*Do We Need a Censor?*" Viscount Brentford is the gentleman who tried to protect the English public from such iniquitous works as *Ulysses* and *The Well of Loneliness*. He is the type, so rampant in the Anglo-Saxon world, to which the words of Dr. Ernest Jones would seem to apply: "It is the people with secret attractions to various temptations who busy themselves with removing these temptations from

[1] *More Essays of Love and Virtue.*

other people; really they are defending themselves under the pretext of defending others, because at heart they fear their own weakness.

As one accused of employing obscene language more freely and abundantly than any other living writer in the English language, it may be of interest to present my own views on the subject. Since the *Tropic of Cancer* first appeared in Paris, in 1934, I have received many hundreds of letters from readers all over the world; they are from men and women of all ages and all walks of life, and in the main they are congratulatory messages. Many of those who denounced the book because of its gutter language professed admiration for it otherwise; very, very few ever remarked that it was a dull book, or badly written. The book continues to sell steadily "under the counter" and is still written about at intervals although it made its appearance thirteen years ago and was promptly banned in all the Anglo-Saxon countries. The only effect which censorship has had upon its circulation is to drive it underground, thus limiting the sales but at the same time insuring for it the best of all publicity—word of mouth recommendation. It is to be found in the libraries of nearly all our important colleges, is often recommended to students by their professors, and has gradually come to take its place beside other celebrated literary works which, once similarly banned and suppressed, are now accepted as classics. It is a book which appeals especially to young people and which, from all that I gather directly and indirectly, not only does not ruin their lives, but increases their morale. The book is a living proof that censorship defeats itself. It also proves once again that the only ones who may be said to be protected by censorship are the censors themselves, and this only because of a law of nature known to all who over-indulge. In this connection I feel impelled to mention a curious fact often brought to my attention by booksellers, namely, that the two classes of books which enjoy a steady and ever-increasing sale are the so-called pornographic, or obscene, and the occult. This would seem to corroborate Havelock Ellis's view which I mentioned earlier. Certainly all attempts to regulate the traffic in obscene books, just as all attempts to regulate the traffic in drugs or prostitution, is doomed to failure wherever civilization rears its head. Whether these things are a definite evil or not, whether or not they are definite and ineradicable elements of our social life, it seems indisputable that they are synonymous with what is called civilization. Despite all that has been said and written for and against, it is evident that with regard to these factors of social life men have never come to that agreement which they have about slavery. It is possible, of course, that one day these things may disappear, but it is also possible, despite the now seemingly universal disapproval of it, that slavery may once again be practiced by human beings.

The most insistent question put to the writer of "obscene" literature is: why did you have to use such language? The implication is, of course, that with conventional terms or means the same effect might have been obtained. Nothing, of course, could be further from the truth. Whatever the language employed, no matter how objectionable—I am here thinking of the most extreme examples—one may be certain that there was no other idiom possible. Effects are bound up with intentions, and these in turn are governed by laws of compulsion as rigid as nature's own. That is something which non-creative individuals seldom ever understand. Someone has said that "the literary artist, having attained understanding, communicates that understanding to his readers. That understanding, whether of sexual or other matters, is certain to come into conflict with popular beliefs, fears and taboos, because these are, for the most part, based on error." Whatever extenuating reasons are adduced for the erroneous opinions of the populace, such as lack of education, lack of contact with the arts, and so on, the fact is that there will always be a gulf between the creative artist and the public because the latter is immune to the mystery inherent in and surrounding all creation. The struggle which the artist wages, consciously or unconsciously, with the public, centers almost exclusively about the problem of a necessitous choice. Putting to one side all questions of ego and temperament, and taking the broadest view of the creative process, which makes of the artist nothing more than an instrument, we are nevertheless forced to conclude that the spirit of an age is the crucible in which, through one means or another, certain vital and mysterious forces seek expression. If there is something mysterious about the manifestation of deep and unsuspected forces, which find expression in disturbing movements and ideas from one period to another, there is nevertheless nothing accidental or bizarre about it. The laws governing the spirit are just as readable as those governing nature. But the readings must come from those who are steeped in the mysteries. The very depth of these interpretations naturally make them unpalatable and unacceptable to the vast body which constitutes the unthinking public.

Parenthetically it is curious to observe that painters, however unapproachable their work may be, are seldom subjected to the same meddling interference as writers. Language, because it also serves as a means of communication, tends to bring about weird obfuscations. Men of high intelligence often display execrable taste when it comes to the arts. Yet even these freaks whom we all recognize, because we are always amazed by their obtuseness, seldom have the cheek to say what elements of a picture had been better left out or what substitutions might have been effected. Take, for example, the early works of George Grosz. Compare the reactions of the intelligent public in his case to the reactions provoked by Joyce when his *Ulysses* appeared. Compare these again with the reactions which Schoenberg's later music inspired. In the case of all three the revulsion which their work first induced was equally strong, but in the case of Joyce the public was more articulate, more voluble, more arrogant in its pseudo-certitude. With books even the butcher and the plumber seem to feel that they have a right to an opinion, especially if the book happens to be what is called a filthy or disgusting one.

I have noticed, moreover, that the attitude of the public alters perceptibly when it is the work of primitive peoples which they must grapple with. Here for some obscure reason the element of the "obscene" is treated with more deference. People who would be revolted by the drawings in *Ecce Homo* will gaze unblushingly at African pottery or sculpture no matter how much their taste or morals may be offended. In the same spirit they are inclined to be more tolerant of the obscene works of ancient authors. Why? Because even the dullest are capable of admitting to themselves that other epochs might, justifiably or not, have enjoyed other customs, other morals. As for the creative spirits of their own epoch, however, freedom of expression is always interpreted as license. The artist must conform to the current and usually hypo-critical, attitude of the majority. He must be original, courageous, inspiring and all that—but never too disturbing. He must say Yes while saying No. The larger the art public, the more tyrannical, complex and perverse does this irrational pressure become. There are always exceptions, to be sure, and Picasso is one of them, one of the few artists in our time table to command the respect and attention of a bewildered and largely hostile public. It is the greatest tribute that could be made to his genius.

The chances are that during this transition period of global wars, lasting perhaps a century or two, art will become less and less important. A world torn by indescribable upheavals, a world preoccupied with social and political transformations, will have less time and energy to spare for the creation and appreciation of works of art. The politician, the soldier, the industrialist, the technician, all those in short who cater to immediate needs, to creature comforts, to transitory and illusory passions and prejudices, will take precedence over the artist. The most poetic inventions will be those capable of serving the most destructive ends. Poetry itself will be expressed in terms of block-busters and lethal gases. The obscene will find expression in the most unthinkable techniques of self-destruction which the inventive genius of man will be forced to adopt. The revolt and disgust which the prophetic spirits in the realm of art have inspired, through their vision of a world in the making will find justification in the years to come as these dreams are acted out.

The growing void between art and life, art becoming ever more sensational and unintelligible, life becoming more dull and hopeless, has been commented on almost ad nauseum. The war, colossal and portentous as it is, has failed to arouse a passion commensurate with its scope or significance. The fervor of the Greeks and the Spaniards was something which astounded the modern world. The admiration and the horror which their ferocious struggles evoked was revelatory. We regarded them as mad and heroic, and we had almost been on the point of believing that such madness, such heroism, no longer existed. But what strikes one as "obscene" and insane rather than mad is the stupendous machine-like character of the war which the big nations are carrying on. It is a war of materiel, a war of statistical preponderance, a war in which victory is coldly and patiently calculated on the basis of bigger and better resources. In the war which the Spaniards and the Greeks waged there was not only a hopelessness about the immediate outcome but a hopelessness as to the eternal outcome, so to speak. Yet they fought, and with tooth and nail, and they will fight again and again, always hopelessly and always gloriously because always passionately. As for the big powers now locked in a death struggle, one feels that they are only grooming themselves for another chance at it, for a chance to win here and now in a victory that will be everlasting, which is an utter delusion. Whatever the outcome, one senses that life will not be altered radically but to a degree which will only make it more like what it was before the conflict started. This war has all the masturbative qualities of a combat between hopeless recidivists.

If I stress the obscene aspect of modern warfare it is not simply because I am against war but because there is something about the ambivalent emotions it inspires which enables me better to grapple with the nature of the obscene. Nothing would be regarded as obscene, I feel, if men were living out their inmost desires. What man dreads most is to be faced with the manifestation, in word or deed, of that which he has refused to live out, that which he has throttled or stifled, buried, as we say now, in his subconscious mind. The sordid qualities imputed to the enemy are always those which we recognize as our own and therefore rise to slay, because only through projection do we realize the enormity and horror of them. Man tries as in a dream to kill the enemy in himself. This enemy, both within and without, is just as, but no more, real than the phantoms in his dreams. When awake he is apathetic about this dream self, but asleep he is filled with terror. I say "when awake," but the question is, *when is he awake, if ever?* To those who no longer need to kill, the man who indulges in murder is a sleep walker. He is a man trying to kill himself in his dreams. He is a man who comes face to face with himself *only in the dream.* This man is the man of the modern world, everyman, as much a myth and a legend as the Everyman of the allegory. Our life to-day is what we dreamed it would be aeons ago. Always it has a double thread running through it, just as in the age-old dream. Always fear and wish, fear and wish. Never the pure fountain of desire. And so we have and we have not, we are and we are not.

In the realm of sex there is a similar kind of sleepwalking and self-delusion at work; here the bifurcation of pure desire into fear and wish has resulted in the creation of a phantasmagorical world in which love plays the role of a chameleon-like scapegoat. Passion is conspicuous by its absence or by monstrous deformations which render it practically unrecognizable. To trace the history of man's attitude towards sex is like threading a labyrinth whose heart is situated in an unknown planet. There has been so much distortion and suppression, even among primitive peoples, that to-day it is virtually impossible to say what constitutes a free and healthy attitude. Certainly the glorification of sex, in pagan times, represented no solution of the problem. And, though Christianity ushered in a conception of love superior to any known before, it did not succeed in freeing man sexually. Perhaps we might say that the tyranny of sex was broken through sublimation in love, but the nature of this greater love has been understood and experienced only by a rare few.

Only where strict bodily discipline is observed, for the purpose of union or communion with God, has the subject of sex ever been faced squarely. Those who have achieved emancipation by this route have, of course, not only liberated themselves from the tyranny of sex but from all other tyrannies of the flesh. With such individuals, the whole body of desire has become so transfigured that the results obtained have had practically no meaning for the man of the world. Spiritual triumphs, even though they effect the man in the street immediately, concern him little, if at all. He is seeking for a solution of life's problems on the plane of mirage and delusion; his notions of reality have nothing to do with ultimate effects; he is blind to the permanent changes which take place above and beneath his level of understanding. If we take such a type of being as the Yogi, whose sole concern is with reality, as opposed to the world of illusion, we are bound to concede that he has faced every human problem with the utmost courage and lucidity. Whether he incorporates the sexual or transmutes it to the point of transcendence and obliteration, he is at least one who has attained to the vast open spaces of love. If he does not reproduce his kind, he at least gives new meaning to the word birth. In lieu of copulating he creates; in the circle of his influence conflict is stilled and the harmony of a profound peace established. He is able to love not only individuals of the opposite sex but all individuals, everything that breathes, in fact. This quiet sort of triumph strikes a chill in the heart of the ordinary man, for not only does it make him visualize the loss of his meagre sex life but the loss of passion itself, passion as he knows it. This sort of liberation, which smashes his thermometrical gauge of feeling, represents itself to him as a living death. The attainment of a love which is boundless and unfettered terrifies him for the very good reason that means the dissolution of his ego. He does not want to be freed for service, dedication and devotion to all mankind; he wants comfort, assurance and security, the enjoyment of his very limited powers. Incapable of surrender, he can never know the healing power of faith; and lacking faith he can never begin to know the meaning of love. He seeks release but not liberation, which is like saying that he prefers death instead of life.

As civilization progresses it becomes more and more apparent that war is the greatest release which life offers the ordinary man. Here he can let go to his heart's content for here crime no longer has any meaning. Guilt is abolished when the whole planet swims in blood. The lulls of peacetime seem only to permit him to sink deeper into the bogs of the sadistic-masochistic complex which has fastened itself into the heart of our civilized life like a cancer. Fear, guilt and murder—these constitute the real triumvirate which rules our lives. *What is obscene then?* The whole fabric of life as we know it to-day. To speak only of what is indecent, foul, lewd, filthy, disgusting, etc., in connection with sex, is to deny ourselves the luxury of the great gamut of revulsion-repulsion which modern life puts at our service. Every department of life is vitiated and corroded with what is so unthinkingly labeled "obscene." One wonders if perhaps the insane could not invent a more fitting, more inclusive term for the polluting elements of life which we create and shun and never identify with our behavior. We think of the insane as inhabiting a world completely divorced from reality, but our own everyday behavior, whether in war or peace, if examined from only a slightly higher standpoint, bears all the earmarks of insanity. "I have said," writes a well-known psychologist, "that this is a mad world, that man is most of the time mad; and I believe that in a way what we call morality is merely a form of madness, which happens to be a working adaptation to existing circumstances."

When obscenity crops out in art, in literature more particularly, it usually functions as a technical device; the element of the deliberate which is there has nothing to do with sexual excitation, as in pornography. If there is an ulterior motive at work it is one which goes far beyond sex. Its purpose is to awaken, to usher in a sense of reality. In a sense, its use by the artist may be compared to the use of the miraculous by the Masters. This last minute quality, so closely allied to desperation, has been the subject of endless debate. Nothing connected with Christ's life, for example, has been exposed to such withering scrutiny as the miracles attributed to him. The great question is: should the Master indulge himself or should he refrain from employing his extraordinary powers? Of the great Zen masters it has been observed that they never hesitate to resort to any means in order to awaken their disciples; they will even perform what we would call sacrilegious acts. And, according to some familiar interpretations of the Flood, it has been acknowledged that even God grows desperate at times and wipes the slate clean in order to continue the human experiment on another level.

It should be recognized, however, with regard to these questionable displays of power, that only a Master may hazard them. As a matter of fact, the element of risk exists only in the eyes of the uninitiated. The Master is always certain of the result; he never plays his trump card, as it were, except at the psychological moment. His behavior, in such instances, might be compared to that of the chemist pouring a last tiny drop into a prepared solution in order to precipitate certain salts. If it is a push it is also a supreme exhortation which the Master indulges in. Once the moment is passed, moreover, the witness is altered forever. In another sense, the situation might be described as the transition from belief to faith. Once faith has been established, there is no regression; whereas with belief everything is in suspense and capable of fluctuation.

It should also be recognized that those who have real power have no need to demonstrate it for themselves; it is never in their

own interests, or for their own glorification, that these performances are made. In fact, there is nothing miraculous, in the vulgar
sense, about these acts, unless it be the ability to raise the
consciousness of the onlooker to that mysterious level of illumination which is natural to the Master. Men who are ignorant of the
source of their powers, on the other hand, men who are regarded
as the powers that move the world, usually come to a disastrous
end. Of their efforts it is truly said that all comes to nought. On
the worldly level nothing endures, because on this level, which is
the level of dream and delusion, all is fear and wish vainly ce-
mented by will.

To revert to the artist again . . . Once he has made use of his
extraordinary powers, and I am thinking of the use of obscenity in
just such magical terms, he is inevitably caught up in the stream of
forces beyond him. He may have begun by assuming that he could
awaken his readers, but in the end he himself passes into another
dimension of reality wherein he no longer feels the need of forcing
an awakening. His rebellion over the prevalent inertia about him
becomes transmuted, as his vision increases, into an acceptance
and understanding of an order and harmony which is beyond man's
conception and approachable only through faith. His vision expands with the growth of his own powers, because creation has its
roots in vision and admits of only one realm, the realm of imagination. Ultimately, then, he stands among his own obscene objur-
gations like the conqueror midst the ruins of a devastated city. He
realizes that the real nature of the obscene resides in the lust to
convert. He knocked to awaken, but it was himself he awakened.
And once awake, he is no longer concerned with the world of
sleep; he walks in the light and, like a mirror, reflects his illumination in every act.

Once this vantage point is reached, how trifling and remote seem
the accusations of moralists! How senseless the debate as to
whether the work in question was of high literary merit or not!
How absurd the wrangling over the moral or immoral nature of his
creation! Concerning every bold act one may raise the reproach of
vulgarity. Everything dramatic is in the nature of an appeal, a
frantic appeal for communion. Violence, whether in deed or
speech, is an inverted sort of prayer. Initiation itself is a violent
process of purification and union. Whatever demands radical treatment demands God, and always through some form of death or
annihilation. Whenever the obscene crops out one can smell the
imminent death of a form. Those who possess the highest clue are
not impatient, even in the presence of death; the artist in words,
however, is not of this order, he is only at the vestibule, as it were,

of the palace of wisdom. Dealing with the spirit, he nevertheless
has recourse to forms. When he fully understands his role as
creator he substitutes his own being for the medium of words. But
in that process there comes the "dark night of the soul" when,
exalted by his vision of things to come and not yet fully conscious
of his powers, he resorts to violence. He becomes desperate over
his inability to transmit his vision. He resorts to any and every
means in his power; this agony, in which creation itself is parodied,
prepares him for the solution of his dilemma, but a solution wholly
unforeseen and mysterious as creation itself.

All violent manifestations of radiant power have an obscene
glow when visualized through the refractive lens of the ego. All
conversions occur in the speed of a split second. Liberation implies
the sloughing off of chains, the bursting of the cocoon. What is
obscene are the preliminary or anticipatory movements of birth,
the preconscious writhing in the face of a life to be. It is in the
agony of death that the nature of birth is apprehended. For in what
consists the struggle if it is not between form and being, between
that which was and that which is about to be? In such moments
creation itself is at the bar; whoever seeks to unveil the mystery
becomes himself a part of the mystery and thus helps to perpetuate
it. Thus the lifting of the veil may be interpreted as the ultimate
expression of the obscene. It is an attempt to spy on the secret
processes of the universe. In this sense the guilt attaching to
Prometheus symbolizes the guilt of man-the-creator, of man-the-
arrogant-one who ventures to create before being crowned with
wisdom.

The pangs of birth relate not to the body but to the spirit. It was
demanded of us to know love, experience union and communion,
and thus achieve liberation from the wheel of life and death. But
we have chosen to remain this side of Paradise and to create
through art the illusory substance of our dreams. In a profound
sense we are forever delaying the act. We flirt with destiny and lull
ourselves to sleep with myth. We die in the throes of our own
tragic legends, like spiders caught in their own webs. If there is
anything which deserves to be called "obscene" it is this oblique,
glancing confrontation with the mysteries, this walking up to the
edge of the abyss, enjoying all the ecstasies of vertigo and yet
refusing to yield to the spell of the unknown. The obscene has all
the qualities of the hidden interval. It is as vast as the Unconscious
itself and as amorphous and fluid as the very stuff of the Unconscious. It is what comes to the surface as strange, intoxicating and
forbidden, and which therefore arrests and paralyzes, when in the
form of Narcissus we bend over our own image in the mirror of

our own iniquity. Acknowledged by all, it is nevertheless despised and rejected, wherefore it is constantly emerging in Protean guise at the most unexpected moments. When it is recognized and accepted, whether as a figment of the imagination or as an integral part of human reality, it inspires no more dread or revulsion than could be ascribed to the flowering lotus which sends its roots down into the mud of the stream on which it is borne.

On the War

I. *Murder the Murderer*
(Excerpt)

I do not say that the men who believe in war as a last resort are necessarily evil, necessarily worse than other men; I say they are stupid, they lack vision, magnanimity, wisdom. When they speak of war as being the last resort can we be certain that they have tried every other means of preserving peace? I am afraid not. I am afraid that even such a sorry figure of an appeaser as Chamberlain had done very little to avert the inevitable. What merit is there in pretending to save the peace of the world when one is unwilling to yield the very things which are the cause of the conflict? It is easy to say we want peace when we are the stronger, when we have the necessities for which the other is hungering. Naturally the one who is desperate enough to risk an open conflict is not playing the game according to our rules. *Naturally* he is the disturber of the peace. *But what made him disturb the peace?* Sheer malice? Sheer diabolical greed, envy, hatred? Even if one has to admit that the Germans are poisoned with hatred, one has also to admit that we who oppose them are not precisely suffused with radiant love. Men do not become poisoned with hatred in a vacuum, nor when surrounded by loving, sympathetic neighbors. No great mystery surrounds the psychosis of the German people. Neither is there any mystery attached to the unwillingness of the British imperialists to part with their illegitimate possessions. Nor is there anything mysterious about the reluctance of the American people to enter a war which concerns the fate of an empire which has always been hostile to our best interests . . .

A period of darkness has set in. The world seems determined to resolve its problems by force. No single individual can stem the tide of hate. We are in the grip of cosmic forces and each one does what he can, or must.

To each man the conflict assumes a different face. Millions of men and women will sacrifice their lives; millions more will be maimed and mutilated. The innocent will suffer with the guilty, the wise with the foolish. It is beyond control now; we are in the hands of Fate.

Useless to say now that it need not have happened. It is not for us to question what happens; it is for us to accept. But there are a thousand ways of accepting the inevitable. In the way we accept lies our ability to transform a situation. No disaster is irremediable. The whole meaning of life is contained in the word suffering. That all the world can be suffering at one time is a fact of tremendous significance.[1] It never has happened before. It is an opportunity which we can reject or use to advantage.

Since I am having my say, I want to reveal what I sincerely believe this opportunity may be. We, the American people, having resisted war to the very last, have now thrown ourselves into the universal conflict. Whether we admit it to ourselves or not, whether or not we have lived up to that faith which the other peoples of the world have in us, *we are the hope of the world*. That is the rock on which America was founded. Let it be our rock now!

Are we at war to extend our empire, to increase our possessions, to gain ascendancy over the other nations of this earth? I believe the great body of American people would answer NO! Like other peoples, we have been misguided. Above all, we had grown callous and indifferent. That was our crime. To-day we are ready to accept our share of suffering, along with the righteous and the unrighteous. Moreover, we are determined to endure what we have never endured before. That was evident the day war was declared.

What can we as a people do beyond anything our allies may expect of us? We can be magnanimous and far-sighted, we can be patient and full of understanding; we can be hard as steel, yet wise and full of tenderness when the time is ripe. We can be all these things because we are the favored people of the earth. Our forefathers, when first they came to this country, were hailed as gods. To our disgrace they behaved as demons. They asked for gold instead of grace. To-day their sins are visited upon us. We are paying now for the crimes committed by our ancestors. They fled their self-imposed prisons because they had a vision of Paradise.

---

[1] Not quite the whole world!—the "civilized" peoples mostly.

Had they acted as the gods they were mistaken for by the aborigines of this continent they could have realized the Paradise which they were seeking. But they were only men and they were weak, and because they were weak the dream of Paradise was forgotten. Dreams are hard to kill; they linger on even when the memory of them is faded. The dream of golden opportunity still clings to the name America no matter what part of the world you may go to. It is regrettable that we, the American people, have fostered a false interpretation of that dream and thereby helped to further poison the world. We have given the impression that America was a place in which to grow rich. We have emphasized gold instead of opportunity. Out of greed we killed the goose that laid the golden egg. Yet, despite the tragic error, we all know that there *was* a golden goose. We are now at the point where we are obliged to interpret the fable intelligently.

What *was* the golden opportunity which was offered the American pilgrim? The opportunity to serve the world, the opportunity to bring about enlightenment and justice. Since the inception of this republic we had no enemies save the mother country, England. We were surrounded by friends. The only great struggle we had was an internal one. Then, in the last war, we were dragged into a world-wide conflict whose significance we only partially understood. The war over, we tried to take refuge again in our comfortable shell, unwilling to accept the responsibilities we had assumed as participants of that great conflict. We refused to sit at the Hague Tribunal and assist in the first crude attempt to establish some kind of international law and order. We refused for years to recognize the one government which had taken the lesson of the war to heart and was endeavoring to bring about a more intelligent and equitable order of human society. With the emergence of the dictators we sat by and watched one little nation after the other swallowed up and enslaved. When France fell we were full of bitterness. We cried "Shame!" though we hadn't lifted a finger to help her. We would have suffered England to undergo the same fate, but the English were made of different stuff. Until the treacherous attack by Japan, which we should have anticipated, considering all the lessons we had been given, we were undecided what course to pursue. Now suddenly we are united and, as in the last war, we are pretending that we are fighting to free the world. The newspapers are doing their best to make the American people believe this beautiful legend, knowing well that the psychology of the American people is based on a sense of utter unreality, that only when we visualize ourselves as saviours and crusaders can we kill with fury and efficiency. "Now at last," I read in to-day's paper, "a single devotion inspires the nation, a great moment has touched us and America has fallen in step to heroic music. We have renounced triviality, indifference and fear, we have taken up the responsibilities of our position in the world, we have turned as one man toward a shining star."[1] It goes on like that, soaring, skyrocketing, to end with the phrase "without compromise—to win."

It is unthinkable that we shall lose. But what do we hope to win? Or better, what do we hope to win to? That is the question which the editorial gentry cleverly evade by grandiloquent phrases such as "ridding the world forever of the Nazi pestilence," and so on. Are we microbe hunters and bug exterminators? Are we merely going to preserve the *tomb* of Christ from the desecrating paw of the infidel? For two thousand years the world has been squabbling over the dead body of Christ. The Christians themselves will admit that God sent his son, a *living* Christ, to redeem the world. He didn't send us a corpse to fight over. In effect, however, that is what the Christian world has done: it has welcomed every excuse to fight in the name of Christ who came to bring peace on earth. There can be no end to this repetitious pattern until each and every one of us become as Christ, until belief and devotion transform our words into deeds and thus make of myth reality.

"To War—and Beyond" reads the caption of the editorial I just cited. We are all interested in what lies beyond the war. Nobody is any longer interested in war for the sake of war. But what comes after the war depends altogether on the spirit in which we wage war. We will accomplish exactly what we aim to accomplish, and no more. In this respect war is no different from peace. The fact that we are desperate instead of lethargic means nothing, if we are not clear as to what we wish to attain. To defeat Hitler and his gang is not a particularly brilliant goal to set oneself. Hitler and his gang could have been defeated without war had we possessed the intelligence, the will, and the purity to undertake the task. Wherever there is indecision, confusion, dalliance and an atmosphere of unreality, you have Hitler. Just as Judas was necessary in order for Christ to enact the drama which was ordained, so Hitler was necessary for this age in order that the world might enact the drama of unification and regeneration. Christ chose Judas to betray him; we have chosen Hitler. All the intermediary figures, the supernumeraries, so to speak, good, honest gentlemen though they be, are dwarfed by this Satanic figure which looms across the horizon. Churchill, Roosevelt, Stalin, none of these is big enough to cope with the monster alone. It is fortunate that they are not, for now it devolves upon the little men, the poor anonymous figures who make up the great mass of humanity, to answer the challenge. Christ chose twelve little men to do his work—not great world figures. . .

In the midst of this incredible toil and bubble new inventions are being turned out by the hour. Finally the great invention of the ages is ushered in—a sort of human Flit. A device which destroys the enemy everywhere instantaneously. Something so ingenious, so simple too, that it needs only to be stamped with a single word, such as *Japanese, German, Bulgarian, Italian*, and it goes directly to the mark, annihilating its victim. Total annihilation of the enemy everywhere! Think of the effect which this produces! At last the ideal victory. Something indeed which the men of this scientific age might well be proud of! Power! Absolute power! No need for Peace Conferences henceforth. No need to ball things up through compromise, chicanery and intrigue, as in the past. All our enemies are dead. Annihilated. The power to rule the world in our own hands. Who now will dare to rise up against us? Magnificent, *what*?

There are those, of course, who will immediately cry "Absurd! Fantastic! Impossible!" A *human Flit?* . . . tsch, tsch, tsch! How many years ago is it that the same was said against the steamboat, the railroad, the aeroplane, the telegraph, the telephone, the electric light, the X-ray? Is it necessary to reel off the whole list of what was once absurd, impossible and fantastic, to say nothing of impracticable, unprofitable, demonic and diabolical? *Whatever man sets his mind on accomplishing he accomplishes*. That is the beautiful and terrible thing about man, that he has within himself the power and the ability to make his dreams come true. . .

Since the democratic wars, which began with Napoleon, the passion for making war has dwindled. The manner in which America went to war in 1917 is significant. Never before in the history of the world had there been coined the slogan—"*a war to end war*." We failed in our high purpose because we were unwilling to accept the responsibility which this magnificent gesture entailed. We were *not* without selfish motives, as we pretended. Hand in hand with the desire to bring about the end of all war was the desire to "make the world safe for democracy." Not real democracy, but the American brand. We did not open the way to debate and experiment. We only enabled our allies, who were full of fear and greed, to re-establish dominion over the defeated. We stood by and watched them shackle and manacle their victims. We did everything possible to abort the one promising experiment which the war brought about.

Now the task has to be performed all over again, this time at greater cost, greater risk, greater sacrifice. During the twenty years of moral stagnation which followed upon the last war the great body of Americans became more than ever disillusioned about making war. We waited to be attacked. We knew we would be attacked. We invited it. It was the only way to salve our conscience. We gained nothing from the last war, not even the gratitude of those whom we saved from destruction. We start out even more confused this time, avowedly to save our own skins and rather shamefacedly to save the world. *We will not save the world*—let us admit that immediately. If God could not do it, by sending his only begotten Son, how can we, a people swollen with pride and self-satisfaction? It doesn't matter whether you believe in the Christ story or not. The legend is profound and tragically beautiful. It has truth in it. The Son of God came to awaken the world by his example. *How he lived* is the important thing, not how he died. We are all crucified, whether we know it or not.

Nations reflect the cowardice and selfishness of the peoples which constitute them. It may have been possible once to serve God and country simultaneously. That is no longer true. The peoples of the earth have a great and compelling urge to unite. The boundaries established by nationalism are no longer valid. People are now murdering one another in a confused effort to break down these boundaries. Those who realize the true nature of the issue are at peace, even though they wield the sword.

Freedom without self-mastery is a snare and a delusion. Do we want power over others, or do we want liberation? The true liberators want to establish a world in which there is neither master nor slave, the democracy which Lincoln advocated. The warrior of the future will murder freely, without orders from above. He will murder whatever is murderous in human nature. He will not be an avenger but a liberator. He will not fight to destroy an ism but to destroy the destroyers, *whoever* they be and *wherever* they be. He will go on fighting even after peace is declared. He will make war until war becomes the lifeless thing which at heart it is.

Murder, murder! It's a fascinating subject. No end to it, seemingly. You know what it's like to kill a spider, an ant, a fly, a mosquito. You do it automatically, without the least compunction. Somehow it's not so easy to adopt that attitude with regard to human beings, even when the latter are annoying or dangerous, as the case may be. In a war such as the present one human beings are being polished off like fleas. To imagine the possibilities ahead, should we really discover that human Flit I spoke of, is almost unthinkable. Right now, at this point in the game, it is difficult to say whether the discoverer would be hailed as a saviour or an enemy to human society. If he springs from *our* side of the fence he will probably be looked upon as the saviour of mankind; if from the other side then as the Devil incarnate. *Is that so, or isn't it?* It's a moral dilemma of the first water. The so-called honest citizen who, in casting his vote for Tweedledum or Tweedledee feels that he has done his duty by the State, will of course refuse to occupy his mind with such a moral problem. It's too fantastic, too remote. He went to the polls last election, both sides promising to keep him out of the war, and he cast a mighty vote. Then the dirty Japs came and stabbed us in the back. Of course neither Tweedledum nor Tweedledee had expected such a dénouement. They were aghast, both of them, at such perfidy. And so war was solemnly declared. We were attacked by a treacherous enemy, our honor was violated. Just yesterday I saw Roosevelt and Churchill posing for the photographers. They were sitting side by side, and Roosevelt was beaming all over. Churchill looked a ringer for Schweik the good soldier. These are the heavenly twins who are going to save the world for us. Angelic creatures, I must say. Mind you, there'll be a bit of hard sledding first. We may have to sacrifice twenty-five or thirty million men, to say nothing of the enemy's losses. But when it's over there'll be an end of Hitler and Mussolini—and perhaps of that feeble-minded yellow-bellied Emperor Hirohito. It'll be worth it, what! A year from now, or two years or five or ten or twenty, we may have the pleasure of again seeing our two leaders arm in arm—when it comes time to inspect the graves of the dead. They will have to go places to bless all the dead this time. But with new inventions coming along they will probably be able to visit all the graves in jig time. If any one reading these lines imagines for one moment that it wasn't necessary to sacrifice all these lives I advise him to keep his mouth closed. There *was* no other way out, you understand. Over 200,000,000 people, hypnotized by their insane leaders, refused to see that the democratic way of life is the best. Somehow, possibly because of the bad example we gave them, they remained unconvinced. Or perhaps they were just lazy-minded and decided that, if they had to fight, they might as well fight for their own way of life. That's a possibility too. Anyway, under the divine tutelage of Roosevelt and Churchill, we are now going to convince them—by extirpating them. Stalin will have something to say about it too, don't forget, because for the moment he's a democrat too. Good old Stalin!

Only a few months ago he was an assassin, a fiend who was putting to death a helpless little country like Finland.[1] Some say that Stalin is even more democratic than Roosevelt or Churchill, believe it or not. They say he doesn't trust his democratic partners completely. I don't know why, because our hands are clean, we always act above board, as they say. We never help the little countries unless they're on the right side of the fence. *Strictly neutral*—until we're attacked and our own rights placed in jeopardy! Spain, Greece, Holland, Denmark, Belgium, Norway—we've always given them fine words of encouragement, haven't we? Gentleman-like, you know. Even with a big country like China we were behaving strictly according to Hoyle—until the Pearl Harbor fiasco. No more scrap-iron now for the dirty Japs—we're through with them. China, you will be rescued too—just wait a bit! *And India?* Well now, that's a horse of another color. Don't be so impatient, dear India. You will be freed, in time. Roosevelt and Churchill will arrange every-thing—when the proper moment comes. First we must get Hitler—he's the one who's responsible for this terrible mess. Impossible even to think straight until he's eliminated. You see how it is, don't you? *Be reasonable!*

Suppose we win the war, as we undoubtedly will, because we *must*, don't you know. Every one will get a square deal, including Hitler, Mussolini and Hirohito the feeble-minded yellow-belly. Austria will become Austrian again; Czechoslovakia Czechoslova-kian; Poland Polish; Denmark Danish; France French; Hungary Hungarian; Greece Greek; China Chinese; Finland Finnish; Latvia Latvian; Spain Spanish. Et cetera, et cetera, et cetera. Everything will be put in place again, just as it was before Hitler. It will be a new A. D. for the world, only this time everybody will have to be satisfied. We won't stand for any grousing. Wilhelmina must be put back on her throne. Haakon must be put back on *his* throne. (That is, if they're still alive and hankering for the job.) Hirohito of course must die, and so must Hitler and Mussolini. We've had enough of these bastards—they damned near ruined the world. And when we polish these maniacs off we don't want any revolu-tion to spring up either. None of that nonsense this time. Revolu-tions are not democratic—they're disturbing, that's what. The Russian revolution, of course, was different. They made a good job of it, as we see now twenty years later. There *are* exceptions, naturally. But all that is in the past. Russia has been doing magnificently recently—just like any other democratic country. In fact, almost too good. We want her to act discreetly when this

[1] Now he's putting her to death again, but this time it's O.K.—she deserved it.

affair is over. Stalin, no monkey business! Yes, we've got to go cautiously when it comes to re-arranging the world. A little country like Bosnia or Croatia—an "enclave," we call it—can cause a lot of trouble. And then there's France, don't forget. Now she's half Vichy and half Pluto. We've got to fuse or weld the irreconcilables—gently, skillfully, of course. With an acetylene torch, if necessary. Can't allow France to slip back into a monarchical form of government. That would be disastrous. The monarchy is all right for Norway, Belgium, Holland and such like—or for England. But not for France. Why? Well *because* . . .

You see, there are going to be little problems coming up. We must be patient and willing to cooperate. That is, *they* must, the other fellows. We wouldn't be sacrificing the lives and fortunes of our good honest citizens did we not know what we were about. We honestly avoided the issue as long as possible, did we not? We had been worried about the world, what it was coming to, ever since Hitler began his crazy antics. But it wasn't our place to interfere—until we were ourselves attacked and dishonored—and by a halfwitted yellow-belly of all things. That really was unforgivable. And yet, if he hadn't spat in our face, who knows—perhaps we wouldn't yet be ready to assume the task of putting the world in order. We have nothing to gain from this conflict. That's clear to every one, I hope. All we want is to see the restoration of the old status quo. We've kept all the maps of the ancient world; we know just what belongs to whom, and we're going to see to it that what's his name gets his what not. And this time, dear fellow-Europeans, dear Chinese, dear Hindus, dear Patagonians, dear Eskimos, dear Zulus, dear Zombies, we want to be spared the humiliation of receiving a kick in the slats for our pains. Though we had to wait until we were treacherously attacked by that degenerate son of the Sun, we do not intend to stop fighting once we have driven the invader from our colonial outposts. We took a terrible slap in the face, but it was good for us, it enabled us to get properly worked up about the plight of the world. To be "the arsenal of the world" was all right as political propaganda—because at bottom, you know, we just loathe and abhor war—but now that we can use the arsenal ourselves we feel better. War is a nasty thing to watch, but once you're in it you feel differently about it. If you want to see an allout war, boy, just keep your eye on us! We'll fry them alive, every man, woman and child that opposes us. Yes sir, no holding us back once we get our dander up. Nagasaki will look like a flaming rum omelette once we concentrate our attention on it. Berlin too, I'm telling you. And if it weren't for the Pope and his dear Vatican, I'd say the same for Rome. But that's a ticklish proposition, the

Vatican. We don't want to blow up his Holiness the Pope accidentally. That's understandable, is it not? The Pope stands for peace—almost at any price. We all do, as a matter of fact—it's only in this matter of the price that we differ from one another. Even the Crusaders were peaceable souls. But they wanted Christ's bones to be left untouched, to lie in Christian soil. And so they fought tooth and nail to destroy the infidels. Some of them returned with the most amazing booty—but that's another story. I was almost on the point of saying that the civilization of Europe began with the return of the victorious Crusaders—you know, Chartres, Amiens, Beauvais, Notre Dame. It would be strange now, wouldn't it, if our Crusaders came back from Moscow and Leningrad, after signing the Peace Treaty, and found themselves afire with the spirit of collective government. That *would* give a queer twist to the situation. Let's hope that the good democratic spirit will survive all temptation. After all, it's a Christian world that we want to save, isn't it? To-morrow is Christmas day and we Christians all over the world will unite in prayer, as we have been doing for nigh on to two thousand years. It seems a little discouraging, perhaps, that after two thousand years we are praying for peace in full uniform, but that's not our fault. If it hadn't been for Hitler and that yellow-faced pagan Hirohito, we'd probably be at peace, isn't that so? It's amazing how, just when we get set for the millennium, some warmonger comes along and upsets our equilibrium. Fortunately we have our own dialectic. That instructs us how to build a permanent peace while being realistically on the alert to make war whenever and wherever necessary. We know what the goal is, which is more, I suppose, than one can say for Hitler and his satellites. The goal is Peace—but to get there you would be a damned fool if you didn't keep a revolver, or at least a hand grenade, in your hip pocket. There have always been, and there still are apparently, two kinds of people in the world: those who want peace and those who want war. Logic dictates that the peaceable ones must extinguish the war-like ones. That is to say, in order to be peaceful you must be a better fighter than the warrior. It sounds like a conundrum at first, but then the history of the world has demonstrated that it is very clear and simple. Wars are getting less and less frequent. We've had about six or eight wars in my life-time, but that's nothing compared to years ago. Before Napoleon's day only professional armies waged war. Nowadays everybody fights—to bring about peace. The last fight will be a splendid one, I'm sure of it. We've only begun to fight, as the saying goes. You see, the more peaceful we get the better we fight. If we were just fighting to fight we might grow slack, because even fighting can grow dull and monotonous if you think only of fighting. But to fight for peace—that's marvelous. That puts iron in you. When the millennium comes we'll all be tough as steel. We'll know how to enjoy peace, just as a murderer learns to enjoy the electric chair. In his zeal to kill, the murderer forgets about the electric chair—but it's always there, always waiting for him. That's his bliss, and when he sizzles and fries he realizes it and thanks the Creator for having made him a murderer. So it is with us. In our zeal to destroy the enemies of peace we forget that war brings about the death and destruction of all that is human and sacred. Peace awaits us, yes—but it is the peace of the grave. The only peace we seem capable of understanding is the peace of death. We make one grand crusade after another in order to rescue the tomb of Christ from the hands of the infidel. We preserve the dead Christ, never the living one. Merry Christmas, I say, and peace on earth! I will not step into St. Patrick's Cathedral to offer up a prayer. I will not appeal to an impotent God to stop the carnage. I will not stand like a savage before the altar of superstition with a javelin in my hand and a mumbo-jumbo incantation on my lips. I will not ask the Creator to bless America without including Japan, German, Italy, Roumania, Bulgaria, Hungary and the other countries of the world. I cannot consider myself as innocent and the other fellow guilty. I am not a hypocrite, neither am I an ignoramus, though the society in which I was reared has done its best to make me behave like both. I say that peace can be brought about any time—*when we want it!* We have found the cunning and the ingenuity to invent the most diabolical weapons of destruction. We are versed in the art of war as no people before us has ever been. War is what we wanted—not peace! And now we have it, I say once again: "Merry Christmas! And a happy New Year!"

The above is scarcely off the typewriter when, on my way to lunch (it is the day before Christmas), I pick up the *N. Y. Post.* At the Italian restaurant, where I usually eat, I spread it open and lo! I come upon the following:

"CHRISTMAS IN MOSCOW"
by
A. T. Steele

It's not about Christmas at all because, as the correspondent explains in his special radio to *The Post*, December 25th will be just another working day to the Russian people. Christmas will come on January 7th in Moscow. No, it's about the failure of the Germans to celebrate Christmas in Moscow this year. There are two items in this message which have a little of the Christmas spirit in them. The first is this:

"I keep thinking of that callow boy with silky growth of down on his cheeks who lay under a snow-burdened fir tree on the battlefield at Klin, which I visited the other day. He was one of many German dead, but I noticed him especially because of his youth, the bandage half wrapped around his head and the way his frozen eyes looked unseeingly upward. He had apparently been wounded and had died of cold.

"Young Otto Seiter is probably listed on Hitler's casualty rolls as 'missing.' But I know he is dead. He won't be home this Christmas or any other Christmas. There are a lot like him."

He goes on to speak of the letters which he retrieved from the battlefield, letters of German wives and mothers to their men and boys. "They make appropriate reading for Christmas Eve," he cables, "because they remind you of something you are prone to forget in the heat of the war—that enemy soldiers are not beasts or monsters but human beings who have been hypnotized into blind allegiance to the mad idea of a half-mad leader. Scarcely any of these letters mentioned politics and only one of them closed with the salutation 'Heil Hitler' . . . In all the letters I examined . . . I found no words of bitterness against the Russians."

Yes, I agree—it sure does make appropriate reading for Christmas Eve. It's rather edifying, if I may say so. *Read it again, please.*

On the front page of this same journal the Pope gives his Five Points for Peace. Also very edifying. The trouble is nobody pays a damned bit of attention to the Pope. He's just a symbol of spiritual power. Anyway, among the other things he says: "True respect for treaties must be observed, and the principles of freedom and equality of rights for all people must underlie the new day." It's obvious that His Holiness is also a forward looker. There's such a gentle, passive, civilized note to his plea—might have been written by Woodrow Wilson himself. I'm making a note to have the Viking Press send him a copy of *The Bertrand Russell Case.* In praying for peace so assiduously this little drama of spiritual sabotage by the good Catholics of America may have escaped his attention.

If some one should give us Germany and Japan this minute, we would be so embarrassed we would hardly know what to do or say . . . We do not have the smallest notion of what we are going to do when we win. We are hopelessly unprepared for victory . . . We must face the truth. The hardest blow that could strike us at the moment would be victory. We would pass it from hand to hand as if it were hot, and would not know where to set it down. Our

*Congress once did conduct some rather magnificent debates as to
what to do with new territories as they came into the democratic
system. We even discussed whether there should be slavery or
freedom in the new States. Both houses now sit tight, with nothing
to say. Not to be able to put into specific, hard words the things
the Colin Kellys are dying for is a confession of ineptness.*

These are not my words, dear, gentle reader. These come to you
through the courtesy of the *N. Y. Post* on Christmas Eve. They
were written by Samuel Grafton in his column called "I'd Rather
Be Right." And most of the time, to do him justice, he is right.
Sometimes he's so damned right that it almost sounds treasonable.
But everybody knows that Sam is on the right side; he can get
away with murder.

I wish I had a little joke to tell now. It's such a solemn moment,
and we've been through so many like it before. "Now is the time,"
as Dorothy Thompson says, "for the United States to wage the
most brilliant psychological warfare against Germany and Italy and
amongst the people of Europe." (Why leave out the Japs, I
wonder?) "But," she adds, "no strategy of psychological warfare
has been developed, and no command and staff capable of waging
it have been created."

Yes, as Dorothy says—"it is a negligence which will prolong the
war, and it should be remedied immediately." But then, if you
follow Sam Grafton's reasoning, on the same page, you will see
that we need a little time—because we haven't the least idea yet
what our victory program should be. It's a bit confusing, to say
the least.

A little joke, as I was saying a minute ago. Yes, Lincoln had his
little joke just before reading the Emancipation Proclamation.
Incidentally, you would think, if you were not a student of history,
that the Emancipation Proclamation came first, and then the attack
on Fort Sumter. But no, it was the other way round. It's like the
Pope again. He talks about good, honest to God peace treaties,
about non-persecution of the Church et cetera, before he knows
what the outcome of the war will be. Anyway, the story goes that
Lincoln had called his cabinet members together on a very important matter. The war was on some time already and the dead were
rather numerous, to say nothing of the halt, the blind, the maimed,
the mutilated. Lincoln has a book in front of him—by Artemas
Ward. He reads a passage aloud to the assembled scarecrows and
he laughs heartily in doing so. Nobody else laughs. So he tries it
again. And again he laughs fit to burst his sides. But the gravediggers look askance. They are at a loss to understand this ill-timed
hilarity. Has he gone off his nut, they wonder? Lincoln feels sorry

for them—for their lack of humor. It's a good book, he tells them, and you ought to sit down and read it. It would do you a world of good. Something like that. Then he quietly reaches into the tail pocket of his flap-doodle walking coat and, extracting the Emancipation Proclamation, he reads it to them quietly and solemnly . . . Whether it be true or not, it's a damned good story. Lincoln had his feet on the ground, as we would say. But his head was in the clouds. He had a quiet, sure confidence that right would prevail—in the end. He was ready to sacrifice any number of lives, his own included, to bring about that end. "As I would not be a *slave*, so I would not be a *master*. This expresses my idea of democracy. Whatever differs from this, to the extent of the difference, is no democracy." Those are Lincoln's words. It's a pity we never gave heed to them. We freed the black salves, or we thought we had, but we forgot to free the white slaves. We freed the Filipinos and the Cubans and the Porto Ricans, but we didn't free ourselves. We rescued France and Belgium from the heels of the German military clique but then we put the Germans in the clink. So now, while Russia deals the death-blow to the Germans, we're getting ready to wipe out Hitlerism and all the other isms, as well as that degenerate yellow-bellied Hirohito.

Nobody can deny that we're the most philanthropic-minded people in the world. A few months ago there were eight or nine million people unemployed in this wonder-working land. Now it's down to about a million, an irreducible minimum, I believe it's called. We work fast, I'll say. And all because that half-witted Hirohito stabbed us in the back. Some say we had no right to be taken by surprise—criminal negligence they call it. Others seem pleased that it turned out so—it proved that we were angels, that we had no intention of going to war with Japan, that our fleet and our fortifications were created only to *frighten* the enemy away. It's six one way and a half dozen the other. I was always of the opinion that if you make cannon you've got to use them some time or other. I'm never surprised when a gun goes off unexpectedly. I expect the unexpected. What does surprise me is that people who believe in making cannon should be aggrieved to see them used so effectively. "In time of peace prepare for war," said the Father of this beloved country. He was a realist, just as Stalin is to-day. He didn't get himself elected a third time by promising to keep his people out of war. He was no half-wit. No sir, he was an aristocrat, a great land-holder with slaves and port and sherry in the cellar. The people were so grateful to him for making this country a democracy that they almost made him a king. About seventy years later there appeared in the State of Massachusetts, noted even then for its hypocrisy, repression and iniquity, a troublesome character who sensed that all was not well with the government of these United States. What's more, he had the courage to say so. He wrote a paper called "Civil Disobedience" which we look upon to-day as a monument to the democratic spirit. Here is a citation from this beautifully embalmed document:

"The progress from an absolute to a limited monarchy, from a limited monarchy to a democracy, is a progress towards a true respect for the individual. Even the Chinese philosopher was wise enough to regard the individual as the basis of the empire. Is a democracy, such as we know it, the last improvement possible in government? Is it not possible to take a step further towards recognizing and organizing the rights of man? There will never be a really free and enlightened State until the State comes to recognize the individual as a higher and independent power, from which all its own power and authority are derived, and treats him accordingly. I please myself with imagining a State at last which can afford to be just to all men, and to treat the individual with respect as a neighbor; which even would not think it inconsistent with its own repose if a few were to live aloof from it, not meddling with it, nor embraced by it, who fulfilled all the duties of neighbors and fellow-men. A State which bore this kind of fruit, and suffered it to drop off as fast as it ripened, would prepare the way for a still more perfect and glorious State, which also I have imagined, but not yet anywhere seen."

That was Henry David Thoreau, author of *Walden* and defender of John Brown, speaking. No doubt the only excuse we can make to-day for such a treasonable anarchistic utterance is to palm him off as a half-witted graduate of the then Transcendentalist School of Philosophy. About the only person I can think of who would have dared to defend him, in our time, had he openly expressed his desire to live a life apart from the most holy and sacrosanct State, is the recently defunct Justice of the Supreme Court, Louis D. Brandeis. In the case of Whitney versus the State of California, Brandeis, whose vote was overruled, wrote a brief in which there appeared these words:

"Those who won our independence by revolution were not cowards. They did not fear political change. They did not exalt order at the cost of liberty. To courageous, self-reliant men, with confidence in the power of free and fearless reasoning applied through the processes of popular government, no danger flowing from speech can be deemed clear and present, unless the incidence of evil apprehended is so imminent that it may befall before there is opportunity for full discussion. If there be time to expose through discussion the falsehood and fallacies, to avert the evil by the processes of education, the remedy to be applied is more speech, not enforced silence. Only an emergency can justify repression. Such must be the rule if authority is to be reconciled with freedom. Such, in my opinion, is the command of the Constitution. It is, therefore, always open to Americans to challenge a law abridging free speech and assembly by showing that there was no emergency justifying it."

Nevertheless, when the good shoe-maker and the poor fish-peddler found themselves at the bar of justice in the benighted State of Massachusetts some few years ago, they were unable to get a fair, honest hearing. Despite all the noble words handed down by the upstanding members of the judiciary, and they are the wordiest people on God's green earth, Sacco and Vanzetti were foully murdered. But just before he went to the chair Vanzetti gave birth to a few lines which are destined to be as immortal as any of Lincoln's or Jefferson's . . .

"If it had not been for these thing, I might have lived out my life talking at street corners to scorning men. I might have died, unmarked, unknown, a failure. Now we are not a failure. This is our career and our triumph. Never in our full life could we hope to do such work for tolerance, for joostice, for man's understanding of man as now we do by accident. Our words—our lives—our pains—nothing! The taking of our lives—lives of a good shoemaker and a poor fish-peddler—all! That last moment belongs to us—that agony is our triumph."

A few days ago, moved by the President's declaration of war the newspapers gave some space to the remarks made by John Haynes Holmes, Minister of the Community Church, N. Y., in tendering his resignation. He had just finished a sermon, it seems, on the 150th anniversary of the Bill of Rights. Mr. Holmes is quoted as saying that "neither as clergyman nor as citizen would he participate in the war," adding however that "neither would he oppose, obstruct or interfere with officials, soldiers or citizens in the performance of what they regard as their patriotic duty."

Then he threw this bombshell:

"I will be loyal and obedient to my government, and loyal and obedient to my God; and when these loyalties conflict, I will choose, as did the Apostles, to 'obey God rather than men.' "

I wait to see if Mr. Holmes will be condemned to prison. In the last world war there were three great figures who, because they openly announced their opposition to war, suffered dire persecution. They were Romain Rolland, Bertrand Russell and Eugene V. Debs. Unimpeachable characters, all three. I'm going to give you

Debs' speech on being condemned to prison, but before I do so I want to mention the Very Reverend Dean Inge's statement about a German theologian named Harnack. "War," writes the gloomy Dean, "is a very horrible thing, an unmixed evil, a reversion to barbarism no less than cannibalism, human sacrifice and judicial torture. Most of us think that we were obliged to resist German agression, which threatens to extinguish liberty, and with liberty all that makes life worth living, over the whole continent of Europe. But no good can ever come out of war. It is a flat negation of Christianity. Even Harnack, a Prussian and the most learned theologian in Europe, said that it is futile to deny that Christ condemned war absolutely." He adds that the Quakers believe they are the only consistent Christians. And what is the history of the Quaker movement? According to recent authority on the subject, the Quaker movement was met with terrific persecution, first from mob violence and later from organized legal procedure. George Fox himself endured eight imprisonments, and more than fifteen thousand Quakers were imprisoned in England before the period of toleration, of whom three hundred and sixty-six died under their sufferings. Four Quakers were hanged on Boston Common and a great number in the American Colonies endured beatings and mutilation.

To-day the Quakers are exempt from military service, in these United States. But what a battle! A man who is not a Quaker, like Eugene V. Debs for example, gets it in the neck. Yet no Quaker could have made a more simple, honest, dignified statement of his views than did Eugene V. Debs. Here are his beautiful, moving words:

"Gentlemen of the Jury, I am accused of having obstructed the war. I admit it. Gentlemen, I abhor war. I would oppose the war if I stood alone. When I think of a cold, glittering steel bayonet being plunged in the white, quivering flesh of a human being, I recoil with horror.

"Men talk about holy wars. There are none. War is the trade of unholy savages and barbarians . . .

"Gentlemen of the Jury, I am accused of being unpatriotic. I object to that accusation. It is not true. I believe in patriotism. I have never uttered a word against the flag. I love the flag as a symbol of freedom . . .

"I believe, however, in a wider patriotism. Thomas Paine said, 'My country is the world. To do good is my religion.' That is the sort of patriotism I believe in. I am an Internationalist. I believe that nations have been pitted against nations long enough in hatred, in strife, in warfare. I believe there ought to be a bond of unity between all of these nations. I believe that the human race consists of one great family. I love the people of this country, but I don't hate a human being because he happens to be born in some other country. Why should I? Like myself, he is the image of his Creator. I would infinitely rather serve him and love him than to hate him and kill him . . .

"Yes, I am opposed to killing him. I am opposed to war. I am perfectly willing on that account to be branded as a traitor. And if it is a crime under the American law to be opposed to human bloodshed, I am perfectly willing to be branded as a criminal and to end my days in a prison cell . . .

"And now, Gentlemen of the Jury, I am prepared for the sentence. I will accept your verdict. What you will do to me does not matter much. Years ago I recognized my kinship with all living beings, and I made up my mind that I was not one whit better than the meanest of earth. I said then, and I say now, that while there is a lower class, I am in it; while there is a criminal element, I am of it; while there is a soul in prison, I am not free."

"Unless from us the future takes place, we are death only," said D. H. Lawrence. A monumental statement. Meanwhile death is piling up all around us. The political and military leaders, if they do not actually make light of it, discount it as they would a promptly paid bill. The bill is victory, they say, and they are willing to pay in advance no matter how many millions of lives it costs. They are even ready to sacrifice their own lives, but fortunately for them most of them are so placed that the risk is slight. When the war is ended the victory will be theirs, no gainsaying it. The dead won't count, nor the millions of maimed and mutilated ones who will go on living until death robs them of the fruits of victory.

Death, especially on a wholesale scale, can raise an awful stench. On the battle-fronts now and then a truce is declared to give the opposing forces an opportunity to bury their dead. It has never occurred to the political and military cliques that it might be an excellent innovation to incorporate among the polite rules of civilized warfare a clause stipulating that every thirty or sixty days a truce shall be declared (for twenty-four hours, let us say) to reconsider the supposed basis of the erstwhile conflict. What would happen, I wonder, if the armies waging war all over the earth, and the friends and relatives supporting these armies, could pause every so often in the process of blood-letting and honestly examine their conscience? Supposing further—and now we get really fantastic—that during these let-ups a vote could be taken on both sides of the fence to see whether the fight should be continued or not. It is not altogether impossible to imagine that perhaps only the higher officers of the armies and navies, together with the congressmen and of course the various dictators, would be in favor of continuing with the slaughter. The great body of men and women, the ones of whom the great sacrifice is being demanded, would most likely yell for peace. Perhaps even "peace at any price"! *If they were given an honest chance!*

The stench of death . . . One day we read that 4,000 Germans were killed on the Russian front. Another day it may be 16,000 or 23,000. Fine! *Progress*, we say. Or, if we wipe out a nest of dirty Japs, still better . . . *bully!* According to this logic, the most magnificent step forward that we could make would be to annihilate them utterly. (Let's get busy and trot out that human Flit I was talking about earlier!) Now the military man will tell you, and utterly sincerely too, that annihilation of the enemy is not the goal at all. The objective, according to the military expert, is merely to render *hors de combat* the enemy's army or navy, as the case may be. That accomplished, the war is won. If it can be done without loss of life, so much the better. The most brilliant defeat that could be inflicted, from the standpoint of these experts, would be a bloodless one. That would indeed be something to record in the annals of history! That would make war look quite jolly, for a change. It would be most superlatively magnificent: a super-duper sort of victory, if you get what I mean. Some people credit Hitler with having had some such idea. He had it all figured out—it was to be a push-over, as we say.

However, to get back to war as we know it, nothing like this is going to happen in our time. War now means just as it did in the past, "blood, sweat and tears"—oodles of it. Not blood, sweat and tears for those who launch it, but for those who have to go through with it. And that means practically everybody, except, as I said before, the favored few who direct the show. The latter are just as eager to give their lives as the little fellows, don't make any mistake about that. Only, because of the peculiar set-up involved in these fracases, they are somehow never privileged to enjoy this supreme sacrifice. They must be protected in order that the others can be most efficiently sacrificed. You can understand what anguish this causes the political and military leaders of any war. (Yet few of them ever pine away because of it. On the contrary, they seem to grow tough as steel.) However, if it were possible to take them by surprise, assure them that nothing they said would be held against them, it's just possible you'd discover that they were fed up with it too. A moment later, to be sure, they would be ready to deny such weak sentiments. "What would the people think?" they'd say. Always that to fall back on. *The people!* It was the people who wanted the war. Of course. Yes, when they're stabbed in the back the people may cry for war, *but*—how does it happen that they get stabbed in the back, and at just the right moment? And so, right or wrong, willing or unwilling, "the war must be fought to a just and victorious conclusion!" From time immemorial every leader has proclaimed that high and mighty truth. That's why the future is always so full of death. Right or wrong, the war must be continued, always. No looking back. No looking forward. *Head down and charge!* That's the order of the day. Victory? Just around the corner. And if not victory, death. Death, death, death. Always death. Or, if you're lucky, your old job back in the mines. The future? It never begins. You had your future yesterday, don't you remember? There is only the present, and the present is never pleasant. Only the future is bright. But then, the future never takes place. The future always recedes, that's the law. When the original Fascists have been vanquished, or exterminated, we'll all be Fascists—that's what the future, if there is to be any future, promises. And that means more death, more blood, sweat and tears, more Churchills, more Roosevelts, more Hitlers, more Stalins. There won't be any more Mussolinis, probably, because he for one has been thoroughly exploded. But there may be another Hirohito, and mark my words, he'll be a yellow-belly too.

It's going to be a lovely world to-morrow, when everything is properly organized and running smoothly. It may take a hundred years, but what's that (Man lives in the eternal—*when he lives*). There may even be another war—or several—between times, but that shouldn't disturb us any. We got through this one, didn't we? You see the logic . . . it runs as smooth as tooth-paste from an old-fashioned tube. Incidentally, you won't have to worry about tooth-paste when the New Day is ushered in; we'll all be fitted with Dr. Cowen's beautiful light-weight platinum teeth. Only cows will chew with their own teeth in the future. Everything's going to be under control, you'll see. Should a new enemy arise (though it's hard to see why he should, with Utopia just in the offing) we'll know how to deal with him. Nothing must or shall hinder our plans for the world-wide improvement of the human race. The human race, of course, will not be understood to include such inferior peoples as the Zulus and the Hottentots, for example. No sir, let's not fall into that sublime error. Only people walking around in pants, with Bibles in their hands and platinum teeth in their mouths, and preferably only those speaking the English language, will be regarded as belonging to the human race.

Utopia, then, will be a world in which the white race (half Slav, half Anglo-Saxon) will know no enemies and will have as neighbors such harmless peoples as the Javanese, the Hindus, the Malays, and perhaps the Arabs too—if they behave. On the fringe of our tremendous colonial possessions there will be the not-quite-human species, who are no longer a menace . . . in other words, the primitives. These will gradually be absorbed into the blood-stream by the process of higher education. They will be "our little brown brothers," so to speak, and will work for us (willingly, of course) like bees and ants. For how otherwise will they be able to make themselves fit to enjoy the fruits of civilization?

There will be only two languages to begin with: Russian and English. After a time the Russians will give up their mother tongue and speak English only. What the Chinese and Hindus will speak will hardly concern us since, though numerically superior, perhaps even morally and spiritually superior, they will be of no consequence in the management of a Utopian world. As for the primitives, they have survived these last fifty to a hundred thousand years without the knowledge of English, so why worry?

There will be no money, of course. Not even the hat money of the Penangs. As it used to say on the silver dollar: *e pluribus unum!* The bookkeeper will be eliminated, and the breed of lawyers too, since most litigation arises over money transactions. The absence of money will also solve the debt problem which arises after every war to end war. No money, no debts! *All for one and one for all*, just like it said once on the silver dollar. The New Deal will go into effect throughout the whole pluralistic universe. Naturally there will have to be a new flag: the flag of Utopia. I should imagine it will be pure white, signifying "peace, purity, and forgiveness of sins." No emblem will be needed, not even the hammer and sickle . . . not even a *plastic* hammer and sickle. Nothing but a white piece of cloth—of the finest material. Under this banner, for the first time in the history of mankind, everybody will get a break, perhaps even the Zulus and the Hottentots. War will be a thing of the past; all our enemies will be dead or incapacitated. Should any new ones threaten to arise, get out the Flit! Simple, what! No need for standing armies any longer. Just oodles of Flit—and a big squirt gun. To be sure, it may be necessary to do a bit of wholesale murdering—clean house, so to speak—before all the enemy are eliminated. It may take ten to twenty years to eradicate the last Jap, German, Bulgarian, Roumanian, Hungarian, Finn or other human pest, but we'll do it, we'll weed them out like vipers. The problem will be what to do with those of mixed blood. It will take a Solomon to decide that issue. However, with the education and training heretofore wasted in turning out admirals, generals and field marshals, we shall undoubtedly pave the way for the emergence of several Solomons. If necessary we can import a few from India or China.

With war eliminated and money eliminated, with the breed of lawyers and bookkeepers wiped out, with politics converted to management, with Solomons sitting in judgment upon all grave matters of dispute, can any intelligent person visualize even the possibility of a miscarriage? Under the slogan "all for one and one for all" the earth will slowly but surely be transformed into a Paradise. There will be no more struggle, except to surpass one another in virtue. There will be no more pain, except that which doctors and dentists impose. We will love one another to death.

Truly, if people would only realize what a glorious future is about to unroll, would they not this instant get down on their knees and devoutly offer up thanks to those great benefactors—Stalin, Churchill, Roosevelt and Madame Chiang Kai-shek? If they were to think about the matter profoundly, would they not also bless Hitler and Mussolini, and above all that yellow-bellied Hirohito, because, if these angelic monsters had not unleashed this grim catastrophe, we would never have thought to usher in the millennium. How true the saying: "It's an ill wind that blows no one some good!" In glory and significance all other wars pale before this one. That Ireland, Sweden, Spain, Portugal, Switzerland, India, Argentina have not evinced the spirit of the crusader is regrettable, but they will doubtless see the wisdom of this heroic strife when we make life more comfortable for them. With the Utopia to follow upon the close of this war the neutral countries will enjoy the same privileges and advantages as the ones that went to war. . . .

With the conclusion of this war it is not even probable that we shall see the dissolution of national boundaries. To eliminate race prejudice no one can say how many more wars it will require. There are thousands of problems for which men will find no solution but war. No system of government now in vogue offers the slightest hope of a future free of war. The remedy for dissent is still, as it was in the past, subjugation or extirpation. The government has never existed which recognizes the freedom and equality of all men. As for freedom of thought, freedom to express one's ideas—not to speak of living them out—where is the government which ever permitted this? Conformity is the rule, and conformity will be the rule as long as men believe in governing one another.

Men of good-will need no government to regulate their affairs.

In every age there is a very small minority which lives without thought of, or desire for, government. These men never brought about a war. So long as civilization lasts it is quite possible that this minority will never be substantially increased. Such men are not the products of our religious organizations or our educational systems; they live outside the cultural pattern of the times. The most we can say, in explanation of their appearance and existence, is that they are evolved beings. And here we must needs touch on the drawback to all schemes, Utopian or otherwise, for the improvement of human society: the failure inherent in all of them to recognize that the human race does not evolve at the same speed nor with the same rhythm. Where there is dream and wish fulfillment merely—and what else can there be if one focuses on society instead of the individual?—there is confusion and disillusionment. Even with red-hot bayonets up their rear, men cannot be prodded all at the same time into Paradise. It is this fact, of course, which the so-called realists, who are always defeatists, seize upon with grim relish in order to excuse and perpetuate the business of murder. With each war they pretend that they are preserving society from a dire fate, or that they are protecting the weak and the helpless. The men of wisdom, who are really the men of good-will, and who are found in every stratum of society and not in any particular class, never make such pretences. They are often accused of being aloof, remote, out of touch with the world. Yet it is to them that all men turn for comfort and guidance in their hour of need. For, even the clod seems to sense that genuine disinterestedness is a source of strength.

If any particular set of men were destined to rule the world it would seem logical that it should be ruled by the men of wisdom. But that is not the case, and there is good reason for it. No one man, no set of men, is capable of ruling the world. The world is ruled by its own inner, mysterious laws. It evolves according to a logic which defies our man-made logic. The higher the type of man, moreover, the less inclined he feels to rule others; he lives in harmony with the world despite the fact that he is in total disagreement with the vast majority, as well as with the leaders of the world. Were there good reason to kill, he could find a thousand justifications to the ordinary man's one. The principal reason, however, for his failure to become embroiled in world conflicts is his absence of fear. Accustomed as he is to live habitually in the world of ideas, he is not frightened when he learns that his neighbor thinks differently from him. Indeed, he might really become alarmed if he found that his neighbors were in agreement with him. The average man, on the contrary, is more frightened of alien ideas than of cold steel or flame throwers. He has spent most of his empty life getting adjusted to the few simple ideas which were thrust on him by his elders or superiors. Anything which menaces this precarious adjustment, which he calls his liberty, throws him into a panic. Let an alien idea become active, and the transition from fear to hate proceeds like clock-work. Trot out the word "enemy," and the whole bloody race behaves as if it had the blind staggers. The nit-wits who never showed the least ability to govern themselves suddenly get the idea that their last mission on earth is to teach the enemy good government. It makes no difference whether this nit-wit be a Communist, Fascist, or Democrat: the reaction is always the same. Just tell him that the other fellow is threatening his liberty, and he reaches for his gun—*automatically*.

And what is the little bundle of ideas around which this precious notion of liberty is formed? Private property, the sanctity of the home, the church he belongs to, the preservation of the political party, or the system, which gives him the privilege of being a drudge all his life. If he could but take one sweeping view of the planet, see what different things the same words mean everywhere, see how all men, including the primitives, believe that whatever they believe is right and just, and of course supremely intelligent, would he be so quick to reach for the sword or the gun? Yes, he would, because he has been educated to understand with his head but not with the rest of his being. As a civilized creature, a man can study and know the ways and customs of a thousand different peoples, yet insist on defending the ways of his own, even though he knows them to be stupid, inadequate or wrong. He will describe with irony and subtle discrimination the reasons why other peoples make war, but he will go to war himself when the time comes, even though he does not believe in killing. He will kill rather than be humiliated by his own people.

In how many wars have people killed who had no desire to kill? Many who killed one another had more in common than with their own compatriots. Were men to seek their real enemies they would have only to turn round and examine the ranks behind them. If men were to realize who their true enemies were, what a scrimmage would ensue! But again, one of the disadvantages of living under civilized rule is that only those may be considered as enemies, and therefore killed or enslaved, whom the governments designate as such. To kill your commanding officer, for example, even though he be the bitterest enemy you have, is strictly taboo. So it goes . . . scholars killing scholars, poets killing poets, workers killing workers, teachers killing teachers, and no one killing the

munitions makers, the politicians, the priests, the military idiots
or any of the other criminals who sanction war and egg one on to
kill one another off.

Just to take one element, the munitions makers, for example:
who could be more international-minded than they? Come war and
they will sell to any side that has the money to buy. Strictly
neutral, these birds, until they see which way the wind blows. No
amount of taxation impoverishes them; the longer the war lasts,
the more the dead pile up, the fatter they grow. Imagine the
colossal absurdity of supporting a body of men whose mission in
life it is to supply us with the means of self-destruction. (Whereas
it is a crime to attempt to take one's own life by one's own means,
no matter how unbearable life becomes!) Nobody considers the
munitions maker—not even the Communist, mind you—as an
enemy. Yet he is the greatest enemy man has. He sits like a vulture
and waits and prays for the day to come when we shall lose our
reason and beg him to furnish us with his most expensive lethal
products. Instead of being looked upon as a leper he is given a
place of honor in human society; often he is knighted for his
indubitably dubious services. On the other hand, Monsieur le
Paris, who really performs a service for society, albeit a most
disagreeable one, is shunned like a pariah. Strange paradox. If
there is any logic to it it is thus: the man who by our own sanction
justly removes a murderer from the ranks of society is a worthless
wretch, whereas the man who provides the means of killing en
masse, for no matter what reason good or bad, deserves a place of
honor in our midst. Corollary logic: murder on a wholesale scale
is always justifiable, as well as profitable and honorable, but
ordinary murder, whether for passion or greed, is so disgraceful
that even the man whose duty it is to make way with the culprit
appears to us as tainted.

. . . Moreover, and above all, and to add to the illogical, the
inconsistent and the paradoxical—does any serious-minded person
believe for one moment that a victorious China, Russia, America,
England will not become more militant, more ready and prepared
for war, more suited to find fresh problems to quarrel over?
German and Japan *may* be put out of harm's way. Agreed. But
what then? Are they the only enemies man will ever have or could
have? Since when have Big Powers agreed with one another, or
laid down their arms and become as lambs? Since when have the
Big Powers treated Little Powers with equal tact and consideration? And what of the Little Powers, when we have liberated them
by our victorious but ruinous campaigns? Will they be grateful and
ready to fall in line with our way of life when their people return

to the desolate, ruined lands which we turned into a stupendous proving ground? Will they perhaps differ with us as to how life and liberty is to be maintained in the future?

Who will rule the coming world? The strong ones. And who are the strong? America, Russia, England, China. (We have not yet finished with Japan. It remains to be seen if she will be thoroughly subjugated and castrated, or if one of the present Big Powers will form an unholy alliance with her, in order to be better prepared for the next conflict, which already impends.) England, we know, will not give up her Empire willingly. France will demand the restoration of her colonies. So will Holland. Perhaps Italy too. Germany of course will never be allowed to have anything but the air to breathe. As for America, she will relinquish everything, that goes without question. The one great Empire which will remain, and which should long ago have fallen to pieces, is the British Empire. This is only fair and just, because the Four Freedoms, being an Anglo-Saxon conception of justice, does not exclude Empires. France will be allowed to grow strong again, because France is a freedom-loving nation, though also an Empire. But France mustn't grow too strong, for then she might become a menace to England's freedom and security, which is based upon a greed for possessions almost unheard of. Everything will have to be maintained in an equilibrium as delicate as the workings of a Swiss watch. The master minds of the new Entente Cordiale, however, will solve all these intricate problems with ease and dispatch. There is no danger of their quarreling among themselves. Oh no, not the slightest! Russia will remain Communist, England an Empire, America a benevolent Democracy (with Roosevelt at the helm until death), and France Republican. China, of course, will remain a complete chaos, as always. The directors of the great show will see eye to eye on all future major problems; as for the minor problems, the future will take care of these.

The great question, to be sure, which will come up as soon as the war ends, is: who will buy whose goods and how? As for the debt problem, that is easily solved. The people will pay off the debts. The people always pay. Though the people never start a war, nor even a revolution, the government somehow always convinces the people that they must pay for these adventures, both before and after. A war is fought for the benefit of the people. By the time the war is over, however, there are no benefits, just debts, death and desolation. All of which has to be paid for.

This time the peoples who make up the victorious nations won't mind the cost because they will have the Four Freedoms. They will also have all sorts of new machines, new labor-saving devices, which will make work a pleasure. (And the harder they work the faster the debts will be paid off; the more ready they will be, too, for the next war.) Yes, there will be all sorts of new inventions, which, if they are not used destructively, will bring untold bliss. There will be, among other things, new airplanes capable of taking us back and forth to China in twenty-four hours—and for a song! Week-ends the workers of the world will be flying around the globe greeting their fellow-workers in Java, Borneo, Mozambique, Saskatchewan, Tierra del Fuego and such places. No need to go to Coney Island any more, or Deauville, or Brighton—there will be far more interesting places at which to spend the week-end. There will be television, too, don't forget. If you don't care to fly around the world in your spare time you can sit quietly by the hearth and watch the Eskimos climbing up and down the slippery icebergs, or look at the primitive peoples in the jungle busy gathering rice, ivory, coffee, tea, rubber, chicle and other useful commodities for our delectation. Every one will be working blissfully, even the Chinese coolies. For, by that time the vast and all-powerful Chiang Kai-shek dynasty will be operating with the smoothness of a high-powered dynamo. The opium traffic will be wiped out, and the heretofore ignorant coolies will be able to understand and appreciate American movies, which are an excellent substitute for opium. We will probably make special Grade D pictures for them at a figure so absurd that even the lowest coolie will be able to afford the price of admission. We will have Grade K or J pictures for "our little brown brothers" too. We will make chewing gum in greater quantities, and Eskimo pies, and malted milk shakes, to say nothing of can openers and other gadgets, so that the little people everywhere may enjoy some of the luxuries of our economic millennium.

The thing to guard against, however, is that the little peoples of the world should not be infected with Communism. Russia will have to be content to communize Siberia, Mongolia, and possibly Japan. But not China! And not the Malay archipelago, nor Africa, nor South America. South America will be somewhat of a problem, especially as miscegenation assumes increasing proportions. It won't do for the peoples of North America, "the melting pot," to begin intermarrying with the black, brown and yellow races. Marrying red-skins is quite another matter; the Indian, it seems, is a hundred percent American, and we don't mind any more if they have a touch of color. But don't let any one think, especially south of the Mason-Dixon line, that the Four Freedoms means freedom for blacks and whites to intermarry! That belongs to the fifth or sixth freedom, and will probably demand another war.

With a plethora of new labor-saving devices flooding the market there will no longer be any question of who is to do the dirty work of the world. *The machine will do it!* No one will need to soil his hands. The machines will work with such efficiency, in fact, that there may be danger of the workers growing bored. Unless the master minds introduce new forms of creative activity. It is quite possible that in the next few hundred years we shall see everybody turning artist. An hour or two at the machine each day, and the rest of the day for art! Perhaps that will be the new order in the world to come. How glorious! *The joy of creation*: something man has never known before, at least not the civilized races. Suddenly, thanks to the ubiquity and the domination of the machine, we will become again as the primitives, only wiser, happier, conscious at last of our blessedness. Everybody dancing, singing, painting, carving, fiddling, drumming, strumming . . . so marvelous! All due to the machine. How simple!

Finally, when every one has become a genius, when genius becomes the norm, there will be no room for envy or rivalry. Art will be truly universal. There will be no need for critics or interpreters; the dealers and middle men will perish, and with them the publishers and editors, the lawyers, the bookkeepers, the politicians, perhaps even the police. Every one will have the kind of home he chooses to live in, and with it a frigidaire, a radio, a telephone, a vacuum cleaner, a washing machine, an automobile, an airplane, a parachute, *and*—a full set of Dr. Cowen's lightweight platinum teeth. The cripples will all have the most wonderful, the most extraordinary, light-weight artificial limbs, which will enable them to run, skip, dance, jump or walk with perfect ease. The insane will have better lunatic asylums, and more humane, more intelligent keepers. The prisons will be more spacious, more sanitary, more comfortable in every way. There will be hospitals in abundance, on every street, and ambulances fitted up like Pullmans. There will be such a variety of pain removers that no one need ever suffer any more, not even the throes of death. Add to this, that when all the world learns English, which will happen inevitably, there won't be the least possibility of a misunderstanding any more. One language, one flag, one way of life. The machine doing all the dirty work, the master minds doing all the thinking: an Entente Cordiale with a vengeance.

That's how it looks for the next five hundred years or so. *Or doesn't it?* Anyway, that's how it *could* look, you must admit. And what's to hinder? Well, we don't know yet, but undoubtedly there will arise some idiot, some fanatic, who will have a better idea to foist upon us. And that will cause trouble. Trouble always starts with "a better idea." It's too soon to predict the nature of the monkey wrench which will wreck the Utopian machine we have just described, but that there will be such a joy-killer we have no doubt. It's in the cards.

So, just to play safe, hold on to your battle-ships and battle wagons, your tanks, your flame-throwers, your bombing machines and everything super-duper in the way of destructive devices—we may have need for them again. One day, out of a clear sky—always a clear sky, mind you!—some fanatic will make an issue of some unforeseeable little incident, magnify it to the proportions of a calamity, and then a fresh catastrophe will be at our door. But if we are armed to the teeth, if we are better prepared than we were this last time, perhaps we shall get it over with more quickly. We must never relinquish the Four Freedoms, remember that! If possible, we must pave the way for a fifth and sixth freedom. Because, the more freedoms we pile up, the nearer we will be to freedom in the abstract.

Each new freedom, to be sure, will entail a few million deaths, as well as the destruction of our principal cities. But, if we achieve ten or twelve freedoms, we won't mind how many millions of lives are sacrificed, nor will we care how many cities are destroyed. After all, we can always make babies, and we can always build new cities—better babies, better cities. If we were able to discover a way to homogenize and irradiate cow's milk we surely will find the way to homogenize and irradiate the minds of our children. If we have to destroy everything now standing, including the Vatican, it will be worth it. What we want is a world in which war will be unthinkable. And, by God, if we have to wipe out the human race in order to achieve it, we will. *Mieux vaut revenir en fantôme que jamais*, as the French say.

So, until that blessed day looms upon the horizon, do please go on murdering one another. Murder as you have never murdered before. Murder the murderers, murder murder, but murder! murder! murder! Murder for God and country! Murder for peace! Murder for sweet murder's sake! Don't stop murdering ever! Murder! Murder! Murder! Murder your mother! Murder your brother! Murder the animals of the field, murder the insects, the birds, the flowers, the grass! Murder the microbes! Murder the molecule and the atom! Murder the electron! Murder the stars, and the sun and moon, if you can get at them! Murder everything off, so that we shall have at last a bright, pure, clean world in which to live in peace, bliss and security until the end of time!

II. Preface to
Remember to Remember
(Excerpt)

America is full of places. Empty places. And all these empty places are crowded. Just jammed with empty souls. All at loose ends, all seeking diversion. As though the chief object of existence were to forget. Everyone seeking a nice, cosy little joint in which to be with his fellow-man and not with the problems which haunt him. Not ever finding such a place, but pretending that it does exist, if not here then elsewhere. Each one saying to himself, like a monomaniac: "It's nice here. A good joint. I'm happy here. I'm going to forget I'm lonely and miserable." And with that one gets really lonely, really miserable. And then you notice some one's talking to you. It's the middle of a beery monologue. This guy's not only lonely and miserable, he's cuckoo. Finally you get so desperate you decide to go home. To do this one has to be really desperate, because home is the last place on earth to go when you're in despair. Of course it's furnished with all the latest improvements—radio, frigidaire, washing machine, vacuum cleaner, Encyclopaedia Britannica, the funny papers, the telephone, steam heat, electric grill, shower bath, etc. All the comforts, so to speak. But never was a people more uncomfortable than the Americans at home. A sort of temperate, cheerless lunacy pervades the atmosphere. Sitting in your easy chair you have only to turn the knob and there comes to you over the ether waves the sound of that bland, especially chosen voice saying: "*The world looks to America!*" If only it could look deep into the heart of America, see what it's like in the bosom of the family! Maybe then the world would turn its face away. Maybe it would be a thousand times better for the world if it ceased to hope and believe in America. This is just a thought.

Of course there are other places beside home, sweet home. Nice, clean places, like the church, for instance. Could anything be nicer and cleaner than the inside of a church—a Protestant church, of course? Only a hospital or the morgue. The outsides of the churches are always a bit gaga, what with the bilious color scheme and the gloomy stained-glass windows, some showing sheep piercing the clouds or else that man Jesus, our Saviour, nailed to his cross. Inside, however, it's almost inviting. Pew after pew, and the psalters hidden away in the back pockets. Standing in the pulpit always one of those good, clean, upright men, a man of God, as they say. A pitcher of water in front of him, in case he gets hoarse or thirsty. How he loves his flock, the dear, good pastor! He loves every single one of them, just like he loves his dear Jesus. Such a good man. If only he wouldn't talk such shit all the time. If only he had a real message!

No, the church is not the place. Neither is the bowling alley, nor the cinema, nor the billiard parlor, nor the drug store; nor the military academy, nor the boarding school, nor the penitentiary, nor the deaf and dumb asylum, nor the bughouse. Each one more empty, more cheerless, more sinister than the other. Even to belong to the Moose or the Elks is no help. Perhaps you have to become a Communist to realize that there just ain't no place to go to. Yet just the other day, when I was visiting Jack London's old place in Glen Ellen, I thought to myself—"here is the nearest thing to Paradise I've ever seen in America." But Jack London didn't live there very much, I was informed. He was too restless. He made a Paradise for himself and then locked himself out.

They say that Pushkin, after he had laughed himself sick reading *Dead Souls*, exclaimed: "What a sad place our Russia is!" That's what I keep saying to myself all the time about America. "What a sad place it is! What a fiasco!" The French, I see, are just beginning to discover this, thanks to the current vogue for American literature. They are amazed, apparently, that American authors have worse things to say about their own country than any foreigner. They admit now that Duhamel's book on America *(Scènes de la Vie Future)* is tame by comparison with the observations of such writers as Faulkner, Steinbeck, Caldwell, Dos Passos and others. They are felicitating our writers on their growing awareness.

That "future life" which Duhamel tried to warn his countrymen about is of course being lived already in Soviet Russia. There it seems to be taken for granted that there is no escape. The Russians are already in the New World, feet foremost. Here we try to pretend that it is possible to live in two worlds at once. Viewed from the Party line, our ablest writers are reactionary. They represent the tail-end of something. There is too much pessimism, too much disillusionment in these social satirists. An up and coming people are full of faith, full of courage, full of optimism.

It should be borne in mind, of course, that our ablest writers have but little influence upon the country at large. The masses will still vote the Republican and Democratic tickets, come what may. Russia is plunging ahead in full consciousness, plunging with boot and spur. We in America are lurching drunkenly in a semi-stupor. The men who enabled us to win the war were for the most part conservative men—professors and technicians, industrialists, inventors. They didn't want a new world; they wanted a return to the good old days. The Russians want a new world and will go to any lengths to get it. And, whether we want it or not, the new world is already in the making. It is a world, however, that nobody likes very much thus far. Even the Russians are not very comfortable in it. To be sure, it is the general expectation among those who believe in a new order that the common man will eventually inherit the fruits of all the inventions and discoveries now being made. But over whose dead body, I'd like to ask? No one seems able to give a convincing explanation of just how this miracle will come about. How will the common man inherit anything if he has no appetite, no taste for Paradise? How will a new order come about if the men who are to compose it have not grown new hearts, new consciences?

When I said a moment ago that America is a sad place, I meant just that. It is sad to think that a country which has the greatest advantages has so little to show for it. It is sad to think that scarcely anyone likes the job he is doing, that scarcely anyone believes in what he is doing, that almost no one, barring the professional optimists, sees any hope in the future. It is even more sad to observe that no real effort is made to do anything about anything. Yes, I know that the workers are constantly organizing, constantly striking or threatening to strike, in order to get better wages, better living conditions. But I also know that, at this rate, they will never get sufficient wages to meet the rising cost of living. The great bugaboo here in America is "the dictatorship of the proletariat." Looking at the rank and file, the so-called "masses," does any one honestly believe that these men and women will dictate the future of America? Can slaves become rulers overnight? These poor devils are begging to be led, and they are being led, but it's up a blind alley.

The war is over and, instead of the Four Freedoms, we have all kinds of tyrannies, all kinds of misery, all kinds of privation. The victors are divided, as always happens. Where are the leaders, who are they, who will make the new world, or help to usher it in? Can you call Stalin one, or President Truman, or de Gaulle, or the Bank of England? Are these the men who incarnate the time spirit? Are these the men who will lead us out of the wilderness?

The new world is being born of necessity, in travail, as all things are born in this human realm. It is being born of forces which we only dimly recognize. The elements which will make the coming world comprise a whole which no political ideology can hope to embrace. Only a new mentality, a new consciousness, only a vision capable of embracing all the conflicting tendencies, of seeing around, beyond and above them, will permit men to adapt themselves to the order and the ambiance of this new world. Once men become imbued with the idea that the "age of plentitude" is inevitable, all the current world views, petty, destructive, mutually exclusive, will vanish like dust. There is not a single political leader to-day who can see beyond his nose, not a single scientist who can reckon with the forces which have already been unleashed, much less marshal or control them. We are only faintly beginning to realize that the world egg is truly shattered, that this happened a few centuries ago, and that in its wake is a staggering cosmos in which men will be forced to play the role of gods.

The atomic bomb is only the first little Christmas present, so to speak, from the blind forces which are shaping the new era. Does any one suppose that we are going to be content with just this one dazzling new toy? How antiquated already are the railroads, the steamships, the automobiles, the aeroplanes, the electrical dynamos! In a jiffy we can be in touch with China, India, Australia, darkest Africa; in a few hours (to-day, that is, but what about to-morrow?) we can be physically transported to any one of these distant places. And here we are lumbering along, millions and billions of us, as if paralyzed, as if deaf and dumb. With the proper will we in America could, almost overnight, supply the whole world with everything it needs. We don't need the support of any country. Everything exists here in superabundance—I mean the physical actuality. As for our potential, no man can estimate it. Wars give only a slight intimation of what this country can do when it feels the vital urge. We are in possession of secrets which, if revealed and exploited, would unleash incalculable power and energy. We could inspire such hope, such courage, such enthusiasm, that the passion of the French revolutionists would seem like a mere breeze. I am thinking now only of what we actually possess, what we actually know, what we can actually visualize, myopic as we are. I say nothing of the suppressed, frustrated dreams of our inventors, our scientists, our technologists, our poets, of what would happen were they encouraged and not discouraged. I say, taking stock of only that which we now know and possess, we could revolutionize life on this earth to an unthinkable degree, and in the space of a few short years. What Russia, for example, hopes to accomplish in the next twenty years would, from this viewpoint, appear childish. To the dreams of our wildest dreamers, I say—"Yes, entirely possible. Possible right now, to-morrow. Possible a thousand times over, and to an extent that not even the wildest dreamer imagines." The future is galloping towards us like a wild horse; we can feel her breath on our necks.

One does not have to belong to any party, any cult, any ism, to sense what lies ahead. One does not have to swear allegiance to this or that to make this new world feasible. If anything, we have to forego these allegiances—they have only been halters and crutches. Our allegiance is always given to dead things. What is alive does not demand allegiance; what is alive commands, whether one gives adherence or not. What is necessary is that we believe and recognize that which is asserting itself, that we put ourselves in rhythm with what is vital and creative.

To-day the world is bound, cramped, stifled by those existing forms of government known as the State. Does the State protect us or do we protect the State? Whatever form of tyranny exists to-day exists by our consent. No matter into what corner of the globe we cast our eye to-day, we see the spectre of tyranny. Perhaps the worst tyranny is that which is created for our own good. There can be no common good unless the individual is recognized first and foremost—and until the last, the weakest, of men is included. Everything proceeds from the living individual. The State is an abstraction, a bogey which can intimidate but never convince us, never win us over completely.

In every State there is an element, like some mortal disease, which works to destroy it. And eventually, through a process of undermining, it does destroy it. No State ever had humanity in mind, only the interests of the State. When will we forget about the State and think of humanity, of ourselves, since it is we, all of us, who make up humanity? When will we think of all instead of just "our own?"

A new world is always more inclusive than the old one. A decadent, dying world is always jealous and possessive in all its parts. Since it can no longer live as a complex organism it strives to live cellularly, atomistically. Birth means disruption. It means the abandonment of one temple for another, the relinquishing of the known and the proven for the adventure of freedom and creation. It means above all—release. Those who are saying No! those who are defending the old order (the sacred temple, the sacred cow), those who are dubious and disillusioned, these do not want release. They want to die in the womb. To every urge they say "but," "if," or—"*impossible!*" Their motto is always the same: "Proceed cautiously!" Their talk is always of concession and compromise, never of faith, trust, confidence.

If the Russians are going to think only of Russia, and Americans of America, the hidden forces which direct the world, the forces which represent *all* humanity, will sooner or later put them in open conflict, incite them to destroy one another. When they talk of disarmament do they not mean stacking arms? If they mean peace, why do they wish to retain their weapons, their arsenals, their spies, their provocateurs? Wherever there is the jealous urge to exclude there is the menace of extinction. I see no nation on earth at present which has an all-inclusive view of things. I say it is impossible for a nation, as such, to hold such a view. Every one will tell you that such a view would be suicidal. Yet it is as clear as the handwriting on the wall that the nations of this earth are finished, though they have not yet come to their end. The dissolving process may continue for a span, but the outcome is certain and definite. Nations will disappear. The human family does not need these water-tight compartments in which to breathe. There is nothing any longer which warrants the survival of the nations, since to be Russian, French, English or American means to be less than what one really is.

Let me digress for a moment on that suicidal policy which a humanitarian instead of a national view of the world is supposed to entrain. I cannot help but think of the fervor with which, during the final days of the war, the helpless nations looked to America or Russia, sometimes to both. Two mighty nations, prepared to make any sacrifice to win the war, dazzled the world by their ability to mobilize seemingly inexhaustible powers, both moral and material. The end accomplished, their miraculous resources, the spiritual ones especially, seem to be drained. More even than during the war, the helpless peoples of the earth need the aid of these two mighty powers. The winning of the war was only half the battle. But where now is the constructive energy to match the spirit of destruction? Mindful of that fervor which we inspired as warriors, I ask myself if we could not inspire a thousand-fold greater fervor if we as a people, every man, woman and child, were to dedicate our lives to the relief and the rehabilitation of Europe and Asia. To protect our homes we were asked to make certain sacrifices. Could we not make the same sacrifices now? Could we not make even greater ones? Why did we destroy valuable stocks, valuable equipment, valuable material when the rest of the world had need of these things? (When even our own people had need of them!) How is it that we can make a surfeit of aeroplanes to destroy other peoples' homes and not make them now in even greater quantity to supply these miserable people with food, clothing and building materials? If we could disrupt our economy, as they say, to kill, maim and destroy, why can we not disrupt it still more to aid, nourish and protect? Are we not guilty now of making war on defenceless people? If we do not raise a hand to prevent people from dying of starvation it is not because we are unable to do so, as our politicians maintain, it is because we do not care to do so. It is because we lack the imagination to see that a people which sits with folded arms while the rest of the world agonizes is just as murderous at heart as the army which devastates their land. If every American considered it his solemn duty to do something for an unknown brother in Europe or Asia, if he regarded it as only right and natural that he share whatever comforts he enjoyed with those in dire need, if he did this as a private citizen, without regard for the policy or diplomacy of his government, if this became a burning issue with every American, do you suppose the present condition "over there" would not alter radically overnight? The mere fact that Americans had the courage—or shall I say "simple decency?"—to formulate such a project would in itself resuscitate millions who now regard themselves as doomed. We are told that we must take care of our own people first, provide them with those necessities and luxuries which they were denied during the war years. But if it had been necessary to continue the war another ten years, would we not have done without these indispensable necessities and luxuries? Would we not have accommodated ourselves to even greater privations? (After all, the war affected us least of all the warring nations, that is indisputable.) Moreover, we ought not to forget that the sacrifices which we make so much of were involuntary sacrifices. The sacrifice I am thinking of would be a voluntary one and its effect, consequently, would be far greater. There would be another difference discernible too, let me add—a people who of their own free will volunteered to sacrifice themselves would wax in joy and strength; they would not be diminished or exhausted as they were from the war effort. It is true, bearing in mind the arguments of wary politicians, that in the midst of such a devotional performance the American people could again be stabbed in the back by some jealous power. One could build up such a fancy—about the Russians, let us say—with considerable eloquence. But supposing we were helping Russia, our potential enemy, too? What answer is there to that, I wonder? And, whether we were stabbed in the back or not, what is more important now, this moment—that we watch the world die on our hands or make an effort to save it? Will we be able to live in a world filled with sick, starving, homeless, helpless people? Who will be our holy "customers?" Will we be forced to eat our own money? Is that the end of national economy?

It is almost foolish to talk about the emptiness of the slogans which were foisted upon the warring peoples of the world by the mouthpieces of universal guilt. It is dubious that any but a weak minority of the respective publics ever believed in these catch phrases. What then were we all fighting for? To win the war, obviously. To win the war and return to a so-called normal mode of existence. But what about this "normal mode of life?" How normal was it? Nobody believed much in the good, comfortable routine that we all longed to return to. In every country, rich or poor, Fascist or Democratic, the conditions were well-nigh intolerable. People may not always have admitted it openly, but it was so. In private conversation, in the bosom of the family, behind locked doors, the same plaint was going up everywhere. Men said to one another, to their wives, to their children: "This is no life. This must end." And then suddenly, in all these countries where this so-called "normal mode of life" prevailed, the citizens were warned that even this simulacrum of life was better than what the enemy threatened to impose; they were told that it were better to sacrifice their lives, their all, for this pseudo-life or there would be eternal hell, eternal slavery. And each of these fear-stricken countries sent its legions of able-bodied men (and women too, and sometimes children) to slaughter one another. With a little package dropped from the sky we Americans accomplished the trick which put an end to the war. We held the trump card. And finally we played it.

Many have wondered, and with justice, why it was that, holding such trumps, we did not carry on, did not put an end everywhere to tyranny and injustice, to misery and privation. We could have cleaned up on a grand scale, and not for our own aggrandisement but to establish a better, saner world. If we could wipe out whole urban populations in far off Japan we ought certainly, one would think, have been able to eliminate all the little Caesars whom we delight in smothering with scorn and ridicule. For that, however, we would have had to do some liquidating right at home, to say nothing of the punishment we would have had to inflict on our Allies. I am putting all this in very simple language—any one ought to be able to understand what I am saying. The question is, "Why didn't we do it?" And the next question is: "Who are *we*?" Immediately you perceive that *we* are not *it*. *We* are always just the people. *We* do not start wars, but the government. If we, the people, had intended to establish the Four Freedoms, what could have hindered us, assuming that *we* won the war, that *we* held those trump cards up our sleeve? No, *we* are never anything but cannon fodder. And so are those who call themselves "we Italians," "we Germans," "we Russians." We will do anything and everything to destroy one another and nothing to preserve ourselves. We elect representatives whom we know in our hearts will betray us. We permit others to regulate our lives for us, and we are amazed and bewildered when they ask us to surrender our lives.

In *The Joy of Man's Desiring*,[1] the peasant Jourdan says: "There is one thing that I do not believe; that is that any one deliberately wants us to be unhappy. I think that things were made so that everybody can be happy. I think that our unhappiness is a sort of disease which we create ourselves, with big chills-and-fever, with bad water, and with the evil that we catch from each other in breathing the same air. I think that if we knew how to live, perhaps we wouldn't be ill. With the habits we've gotten into now, all our life is a struggle; we strike out in the water, we fight, to keep from going under. Our whole life long. Whether it be your animals, whether it be your seeds, your plants, your trees, you've got to police against them all. What we want, it seems that the entire world does not want. They seem to do it on purpose. That must have given us a distaste for everything, in the end. That must have forced our bodies to produce any old way, how can we tell? . . . The world forces us to shed blood. Perhaps we are unconsciously creating a special kind of blood, a blood of distaste, and instead of there flowing through our bodies, everywhere—in our arms, in our thighs, in our hearts, in our stomachs, in our lungs—a blood of desire, our great pipe system washes us with a blood of disgust."

I have hopes of some day adding a third volume to this *Nightmare*. In it I should like to speak only of what could be. I would like to take this country of ours and recreate it—in the image of the hope which it once inspired. I too believe "that things were made so that everybody can be happy." I see evidence of this truth constantly. Native of a land which has been richly blessed, I was imbued from infancy, I might almost say, with the conviction that we have the power to do well-nigh anything. My earliest recollections are of plenitude, of peace, of joy. I had a golden childhood amidst humble surroundings. My people were ordinary folk, gifted in no way. It is true, they were the product of immigrants—there was a certain advantage in that. But are we not all, in America, the products of immigrants at some point along the line? America was made entirely by foreigners. What makes us Americans, and not simply the sons and daughters of foreigners, is that we used to believe we could accomplish miracles. We were born in the middle of the horn of plenty. We had no enemies on our backs, unless it was "the mother country," England. We had the good-will of the world. We had no desire to take over the world and run it.

[1] By Jean Giono, Viking Press, N. Y. Edition exhausted.

To-day all that is past. We have been forced to take a hand in the running of the world; we have been forced to share our treasures; we have been forced to make enemies and to fight them. In doing these things we have also been forced to take stock of ourselves. We have been obliged to ask ourselves whether we are a force for good or for evil. That we are a force we know, and the knowledge of it, the responsibility which it entails, frightens us. What many Americans are asking themselves is this: "What have we to give the world, now that we have succeeded in dismantling it? Can we put it together again?" Many of us wonder if we shall ever be able to disintoxicate ourselves—for we are drunk, drunk with a power beyond us. Despite all back-sliding, always we have stoutly maintained that we want only peace. But never have we been more ready, more willing, to engage in war. We seem to invite trouble. We stand like the big bully who has cleaned up the whole neighborhood, and we ask defiantly: "Who next?" I don't say we, the people, but we, the government of the United States. Like all governments, our government too pretends that it wishes to protect the interests of its citizens. As if every Tom, Dick and Harry had some foreign interests which he was eager to preserve. We are told about the oil wells in some distant region of the earth, and how important it is that this country or that should not get hold of them. (We talk about them as if they existed in a no-man's land, the public domain of King Nod.) We are warned that the next war will probably be started over the possession of these foreign oil fields. When the time is ripe for it, the common man in America, in Russia, in Great Britain, and in other places too, will be persuaded by the right propaganda that the most vital thing in his short life is for one of us countries to gain possession of those oil reserves. We will be told that "we" need them, that our very lives are dependent on the possession of these natural resources. By that time it is quite possible, indeed even most probable, that one of these progressive nations will have found the way to reach the moon, possibly other nearby planets. It is altogether conceivable, in view of the universal fear, distrust, panic and alarm, that these neighboring planets will be used as hide-outs for the monstrous new engines of war which will be invented. Anything is possible.

Fifty, or even twenty, years ago, the thought of being able to visit the moon seemed the most stupendous feat imaginable. And now, now that the moon is almost within reach, the probabilities are that we shall think of it only in terms of military strategy. Think to what an extent our fears can lead us! How tragic for the universe at large that our war-like spirit envisages the possibility of bursting its terrestrial bounds and seeks to fill the heavens with its thunder! To satisfy our lust for destruction we are ready to invade the stars, exploit the very heavens.

To some, of course, this will sound like the wildest fancy. But in ten years the wildest flights of fantasy may well become stark reality. We are moving with a pace which is electrifying. A return to a slower, easier rhythm is impossible. Acceleration, more and more acceleration, that is the key-note of this new epoch. The pace is set for us by our inventions. Each invention augments the magnitude of the gear, the gear of a vehicle whose form is not even discernible yet. Would you know where lies the seat of our heart's desire? Look to our great inventions. We pretend that we created them for our own use, but we are no longer the masters, we are the victims. We and our inventions are one. In every sense they answer to our deepest desires. When we yearned to be able to kill a man at long range we invented the rifle; when we yearned to communicate with a fellow mortal at a distance, we invented the telephone; when we yearned to turn night into day we invented the electric bulb; when we no longer yearned to have children we invented the contraceptive; when we became impatient with piece-meal destruction, we invented the high explosive. When we get ready to destroy the earth we shall doubtless have invented the means of migrating to another planet.

We in America are the most inventive people on earth. It is in our blood. Back of this mania for invention exists the delusion that we are making things easier for ourselves. Easier and better. Or else bigger and better. We despise work and yet we toil like slaves. We never think beforehand of the consequences which a new invention entails. Only now, now that we have invented the atomic bomb, do we begin to ponder about such things. (Nobel, the father of dynamite, foresaw the dilemma long ago.) Suddenly we have become acutely aware of the Janus-like quality of the atom bomb. That swords could be beaten into plough-shares, this is something we all knew from childhood, though none ever acted on it. But when it finally sunk into us that the world's most destructive weapon could be converted to the most expansive utilitarian ends, something like "a shock of recognition" swept the world. Indeed, at this particular moment, the world may be said to be vainly struggling to recover from a double shock, namely the recognition that it must choose between annihilation and paradise. That middle ground, to which the men of the old order so desperately cling, that in-between realm which we once regarded as human and which we characterized with appellations such as Culture and Civilization, has become like quicksand under our feet.

If it is possible for a mere novelist to present us with a picture of the future, such as Werfel gave us in *Star of the Unborn*, what is not possible in the next fifty years? I say this because reality has a way of catching up with the dreams of poets in short order. Werfel situated his fictive world in a time one hundred thousand years distant. The inciting imaginative challenge which Jules Verne made to the men of his generation, Werfel has made to our generation. Much that Werfel's phantasy prefigured could be actualized in less than five hundred years. One crawls on all fours for aeons, seemingly, but the moment one stands erect one can not only walk and run, but fly. One babbles until one has acquired a vocabulary; after that it does not take much to establish communication with God. We make machines which defy the laws of gravitation, but will the time not soon be here when gravitation itself will be exploited, as now we exploit that mysterious force called electricity? How long will we bother with cumbersome machines, with tools even of the finest precision? Is not the machine a rude model, a crude hieroglyph, if you like, of a language which, when understood, will give us a movable and inexhaustible alphabet enabling us to translate instantaneously from impulse to desire, from desire to thought, from thought to act, and from act to fulfillment?

We have entered a new magnetic field of energy, one which will condition us to live like gods. It will no longer be possible, as at present, to bury the clues to these mysterious forces in our patent offices; our children already inhabit an imaginative world more daring, more in keeping with the new age, than the mental world of the present-day adult. The sparks which have been kindled will grow into flames. We cannot put the brakes on this spirit of investigation and exploration. The earth is rushing onward, carrying us along like detritus.

When the desire to be in a distant place becomes greater than the physical means of getting there, we will most certainly discover how to be in that place *without the use of a conveyance*. If we truly want to hear and see what is going on in distant parts of the earth (or distant parts of the universe), it is not only possible but altogether probable that we will dispense with all our instruments. There can well come a moment of impatience, a moment of need, a moment of inspirational fervor so great that the way will be broken open—and we will perform those seeming miracles which have been spoken of in all ages. To open up a new realm of consciousness will be no more impossible than to make sound, light or heat issue from the end of a wire. Indeed, it will be absolutely necessary to attain this higher state of consciousness. At the present level the human intellect is unable to cope with the forces it has unleashed. The irrational world is rapidly gaining the ascendancy. There is no hope of achieving that harmonious unity of the psyche, now more than ever indispensable, with the intellect functioning like an adding machine. The mind and consciousness of man will have to expand to meet the demands of that soul which will reflect the new universal spirit. In our souls we know that the universe is not a haphazard affair. In our souls we know that nothing is impossible. In our souls we know that death is only a shadow which accompanies us. Our poverty-stricken, terrorized minds may tell us differently, but this mind which would keep us in fear and trembling is only the kernel of a greater mind. We are made of the same substance as the stars, the same substance as the gods. We are one with the universe, and we know it quietly in moments of crisis. It is for this reason we are able to sacrifice ourselves on occasion. We know that in some unknown accounting, by some bookkeeping which is beyond our comprehension, nothing is lost. Indeed, we know more, we know a better thing than that . . . we know that the more willing we are to lose everything the more certain we are to gain all. Weak man, shrewd men, sombre, worldly men, have tried to deny this. They have tried to make us believe that our lives are petty and vain, that we live to no end, counseling us at the same time to make the most of it while we can. But when a great issue arises, the influence of these men evaporates like sweat.

We are only gradually shaking off the tyranny of the Church. Now we face another tyranny, perhaps worse: the tyranny of the State. The State seeks to make of its citizens obedient instruments for its glorification. It promises them happiness—in some distant future—as once the Church held out the hope of reaching Paradise. To preserve its interests, the State is perpetually obliged to make war. The chief concern of a State is to be ready and fit for the next conflict. The important thing, which is the enjoyment of life, now, this moment, every moment, is constantly postponed because of the necessity to be prepared for war. Every new invention is appraised from this standpoint. The last thing which any State thinks of is how to make its citizens comfortable and joyous. The wages of the average man barely suffice, and often do not suffice at all, to meet the cost of living. I am speaking now of the richest country on earth—America. What conditions are like in the rest of the world beggars description. One can say to-day without fear of contradiction that never since the dawn of civilization has the world been in a worse state.

To aid our fellow sufferers throughout the world we are urged on the one hand to give all we can, and on the other hand we are informed that no matter how much we give it will be but a drop in the bucket. The despair which seizes the sensitive individual, confronted with this dilemma, is fathomless. One knows that there must be a way out, but who holds the answer? The way has to be created. There must be a desire, an overwhelming desire, to find a solution. To think for one moment that it will be found by the representatives of our various governments is the gravest delusion. These men are thinking only of saving their faces. Each one is pitted against the other, is obliged to win some sort of petty victory over the other, in order to maintain his position. While these mouthpieces talk about peace and order, about freedom and justice, the men behind them, the men who support them and keep them up front, so to speak, are mobilizing all their forces to keep the world in a state of perpetual conflict. In China at this very moment America and Russia are playing the same game that was played in Spain a few years ago. There is no secret about it. Yet every day we are told through the newspapers and over the radio that America and Russia are seeking to understand one another, to live amicably in the same world.

It is not easy to see how the peoples of either of these great countries can liberate themselves. The American people are supine, the Russian people are acquiescent. In neither of them is there the slightest revolutionary ardor. In opportunities for self-development they are richer than any other people in the world. They could not only support themselves comfortably, they could between them assume the burdens of the starving nations of the earth.

And what is it they are worried about? Why are these two nations still at loggerheads? Because each is fearful of the other's influence upon the rest of the world. One of these countries represents itself as a Communist nation, the other as a Democratic nation. Neither of them are what they pretend to be. Russia is no more Communist than America is Democratic. The present Russian government is even more autocratic than that of the Czars. The present American government is more tyrannical than that of the British in the time of the thirteen Colonies. There is less freedom now in both these countries than there ever was. How will such peoples free the world? They do not seem to know the meaning of freedom.

It seems almost inevitable now that these two countries are determined to destroy, and will succeed in destroying, one another. And in the process of destroying each other they will destroy a large part of the civilized world. England is weak, France is helpless, Germany is prostrate, and Japan will be only too delighted to watch and wait, biding her time to make herself strong again. Of all the countries which participated in the war, Japan learned her lesson best. When the West is in ruins she will rise again, invade Europe, take it over.

"Nonsense! Ridiculous!" the critics will scream. And, burying their heads in the sand, they will whistle from their rear ends. For once, Democrats, Republicans, Fascists, Communists will agree. "Impossible!" they will shout. Well, this is a lone man's view. I have no axe to grind, no Party to sustain, no ism to further. All I clamor for is that freedom, that security, that peace and harmony which all these conflicting groups advocate and promise. I don't want it when I'm dead. I want it now. Everything I do is with that purpose in mind.

I ask no one to sacrifice himself in order to promote my ideas. I demand no allegiance, no taxes, no devotion. I say—free yourself to the best of your ability! The more freedom you obtain for yourself, the more you create for me, for every one. I would like you to have all that you desire, praying at the same time that you wish as much for the next man. I urge you to create and to share your creation with those less fortunate. If some one asks you to vote for him at the next election, ask him, I beg you, what he can do for you that you cannot do yourself. Ask him whom *he* is voting for. If he tells you the truth, then go to the polls and vote for yourself. Most any one who reads this could do a better job than the man now doing it. Why create these jobs? Why ask some one else to regulate your affairs? What are you doing that is so important? Does the man who asks for your vote find you your job, does he provide your family with food and shelter, does he put clothes on your back, does he provide the education you need . . . does he even bother to see that you get a decent burial? The only time he is concerned about you is when you can make money for him. No matter how little you make he wants part of it. He keeps you poor on the pretext that he is doing something for your benefit. And you are too lazy to protest, knowing full well that he thinks about no one but himself. From childhood you were taught that it is right and just to delegate your powers to some one else. You never questioned it because everything you are taught in school has one purpose: the glorification of your country. Somehow, though it is *your* country, you seem to have no part in it until the time comes to surrender your life. Your whole life is spent in trying to get a hearing. You're always on the door-step, never inside.

Wherever one goes in this civilized world one always finds the same set-up. The little man, the man who does the dirty work, *the producer*, is of no importance, receives no consideration, and is always being asked to make the greatest sacrifice. Yet everything depends on this forgotten man. Not a wheel could turn without his support and cooperation. It is this man, whose number is legion, who has no voice whatever in world affairs. These matters are beyond his grasp, supposedly. He has only to produce; the others, the politicians, they will run the world. One day this poor little man, this forgotten son, this nobody on whose toil and industry everything depends, will see through the farce. Uninstructed though he may be, he knows full well how rich is the earth, how little he needs to live happily. He knows, too, that it is not necessary to kill his fellow-man in order to live; he knows that he has been robbed and cheated from time immemorial; he knows that if he can't run his affairs properly, nobody else can. He is suffocated with all this bitter knowledge. He waits and waits, hoping that time will alter things. And slowly he realizes that time alters nothing, that with time things only grow worse. One day he will decide to act. "Wait!" he will be told. "Wait just a little longer." But he will refuse to wait another second.

When that day comes, watch out! When the little man all over the world becomes so desperate that he cannot wait another minute, another second, beware O world! Once he decides to act for himself, act on his own, there will be no putting him back in harness. There will be nothing you can promise him which will equal the joy of being free, being rid of the incubus. To-day he is still yours, still the pawn which can be shuffled about, but to-morrow there may be such a reversal of all precedent as to make your hearts quake. To-day you may still talk the absurd language of the Stone Age; to-day you may still coerce the young into preparedness for the next conflict; to-day you may still convince the blind and the ignorant that they should be content to do without the things you find indispensable; to-day you may still talk about your possessions, your colonies, your empires. But your days are numbered. You belong in the museum, with the dinosaur, the stone axe, the hieroglyph, the mummy. The new age will come into being with your disappearance from the face of the earth.

At the dawn of every age there is distinguishable a radiant figure in whom the new time spirit is embodied. He comes at the darkest hour, rises like a sun, and dispels the gloom and stagnation in which the world was gripped. Somewhere in the black folds which now enshroud us I am certain that another being is gestating, that he is but waiting for the zero hour to announce himself. Hope never dies, passion can never be utterly extinguished. The dead-lock will be broken. Now we are sound asleep in the cocoon; it took centuries and centuries to spin this seeming web of death. It takes but a few moments to burst it asunder. Now we are out on a limb, suspended over the void. Should the tree give way, all creation vaults to its doom. But what is it that tells us to hasten the hour of birth? What is it that, at precisely the right moment, gives us the knowledge and the power to take wing, when heretofore we knew only how to crawl ignominiously on our bellies? If the caterpillar through sleep can metamorphose into a butterfly, surely man during his long night of travail must discover the knowledge and the power to redeem himself.

BIG SUR
AND
AFTER

•

(1945–1980)

Chronological

Early in 1930 I left New York with the intention of going to Spain. I never got there. Instead, I remained in France until June 1939, when I left for Greece to take a much needed vacation. Forced out of Greece early in 1940 because of the war, I returned to New York. Before becoming a resident of California I made the "air-conditioned nightmare" trip around America, which consumed a full year. During this period of almost two and a half years I wrote *The Colossus of Maroussi, The World of Sex, Quiet Days in Clichy,* parts of *The Air-conditioned Nightmare,* and the first book of *The Rosy Crucifixion (Sexus).*

In June 1942 I arrived in California to stay. For over a year I lived in Beverly Glen, just outside Hollywood. There I met Jean Varda, who induced me to come to Monterey on a visit. This was in February 1944. I stayed with Varda, in his Red Barn, for several weeks and then, at his suggestion, made a trip to Big Sur to meet Lynda Sargent. Lynda was then living in the log cabin around which the celebrated "Nepenthe" has since been built. I stayed on as a house guest for about two months, at which time Keith Evans, who was then in the service, offered me the use of his cabin on Partington Ridge. (Thanks to Lynda Sargent's efforts.) Here I remained from May 1944 until January 1946, during which time I made a brief trip to New York, remarried in Denver, and became the father of a daughter, Valentine. Upon Keith Evans' return to civil life we were obliged to seek other quarters. In January 1946 we moved to Anderson Creek, three miles down the road, where we rented one of the old convicts' shacks situated at the edge of a cliff. In February 1947 we returned to Partington Ridge, to occupy the house which Jean Wharton had originally built for herself. It was towards the very end of this year that

Conrad Moricand arrived, to last only about three months. In 1948 a son, Tony, was born.

Partington Ridge is about fourteen miles south of the Big Sur Post Office and some forty odd miles from Monterey. Except for a pleasure trip to Europe in 1953, when I married again, I have been living on the Ridge ever since February 1947.

Big Sur

The little community of one, begun by the fabulous "outlander," Jaime de Angulo, has multiplied into a dozen families. The hill (Partington Ridge) is now nearing the saturation point, as things go in this part of the world. The one big difference between the Big Sur I encountered eleven years ago and that of today is the advent of so many new children. The mothers here seem to be as fecund as the soil. The little country school, situated not far from the State Park, has almost reached its capacity. It is the sort of school which, most unfortunately for our children, is rapidly disappearing from the American scene.

In another ten years we know not what may happen. If uranium or some other metal vital to the warmongers is discovered in these parts, Big Sur will be nothing but a legend.

Today Big Sur is no longer an outpost. The number of sightseers and visitors increases yearly. Emil White's "Big Sur Guide" alone brings swarms of tourists to our front door. What was inaugurated with virginal modesty threatens to end as a bonanza. The early settlers are dying off. Should their huge tracts of land be broken up into small holdings, Big Sur may rapidly develop into a suburb (of Monterey), with bus service, barbecue stands, gas stations, chain stores and all the odious claptrap that makes Suburbia horrendous.

This is a bleak view. It may be that we will be spared the usual horrors which accompany the tides of progress. Perhaps the millennium will be ushered in before we are taken over!

I like to think back to my early days on Partington Ridge, when there was no electricity, no butane tanks, no refrigeration—and the mail came only three times a week. In those days, and even later when I returned to the Ridge, I managed to get along without a car. To be sure, I did have a little cart (such as children play

553

with), which Emil White had knocked together for me. Hitching myself to it, like an old billy goat, I would patiently haul the mail and groceries up the hill, a fairly steep climb of about a mile and a half. On reaching the turn near the Roosevelts' driveway, I would divest myself of everything but a jock-strap. What was to hinder?

The callers in those days were mostly youngsters just entering or just leaving the service. (They're doing the same today, though the war ended in '45.) The majority of these lads were artists or would-be artists. Some stayed on, eking out the weirdest sort of existence; some came back later to have a serious go at it. They were all filled with a desire to escape the horrors of the present and willing to live like rats if only they might be left alone and in peace. What a strange lot they were, when I think on it! Judson Crews of Waco, Texas, one of the first to muscle in, reminded one—because of his shaggy beard and manner of speech—of a latter-day prophet. He lived almost exclusively on peanut butter and wild mustard greens, and neither smoked nor drank. Norman Mini, who had already had an unusual career, starting as in Poe's case with his dismissal from West Point, stayed on (with wife and child) long enough to finish a first novel—the best first novel I have ever read and, as yet, unpublished. Norman was "different" in that, though poor as a church mouse, he clung to his cellar, which contained some of the finest wines (native and foreign) anyone could wish for. And then there was Walker Winslow, who was then writing *If a Man Be Mad*, which turned out to be a best seller. Walker wrote at top speed, and seemingly without interruption, in a tiny shack by the roadside which Emil White had built to house the steady stream of stragglers who were forever busting in on him for a day, a week, a month or a year.

In all, almost a hundred painters, writers, dancers, sculptors and musicians have come and gone since I first arrived. At least a dozen possessed genuine talent and may leave their mark on the world. The one who was an unquestionable genius and the most spectacular of all, aside from Varda, who belongs to an earlier period, was Gerhart Muench of Dresden. Gerhart belongs in a category all by himself. As a pianist he is phenomenal, if not incomparable. He is also a composer. And in addition, a scholar, erudite to the finger tips. If he had done no more for us than to interpret Scriabin—and he did vastly more, all without result, alas!—we of Big Sur ought be forever indebted to him.

Speaking of artists, the curious thing is that few of this stripe ever last it out here. Is something lacking? Or is there too much . . . too much sunshine, too much fog, too much peace and contentment?

Almost every art colony owes its inception to the longing of a mature artist who felt the need to break with the clique surrounding him. The location chosen was usually an ideal one, particularly to the discoverer who had spent the better years of his life in dingy holes and garrets. The would-be artists, for whom place and atmosphere are all important, always contrive to convert these havens of retreat into boisterous, merry-making colonies. Whether this will happen to Big Sur remains to be seen. Fortunately there are certain deterrents.

It is my belief that the immature artist seldom thrives in idyllic surroundings. What he seems to need, though I am the last to advocate it, is more first-hand experience of life—more bitter experience, in other words. In short, more struggle, more privation, more anguish, more disillusionment. These goads or stimulants he may not always hope to find here in Big Sur. Here, unless he is on his guard, unless he is ready to wrestle with phantoms as well as bitter realities, he is apt to go to sleep mentally and spiritually. If an art colony is established here it will go the way of all the others. Artists never thrive in colonies. Ants do. What the budding artist needs is the privilege of wrestling with his problems in solitude—and now and then a piece of red meat.

The chief problem for the man who endeavors to live apart is the idle visitor. One can never decide whether he is a curse or a blessing. With all the experience which these last few years have provided, I still do not know how, or whether, to protect myself against the unwarranted intrusion, the steady invasion, of that prying, curious-minded species of "homo fatuoso" endowed with the annoying faculty of dropping in at the wrong moment. To seek a hide-out more difficult of access is futile. The fan who wants to meet you, who is *determined* to meet you, if only to shake your hand, will not stop at climbing the Himalayas.

In America, I have long observed, one lives exposed to all comers. One is expected to live thus or be regarded as a crank. Only in Europe do writers live behind garden walls and locked doors.

In addition to all the other problems he has to cope with, the artist has to wage a perpetual struggle to fight free. I mean, find a way out of the senseless grind which daily threatens to annihilate all incentive. Even more than other mortals, he has need of harmonious surroundings. As writer or painter, he can do his work most anywhere. The rub is that wherever living is cheap, wherever nature is inviting, it is almost impossible to find the means of acquiring that bare modicum which is needed to keep body and soul together. A man with talent has to make his living on the side or do his creative work on the side. A difficult choice!

If he has the luck to find an ideal spot, or an ideal community, it does not follow that his work will there receive the encouragement he so desperately needs. On the contrary, he will probably find that no one is interested in what he is doing. He will generally be looked upon as strange or different. And he *will* be, of course, since what makes him tick is that mysterious element "X" which his fellow-man seems so well able to do without. He is almost certain to eat, talk, dress in a fashion eccentric to his neighbors. Which is quite enough to mark him out for ridicule, contempt and isolation. If, by taking a humble job, he demonstrates that he is as good as the next man, the situation may be somewhat ameliorated. But not for long. To prove that he is "as good as the next man" means little or nothing to one who is an artist. It was his "otherness" which made him an artist and, given the chance, he will make his fellow-man other too. Sooner or later, in one way or another, he is bound to rub his neighbors the wrong way. Unlike the ordinary fellow, he will throw everything to the winds when the urge seizes him. Moreover, if he *is* an artist, he will be compelled to make sacrifices which worldly people find absurd and unnecessary. In following the inner light he will inevitably choose for his boon companion poverty. And, if he has in him the makings of a great artist, he may renounce everything, even his art. This, to the average citizen, particularly the good citizen, is preposterous and unthinkable. Thus it happens now and then that, failing to recognize the genius in a man, a most worthy, a most respected, member of society may be heard to say: "Beware of that chap, he's up to no good!"

The world being what it is, I give it as my candid opinion that anyone who knows how to work with his two hands, anyone who is willing to give a fair day's work for a fair day's pay, would be better off to abandon his art and settle down to a humdrum life in an out of the way place like this. It may indeed be the highest wisdom to elect to be a nobody in a relative paradise such as this rather than a celebrity in a world which has lost all sense of values. But this is a problem which is rarely settled in advance.

There is one young man in this community who seems to have espoused the kind of wisdom I refer to. He is a man with an independent income, a man of keen intelligence, well educated, sensitive, of excellent character, and capable not only with his hands but with brain and heart. In making a life for himself he has apparently chosen to do nothing more than raise a family, provide its members with what he can, and enjoy the life of day to day. He does everything single-handed, from erecting buildings to raising crops, making wines, and so on. At intervals he hunts or fishes, or just takes off into the wilderness to commune with nature. To the average man he would appear to be just another good citizen, except that he is of better physique than most, enjoys better health, has no vices and no trace of the usual neuroses. His library is an excellent one, and he is at home in it; he enjoys good music and listens to it frequently. He can hold his own at any sport or game, can vie with the toughest when it comes to hard work, and in general is what might be called "a good fellow," that is, a man who knows how to mix with others, how to get along with the world. But what he also knows and does, and what the average citizen can not or will not do, is to enjoy solitude, to live simply, to crave nothing, and to share what he has when called upon. I refrain from mentioning his name for fear of doing him a disservice. Let us leave him where he is, Mr. X, a master of the anonymous life and a wonderful example to his fellow-man.

While in Vienne (France) two years ago I had the privilege of making the acquaintance of Fernand Rude, the *sous-préfet* of Vienne, who possesses a remarkable collection of Utopian literature. On leaving, he presented me with a copy of his book, *Voyage en Icarie*,[1] which is the account of two workers from Vienne who came to America just a hundred years ago to join Étienne Cabet's experimental colony at Nauvoo, Illinois. The description given of American life, not only at Nauvoo but in the cities they passed through—they arrived at New Orleans and left by way of New York—is worth reading today, if only to observe how essentially unchanged is our American way of life. To be sure, Whitman was giving us about this same time (in his prose works) a similar picture of vulgarity, violence and corruption, in high and low places. One fact stands out, however, and that is the inborn urge of the American to experiment, to try out the most crack-brained schemes having to do with social, economic, religious and even sex relations. Where sex and religion were dominant, the most amazing results were achieved. The Oneida Community (New York), for example, is destined to remain as memorable an experiment as Robert Owen's in New Harmony (Indiana). As for the Mormons, nothing comparable to their efforts has ever been undertaken on this continent, and probably never will again.

In all these idealistic ventures, particularly those initiated by

---

[1] The title is taken from the book of the same name by Étienne Cabet wherein the latter describes his (imaginary) Utopia. A remarkable work in this, that though Communistic in the romantic sense, it is an accurate blueprint of the totalitarian governments we now have.

religious communities, the participants seemed to possess a keen sense of reality, a practical wisdom, which in no way conflicted (as it does in the case of ordinary Christians) with their religious views. They were honest, law-abiding, industrious, self-sustaining, self-sufficient citizens with character, individuality and integrity, somewhat corroded (to our present way of thinking) by a Puritan sobriety and austerity, but never lacking in faith, courage and independence. Their influence on American thought, American behavior, has been most powerful.

Since living here in Big Sur I have become more and more aware of this tendency in my fellow-American to experiment. Today it is not communities or groups who seek to lead "the good life" but isolated individuals. The majority of these, at least from my observation, are young men who have already had a taste of professional life, who have already been married and divorced, who have already served in the armed forces and seen a bit of the world, as we say. Utterly disillusioned, this new breed of experimenter is resolutely turning his back on all that he once held true and viable, and is making a valiant effort to start anew. Starting anew, for this type, means leading a vagrant's life, tackling anything, clinging to nothing, reducing one's needs and one's desires, and eventually—out of a wisdom born of desperation—leading the life of an artist. Not, however, the type of artist we are familiar with. An artist, rather, whose sole interest is in creating, an artist who is indifferent to reward, fame, success. One, in short, who is reconciled from the outset to the fact that the better he is the less chance he has of being accepted at face value. These young men, usually in their late twenties or early thirties, are now roaming about in our midst like anonymous messengers from another planet. By force of example, by reason of their thoroughgoing nonconformity and, shall I say, "nonresistance," they are proving themselves a more potent, stimulating force than the most eloquent and vociferous of recognized artists.

The point to note is that these individuals are not concerned with undermining a vicious system but with leading their own lives—on the fringe of society. It is only natural to find them gravitating toward places like Big Sur, of which there are many replicas in this vast country. We are in the habit of speaking of "the last frontier," but wherever there are "individuals" there will always be new frontiers. For the man who wants to lead the good life, which is a way of saying *his own life,* there is always a spot where he can dig in and take root.

But what is it that these young men have discovered, and which, curiously enough, links them with their forebears who deserted

Europe for America? That the American way of life is an illusory kind of existence, that the price demanded for the security and abundance it pretends to offer is too great. The presence of these "renegades," small in number though they be, is but another indication that the machine is breaking down. When the smashup comes, as now seems inevitable, they are more likely to survive the catastrophe than the rest of us. At least, they will know how to get along without cars, without refrigerators, without vacuum cleaners, electric razors and all the other "indispensables" . . . probably even without money. If ever we are to witness a new heaven and a new earth, it must surely be one in which money is absent, forgotten, wholly useless.

Here I should like to quote from a review of *Living the Good Life,* by Helen and Scott Nearing.[1] Says the editor: "What we are trying to suggest is that the solution for a cluttered, frustrated existence is not merely in moving to the country and attempting to practise 'the simple life.' The solution is in an attitude towards human experience which makes simple physical and economic arrangements almost a moral and esthetic necessity. It is the larger purpose in life which gives to its lesser enterprises—the obtaining of food, shelter and clothing—their essential harmony and balance. So often people dream of an ideal life "in community," forgetting that a "community" is not an end in itself, but a frame for higher qualities—the qualities of the mind and the heart. Making a community is not a magic formula for happiness and good; making a community is the result of the happiness and the good which people already possess in principle, and the community, whether of one family or several, is the infinitely variable expression of the excellences of human beings, and not their cause. . . ."

Digging in at Big Sur eleven years ago, I must confess that I had not the least thought or concern about the life of the community. With a population of one hundred souls scattered over several hundred square miles, I was not even conscious of an existent "community." My community then comprised a dog, Pascal (so named because he had the sorrowful look of a thinker), a few trees, the buzzards, and a seeming jungle of poison oak. My only friend, Emil White, lived three miles down the road. The hot sulphur baths were three miles farther down the road. There the community ended, from my standpoint.

I soon found out how mistaken I was, of course. It was no time before neighbors began popping up from all sides—out of the brush, it seemed—and always laden with gifts, as well as the most

[1] From *Manas,* Los Angeles, March 23, 1955.

discreet and sensible advice, for the "newcomer." Never have I known better neighbors! All of them were endowed with a tact and subtlety such as I never ceased to marvel at. They came only when they sensed you had need of them. As in France, it seemed to me that I was once again among people who knew how to let you be. And always there was a standing invitation to join them at table, should you have need of food or company.

Being one of those unfortunate "helpless" individuals who knew nothing but city ways, it wasn't long before I had to call upon my neighbors for aid of one kind or another. Something was always going amiss, something was always getting out of order. I hate to think what would have happened had I been left entirely to my own resources! Anyway, with the assistance that was always willingly and cheerfully extended, I received instruction in how to help myself, the most valuable gift that can be offered. I discovered all too quickly that my neighbors were not only extremely affable, helpful, generous in every way, but that they were far more intelligent, far wiser, far more self-sufficient than I had fatuously thought myself to be. The community, from being at first an invisible web, gradually became most tangible, most real. For the first time in my life I found myself surrounded by kind souls who were not thinking exclusively of their own welfare. A strange new sense of security began to develop in me, one I had never known before. In fact, I would boast to visitors that, once a resident of Big Sur, nothing evil could possibly happen to one. I would always add cautiously: "But one has first to prove himself a good neighbor!" Though they were addressed to my visitor, I meant these words for myself. And often, when the visitor had departed, I would repeat them to myself like a litany. It took time, you see, for one who had always lived the jungle life of the big city to realize that he too could be "a neighbor."

Here I must say flatly, and not without a bad conscience, that I am undoubtedly the worst neighbor any community could boast of. That I am still treated with more than mere tolerance is something which still surprises me.

Often I am so completely out of it all that the only way I can "get back" is to look at my world through the eyes of my children. I always begin by thinking back to the glorious childhood I enjoyed in that squalid section of Brooklyn known as Williamsburg. I try to relate those squalid streets and shabby houses to the vast expanse of sea and mountain of this region. I dwell on the birds I never saw except for the sparrow feasting on a fresh pile of manure, or a stray pigeon. Never a hawk, a buzzard, an eagle, never a robin or a hummingbird. I think of the sky which was always hacked to pieces by roof-tops and hideous smoking chimneys. I breathe again the air that filled the sky, an atmosphere without fragrance, often leaden and oppressive, saturated with the reek of burning chemicals. I think of the games we played in the street, ignorant of the lure of stream and forest. I think, and with tenderness, of my little companions, some of whom later went to the penitentiary. Despite it all, it was a good life I led there. A wonderful life, I might say. It was the first "Paradise" I knew, there in that old neighborhood. And though forever gone, it is still accessible in memory.

But *now,* when I watch the youngsters playing in our front yard, when I see them silhouetted against the blue white-capped Pacific, when I stare at the huge, frightening buzzards swirling lazily above, circling, dipping, forever circling, when I observe the willow gently swaying, its long fragile branches drooping ever lower, ever greener and tenderer, when I hear the frog croaking in the pool or a bird calling from the bush, when I suddenly turn and espy a lemon ripening on a dwarfish tree or notice that the camellia has just begun to bloom, I see my children set against an eternal background. They are not even *my* children any longer, but just children, children of the earth . . . and I know they will never forget, never forsake, the place where they were born and raised. In my mind I am with them as they return from some distant shore to gaze upon the old homestead. My eyes are moist with tears as I watch them moving tenderly and reverently amid a swarm of golden memories. Will they notice, I wonder, the tree they were going to help me plant but were too busy then having fun? Will they stand in the little wing we built for them and wonder how on earth they ever fitted into such a cubicle? Will they pause outside the tiny workroom where I passed my days and tap again at the windowpane to ask if I will join them at play—*or must I work some more?* Will they find the marbles I gathered from the garden and hid so that they would not swallow them? Will they stand in reverie at the forest glade, where the little stream prattles on, and search for the pots and pans with which we made our make-believe breakfast before diving into the woods? Will they take the goat path along the flank of the mountain and look up in wonder and awe at the old Trotter house teetering in the wind? Will they run down to the Rosses, if only in memory, to see if Harrydick can mend the broken sword or Shanagolden lend us a pot of jam?

For every wonderful event in my golden childhood they must possess a dozen incomparably more wonderful. For not only did they have their little playmates, their games, their mysterious adventures, as did I, they had also skies of pure azure and walls of fog moving in and out of the canyons with invisible feet, hills in winter of emerald green and in summer mountain upon mountain of pure gold. They had even more, for there was ever the unfathomable silence of the forest, the blazing immensity of the Pacific, days drenched with sun and nights spangled with stars and—"Oh, Daddy, come quick, see the moon, it's lying in the pool!" And besides the adoration of the neighbors, a dolt of a father who preferred wasting his time playing with them to cultivating his mind or making himself a good neighbor. Lucky the father who is merely a writer, who can drop his work and return to childhood at will! Lucky the father who is pestered from morn till sundown by two healthy, insatiable youngsters! Lucky the father who learns to see again through the eyes of his children, even though he become the biggest fool that ever was!

The Cult of
Sex and Anarchy

I had gone to bed to nurse a cold when it started, the hemorrhage. Whenever I take to bed (in broad daylight), which is my way of curing colds, hemorrhoids, melancholia or any ailment real or imaginary, I always put beside the bed a little bench laden with cigarettes, ash tray and reading matter. Just in case. . . .

After I had whiled away an hour or two in delicious reverie, I reached for the issue of *La Nouvelle Revue Française* which my friend Gerald Robitaille had sent me. It was the issue dedicated to Charles-Albert Cingria, who had passed away a few months before. In his letter Gerald asked if I had ever heard of Cingria. I had indeed. It so happens that I met Cingria, for the first and only time, at the home of Bravig Imbs, in Paris. It was a whole afternoon and evening that I spent, most fortunately, in Cingria's company. These few short hours stand out as one of the events in my life.

What I had not known, until I picked up the *revue,* was that at the time of this meeting Cingria was traversing one of the worst periods in his life. Who would have suspected that this man who had the look of a clown, or a defrocked priest, this man who never ceased talking, joking, laughing, drinking—it was New Year's Eve and we were consuming pitchers of eggnog—who would have dreamed, as I say, that this man would leave us to return to a miserable hole in the hall, where crusts of bread were hidden away under bureaus and commodes and where he could plainly hear the noises made by everyone who went to the W.C.[1]

As I read the tributes that were paid him, as I perceived what a remarkable personality his was, what a fantastic life he had led, what precious things he had written, my head began to whirl.

[1] See the passage from Cingria's diary quoted by Pierre Guéguen in the March 1, 1955 issue of the *N.R.F.* His text is called *"Le Dandy."*

563

Thrusting the *revue* aside—I couldn't possibly read another line—the hemorrhage suddenly broke loose. Like a drunken boat I tossed about, wallowing in the flood of memories which assailed me. After a time I rose, found a notebook, and began inditing cryptic cues. It went on for several hours. I forgot that I had a cold, forgot what time it was.

It was after midnight when I reluctantly laid down the pencil and switched off the lights. As I closed my eyes I said to myself: "Now is the time to tell about your life in Big Sur."

And so I shall tell it, in the same disorderly fashion that it came to me the other day as I lay abed. . . .

I suspect that many who read my books, or talk about my life, believe that I am living in an ivory tower. If I am, it is a tower without walls in which fabulous and often "anachronistic" things happen. In following this fantasia the reader should bear in mind that cause and event, chronology, order of any kind—except the illogical order of life itself—is absent.

Picture a day, for example, an excruciating one, in which I have been interrupted at least half a dozen times, and then . . . well, after an exciting talk with a writer who has just come from Paris (or Rome or Athens), after another talk with a bore who wants to know every detail about my life, past and present, and whom I discover (too late) has never read a single one of my books, after examining the cesspool to see why it doesn't work, after shooing away three students who stand at the door and apologetically explain that all they want of me is my opinion of Job—yes, Job, no less!—and they are not joking, only too serious, alas! after one thing and another, with intermittent attempts to resume where I left off (the middle of a sentence), comes the incomparable Varda with a bouquet of *"jeunes filles en fleur."* Observing that I am unusually quiet, and not realizing that it is a result of exhaustion, he exclaims: "And here I have been telling these girls what a wonderful *raconteur* you are! Come, do tell them something about your 'anecdotal life'!" (A phrase of Zadkine's.)

Strangely enough, at one in the morning, the table littered with empty glasses, bread crumbs and bits of rind, the guests departed at last, silence once again enveloping us, what is it that is singing in my head but a line from one of Cendrars' books, an enigmatic line, in his own inimitable French, which had me electrified a few nights before. There is no relation whatsoever between this line of Cendrars' and the multitudinous events of the day. We, Varda and I, had not even mentioned Cendrars' name, which is unusual because, with certain of my friends—Varda, Gerhart Muensch, Giles Healey, Ephraim Doner—we sound off with Cendrars and finish with Cendrars. So there I sit with that curious, tantalizing line of his, trying to recall what evoked it and wondering how I shall finish the sentence I left on the roller hours and hours ago. I ask myself—I've asked it over and over—how ever did this extraordinary man, Cendrars, turn out so many books in such a short time (I refer to the period right after the Occupation) with only one hand, his left hand, and no secretary to aid him, no heat, little food, his beloved sons killed in the war, his huge library destroyed by the Huns, and so on. I sit there reliving, or trying to relive, his life, his books, his thoughts, his emotions. My day, full as it was, only begins there in the ocean of his prodigious being. . . .

It was "one of those days" when a woman with whom I had exchanged some correspondence arrived from Holland. My wife had only recently left me and I was alone with my little girl. She was only in the room a few minutes when I sensed that an instantaneous and mutual antipathy had sprung up between the two. I apologized to my visitor for continuing with the chores—I had decided to wash the floor and wax it—and felt most grateful when she offered to do the dishes for me. Meanwhile Val, my daughter, was making things even more difficult than usual; she seemed to take a perverse delight in interrupting our conversation, erratic as it was with all the hopping about I was doing. Then she went to the toilet, only to announce a moment later that it wouldn't flush. At once I dropped the mop, dashed for the pickaxe, and began removing the dirt which covers the septic tank. I had hardly begun when it started to rain. I continued nevertheless, somewhat annoyed, I confess, by my visitor's frequent comings and goings, by her hysterical exhortations to abandon the task. Finally I managed to get my arm into the inlet which, as usual, was encrusted with snarled roots. As I pulled the blockage away, out came the water—and with it what had been dropped in the toilet bowl. I was a pretty sight when I came back to the house to clean up. The floor, of course, was a mess, and the furniture still piled on the table and the bed.

My visitor, who had built up a picture of me as a world-famous writer, a man living apart in that sublime place called Big Sur, began to berate me—or perhaps she thought she was consoling me—for trying to do so many things which had nothing to do with my work. Her talk sounded so absurd to me that, somewhat flabbergasted, I asked her curtly who she thought was to do the dirty work . . . *God?* She continued in her vague way to dwell on what I ought not to be doing, meaning cleaning, cooking, gardening, taking care of a child, fixing cesspools and so on. I was getting hot under the collar when suddenly I thought I heard a car pull up in the turn around. I stepped outside and, sure enough, there was Varda tripping down the steps, followed by his usual retinue of friends and admirers.

"Well, well! How are you? What a surprise!"

Handshakes, introductions all around. The usual exclamations. "What a marvelous place!" (Even in the rain.)

My visitor from Holland drew me aside. With an imploring look she whispered: "What do we do now?"

"Put a good face on it," I said, and turned my back on her.

A few minutes later she tugged at my sleeve again to inquire plaintively if *I* would have to prepare a meal for all these people.

I skip what followed during the next few hours to give you her parting words: "I never dreamed that Big Sur was like this!"

Under my breath I added: "Nor did I!"

And there stands Ralph! Though it's midsummer he's wearing a heavy overcoat and fur-lined gloves. He has a book in his hand and, like a Tibetan monk, he's leisurely pacing back and forth, back and forth. I had been so occupied pulling up weeds that I hadn't noticed him immediately. It was only when I lifted my head to go in search of a mattock, which I had left near the fence, that I was aware of his presence in the turn around. Realizing that he was a queer one, I thought I might snatch the implement and sneak away without being hooked. I would just pay no attention to him; he might be sensitive and move off in a huff. But as I started toward the fence this queer apparition approached and started speaking to me. He spoke in such a low tone that I was obliged to move in closer. That was the clincher.

"Are you Henry Miller?" he says.

I nodded, though my impulse was to say no.

"I came to see you because I want to have a talk with you."

("Christ, here it begins," I said to myself.)

"I was just driven away"—brutally or insultingly, I believe he added—"by a woman. Maybe it was your wife."

To this I simply grunted.

He continued by informing me that he too was a writer, that he had run away from it all (meaning job and home) to live his own life.

"I came to join the cult of sex and anarchy," he said, quietly and evenly, as if he were talking about toast and coffee.

I told him there was no such colony.

"But I read about it in the papers," he insisted. He started to pull a newspaper out of his pocket.

"That was all an invention," said I. "You musn't believe every-thing you see in the papers." I gave a forced laugh.

He seemed to doubt my words. Went on to tell me why he thought he would make an eligible member—even if there were no colony. *(sic)* I cut him short. Told him I had work to do. He would have to excuse me.

Now his feelings were hurt. There followed a brief exchange of question and answer—rather impertinent questions, rather caustic answers—which only seemed to increase his disturbance. Sud-denly he opened the book he was holding and, turning the pages rapidly, he found the passage he was looking for. He then pro-ceeded to read it aloud.

It was a passage from the *Hamlet* letters in which my friend and co-author, Michael Fraenkel, had raked me over the coals. Had excoriated me, in fact.

When he had finished reading he looked at me coldly and accusingly, to say: "I guess that fits, doesn't it?"

I opened the gate and said: "Ralph, what in hell's the matter with you? Come on down and talk it over!"

I ushered him into my little den, sat him down, handed him a cigarette and urged him to unbosom himself.

In a few minutes he was in tears. Just a poor, defenseless, brokenhearted boy.

The same evening I dispatched him, with a note, to Emil White at Anderson Creek. He had told me that he would head for Los Angeles, where he had an aunt, now that he knew there was no cult of sex and anarchy. I thought he would spend the night at Emil's and move on. But, after a good dinner and a good night's rest, he discovered that Emil owned a typewriter. In the morning, after a good breakfast, he sat down to the machine and, though he had never written a line before, he suddenly took it into his head to write a book. After a few days Emil gently informed him that he couldn't put him up indefinitely. This didn't floor Ralph. Not at all. He informed Emil that it was just the sort of place he had always wanted to live in and that, if Emil would help him, he would find a job and earn his keep.

To make it brief, Ralph stayed on at Big Sur about six months, doing odd jobs, floating from one ménage to another, always getting into trouble. In general, behaving like a spoiled child. In the interim I received a letter one day from Ralph's father, some-where in the Midwest, telling me how grateful he was to all of us for looking after Ralph. He related the trials and ordeals they had been through at home trying to get Ralph to lead a normal, sensible life. It was the usual story of the problem child, one I was only too familiar with from the old days when I hired and fired for the Cosmodemonic Telegraph Company.

One of the strange things about Ralph's behavior was that he was always turning up minus some necessary part of his apparel. He had shown up on a summer's day in a heavy overcoat and gloves. Now that it was cold he would show up naked to the waist. What about his shirt and jacket? He had burned them! He didn't like them any more, or else he had taken a dislike to the person who had given them to him. (We had all supplemented his wardrobe at one time or another.)

On a cold, nasty day in winter, as I was driving along a side street in Monterey, whom should I spy but Ralph, half-naked, shivering, and looking altogether woebegone. Lilik Schatz was with me. We got out and dragged Ralph to a cafeteria. He hadn't eaten for two days—ever since they had let him out of the clink, it seems. What disturbed him more than the cold was the fear that his father might come to fetch him.

"Why can't you let me stay with you?" he repeated over and over. "I wouldn't give you any trouble. You understand me, the others don't. I want to be a writer—like you."

We had been over this ground a number of times before. I could only repeat what I had told him, that it was hopeless.

"But I'm different now," he said. "I know better." He kept boring in, determined, like a child, to have his way. Lilik tried to reason with him but got nowhere. "You don't understand me," he would say.

Finally I became exasperated. "Ralph," I said, "you're just a plain nuisance. Nobody can put up with you. You're a pest. I'm not taking you home with me and I'm not going to look after you. I'm going to let you starve and freeze—it's the only way you'll come to your senses."

With this I got up and walked to the door. Ralph followed us to the car and, with one foot on the running board, continued to plead his case. I took off my coat, put it around his shoulders, and told Lilik to start the motor.

"You're on your own, Ralph!" I shouted, as we waved goodbye.

He seemed rooted to the spot, his lips still moving.

A few days later I heard that he had been picked up for being a vagrant and shipped home to his parents. That was the last I heard of him.

There's a knock at the door. I open it to find a clump of visitors wreathed in smiles. The usual declarations—"Just passing through. Thought we would look you up."

I don't know them from Adam. However . . . "Come on in!"

The usual preliminaries . . . "Beautiful place you have . . . How did you find it? . . . I thought you had children . . . Not disturbing you, I hope?"

Out of a clear sky one of them, a woman, pipes up: "Do you have any water colors for sale? I've always thought I'd like to own a Henry Miller water color."

I jumped. "Are you serious?"

She was indeed. "Where are they? Where are they?" she cried, hopping about from one corner of the room to the other.

I trot out the few I have on hand and spread them on the couch. As she looks through the pile I busy myself fixing drinks and preparing the dogs' meals. (First the dogs, then the visitors.)

I can hear them moving about, examining the paintings on the walls, none of them mine. I give no heed.

Finally the woman who expressed a desire to buy takes me by the sleeve and leads me to a door where my wife's work is tacked up. It's a carnival scene, blazing with color, full of people and things. A really jolly picture, but not a water color.

"Haven't you any more like *this?*" she asks. "It's just enchanting. A fantasy, isn't it?"

"No," I reply, not bothering to explain, "but I have one with a rainbow, did you notice? How about *rocks?* I've just discovered how to make rocks . . . not easy, you know." And with this I go into a long discourse as to how each picture represents a theme, or to put it another way, a problem. "A pleasure problem," I add. "I'd be a fool to give myself torture problems, wouldn't I?"

Carried away by these glib remarks, I then endeavored to explain that my work was nothing but an attempt to paint my own evolution as a painter. A highly dubious explanation which I scotched by adding: "Most of the time I just make pictures." Which must have sounded equally foolish and sententious.

Since she showed no signs of wilting or crumpling, I went on to say that only a year or so ago I painted nothing but buildings, crowds of buildings . . . so many, indeed, that sometimes the paper wasn't large enough to hold them all.

"I always began with the Potala," I said.

"The *Potala?*"

"Yes, in Lhasa. You must have seen it in the movies. The edifice with a thousand rooms—where the Dalai Lama lives. Built long before the Commodore Hotel."

At this point I am aware that the other visitors are not altogether at ease. Another drink would do the trick, but I'm not getting off my horse yet. Even if I ruin the sale, which is what I usually do, I've got to carry on. I take another tack, just as a feeler. A long, utterly irrelevant disquisition on some little-known French painter whose jungle scenes have haunted me for years. (How he could intermingle, interweave, intertwine boughs, leaves, heads, limbs, spears, pieces of sky—even rain, if he chose to—all with perfect clarity. And why not geometric precision? "And with geometric precision," I throw in.) Once again I feel that everyone is growing restive. Harassed, I make a feeble joke about jungle scenes being so delicious because, if you lose your touch, you can just scramble things. (I meant, of course, that it has always been easier, more instinctive, for me to make scrambled eggs than clear-cut trunks, boughs, leaves, flowers, shrubs.) "In the old days"—making a frantic switch—"I did nothing but portraits. I called them self-portraits because they all turned out like *me*." (Nobody laughs.) "Yes, I must have made over a hundred. . . ."

"Excuse me, but could I look at that painting on the door again?" It's my buyer.

"Certainly, certainly."

"I like it *so* much!"

"It's not mine, you know. My wife did it."

"I thought so. I mean, I knew it wasn't yours." It was said simply, with no malicious overtone.

She takes a good, thirsty look, then walks over to the bed over which the water colors are strewn and, selecting my favorite, one I had hoped to keep, she asks: "Would you let me have *this?*"

"I'd rather not, to be frank. But if you insist. . . ."

"Is there something wrong with it?" She let it fall on the bed like a dead leaf.

"No, not exactly." I picked it up, almost tenderly. "It's merely that I hoped to keep it for myself. It's the one *I* like best."

I made the *I* prominent to give her a way out. I was convinced that by this time *my* views on art must have impressed her as being screwy. To make doubly sure, I added that my friend Emil, a painter down the road, didn't think very much of it. "Too subjective."

The effect this had, unfortunately, was to make her eager to examine the painting more thoroughly. She bent over it, studied it, as if she had a magnifying glass to her eye. She turned it around several times. Apparently it looked good to her upside down, for suddenly she said: "I'll take it. That is, if I can afford it."

I could have doubled my price and scared her off, but I didn't have the heart for it. My feeling was that she had earned it—by trial and ordeal. So I made an even lower price than I had originally thought to ask and we sealed the bargain. She would have liked a frame to go with it, but unfortunately I had none to offer.

As they were about to leave she asked if I thought my wife would care to sell the one she liked so much. "It's a possibility," I replied. Then, impulsively, she stepped inside the doorway, took a quick look around, and said: "Maybe I ought to take another one along. Do you mind if I look through them again?"

I didn't mind too much. All I thought was—*how long?*

Fumbling through the pile once again she paused—apprecia-tively, I thought—to look more closely at one which nobody in his right senses would look at twice.

"What on earth can *this* be?" she cried, holding the painting aloft and struggling to repress her laughter.

"El Alamein, I call it. Where Rommel tricked the British—wasn't that it?"

(I had previously given her a windy spiel about another title, "The Battle of Trafalgar," so named because it was full of bat-tered, capsized boats. I had had trouble making waves, hence the battered, capsized boats.)

"Did you say Rommel?" she asked.

"Yes, Rommel. That's him there in the foreground." I indicated where with my index finger.

She smiled benignly. "I thought it was a scarecrow."

"Cancer—schmanser, what's the difference?" Might as well put a good face on it.

"And what are those dark spots, those blobs, up near the hills? They *are* hills, aren't they?"

"Tombstones. After the battle, you see . . . I'm going to put inscriptions on them. Yes, I thought to write the inscriptions in white. They'll be hard to decipher, of course. Besides, they'll be in Hebrew."

"In Hebrew?"

"Why not? Who reads inscriptions on tombstones anyway?"

By this time her friends were calling for her. They were hoping to find time to visit another celebrity, in Watsonville.

"I'd better run," she said. "Maybe I'll write and ask you to send me one by mail. One less . . . less esoteric." She giggled.

As she flew up the steps she waved her hand. "Ta-ta!" she cried.

"Ta-ta!" I echoed. "If you don't like the one you bought, just mail it back. It'll have a good home here."

After dinner that evening, thinking to empty my mind of images, I took the lantern and, going to a spot in the garden where the poison oak was thick, I hung the lantern to the bough of a tree and fell to. What a pleasure, what a ferocious pleasure, to pull up long, vicious roots of poison oak! (With gloves on.) Better than making water colors, sometimes. Better than *selling* water colors, certainly. But, as with painting, you can never be sure of the outcome. You may think you have a Rommel, only to find out it is nothing but a scarecrow. And now and then, in your ferocious haste, you pull up pomegranates instead of camphor weed.

Down at Lucia, some time after Norman Mini decamped, a chap named Harvey took over—as chief cook and bottle-washer. He pitched a tent right in the midst of the brush, the poison oak, the rattlesnakes, the fog and the bottle-flies, and there he made his abode with a wife and two small children. In this tent he tried to paint, to practice the violin and to write. He wanted most of all to write.

If ever I spotted a born writer, this fellow Harvey was certainly it. When he talked, and he was a good talker, a wonderful story-teller, it sounded as if he were reading from a book. Everything he related had form, structure, clarity and meaning.

But Harvey wasn't satisfied with this gift. He wanted to write.

Occasionally, on his day off, he would drop in on me. He was always apologetic about taking up my time—which didn't prevent him from lingering for hours—but his excuse was, and he meant it sincerely, that he had need of me. To be honest, he was one man I always enjoyed listening to. For one thing, he possessed a profound knowledge of English literature, beginning from the beginning. I believe he had once been a teacher of English literature. He had been many other things too. He had taken a job as cook and handy man at Lucia, a lonely spot, because he thought it would give him a chance to try his hand at writing. Why he thought so I don't know. The job afforded him little spare time and the overcrowded tent was hardly an ideal work place. Besides, with the violin exercises and the easel painting only a da Vinci could have hoped to write too. But that was Harvey's way of going about it.

"I *want* to write," he would say, "and I just can't. It won't come. I sit at the machine for hours at a stretch and all I can produce is a few lines. And even these few lines are no good."

Every time he took leave of me he would remark how good he

felt, how buoyed up. "Tomorrow," he would say, "I feel that it will go like a breeze." And then he would thank me warmly.

It went on like this for weeks and weeks, with only a trickle coming out despite our peptonic talks.

One of the fascinating things about Harvey, whose case is by no means unique, is that despite all the blockage, the paralysis (before the machine), he could relate the contents of a long novel—one of Dostoevsky's, for instance—with uncanny accuracy of detail, emphasizing and underlining the most complicated passages in a manner such as one imagines only writers can. In a single session Harvey could cover analytically, didactically and ecstatically such a string of writers as Henry James, Melville, Fielding, Laurence Sterne, Stendhal, Jonathan Swift, Hart Crane. Listening to Harvey talking books and authors was far more absorbing (to me) than listening to a celebrated professor of literature. He had a way of identifying himself with each and every author, a way of insinuating his own agonies into what probably were once theirs. He knew how to select, evaluate and elucidate, no gainsaying it.

But this ability, as one can readily surmise, came all too easy for our friend Harvey. It was as nothing for him to discuss the fine points of an intricate Henry James story while cooking and recooking a penguin. (He did actually carry off a wounded penguin which he found one day on the highway, and after three days and nights of wrestling with it, he did serve up a delicious meal!)

One afternoon, in the midst of a lengthy disquisition on the merits and demerits of Walter Pater, I suddenly put up my hand. An intriguing idea had flashed through my mind. An idea, needless to say, not even remotely connected with Walter Pater.

"Hold it, Harvey!" I cried and, reaching for his glass, I filled it to the brim. "Harvey, my good man, I think I've got something for you."

Harvey hadn't the least idea of what was going through my head. He looked at me blankly.

"Look here," I began, almost trembling with inner excitement, "to begin with, forget Walter Pater—and Henry James and Stendhal and all the other birds you like to shoot at. Fuck them! You're finished with them . . . they're just dead ducks. Your trouble is that you know too much . . . too much for your own good, I mean. I want you to bury these guys, wipe them out of your consciousness. Don't open another book, nor a magazine. Not even the dictionary. At least, not until you've tried what I'm about to suggest."

Harvey stared at me in a puzzled way, patiently waiting for the clue.

"You're always saying that you can't write. You tell me that every time you come. I'm sick of hearing it. What's more, I don't believe it. Maybe you can't write as you would like to write, but write you can! Even an idiot can learn to write, if he sticks at it long enough. Now here's my thought . . . I want you to leave soon"—I said this because I knew that if he started inquiring into my scheme it would all evaporate in talk—"yes, I want you to go home, get a good night's rest, and tomorrow, before breakfast, if possible, sit down to the machine and explain to it why it is that you can't write. Nothing more, nothing else. Is that clear? Don't ask me why I urge it, just try it out!"

I was surprised that he made no attempt to interrupt me. He had a queer expression on his face, as if he had just been given a jolt.

"Harvey," I continued, "even though the two are not the same—I mean talking and writing—I've noticed that you can talk most eloquently about anything under the sun. And you can talk about yourself, your own problems, just as brilliantly as you can about the next fellow. In fact, you're even better when you're talking about yourself. And that's what you're doing all the time, anyway, even when you pretend to be talking about Henry James or Herman Melville or Leigh Hunt. A man who has the verbal gift—and you certainly have it—shouldn't be stymied by a piece of white paper. Forget that it's a piece of white paper . . . pretend that it's an ear. Talk to it! Talk into it! With your fingers, of course. . . . Can't write! What nonsense! Of course you can write. You're a Niagara. . . . Now go home and do as I say. Let's end it right here. And remember, you're to write only about why you can't write. See what happens. . . ."

It took some firmness on my part to make Harvey run off, just like that, and not "go into it," as he was dying to do. But he did ease himself out. In fact, he was almost on the trot by the time he reached the car.

A week or two passed, then three or four, but no sign of Harvey. I was beginning to think my idea was not such a brilliant one after all. Then one day he showed up.

"Well, well!" I exclaimed. "So you're still alive! Tell me, did it work?"

"It sure did," he said. "I've been writing steadily ever since you put the bug in my head that day." He went on to explain that he was throwing up the job at Lucia. He was going back East where he came from.

"When I leave I'll put that bundle of manuscript in your mail-box. Take a glance at it if you ever have the time, will you?"

I promised faithfully that I would. Some few days later Harvey picked up and moved. But there was no bundle of manuscript in my mailbox. After a few weeks I received a letter from him in which he explained that he hadn't left the manuscript in my mailbox because he didn't think it was worth bothering me about. It was much too long, for one thing. Besides, he had given up the idea of becoming a writer. He didn't say what he was going to do for a living but I had the impression that he was going back to the teaching profession. That's the usual way out. When everything else fails, teach!

I've never heard from Harvey since. I've no idea what he's doing today. I'm still convinced that he's a writer; still convinced that one day he'll go back to it and stick to it. Why I speak with such conviction I don't know.

The tragic thing today is that, in the case of men like Harvey, even when they do break through the "sound barrier" they are killed off almost immediately. Either they write too well or not bad enough. Because of their great knowledge and familiarity with good literature, because of their innate taste and discrimination, they have difficulty in finding the level on which to reach the reading public. They particularly lack that liberating instinct so well formulated by the Zen masters: *"Kill the Buddha!"* They want to become another Dostoevsky, another Gide, another Melville.

On sober thought, my advice to Harvey (and to all who find themselves in Harvey's boots) struck me as being sound and sensible. If you can't give the is-ness of a thing give the not-ness of it! The main thing is to hook up, get the wheels turning, sound off. When your brakes jam, try going in reverse. It often works.

Once traction is established, the most important thing—how to reach the public, or better, how to create your own public!—still remains to be faced. Without a public it's suicide. No matter how small, there has to be an audience. I mean, an appreciative, enthusiastic audience, a selective audience.

What few young writers realize, it seems to me, is that they must find—create, invent!—the way to reach their readers. It isn't enough to write a good book, a beautiful book, or even a better book than most. It isn't enough even to write an "original" book! One has to establish, or re-establish, a unity which has been broken and which is felt just as keenly by the reader, who is a potential artist, as by the writer, who believes himself to be an artist. The theme of separation and isolation—"atomization," it's now called—has as many facets to it as there are unique individuals. And we are all unique. The longing to be reunited, with a common purpose and an all-embracing significance, is now universal. The writer who wants to communicate with his fellow-man, and thereby establish communion with him, has only to speak with sincerity and directness. He has not to think about literary standards—he will make them as he goes along—he has not to think about trends, vogues, markets, acceptable ideas or unacceptable ideas: he has only to deliver himself, naked and vulnerable. All that constricts and restricts him, to use the language of not-ness, his fellow-reader, even though he may not be an artist, feels with equal despair and bewilderment. The world presses down on all alike. Men are not suffering from the lack of good literature, good art, good theatre, good music, but from that which has made it impossible for these to become manifest. In short, they are suffering from the silent, shameful conspiracy (the more shameful since it is unacknowledged) which has bound them together as enemies of art and artist. They are suffering from the fact that art is not the primary, moving force in their lives. They are suffering from the act, repeated daily, of keeping up the pretense that they can go their way, lead their lives, without art. They never dream—or they behave as if they never realize—that the reason why they feel sterile, frustrated and joyless is because art (and with it the artist) has been ruled out of their lives. For every artist who has been assassinated thus (unwittingly?) thousands of ordinary citizens, who might have known a normal joyous life, are condemned to lead the purgatorial existence of neurotics, psychotics, schizophrenics. No, the man who is about to blow his top does not have to fix his eye on the *Iliad,* the *Divine Comedy* or any other great model; he has only to give us, in his own language, the saga of his woes and tribulations, the saga of his non-existentialism. In this mirror of not-ness everyone will recognize himself for what he is as well as what he is not. He will no longer be able to hold his head up either before his children or before his neighbors; he will have to admit that he—not the other fellow—is that terrible person who is contributing, wittingly or unwittingly, to the speedy downfall and disintegration of his own people. He will know, when he resumes work in the morning, that everything he does, everything he says, everything he touches, pertains to the invisible poisonous web which holds us all in its mesh and which is slowly but surely crushing the life out of us. It does not matter what high office the reader may hold—he is as much a villain and a victim as the outlaw and the outcast.

Who will print such books, who will publish and disseminate them?

No one!

You will have to do it yourself, dear man. Or, do as Homer did:

travel the highways and byways with a white cane, singing your song as you go. You may have to pay people to listen to you, but that isn't an insuperable feat either. Carry a little "tea" with you and you'll soon have an audience.

Fan Mail

If ever I should find time hanging heavy on my hands I know what to do: hop in my car, drive to Los Angeles, and search out the files which are kept in steel cabinets in the Special Collections Division of the University Library there. In these files are the thousands of letters which, at their urgent request, I have been turning over to the library ever since I have been in Big Sur. They are for posterity, I suppose. Unfortunately, some of the best ones, the maddest, the craziest, I burned (at my wife's instigation) shortly before the library made its request. Before that, in New York, and again in Paris (when leaving for Greece), I got rid of a short ton of correspondence which I then thought of no importance, even for "posterity."

With the letters, *bien entendu,* arrive manuscripts, beautifully printed poems, books of indescribable variety, checks, wedding and funeral announcements (why not divorce notices also?), photos of newborn infants (the spawn of my fans), theses (dozens of them), lecture programs, excerpts from books, clippings, reviews in a dozen different languages, requests for photos or autographs, plans for a new world, appeals for funds, pleas to help stop the execution of this or that innocent one, pamphlets and monographs ranging in subject matter from dietary cures to the true nature of Zoroastrianism.

It is assumed that I am vitally interested in all these subjects, projects and proposals. What I am most interested in, naturally, is checks. If I see an envelope which bears promise of containing a check, that is the one I open first. Next in order come those which bear the postmark of exotic countries. The ones I put away to read some rainy day are the thick envelopes which I know in advance contain abortive stories, essays or poems which I am generally told that I may consign to the waste basket if I choose—the sender

578

never has the courage to do this himself! On the other hand, a real fat one from someone I adore I may save until I go to the sulphur baths, there to enjoy it in peace and quiet. But how rare are these in comparison with the slew of crap which pours in day in and day out!

Sometimes it is a very brief letter, in an exquisite or else an execrable hand, which will "send" me. It is usually from a foreigner who is also a writer. A writer I have never heard of before. The short letters which exasperate me are from ultralucid spirits to whom I have presented a knotty, complicated, usually legal or ethical, problem, and who are adept in cutting through fog and grease with three or four scimitar-like lines which always leave me exactly where I was before posing the problem. The type I have in mind is the judicial type. The better the lawyer, the bigger the judge, the briefer and more bewildering the reply.

Let me say at the outset that the most vapid letter writers are the British. Even their handwriting seems to reveal a paucity of spirit which is glaring. From a calligraphic standpoint, they appear to be crouching behind their own shadows—skulking like poltroons. They are congenitally incapable of coming out with it, whatever it may be that impelled them to write me. (Usually I discover that it is about themselves, their spiritual poverty, their crushed spirits, their lowered horizon.) There are exceptions, to be sure. Splendid, remarkable exceptions. As epistolary virtuosi, no one can equal Lawrence Durrell, the poet, or John Cowper Powys, the returned Welshman. Durrell's letters awaken the same sure delight which comes with viewing a Persian miniature or a Japanese wood-block print. I am not thinking of the physical aspect of his letters, though this too plays a part, but the language itself. Here is a happy master of prose whose style is pure and limpid, whose lines sing, bubble, effervesce, whether writing a letter or writing a treatise. From wherever he sits penning his letter there is wafted the fragrance, the wonder and the eternality of landscape, to which is added the spice of fable and myth, of legend and folklore, of customs, ritual and architecture. He has written me, Lawrence Durrell, from such places as Cos, Patmos, Knossus, Syracuse, Rhodes, Sparta, Delphi, Cairo, Damascus, Jerusalem, Cyprus. The very names of these stopping places make my mouth water. And he has put them all in his books and in his poems. . . .

As for "Friar John," as Powys sometimes styles himself, the very look of his letters puts me in ecstasy. He probably writes with a pad on his knee, a paid which is pivoted on invisible ball bearings. His lines flow in a labyrinthian curve which permits them to be read upside down, swinging from a chandelier or climbing a wall. He is always exalted. Always. Trifles become monumental. And this despite the fact that he has lost the use of one eye, has no teeth to chew with, and until fairly recently—he is now in his eighties—suffered unremittingly from gastric or duodenal ulcers. The oldest of all my correspondents (excepting Al Jennings), he is also the youngest and the gayest, the most liberal, the most tolerant, the most enthusiastic of all. Like William Blake, I feel certain that he will die singing and clapping his hands.

Few are they who are able to write freely and effortlessly about anything and everything—as Chesterton and Belloc did. The name of the sender usually apprises me of the nature of the contents of a letter. One writes perpetually about his ailments, another about his financial difficulties, another about his domestic problems, another about his run-ins with publisher or dealer; one guy is hepped on pornography and obscenity, can never get off the subject; another talks only about Rimbaud or about William Blake; another about the Essenes; another about the stratospheric complexities of Indian metaphysics; another about Rudolf Steiner or the "masters" in the Himalayas; some are Dianetic bloodhounds, others Zen enthusiasts; some write only of Jesus, Buddha, Socrates and Pythagoras. You might suppose the latter breed to be stimulating minds. On the contrary, they are the dullest, the windiest, the dryest of all. Genuine "gaseous vertebrates." They are only surpassed in dullness by the nimble wits who are always ready to relay the latest joke overheard at the office or in a public toilet.

The letters that really set me up for a few days are the "isotopes" which come by carrier pigeon—from cranks, freaks, nuts and plain lunatics. What a splendid insight into an author's life we would have if such missives were collected and published occasionally. Whenever a celebrated author dies there is a stampede to unearth the correspondence exchanged between him and other world-wide celebrities. Sometimes these make good reading, often not. As a devotee of French literary weeklies, I often find myself reading snatches of correspondence between men like Valéry and Gide, for example, and wondering all the while why I am so sleepy.

Some of those I roughly classify as "nuts" are not wacky at all but eccentric, raffish, perverse and, being genuine solipsists, all of them, of course at odds with the world. I find them most humorous when they are pathetically whining about the cruelty of fate. This may sound malicious, but it is a fact that nothing is more hilarious to read about than the troubles of a person who is "somehow" always in trouble. What seem like mountains to this type are always molehills to us. A man who can enlarge on the tragedy of a hangnail, who can elaborate on it for five and six pages, is a comedian from heaven sent. Or a man who can take your work apart with hammer and tong, analyze it to nothingness, and hand you the missing members in an old-fashioned *bidet* which he normally uses for serving spaghetti.

There was one sly coyote who used to write me direct from the asylum, a chap to whom in a moment of weakness I had sent a photograph and who for weeks thereafter bombarded me with letters ten, twenty, thirty pages long, in pencil, crayon and celery stalks—always about my supposed kidney trouble. He had noticed the pouches under my eyes (an inheritance from Franz Josef on the paternal side) and he had deduced that I was destined for a speedy end. *Unless* I followed his recommendations for the care and preservation of the bladder, which required a number of installments to elucidate. The regimen he prescribed began with physical exercises of a highly unorthodox character and were to be performed without the slightest deviation six times a day, one of these times being in the middle of the night. Any one of these exercises would have tied the perfect gymnast into a sailor's knot. The exercises were to be accompanied by dietary feats which only a madman could think up. For example. . . .

"Eat only the stem of the spinach plant, but grind first with a pestle, then mix in chickweed, parsley, dandelion that has gone to seed, nutmeg and the tail of any rodent which has not been domesticated.

"Eschew all meats except the flesh of the guinea pig, the wild boar, the kangaroo (now put up in tins), the onager of Asiatic origin—not the European variety!—the muskrat and the garter snake. All small birds are good for the bladder, excepting the finch, the dart and the miner bird."

He counseled strongly against standing on one's head, which he described as an atavistic praxis of supernatural origin. Instead, he recommended walking on all fours, particularly over precipitous terrain. He thought it advisable, nay indispensable, to nibble between meals, particularly to nibble minute particles of caraway seeds, sunflower seeds, watermelon seeds, or even gravel and bird seed. I was not to take much water, nor tea, coffee, cocoa and tisanes, but to drink as much whiskey, vodka, gin as I could—a teaspoonful at a time. All liqueurs were taboo, and sherry, no matter what the origin, was to be shunned as one would a witch's brew. He explained in a footnote that he had to be stringent in this regard because, after years of research (in a laboratory, suppos-edly) he had discovered that sherry, however and wherever manufactured, contained traces of the arnica root, liverwort and henbane, all poisonous to the human organism though rarely deleterious when given to convicts in the death-cell or to microorganisms employed in approved formulae for the making of antibiotics. Even if I were at the point of death, I was not to resort to any of the sulfa drugs, penicillin or any of the allied miracle drug family based on mud, urine and fungus.

Aside from the rapidity with which time flies, unbelievably so!, there is another aspect of life at Big Sur which always stupefies me, *viz.*, the amount of trash which accumulates daily. The trash has to do with my correspondents. For, in addition to photographs, theses, manuscripts and so on which accompany the letters, come articles of clothing, stationery, talismans and amulets, albums of records, rare coins, rubbings *(frottages),* medallions, ornamental trays, Japanese lanterns and Japanese gimcrackery, art supplies, catalogues and almanacs, statuettes, seeds from exotic blooms, exquisite tins of cigarettes, neckties galore, hand-winding phonographs, carpet slippers from Jugoslavia, leather pantouffles from India, pocketknives with multiple accessories, cigarette lighters (none that ever work!), magazines, stock market reports, paintings (huge ones sometimes, which cost time and money to return), Turkish and Greek pastries, imported candies, rosaries, fountain pens, wines and liqueurs, occasionally a bottle of Pernod, pipes which I never smoke (but never cigars!), books of course, sometimes complete sets, and food: salami, lachs, smoked fish, cheeses, jars of olives, preserves, jams, sweet and sour pickles, corn bread (the Jewish variety), and now and then a bit of ginger. There is hardly a thing I need which my correspondents cannot supply me with. Often, when short of cash, they send me postage stamps—filched from the till, no doubt. The children also receive their share of gifts, from toys of all kinds to delicious sweets and exquisite items of wearing apparel. Whenever I make a new friend in some outlandish part of the world I invariably remind him to send the children something "exotic." One such, a student in Lebanon, sent me the Koran in Arabic, a diminutive volume in fine print, which he urged me to teach the youngsters when they came of age.

One can easily see, therefore, why we always have plenty with which to start a fire. Why we always have enough paper, cardboard and twine to wrap books and parcels. In the old days, when I had to walk up and down the hill, the gift business presented a problem. Now, with a Jeep station wagon, I can haul a cartload if need be.

Certain individuals who write me regularly never fail to repeat like a refrain—"Be sure to let me know if you need anything. If I don't have it or can't get it, I know someone who can and will. Don't hesitate to call on me—for anything!'' (Only Americans write this way. Europeans are more conservative, so to speak. As for the Russians—the exiled ones—they will offer you heaven too.) In this group there are certain individuals who by any standard of measurement are exceptional. One is a radio operator for an air line, another is a biochemist who runs a laboratory in Los Angeles, another is a student of Greek parentage, another is a young script writer from Beverly Hills. When a package comes from V., the radio operator, I am apt to find literally anything in it, barring an elephant. The main item in the package is always carefully wrapped in wads of newspaper (newspapers from India, Japan, Israel, Egypt, anywhere he happens to be at the time) together with French, German and Italian illustrated weeklies. In the French weeklies I am always certain to find at least one text on a subject which I happen to be interested in at that moment. It's as if he divined my need! Anyway, sandwiched in and around the precious object he has sent will be Turkish delight, fresh dates from the Orient, sardines from Portugal, smoked Japanese oysters and other little delicacies he thought up at the last minute. . . . F., the laboratory man, when shipping typewriter paper, carbon or ribbons that I am in need of, never fails to include a newfangled pen or pencil, a bottle of extra-ultra vitamins, a jar of lachs, a huge salami and a loaf or two of genuine corn bread, the one and only bread, as fas as I am concerned, and now getting to be as scarce, and almost as expensive, as sturgeon. He would send sweet butter too, if it traveled well. . . . K. and M., the other two, always offer to type my scripts or get things printed for me. If I ask for one or two tubes of water colors they send me a year's supply, to say nothing of blocks of excellent water-color paper. K. used to keep his grandmother busy knitting socks and sweaters for me—and making loukoumi for the children.

Some, like Dante Z., render service by doing research work for me. Dante will go through the thickest tomes and give me a summary of the contents, or track down a buried passage which, at the moment, I deem important to have on tap in my files, or translate difficult passages from obscure works, or find out if such and such an author wrote such and such a work and why, or dig into ancient medical treatises for data which I may never use but which I like to have on hand in the event that I engage in dispute with some learned ass.

Or there is a great soul like Dr. Leon Bernstein who will, if I ask it, take a plane to visit a poverty-stricken devil who is in need of treatment, and not only will he do everything that is needed (gratis) but he will see to it that the poor devil is provided for during the long period of convalescence.

Is it any wonder that John Cowper Powys is forever extolling the Jews and the Negroes? Without the latter, as I have often remarked, America would be a joyless, immaculate, superabundant museum of monotonous specimens labelled "the white race." Without the Jews, charity would begin at home and stay there. Every artist, in America certainly, must be indebted a hundred times over to his Jewish friends. And indebted not for material services only. Think, *chers confrères,* who is the first among your friends to give encouragement, to read your work, look at your paintings, show your work around, *buy* your work (on the instalment plan, if necessary). *Buy* it, I say, and not beg off with the lame excuse—"If only I could afford it!" Who lends you money to carry on, even when he has no money to spare? Who else but the Jew will say: "I know where to borrow it for you, don't you do a thing!" Who is it thinks to send you food, clothing, and the other vital necessities of daily life? No, the artist—in America, at least—cannot avoid coming into contact with the Jew, becoming friends with him, imitating him, imbibing from him the courage, the patience, the tolerance, the persistence and the tenacity which this people has in its blood, because, to be an artist is to lead a dog's life, and most Jews begin life that way. Others do too, certainly, but they seem to forget it as they rise in life. The Jew seldom forgets. How can he, living in the midst of a drama which is endlessly repeated?

And now I think of the letters which come regularly from Palestine, from Lilik Schatz, son of Boris, who has become my brother-in-law. Lilik lived for several years at Krenkel Corners, which is a sunken hollow midway between Partington Ridge and Anderson Creek. While living in Berkeley he made a trip to Big Sur one day expressly to induce me to do a silk-screen book with him, which we did, after much labor and struggle, and from scratch.[1] This book, *Into the Night Life,* the conception, the making, and its sale (which remains steadily at zero), was the beginning of a great friendship. It was only after he had returned to his home in Jerusalem that I got to know his wife's sister, Eve, and married her. If I hadn't found Eve I would be a dead duck today.

But the letters. . . . To begin with, know ye all that Lilik, the son of Boris, who was the son of Bezalel as built the Ark, has the

---

[1] See his account of this enterprise in the illustrated brochure dealing with the production of the book.

extraordinary gift of being able to talk in any tongue. Not that he is a linguist, though he does know half a dozen languages moderately well, including his native Hebrew. It is not knowledge of a language that he needs in order to communicate with his neighbor, be that man a Turk, an Arab, a Ceylonese, a Peruvian of the Andes, a pygmy or a Chinese mandarin. Lilik's procedure is to start talking at once—with tongue, hands, feet and ears—explicating mimetically as he goes along by grunts and squeals, dance steps, Indian signs, Morse code and so on. It's all sustained and borne along by an overflowing current of sympathy, empathy, identity, or whatever you wish to call that fundament of good will, good nature, brotherhood, sisterhood, divine benevolence and understanding which is his special heritage. Yes, Lilik can talk to a stone wall and get a response from it. Some of the living tombstones I have seen him plead with, when he desperately needed to sell a painting or an *objet d'art* from his father's collection, were more deaf, more impenetrable, than any stone wall. There are human beings, as we all know, who freeze at the mere mention of a painting for sale. There are some who turn to stone whenever there is the slightest hint that they may be called upon to relinquish so much as a moldy crust of bread.

If Lilik had a rough time of it in Big Sur, he's having an equally rough time of it in his home town, Jerusalem. But his letters never sound that way. No, Lilik begins—invariably—with himself seated on the terrace of a noisy café and some poor devil begging to shine his shoes or sell him a rug which he doesn't need. (It varies . . . sometimes it's the dessicated toenail of a saint that's being offered to him.) Even if it's raining, the sun is always out (in his heart) and he, the professor *(cher mâitre, cher ami),* is in particularly fine fettle, either because he is just about to tackle a new series of oils or because he has just ended a bout of work. His letters start with the place, the moment, the immediate thought, the way he feels— whether short of breath, constipated, or delighted with his warm beer. In a few lines he manages to evoke the atmosphere of the crowd, the market place, the cemetery hard by, the waiters running to and fro, the peddlers and mendicants wheedling and whining, the chickens being plucked (by toothless hags), the mountebanks performing their stints, the smell of food, grime, sweat and drink, the clove he just swallowed by mistake, yesterday's delicious garlic (we used to airmail him a clove of garlic at a time), the juicy colors which he will squeeze on to his palette the moment he gets home. *Und so weiter.*

Every other word is mispelled, whether written in English, German, Russian or French. It would take a mental acrobat to deliberately distort, or transmogrify, words the way Lilik does unwittingly. Only a homely word like fart comes off intact, so to say. And there is lots of farting in his jubilant epistles—on his own part and on the part of those around him. The Israelis apparently do not blush or hasten to excuse themselves when they "break wind," as we say in polite literature.

"At this moment," he will write, "we are having trouble again with the Arabs, or the Arabs with us." Homeward bound, he may have to duck into a doorway several times in order to escape stray bullets. Every time he leaves the house his wife, Louise, wonders if he will come back dead or alive. But Lilik, from all accounts, doesn't give much heed to these goings on; it's all part of the daily routine. What interests him, what makes him *chuckle*—there's a word he could never succeed in spelling if he went to school for three solid years!—is the news from the outside world. Perhaps getting it in Hebrew makes it appear even more complicated than it does to us. From that sunny café (even if it's raining) where he sits leisurely sipping his warm beer, leisurely nibbling at a piece of stale cheese, the world outside seems what it truly is—absolutely cockeyed. Sure, he says, we may be having our troubles with the Arabs—he never says "with the bloody Arabs"—but what about Formosa, what about China, Indonesia, Russia, Japan, North Africa and South Africa, West Germany and East Germany, and so on, meaning up and down, back and forth, round and about the grisly gridiron on which the "civilized" nations of the world are matching wits, stoking fires, pushing each other around, shoving, grabbing, scrambling, lying to one another and insulting one another, jeering or menacing, patching up coalitions here, breaking down alliances there, disarming some nations and arming others to the teeth, talking peace and progress and preparing to murder *en masse,* promising this group of devil dogs the latest models in all-out destruction while cautiously limiting others to obsolete fleets, tanks, bombers, rifles, machine guns, hand grenades and flame-throwers, which were once effective in "saving civilization" but are now scarcely more destructive than Fourth of July firecrackers, and firecrackers may soon be eliminated altogether, even for Fourth of July celebrations, because they are dangerous for children to handle, whereas atom bombs, when kept neatly in stockpiles, wouldn't hurt a fly. As he slyly puts it, quoting Professor Slivovitz, "the analects of logistics, when fed through I.B.M. machines, add up to little more than matzoth balls." What Lilik implies, talking through his dummy professor, is that the voice of insanity can be heard above the evening call to prayer. What we need, as the professor would say, are not more amplifiers, or better amplifiers, but reductors, filters, screens, which will enable us to distinguish between the maudlin ravings of a statesman and the cooing of a turtle dove. . . . I must leave him, dear Lilik, in the peace and serenity of four in the afternoon when bullfighters meet their death and diplomats stab us in the back over their atom bomb cocktails.

(So you grew a peenus, Mrs. Feitelbaum? *Nu,* what else is new?)

Other voices, other rooms; other worries, other microbes. I don't know why, but speaking of the lack of garlic brings to mind the image of that forlorn Basque girl whom I found standing on the road outside our house one late afternoon in winter, her thin, busted shoes waterlogged, her hands numb with cold, too timid to knock at the door but determined to see me if she had to stand there in the rain all night.

What was her urgent mission? To inquire if I were acquainted with Nietzsche's philosophy of "peace and disarmament" as given in the second volume of *Thoughts Out of Season.* The poor girl, what she needed was nourishment, not more "peace and dismemberment." I brought her in, sat her by the fire, dried her skirt and stockings, and had my wife throw a good meal into her. Then, after I had listened to as much as I could take for one evening, I drove her down to Emil White's and begged him to put her up for the night and see that she got a lift in the morning. (She was headed for L.A. No money, no car. All the nuts and crackpots seem headed for L.A. And they all travel light, like the birds of the air.)

Finding the atmosphere congenial at Anderson Creek—the old story!—she lingered on for a week before hitting the road. She offered Emil a lay before leaving, to show her gratitude, but he wasn't tempted. Too much "peace and dismemberment."

Three or four weeks later I received a letter from her—she was now in Montana—giving me a detailed account of the troubles which a certain tribe of Indians was having with our Federal government and conveying an earnest message from the head of the tribe to come immediately so that I might be informed at first hand of the complicated situation. She stated that they, the headmen of the tribe, would endeavor to persuade me to act as intermediary for them in Washington, D.C. I *of course* immediately chartered a private plane and, flying low over Duck Creek, impressed into my service a secretary, interpreter and full-fledged stenotypist.

Lying awake that night, I thought of a humorous episode which took place in that make-believe world of Washington, D.C., shortly after my return from Europe. Someone in the upper circles, whose acquaintance I had made by hazard in another part of the world, had invited me to a luncheon at a famous club in the heart of our spotless capital. I thought I would be dining with a few of his intimate friends, the usual devotees of "tropical" literature. As one guest after another swept through the revolving door, I noticed that they all had under their arms packages which looked suspiciously alike. It also seemed to me that these guests were one and all men of standing. They were, indeed, as I soon learned. Each one was an official from those departments of the government whose duty it is to be on the lookout for, track down, and bring to just punishment the culprits who deal in pornographic literature. As I was at that time the chief culprit in the government's eye, these representatives of truth and enlightenment were paying me a signal honor in bringing the offending books to be autographed. I must say that they all seemed like good fellows well met, not one of them deranged or undermined, damaged or deteriorated, by my "filthy" books. After apologies for being engaged in such unclean work—apologies given sincerely and accepted sincerely—they pressed me, each in turn, to think of something "original" to inscribe above my signature.

When I thought I had signed them all, an official more imposing looking than the others unwrapped a special package and, dumping a few copies (of this same "tropical" literature), said to me in low tones: "This one, if you will be so kind, I would like inscribed to Secretary So-and-So." When I had faithfully done as bidden, he murmured in an even lower tone of voice: "And this one is for President So-and-So." As he reached for the third copy, I said to myself: "This must be for his Most Holy Eminence, the Pope of Rome!" But it wasn't. It was for one of the nonentities in the Cabinet. The last one he asked me to inscribe, always with the same polite "if you will be so kind!", was destined for the Ambassador from Soviet Russia. It developed that this emissary had requested his wife, who was then visiting Washington, to bring back the most obscene work of mine she could lay hands on. She was to bring it back in person, not entrust it to the diplomatic pouch. At this point, my gorge rising, I excused myself and went to the men's room to throw up. I succeeded only in bringing up some bile. . . .

Not a word of all this is true, of course. Just the ravings of "a Brooklyn boy."

Speaking of this same "tropical" literature, I must add a word about the filthy, tattered, chewed up copies which are sent me from time to time by fans who, in the course of dumping antiquated phonographs and water pistols upon the unsuspecting aborigines of the hinterlands, make occasional visits to bordels and other "slaughterhouses of love" in order, no doubt, to wash away their sins. Since living here in Big Sur I must have received at least a dozen copies of the banned books which these nonchalant marauders filched from the private libraries which are (naturally) to be found in these unorthodox retreats. One wonders who the readers are—the madam, the girls, or the clients? Whoever had read the copies sent me had read them attentively, assiduously and often with a critical eye. Some corrected my spelling, some improved my punctuation, some added phrases here and there which would have thrilled a James Joyce or a Rabelais by their inventiveness. Others, under the influence of drink, no doubt, littered the margins with epithets such as I have never seen anywhere, neither in our own public toilets nor in the toilets of French newspapers, where invention and ribaldry run riot.

Of all the tidbits which pop up in the mail the ones which excite me the most, which leave me dreaming longest, are the picture postcards from the assholes of creation. Imagine getting a postcard from a digger attached to some archaeological expedition in the dreary wastes of Asia Minor who says he has just stumbled on a copy of *Sexus* in the village of Christ knows what name! Or a cryptic message from a celebrated artist whom you have worshipped all your life but never dared write, though in your head you've written him letters yards long, and he says: "Having lunch here (on the banks of the Nile, the Ganges or the Brahmaputra) with some devoted followers of yours"; and there follow the signatures of the starry members of the Pleiades. Or from some atoll in the far Pacific a message scrawled with a broom handle states that the Colonel or the Brigadier-General lifted "my only copy of *Capricorn,* please get me another!" Adding, not entirely for effect—"before I am liquidated." Or comes a letter in a language unknown to you, informing you that the sender has just run across a wonderful passage in a manuscript—a passage about *Capricorn* again—written by a man who died alone on a coral reef. Or an elderly gentleman, once a reviewer and one of the first to acclaim you, writes on crested stationery from his castle in the Hebrides, inquiring if you are still alive, have you written anything since and what is it, adding (sorrowfully): "You see, I've been knighted since!" Since what? Possibly since writing the review which cost him his job!

All these messages, inquiries, fond wishes and tokens of affection and remembrance create an elation which may last for days, not because you're puffed up but because, just as when you were very young and very much in love with a will-o'-the-wisp, some bedraggled Gypsy, reading your hand, drove you to fever pitch telling you all the things you already knew when all you wanted to hear were those three magic words—*"She loves you!"*

When the Armenian soothsayer, in Athens, was predicting the varied and exciting voyages I was yet to undertake, when he was indicating the general directions of these voyages, one indubitably toward the Orient, another unmistakably toward the South Pacific, and so on, the question which was hammering in my brain was: "Be specific! Tell me if I shall ever get to Lhasa, to Mecca, to Timbuctoo!" Today I realize that if I do not get there in person one of my "emissaries" will, and I'll one day know everything I long to know, not in the life to come but in this life here on earth.

Paradise Lost

It was Anaïs Nin who introduced me to Conrad Moricand. She brought him to my studio in the Villa Seurat one day in the fall of 1936. My first impressions were not altogether favorable. The man seemed somber, didactic, opinionated, self-centered. A fatalistic quality pervaded his whole being.

It was late afternoon when he arrived, and after chatting a while, we went to eat in a little restaurant on the Avenue d'Orléans. The way he surveyed the menu told me at once that he was finicky. Throughout the meal he talked incessantly, without its spoiling his enjoyment of the food. But it was the kind of talk that does not go with food, the kind that makes food indigestible.

There was an odor about him which I could not help but be aware of. It was a mélange of bay rum, wet ashes and *tabac gris,* tinctured with a dash of some elusive, elegant perfume. Later these would resolve themselves into one unmistakable scent—the aroma of death.

I had already been introduced to astrologic circles before meeting Moricand. And in Eduardo Sanchez, a cousin of Anaïs Nin, I had found a man of immense erudition, who, on the advice of his analyst, had taken up astrology therapeutically, so to speak. Eduardo often reminded me of the earthworm, one of God's most useful creatures, it is said. His powers of ingestion and digestion were stupendous. Like the worm, his labors were primarily for the benefit of others, not himself. At the time Eduardo was engrossed in a study of the Pluto-Neptune-Uranus conjunctions. He had delved deep into history, metaphysics and biography in search of material to corroborate his intuitions. And finally he had begun work on the great theme: Apocatastasis.

With Moricand I entered new waters. Moricand was not only an astrologer and a scholar steeped in the hermetic philosophies, but

591

an occultist. In appearance there was something of the mage about
him. Rather tall, well built, broad shouldered, heavy and slow in
his movements, he might have been taken for a descendant of the
American Indian family. He liked to think, he later confided, that
there was a connection between the name Moricand and Mohican.
In moments of sorrow there was something slightly ludicrous about
his expression, as if he were consciously identifying himself with
the last of the Mohicans. It was in such moments that his square
head with its high cheek bones, his stolidity and impassivity, gave
him the look of anguished granite.

Inwardly he was a disturbed being, a man of nerves, caprices
and stubborn will. Accustomed to a set routine, he lived the
disciplined life of a hermit or ascetic. It was difficult to tell whether
he had adapted himself to this mode of life or accepted it against
the grain. He never spoke of the kind of life he would have liked to
lead. He behaved as one who, already buffeted and battered, had
resigned himself to his fate. As one who could assimilate punishment better than good fortune. There was a strong feminine streak
in him which was not without charm but which he exploited to his
own detriment. He was an incurable dandy living the life of a
beggar. And living wholly in the past!

Perhaps the closest description I can give of him at the outset of
our acquaintance is that of a Stoic dragging his tomb about with
him. Yet he was a man of many sides, as I gradually came to
discover. He had a tender skin, was extremely susceptible, particularly to disturbing emanations, and could be as fickle and emotional as a girl of sixteen. Though he was basically not fair-minded,
he did his utmost to be fair, to be impartial, to be just. And to be
loyal, though by nature I felt that he was essentially treacherous.
In fact, it was this undefinable treachery which I was first aware of
in him, though I had nothing on which to base my feelings. I
remember that I deliberately banished the thought from my mind,
replacing it with the vague notion that here was an intelligence
which was suspect.

What I looked like to him in those early days is a matter of
conjecture on my part. He did not know my writings except for a
few fragments which had appeared in translation in French revues.
He, of course, knew my date of birth and had presented me with
my horoscope shortly after I became acquainted with him. (If I am
not mistaken, it was he who detected the error in my hour of birth
which I had given as midnight instead of noon.)

All our intercourse was in French, in which I was none too
fluent. A great pity, because he was not only a born conversationalist but a man who had an ear for language, a man who spoke

French like a poet. Above all, a man who loved subtleties and nuances! It was a dual pleasure I enjoyed whenever we came together—the pleasure of receiving instruction (not only in astrology) and the pleasure of listening to a musician, for he used the language much as a musician would his instrument. In addition there was the thrill of listening to personal anecdotes about celebrities whom I knew only through books.

In brief, I was an ideal listener. And for a man who loves to talk, for a monologist especially, what greater pleasure could there be for him than in having an attentive, eager, appreciative listener?

I also knew how to put questions. Fruitful questions.

All in all, I must have been a strange animal in his eyes. An expatriate from Brooklyn, a francophile, a vagabond, a writer only at the beginning of his career, naive, enthusiastic, absorbent as a sponge, interested in everything and seemingly rudderless. Such is the image I retain of myself at this period. Above all, I was gregarious. (He was anything but.) And a Capricorn, though not of the same decan. In age we were but a few years apart.

Apparently I was something of a stimulant to him. My native optimism and recklessness complemented his ingrained pessimism and cautiousness. I was frank and outspoken, he judicious and reserved. My tendency was to exfoliate in all directions; he, on the other hand, had narrowed his interests and focused on them with his whole being. He had all the reason and logic of the French, whereas I often contradicted myself and flew off at tangents.

What we had in common was the basic nature of the Capricorn. In his *Miroir d' Astrologie*[1] he has summed up succinctly and discriminatingly these common factors to be found in the Capricorn type. Under *"Analogies"* he puts it thus, to give a few fragments:

"Philosophers. Inquisitors. Sorcerers. Hermits. Gravediggers. Beggars.

"Profundity. Solitude. Anguish.

"Chasms. Caverns. Abandoned places."

Here are a few Capricorns of varying types which he gives: "Dante, Michelangelo, Dostoevsky, El Greco, Schopenhauer, Tolstoy, Cézanne, Edgar Allan Poe, Maxim Gorky. . . ."

Let me add a few of the more common qualities they possess, according to Moricand.

"Grave, taciturn, closed. Love solitude, all that is mysterious, are contemplative.

"They are sad and heavy.

[1] Paris: Au Sans Pareil, 1928.

"They are born old.

"They see the bad before the good. The weakness in everything leaps immediately to their eyes.

"Penitence, regrets, perpetual remorse.

"Cling to the remembrance of injuries done them.

"Seldom or never laugh; when they do, it is a sardonic laugh.

"Profound but heavy. Burgeon slowly and with difficulty. Obstinate and persevering. Indefatigable workers. Take advantage of everything to amass or progress.

"Insatiable for knowledge. Undertake long-winded projects. Given to the study of complicated and abstract things.

"Live on several levels at once. Can hold several thoughts at one and the same time.

"They illumine only the abysses."

There are the three decans or divisions to each house. For the first decan—I was born the 26th of December—he gives this:

"Very patient and tenacious. Capable of anything in order to succeed. Arrive by dint of perseverance, but step by step. . . . Tendency to exaggerate the importance of earthly life. Avaricious of self. Constant in their affections and in their hatreds. Have a high opinion of themselves."

I quote these observations for several reasons. The reader will discover, each in his own way, the importance which may or may not be attached to them.

But to get on. . . . When I first met him, Moricand was living— *existing* would be better—in a very modest hotel called the Hotel Modial in the rue Notre Dame de Lorette. He had but recently weathered a great crisis—the loss of his fortune. Completely destitute, and with no ability or concern for practical affairs, he was leading a hand-to-mouth existence. For breakfast he had his coffee and croissants in his room, and often he had the same for dinner too, with no lunch in between.

Anaïs was a godsend. She aided him with modest sums as best she could. But there were others, quite a few indeed, whom she likewise felt compelled to aid. What Moricand never suspected was that, in presenting him to me, Anaïs hoped to unload some of her burden. She did it gently, tactfully, discreetly, as she did all things. But she was definitely finished with him.

Anaïs knew quite well that I was unable to support him, unless morally, but she also knew that I was ingenious and resourceful, that I had all manner of friends and acquaintances, and that if I was sufficiently interested I would probably find a way to help him, at least temporarily.

She was not far wrong in this surmise.

Naturally, from my standpoint, the first and most important thing was to see that the poor devil ate more regularly, and more abundantly. I hadn't the means to guarantee him three meals a day, but I could and did throw a meal into him now and then. Sometimes I invited him out to lunch or dinner; more often I invited him to my quarters where I would cook as bountiful and delicious a meal as possible. Half-starved as he was most of the time, it was small wonder that by the end of the meal he was usually drunk. Drunk not with wine, though he drank copiously, but with food, food which his impoverished organism was unable to assimilate in such quantities. The ironic thing was—and how well I understood it!—that by the time he had walked home he was hungry all over again. Poor Moricand! How very, very familiar to me was this ludicrous aspect of his tribulations! Walking on an empty stomach, walking on a full stomach, walking to digest a meal, walking in search of a meal, walking because it is the only recreation one's pocketbook permits, as Balzac discovered when he came to Paris. Walking to lay the ghost. Walking instead of weeping. Walking in the vain and desperate hope of meeting a friendly face. Walking, walking, walking. . . . But why go into it? Let's dismiss it with the label—"ambulatory paranoia."

To be sure, Moricand's tribulations were without number. Like Job, he was afflicted in every way. Altogether devoid of the latter's faith, he nevertheless displayed remarkable fortitude. Perhaps all the more remarkable in that it was without foundation. He did his best to keep face. Rarely did he break down, in my presence at least. When he did, when tears got the better of him, it was more than I could bear. It left me speechless and impotent. It was a special kind of anguish he experienced, the anguish of a man who is incapable of understanding why he of all men should be singled out for punishment. He led me to believe, always indirectly, that never had he done his fellow-man an injury with intent and deliberation. On the contrary, he had always tried to be of help. He liked to believe, and I have no doubt he was sincere, that he harbored no evil thoughts, bore no one any ill will. It is true, for example, that he never spoke ill of the man who was responsible for his comedown in the world. He attributed this misfortune entirely to the fact that he was too trusting. As though it were his own fault and not the fault of the one who had taken advantage of his confidence.

Using what little wits I possessed, for I was scarcely more capable than he in practical matters, I finally hit upon the idea of asking my friends to have Moricand do their horoscopes for a modest fee. I believe I suggested a hundred francs as a fee, but it may only have been fifty. One could then get a very decent meal for from twelve to fifteen francs. As for Moricand's room rent, it could not have been more than three hundred francs per month, possibly less.

All went well until I exhausted my list of friends and acquaintances. Then, not to let Moricand down, I began inventing people. That is to say, I would give him the name, sex, date, hour and place of birth of individuals who did not exist. I paid for these horoscopes out of my own pocket, naturally. According to Moricand, who had not the least suspicion of the turn things had taken, these imaginary subjects comprised an astounding variety of characters. Occasionally, faced with a most incongruous chart, he would express a desire to meet the subject, or would press me for intimate details which of course I would offer with the ease and nonchalance of one who knew whereof he spoke.

When it came to reading personalities, Moricand impressed one as possesssing certain powers of divination. His sixth sense, as he called it, served him well in interpreting a chart. But often he had no need of a chart, no need of dates, places, and so on. Never shall I forget the banquet given by the group sponsoring the revue *Volontés* which was directed by Georges Pelorson. Eugene Jolas and I were the only Americans in the group, the rest were all French. There must have been about twenty of us at table that evening. The food was excellent and the wine and liqueurs plentiful. Moricand sat opposite me. On one side of him sat Jolas and on the other, I believe, Raymond Queneau. Every one was in excellent spirits, the conversation running high.

With Moricand in our midst, it was inevitable that sooner or later the subject of astrology must come up for discussion. There he was, Moricand, cool as a cucumber, and filling his breadbasket to the best of his ability. Lying in wait, as it were, for the jeers and derision which he doubtless anticipated.

And then it came—an innocent question by an unsuspecting nobody. Immediately a sort of mild insanity pervaded the atmosphere. Questions were being hurled from all directions. It was as if a fanatic had suddenly been uncovered—or worse, a lunatic. Jolas, who was a little under the weather by now and consequently more aggressive than usual, insisted that Moricand give demonstrable proofs. He challenged Moricand to single out the various zodiacal types seated about him. Now Moricand had undoubtedly made such classification in his head during the course of his conversation with this one and that. He could not help doing so by virtue of his calling. It was everyday routine with him, when talking to an individual, to observe the person's manner of speech, his gestures, his tics and idiosyncrasies, his mental and physical build, and so on. He was acute enough, adept enough, to distinguish and classify the more pronounced types present at the table. So, addressing himself to one after another whom he had singled out, he named them: Leo, Taurus, Libra, Virgo, Scorpio, Capricorn, and so on. Then, turning to Jolas, he quietly informed him that he believed he could tell him the year and day of his birth, perhaps the hour too. So saying, he took a good pause, raised his head slightly, as if studying the look of the heavens on the appointed day, then gave the exact date and, after a further pause, the approximate hour. He had hit it right on the nose. Jolas, who was dumbfounded, was still catching his breath as Moricand went on to relate some of the more intimate details of his past, facts which not even Jolas' close friends were aware of. He told him what he liked and what he disliked; he told him what maladies he had suffered from and was likely to suffer from in the future; he told him all manner of things which only a mind-reader could possibly divulge. If I am not mistaken, he even told him the location of a birthmark. (A shot in the dark like this was a trump card that Moricand loved to play when he had things well in hand. It was like putting his signature to a horoscope.)

That was one occasion when he ran true to form. There were others, some of them more eerie, more disturbing. Whenever it happened it was a good act. Far better than a spiritualistic séance.

Thinking of these performances, my mind always reverts to the room he occupied on the top floor of his hotel. There was no elevator service, naturally. One had to climb the five or six flights to the attic. Once inside, the world outside was completely forgotten. It was an irregular shaped room, large enough to pace up and down in, and furnished entirely with what belongings Moricand had managed to salvage from the wreck. The first impression one had, on entering, was that of orderliness. Everything was in place, but exactly in place. A few millimeters this way or that in the disposal of a chair, an *objet d'art,* a paper knife, and the effect would have been lost—in Moricand's mind, at least. Even the arrangement of his writing table revealed this obsession with order. Nowhere at any time was there ever any trace of dust or dirt. All was immaculate.

He was the same about his own person. He always appeared in clean, starched linen, coat and pants pressed (he probably pressed them himself), shoes polished, cravat arranged just so and to match his shirt of course, hat, overcoat, rubbers and suchlike neatly arranged in the clothes closet. One of the most vivid remembrances he had of his experience in the First World War—he had served in the Foreign Legion—was of the filth which he had been obliged to endure. He once recounted to me at great length how he had stripped and washed himself from head to toe with wet snow (in the trenches) after a night in which one of his comrades had vomited all over him. I had the impression that he would far rather have suffered a bullet wound than an ordeal of this nature.

What sticks in my crop about this period, when he was so desperately poor and miserable, is the air of elegance and fastidiousness which clung to him. He always seemed more like a stockbroker weathering a bad period than a man utterly without resources. The clothes he wore, all of excellent cut as well as of the best material, would obviously last another ten years, considering the care and attention he gave them. Even had they been patched, he would still have looked the well-dressed gentleman. Unlike myself, it never occurred to him to pawn or sell his clothes in order to eat. He had need of his good clothes. He had to preserve a front were he to maintain even interrupted relations with *le monde*. Even for ordinary correspondence he employed good stationery. Slightly perfumed too. His handwriting, which was distinctive, was also invested with the traits I have underlined. His letters, like his manuscripts and his astrological portraits, bore the stamp of a royal emissary, of a man who weighed every word carefully and would vouch for his opinions with his life.

One of the objects in this den he inhabited I shall never forget as long as I live. The dresser. Towards the end of an evening, usually a long one, I would edge toward this dresser, wait for a propitious moment when his glance was averted, and deftly slip a fifty- or hundred-franc note under the statuette which stood on top of the dresser. I had to repeat this performance over and over because it would have embarrassed him, to say the least, had I handed him the money or sent it to him in the mail. I always had the feeling, on leaving, that he would give me just time enough to reach the nearest Métro station, then duck out and buy himself a *choucroute garnie* at a nearby *brasserie*.

I must also say that I had to be very careful about expressing a liking for anything he possessed, for if I did he would thrust it on me in the manner of a Spaniard. It made no difference whether I admired a cravat he was wearing or a walking stick, of which he still had a number. It was thus I inadvertently acquired a beautiful cane which Moïse Kisling had once given him. On one occasion it demanded all my powers of persuasion to prevent him from giving me his only pair of gold cuff links. Why he was still wearing starched cuffs and cuff links I never dared ask him. He would probably have answered that he had no other kind of shirts.

On the wall by the window, where he had arranged his writing table caticornered, there were always pinned up two or three charts of subjects whose horoscopes he was studying. He kept them there at his elbow just as a chess player keeps a board handy on which he has a problem arranged. He believed in allowing time for his interpretations to simmer. His own chart hung beside the others in a special niche.

He regarded it at frequent intervals, much as a mariner would a barometer. He was always waiting for an "opening." In a chart, he told me, death manifested itself when all the exits were blocked. It was difficult, he averred, to detect the advent of death in advance. It was much easier to see it after a person had died; then everything became crystal clear, dramatic from a graphic standpoint.

What I recall most vividly are the red and blue pencil marks he employed to indicate the progress or regression of the span of chance in his chart. It was like watching the movement of a pendulum, a slow moving pendulum which only a man of infinite patience would bother to follow. If it swung a little this way, he was almost jubilant; if it swung a little the other way, he was depressed. What he expected of an "opening" I still do not know, since he was never prepared to make any apparent effort to improve his situation. Perhaps he expected no more than a breather. All he could possibly hope for, given his temperament, was a windfall. Certainly nothing in the way of a job could have meant anything to him. His one and only desire was to continue his researches. Seemingly, he had reconciled himself to his limitations. He was not a man of action, not a brilliant writer who might some day hope to liberate himself by the pen, nor was he flexible and yielding enough to beg his way. He was simply Moricand, the personality so clearly revealed by the chart which he himself had drawn up. A "subject" with a bad Saturn, among other things. A sad wizard who in moments of desperation would endeavor to extract a thin ray of promise from his star Regulus. In short, a victim doomed to live a dolorous, circumscribed life.

"We all get a break some time or other," I used to say to him. "It can't rain all the time! And what about that saying—'It's an ill wind that blows no one some good'?"

If he was in a mood to listen I might even go further and say: "Why don't you forget the stars for a while? Why not take a vacation and act *as if* fortune were yours? Who knows what might happen? You might meet a man in the street, an utter stranger, who would be the means of opening these doors you regard as locked. There is such a thing as grace too. It could happen, you know, if you were in the right mood, if you were prepared to let something happen. And if you forgot what was written in the sky."

To a speech of this sort he would give me one of those strange looks which signified many things. He would even throw me a smile, one of those tender, wistful smiles which an indulgent parent gives a child who poses an impossible problem. Nor would he rush to offer the answer which he had ever at his disposal and which, no doubt, he was weary of stating when thus cornered. In the pause which followed he gave the impression that he was first testing his own convictions, that he was rapidly surveying (for the thousandth time) all that he had ever said or thought about the subject, that he was even giving himself an injection of doubt, widening and deepening the problem, giving it dimensions which neither I nor anyone else could imagine, before slowly, ponderously, coldly and logically formulating the opening phrases of his defense.

"Mon vieux," I can hear him saying, "one must understand what is meant by chance. The universe operates according to law, and these laws obtain as much for man's destiny as for the birth and movements of the planets." Leaning back in his comfortable swivel chair, veering slightly round to focus better on his chart, he would add: "Look at *that!"* He meant the peculiar and particular impasse in which he was fixed at the moment. Then, extracting my chart from the portfolio which he always kept handy, he would beg me to examine it with him. "The only chance for me at this moment," he would say most solemnly, "is *you.* There *you* are!" And he would indicate how and where I fitted into the picture. "You and that angel, Anaïs. Without you two I would be a goner!"

"But why don't you look at it more positively?" I would exclaim. "If we are there, Anaïs and I, if we are all that you credit us with being, why don't you put all your faith and trust in us? Why don't you let us help you to free yourself? There are no limits to what one person can do for another, is that not so?"

Of course he had an answer to that. His great failing was that he had an answer for everything. He did not deny the power of faith. What he would say quite simply was that he was a man to whom faith had been denied. It was there in his chart, the absence of faith. What could one do? What he failed to add was that he had chosen the path of knowledge, and that in doing so he had clipped his own wings.

Only years later did he offer me a glimpse into the nature and origin of this castration which he referred to as lack of faith. It had to do with his boyhood, with the neglect and indifference of his parents, the perverse cruelty of his schoolmasters, one in particular, who had humiliated and tortured him in inhuman fashion. It was an ugly, woeful story, quite enough to account for his loss of morale, his spiritual degradation.

As always before a war, there was fever in the air. With the end approaching, everything became distorted, magnified, speeded up. The wealthy were as active as bees or ants, redistributing their funds and assets, their mansions, their yachts, their gilt-edged bonds, their mine holdings, their jewels, their art treasures. I had at the time a good friend who was flying back and forth from one continent to another catering to these panicky clients who were trying to get out from under. Fabulous were the tales he told me. Yet so familiar. So disguistingly familiar. (Can anyone imagine an army of millionaires?) Fabulous too were the tales of another friend, a chemical engineer, who would turn up at intervals for dinner, just back from China, Manchuria, Mongolia, Tibet, Persia, Afghanistan, wherever there was deviltry afoot. And always with the same story—of intrigue, plunder, bribery, treachery, plots and projects of the most diabolical sort. The war was still a year or so away, but the signs were unmistakable—not only for the Second World War but for the wars and revolutions to follow.

Even the "bohemians" were being routed out of their trenches. Amazing how many young intellectuals were already dislocated, dispossessed, already being pushed about like pawns in the service of their unknown masters. Every day I was receiving visits from the most unexpected individuals. There was only one question in every one's mind: *when?* Meanwhile make the most of it! And we did, we who were hanging on till the last boat call.

In this merry, devil-may-care atmosphere Moricand took no part. He was hardly the sort to invite for a festive evening which promised to end up in a brawl, a drunken stupor, or a visit from the police. Indeed, the thought never entered my head. When I did invite him over for a meal I would carefully select the two or three guests who were to join us. They were usually the same ones each time. Astrological buddies, so to speak.

Once he called on me unannounced, a rare breach of protocol for Moricand. He seemed elated and explained that he had been strolling about the quays all afternoon. Finally he fished a small package out of his coat pocket and handed it to me. "For *you!*" he said, with much emotion in his voice. From the way he said it I understood that he was offering a gift which only I could appreciate to the full.

The book, for that's what it was, was Balzac's *Seraphita*.

Had it not been for *Seraphita* I doubt very much that my adventure with Moricand would have terminated in the manner it did. It will be seen shortly what a price I paid for this precious gift.

What I wish to stress at this point is that, coincident with the feverishness of the times, the increased tempo, the peculiar derangement which everyone suffered, writers more than others perhaps, there was noticeable, in my own case at any rate, a quickening of the spiritual pulse. The individuals who were thrown across my path, the incidents which occurred daily and which to another would have seemed like trifles, all had a very special significance in my mind. There was an *enchainement* which was not only stimulating and exciting but often hallucinating. Just to take a walk into the outskirts of Paris—Montrouge, Gentilly, Kremlin-Bicêtre, Ivry—was sufficient to unbalance me for the rest of the day. I enjoyed being unbalanced, derailed, disoriented early in the morning. (The walks I refer to were "constitutionals," taken before breakfast. My mind free and empty, I was making myself physically and spiritually prepared for long sieges at the machine.) Taking the rue de la Tombe-Issoire, I would head for the outer boulevards, then dive into the outskirts, letting my feet lead me where they would. Coming back, I always steered instinctively for the Place de Rungis, which in some mysterious way connected itself with certain phases of the film *L'Age d'or,* and more particularly with Luis Bunuel himself. With its queer street names, its atmosphere of not belonging, its special assortment of gamins, urchins and monsters who hailed from some other world, it was for me an eerie and seductive neighborhood. Often I took a seat on a public bench, closed my eyes for a few moments to sink below the surface, then suddenly opened them to look at the scene with the vacant stare of a somnambulist. Goats from the *banlieue,* gangplanks, douche bags, safety belts, iron trusses, *passerelles* and *sauterelles* floated before my glazed eyeballs, together with headless fowl, beribboned antlers, rusty sewing machines, dripping ikons and other unbelievable phenomena. It was not a community or neighborhood but a vector, a very special vector created wholly for my artistic benefit, created expressly to tie me into an emotional knot. Walking up the rue de la Fontaine à Mulard, I struggled frantically to contain my ecstasy, struggled to fix and hold in my mind (until after breakfast) three thoroughly disparate images which, if I could fuse them successfully, would enable me to force a wedge into a difficult passage (of my book) which I had been unable to penetrate the day before. The rue Brillat-Savarin, running like a snake past the Place, balances the works of Eliphas Lévi, the rue Butte aux Cailles (farther along) evokes the Stations of the Cross, the rue Félicien Rops (at another angle) sets bells to ringing and with it the whir of pigeon wings. If I was suffering from a hangover, as I frequently was, all these associations, deformations and interpenetrations became even more quixotically vivid and colorful. On such days it was nothing to receive in the first mail a second or third copy of the *I Ching,* an album of Scriabin, a slim volume concerning the life of James Ensor or a treatise on Pico della Mirandola. Beside my desk, as a reminder of recent festivities, the empty wine bottles were always neatly ranged: Nuits Saint-Georges, Gevrey-Chambertin, Clos-Veugeot, Vosne Romanée, Meursault, Traminer, Château Haut-Brion, Chambolle-Musigny, Montrachet, Beaune, Beaujolais, Anjou and that *"vin de prédilection"* of Balzac's—Vouvray. Old friends, even though drained to the last drop. Some still retained a slight bouquet.

Breakfast, *chez moi.* Strong coffee with hot milk, two or three delicious warm croissants with sweet butter and a touch of jam. And with the breakfast a snatch of Segovia. An emperor couldn't do better.

Belching a little, picking my teeth, my fingers tingling, I take a quick look around (as if to see if everything's in order!), lock the door, and plunk myself in front of the machine. Set to go. My brain afire.

But what drawer of my Chinese cabinet mind will I open first? Each one contains a recipe, a prescription, a formula. Some of the items go back to 6,000 B.C. Some still further back.

First I must blow the dust away. Particularly the dust of Paris, so fine, so penetrating, so nearly invisible. I must submerge to the root taps—Williamsburg, Canarsie, Greenpoint, Hoboken, the Gowanus Canal, Erie Basin, to playmates now moldering in the grave, to places of enchantment like Glendale, Glen Island, Sayville, Patchogue, to parks and islands and coves now transformed into garbage dumps. I must think French and write English, be very still and talk wild, act the sage and remain a fool or a dunce. I must balance what is unbalanced without falling off the tightrope. I must summon to the hall of vertigo the lyre known as the Brooklyn Bridge yet preserve the flavor and the aroma of the Place de Rungis. It must be of this moment but pregnant with the ebb of the Great Return. . . .

And it was just at this time—too much to do, too much to see, too much to drink, too much to digest—that, like heralds from distant yet strangely familiar worlds, the books began to come. Nijinsky's *Diary, The Eternal Husband, The Spirit of Zen, The Voice of the Silence, The Absolute Collective,* the *Tibetan Book of the Dead, l' Eubage,* the *Life of Milarepa, War Dance, Musings of a Chinese Mystic.* . . .

Some day, when I acquire a house with a large room and bare walls, I intend to compose a huge chart or graph which will tell better than any book the story of my friends, and another telling the story of the books in my life. One on each wall, facing each other, impregnating each other, erasing each other. No man can hope to live long enough to round out these happenings, these unfathomable experiences, in words. It can only be done symbolically, graphically, as the stars write their constellated *mysterium*.

Why do I speak thus? Because during this period—too much to do, too much to see, taste, and so forth—the past and the future converged with such clarity and precision that not only friends and books but creatures, objects, dreams, historical events, monuments, streets, names of places, walks, encounters, conversations, reveries, half-thoughts, all came sharply into focus, broke into angles, chasms, waves, shadows, revealing to me in one harmonious, understandable pattern their essence and significance.

Where my friends were concerned, I had only to think a moment in order to evoke a company or a regiment. Without effort on my part they ranged themselves in order of magnitude, influence, duration, proximity, spiritual weight and density, and so on. As they took their stations I myself seemed to be moving through the ether with the sweep and rhythm of an absent-minded angel, yet falling in with each in turn at exactly the right zodiacal point and at precisely the destined moment, good or bad, to tune in. What a medley of apparitions they presented! Some were shrouded in fog, some sharp as sentinels, some rigid as phantom ice-bergs, some wilted like autumn flowers, some racing toward death, some rolling along like drunks on rubber wheels, some pushing laboriously through endless mazes, some skating over the heads of their comrades as if muffled in luminol, some lifting crushing weights, some glued to the books in which they borrowed, some trying to fly though anchored with ball and chain, but all of them vivid, named classified, identified according to need, depth, insight, flavor, aura, fragrance and pulse beat. Some were suspended like blazing planets, others like cold, distant stars. Some burgeoned with frightening rapidity, like novae, then faded into dust; some moved along discreetly, always within calling distance, as it were, like beneficent planets. Some stood apart, not haughtily but as if waiting to be summoned—like authors (Novalis, for example) whose names alone are so freighted with promise that one postpones reading them until that ideal moment which never arrives.

And Moricand, had he any part in all this scintillating turmoil? I doubt it. He was merely part of the décor, another phenomenon pertinent to the epoch. I can see him still as he then appeared in my mind's eye. In a penumbra he lurks, cool, gray, imperturbable, with a twinkle in his eyes and a metallic *"Ouais!"* shaping his lips. As if saying to himself: *"Ouais!* Know it all. Heard it before. Forgot it long ago. *Ouais! Tu parles!* The labyrinth, the chamois with the golden horns, the grail, the argonaut, the *kermesse à la* Breughel, the wounded groin of Scorpio, the profanation of the host, the Areopagite, translunacy, symbiotic neurosis, and in a wilderness of pebbles a lone katydid. Keep it up, the wheel is softly turning. A time comes when. . . ." Now he is bent over his *pantâcles*. Reads with a Geiger counter. Unlatching his gold fountain pen, he writes in purple milk: Porphyry, Proclus, Plotinus, Saint Valentin, Julian the Apostate, Hermes Trismegistus, Apollonius of Tyana, Claude Saint-Martin. In his vest pocket he carries a little phial; it contains myrrh, frankincense and a dash of wild sarsparilla. *The odor of sanctity!* On the little finger of his left hand he wears a jade ring marked with yin and yang. Cautiously he brings out a heavy brass watch, a stem-winder, and lays it on the floor. It is 9:30, sidereal time, the moon on the cusp of panic, the ecliptic freckled with cometary warts. Saturn is there with her ominous milky hue. *"Ouais!"* he exclaims, as if clinching the argument. "I say nothing against anything. I observe. I analyze. I calculate. I distillate. Wisdom is becoming, but knowledge is the certainty of certitude. To the surgeon his scalpel, to the gravedigger his pick and shovel, to the analyst his dream books, to the fool his dunce cap. As for me, I have a bellyache. The atmosphere is too rarefied, the stones too heavy to digest. *Kali Yuga.* Only 9,765,854 years to go and we will be out of the snake pit. *Du courage, mon vieux!"*

Let us take a last look backward. The year is 1939. The month is June. I am not waiting for the Huns to rout me out. I am taking a vacation. Another few hours and I shall be leaving for Greece.

All that remains of my presence in the studio at the Villa Seurat is my natal chart done in chalk on the wall facing the door. It's for whomever takes over to ponder on. I'm sure it will be an officer of the line. Perhaps an erudite.

Oh yes, and on the other wall, high up near the ceiling, these two lines:

> *Jetzt müsste die Welt versinken,*
> *Jetzt muszte ein Wunder gescheh'n.*

Clear, what?

And now it is my last evening with my good friend Moricand. A modest repast in a restaurant on the rue Fontaine, diagonally opposite the living quarters of the Father of Surrealism. We spoke of him as we broke bread. *Nadja* once more. And the "Profanation of the Host."

He is sad, Moricand. So am I, in a faint way. I am only partly there. My mind is already reaching out for Rocamadour where I expect to be on the morrow. In the morning Moricand will once again face his chart, observe the sway of the pendulum—undoubtedly it has moved to the left!—see if Regulus, Rigel, Antares or Betelgeuse can aid him just a wee, wee bit. Only 9,765,854 years before the climate changes. . . .

It's drizzling as I step out of the Métro at Vavin. I've decided I must have a drink all by my lonesome. Does not the Capricorn love solutide? *Ouais!* Solitude in the midst of hubbub. Not heavenly solitude. Earthly solitude. *Abandoned places.*

The drizzle turns into a light rain, a gray, sweetly melancholy rain. A beggar's rain. My thoughts drift. Suddenly I'm gazing at the huge chrysanthemums my mother loved to raise in our dismal back yard in the street of early sorrows. They are hanging there before my eyes, like an artificial bloom, just opposite the lilac bush which Mr. Fuchs, the hundski picker, gave us one summer.

Yes, the Capricorn is a beast of solitude. Slow, steady, persevering. Lives on several levels at once. Thinks in circles. Fascinated by death. Ever climbing, climbing. In search of the edelweiss, presumably. Or could it be the *immortelle?* Knows no mother. Only "the mothers." Laughs little and usually on the wrong side of the face. Collects friends as easily as postage stamps, but is unsociable. Speaks truthfully instead of kindly. Metaphysics, abstractions, electromagnetic displays. Dives to the depths. Sees stars, comets, asteroids where others see only moles, warts, pimples. Feeds on himself when tired of playing the man-eating shark. A paranoiac. An *ambulatory* paranoiac. But constant in his affections—*and his hatreds. Ouais!*

From the time the war broke out until 1947 not a word from Moricand. I had given him up for dead. Then, shortly after we had installed ourselves in our new home on Partington Ridge, a thick envelope arrived bearing the return address of an Italian princess. In it was enclosed a letter from Moricand, six months old, which he had requested the princess to forward should she ever discover my address. He gave as his address a village near Vevey, Switzerland, where he said he had been living since the end of the war. I answered immediately, telling him how glad I was to know that he was still alive and inquiring what I could do for him. Like a cannon ball came his reply, giving a detailed account of his circumstances which, as I might have guessed, had not improved. He was living in a miserable pension, in a room without heat, starving as usual, and without even the little it takes to buy cigarettes. Immediately we began sending him foodstuffs and other necessities of which he was apparently deprived. And what money we could spare. I also sent him international postal coupons so that he would not be obliged to waste money on stamps.

Soon the letters began to fly back and forth. With each succeeding letter the situation grew worse. Obviously the little sums we dispatched didn't go very far in Switzerland. His landlady was constantly threatening to turn him out, his health was getting worse, his room was insupportable, he had not enough to eat, it was impossible to find work of any kind, *and*—in Switzerland you don't beg!

To send him larger sums was impossible. We simply didn't have that kind of money. What to do? I pondered the situation over and over. There seemed to be no solution.

Meanwhile his letters poured in, always on good stationery, always airmail, always begging, supplicating, the tone growing more and more desperate. Unless I did something drastic he was done for. That he made painfully clear.

Finally I conceived what I thought to be a brilliant idea. Genial, nothing less. It was to invite him to come and live with us, share what we had, regard our home as his own for the rest of his days. It was such a simple solution I wondered why it had never occurred to me before.

I kept the idea to myself for a few days before broaching it to my wife. I knew that it would take some persuading to convince her of the necessity for such a move. Not that she was ungenerous, but that he was hardly the type to make life more interesting. It was like inviting Melancholia to come and perch on your shoulder.

"Where would you put him up?" were her first words, when finally I summoned the courage to broach the subject. We had only a living room, in which we slept, and a tiny wing adjoining it where little Val slept.

"I'll give him my studio," I said. This was a separate cubicle hardly bigger than the one Val slept in. Above it was the garage which had been partly converted into a workroom. My thought was to use that for myself.

Then came the big question: "How will you raise the passage money?"

"That I have to think about," I replied. "The main thing is, are you willing to risk it?"

We argued it back and forth for several days. Her mind was full of premonitions and forebodings. She pleaded with me to abandon the idea. "I know you'll only regret it," she croaked.

What she could not understand was why I felt it imperative to assume such a responsibility for one who had never really been an intimate friend. "If it were Perlès," she said, "it would be different; he means something to you. Or your Russian friend, Eugene. But Moricand? What do you owe *him?*"

This last touched me off. What did I owe Moricand? Nothing. *And everything.* Who was it put *Seraphita* in my hands?

I endeavored to explain the point. Halfway along I gave up. I saw how absurd it was to attempt to make such a point. A mere book! One must be insane to fall back on such an argument.

Naturally I had other reasons. But I persisted in making *Seraphita* my advocate. Why? I tried to get to the bottom of it. Finally I grew ashamed of myself. What did I have to justify myself? Why make excuses? The man was starving. He was ill. He was penniless. He was at the end of his rope. Weren't these reason enough? To be sure, he had been a pauper, a miserable pauper, all the years I had known him. The war hadn't changed anything; it had only rendered his situation more hopeless. But why quibble about his being an intimate friend or just a friend? Even if he had been a stranger, the fact that he was throwing himself on my mercy was enough. One doesn't let a drowning man sink.

"I've just got to do it!" I exclaimed. "I don't know how I'm going to do it, but I will. I'm writing him today." And then, to throw her a bone, I added: "Perhaps he won't like the idea."

"Don't worry," she said, "he'll grab at a straw."

So I wrote and explained the whole situation to him. I even drew a diagram of the place, giving the dimensions of his room, the fact that it was without heat, and adding that we were far from any city. "You may find it very dull here," I said, "with no one to talk to but us, no library to go to, no cafés, and the nearest cinema forty miles away. But at least you will not have to worry anymore about food and shelter." I concluded by saying that once here he would be his own master, could devote his time to whatever pleased him, in fact he could loaf the rest of his days away, if that was his wish.

He wrote back immediately, telling me that he was overjoyed, calling me a saint and a savior, et cetera, et cetera.

The next few months were consumed in raising the necessary funds. I borrowed whatever I could, diverted what few francs I had to his account, borrowed in advance on my royalties, and finally made definite arrangements for him to fly from Switzerland to England, there take the *Queen Mary* or *Elizabeth,* whichever it was, to New York, and fly from New York to San Francisco, where I would pick him up.

During these few months when we were borrowing and scraping I managed to maintain him in better style. He had to be fattened up or I would have an invalid on my hands. There was just one item I had failed to settle satisfactorily, that was to liquidate his back rent. The best I could do, under the circumstances, was to send a letter which he was to show his landlady, a letter in which I promised to wipe out his debt just as soon as I possibly could. I gave her my word of honor.

Just before leaving he dispatched a last letter. It was to reassure me that, as regards the landlady, everything was jake. To allay her anxiety, he wrote, he had reluctantly given her a lay. Of course he couched it in more elegant terms. But he made it clear that, disgusting though it was, he had done his duty.

It was just a few days before Christmas when he landed at the airport in San Francisco. Since my car had broken down I asked my friend Lilik (Schatz) to meet him and put him up at his home in Berkeley until I could come and fetch him.

As soon as Moricand stepped off the plane he heard his name being called. "Monsieur Moricand! Monsieur Moricand! *Attention!*" He stopped dead and listened with open mouth. A beautiful contralto voice was speaking to him over the air in excellent French, telling him to step to the information desk, where someone was waiting for him.

He was dumbfounded. What a country! What service! For a moment he felt like a potentate.

It was Lilik who was waiting for him at the information desk. Lilik who had coached the girl. Lilik who whisked him away, fixed him a good meal, sat up with him until dawn and plied him with the best Scotch he could buy. And to top it off he had given him a picture of Big Sur which made it sound like the paradise which it is. He was a happy man, Conrad Moricand, when he finally hit the hay.

In a way, it worked out better than if I had gone to meet him myself.

When a few days passed and I found myself still unable to get to San Francisco, I telephoned Lilik and asked him to drive Moricand down.

They arrived the next day about nine in the evening.

I had gone through so many inner convulsions prior to his arrival that when I opened the door and watched him descend the garden steps I was virtually numb. (Besides, the Capricorn seldom reveals his feelings all at once.)

As for Moricand, he was visibly moved. As we pulled away from an embrace I saw two big tears roll down his cheeks. He was "home" at last. Safe, sound, secure.

The little studio which I had turned over to him to sleep and work in was about half the size of his attic room in the Hotel Modial. It was just big enough to hold a cot, a writing table, a chiffonier. When the two oil lamps were lit it gave off a glow. A Van Gogh would have found it charming.

I could not help but notice how quickly he had arranged everything in his customary neat, orderly way. I had left him alone for a few minutes to unpack his bags and say an Ave Maria. When I returned to say goodnight I saw the writing table arranged as of yore—the block of paper resting slantwise on the triangular ruler, the large blotting pad spread out, and beside it his ink bottle and pen together with an assortment of pencils, all sharpened to a fine point. On the dresser, which had a mirror affixed to it, were laid out his comb and brush, his manicure scissors and nail file, a portable clock, his clothes brush and a pair of small framed photographs. He had already tacked up a few flags and pennants, just like a college boy. All that was missing to complete the picture was his birth chart.

I tried to explain how the Aladdin lamp worked, but it was too complicated for him to grasp all at once. He lit two candles instead. Then, apologizing for the close quarters he was to occupy, referring to it jokingly as a comfortable little tomb, I bade him goodnight. He followed me out to have a look at the stars and inhale a draught of clean, fragrant night air, assuring me that he would be perfectly comfortable in his cell.

When I went to call him the next morning I found him standing at the head of the stairs fully dressed. He was gazing out at the sea. The sun was low and bright in the sky, the atmosphere extremely clear, the temperature that of a day in late spring. He seemed entranced by the vast expanse of the Pacific, by the far off horizon so sharp and clear, by the bright blue immensity of it all. A vulture hove into sight, made a low sweep in front of the house, then swooned away. He seemed stupefied by the sight. Then suddenly he realized how warm it was. "My God," he said, "and it is almost the first of January!"

"C'est un vrai paradis," he mumbled as he descended the steps.

Breakfast over, he showed me how to set and wind the clock which he had brought me as a gift. It was an heirloom, his last possession, he explained. It had been in the family for generations. Every quarter of an hour the chimes struck. Very softly, melodiously. He handled it with the utmost care while explaining at great length the complicated mechanism. He had even taken the precaution to look up a watch-maker in San Francisco, a reliable one, to whom I was to entrust the clock should anything go wrong with it.

I tried to express my appreciation of the marvelous gift he had made me, but somehow, deep inside, I was against the bloody clock. There was not a single possession of ours which was precious to me. Now I was saddled with an object which demanded care and attention. "A white elephant!" I said to myself. Aloud I suggested that *he* watch over it, regulate it, wind it, oil it, and so on. "You're used to it," I said. I wondered how long it would be before little Val—she was only a little over two—would begin tinkering with it in order to hear the music.

To my surprise, my wife did not find him too somber, too morbid, too aged, too decrepit. On the contrary, she remarked that he had a great deal of charm—and *savoir-faire*. She was rather impressed by his neatness and elegance. "Did you notice his hands? How beautiful! The hands of a musician." It was true, he had good strong hands with spatulate fingers and well-kept nails, which were always polished.

"Did you bring any old clothes?" I asked. He looked so citified in his dark business suit.

He had no old clothes, it turned out. Or rather he had the same good clothes which were neither new nor old. I noticed that he was eyeing me up and down with mild curiosity. I no longer owned a suit. I wore corduroy pants, a sweater with holes in it, somebody's hand-me-down jacket, and sneakers. My slouch hat—the last I was to own—had ventilators all around the sweat band.

"One doesn't need clothes here," I remarked. "You can go naked, if you want."

"*Quelle vie!*" he exclaimed. "*C'est fantastique.*"

Later that morning, as he was shaving, he asked if I didn't have some talcum powder. "Of course," I said, and handed him the can I used. "Do you by chance have any Yardley?" he asked. "No," I said, "why?"

He gave me a strange, half-girlish, half-guilty smile. "I can't use anything but Yardley. Maybe when you go to town again you can get me some, yes?"

Suddenly it seemed as if the ground opened under my feet. Here he was, safe and secure, with a haven for the rest of his life in the midst of "*un vrai paradis,*" and he must have Yardley's talcum powder! Then and there I should have obeyed my instinct and said: "Beat it! Get back to your Purgatory!"

It was a trifling incident and, had it been any other man, I would have dismissed it immediately, put it down as a caprice, a foible, an idiosyncrasy, anything but an ominous presage. But of that instant I knew my wife was right, knew that I had made a grave mistake. In that moment I sensed the leech that Anaïs had tried to get rid of. I saw the spoiled child, the man who had never done an honest stroke of work in his life, the destitute individual who was too proud to beg openly but was not above milking a friend dry. I knew it all, felt it all, and already foresaw the end.

Each day I endeavored to reveal some new aspect of the region to him. There were the sulphur baths, which he found marvelous—better than a European spa because natural, primitive, unspoiled. There was the "virgin forest" hard by, which he soon explored on his own, enchanted by the redwoods, the madrones, the wild flowers and the luxuriant ferns. Enchanted even more by what he called "neglect," for there are no forests in Europe which have the unkempt look of our American forests. He could not get over the fact that no one came to take the dead limbs and trunks which were piled crisscross above one another on either side of the trail. So much firewood going to waste! So much building material lying unused, unwanted, and the men and women of Europe crowded together in miserable little rooms without heat. "What a country!" he exclaimed. "Everywhere there is abundance. No wonder the Americans are so generous!"

My wife was not a bad cook. In fact, she was a rather good cook. There was always plenty to eat and sufficient wine to wash the food down. California wines, to be sure, but he thought them excellent, better in fact than the *vin rouge ordinaire* one gets in France. But there was one thing about the meals which he found difficult to adjust to—the absence of soup with each meal. He also missed the suite of courses which is customary in France. He found it hard to accommodate himself to a light lunch, which is the American custom. Midday was the time for the big meal. Our big meal was at dinner. Still, the cheeses weren't bad and the salads quite good, all things considered, though he would have preferred *l'huile d'arachide* (peanut oil) to the rather copious use of olive oil which we indulged in. He was glad we used garlic liberally. As for the *bifteks,* never had he eaten the like abroad. Now and then we dug up a little cognac for him, just to make him feel more at home.

But what bothered him most was our American tobacco. The cigarettes in particular were atrocious. Was it not possible to dig up some *gauloises bleues,* perhaps in San Francisco or New York? I opined that it was indeed but that they would be expensive. I suggested that he try Between the Acts. (Meanwhile, without telling him, I begged my friends in the big cities to rustle up some French cigarettes.) He found the little cigars quite smokable. They

reminded him of something even more to his liking—cheroots. I
dug up some Italian stogies next time I went to town. Just ducky!
Good! We're getting somewhere, thought I to myself.

One problem we hadn't yet solved was stationery. He had need,
he maintained, for paper of a certain size. He showed me a sample
which he had brought with him from Europe. I took it to town to
see if it could be matched. Unfortunately it couldn't. It was an odd
size, a size we had no demand for apparently. He found it impossible to believe that such could be the case. America made everything, and in abundance. Strange that one couldn't match an
ordinary piece of paper. He grew quite incensed about it. Holding
up the sample sheet, flicking it with his fingernail, he exclaimed:
"Anywhere in Europe one can find this paper, exactly this size.
And in America, which has everything, it can't be found. *C'est
emmerdant!*"

To be frank, it was shitty to me too, the bloody subject. What
could he be writing that demanded the use of paper precisely that
size? I had got him his Yardley talc, his *gauloises bleues,* his eau
de cologne, his powdered, slightly perfumed pumice stone (for a
dentifrice), and now he was plaguing me about paper.

"Step outside a moment, won't you?" I begged. I spoke quietly,
gently, soothingly. "Look out there . . . look at that ocean! Look
at the sky!" I pointed to the flowers which were in bloom. A
hummingbird had just made as if to alight on the rose bush in front
of us. All its motors were whirring. *"Regardez-moi ça!" I* exclaimed. I allowed a due pause. Then, in a very even tone of voice
I said: "When a man has all this, can he not write just as well on
toilet paper if he has to?"

It registered.

"Mon vieux," he began, "I hope you don't think I am
exigent. . . ."

"I do indeed," said I.

"You must forgive me. I'm sorry. Nobody could be more
grateful than I for all you have done."

"My dear Moricand, I am not asking for gratitude. I'm asking
for a little common sense." (I wanted to say "horse sense" but
couldn't think of the equivalent in French immediately.) "Even if
we had no paper at all I would expect you to be happy. You're a
free man now, do you realize that? Why, god-damn it, you're
better off than I am! Look, let's not spoil all this"—I gestured
loosely toward the sky, the ocean, the birds of the air, the green
hills—"let's not spoil all this with talk of paper, cigarettes, talcum
powder and such nonsense. What we should be talking about is—
God."

He was crestfallen. I felt like apologizing then and there, but I didn't. Instead I strode off in the direction of the forest. In the cool depths I sat down beside a pool and proceeded to give myself what the French call an *examen de conscience*. I tried to reverse the picture, put myself in his boots, look at myself through *his* eyes. I didn't get very far, I must confess. Somehow, I just could not put myself in his boots.

"Had my name been Moricand," said I softly to myself, "I would have killed myself long ago."

In one respect he was an ideal house guest—he kept to himself most of the day. Apart from meal times, he remained in his room almost the entire day, reading, writing, perhaps meditating too. I worked in the studio-garage just above him. At first the sound of my typewriter going full blast bothered him. It was like the rat-a-tat-tat of a machine gun in his ears. But gradually he got used to it, even found it stimulating, he said. At lunch and dinner he relaxed. Being so much on his own, he seized these occasions to engage us in conversation. He was the kind of talker it is difficult to disengage once he has sunk his hooks into you. Lunch times I would often pull myself away abruptly, leaving him to work it out as best he could with my wife. Time is the one thing I regard as precious. If I had to waste time, I preferred to waste it in taking a nap rather than in listening to my friend Moricand.

Dinner was another matter. It was hard to find an excuse for terminating these sessions at my own time. It would have been a pleasure to glance at a book after dinner, since there was never any time for reading during the day, but I never got the chance. Once we were seated for the evening meal we were in for it till he had exhausted himself. Naturally, our conversations were all in French. Moricand had intended to learn a little English but after a few attempts gave it up. It was not a "sympathetic" language to him. It was even worse than German, he thought. Fortunately, my wife spoke some French and understood a lot more, but not enough to follow a man with Moricand's gift of speech. I couldn't always follow him myself. Every now and then I would have to halt the flow, ask him to repeat what he had just said in simpler language, then translate it for my wife. Now and then I would forget myself and give him a spate of English, soon arrested of course by his blank look. To translate these bursts was like sweating out a cold. If, as frequently happened, I had to explain something to my wife in English, he would pretend that he understood. She would do the same when he conveyed something confidential to me in French. Thus it happened that often the three of us were talking three different subjects, nodding, agreeing with one another, saying Yes when we meant No, and so on, until the confusion became so great that we all threw up our hands simultaneously. Then we would begin all over, sentence by sentence, thought by thought, as if struggling to cement a piece of string.

Nevertheless, and despite all frustration, we managed to understand one another exceedingly well. Usually it was only in the long, overembroidered monologue that we lost him. Even then, astray in the complicated web of a long-drawn-out story or a windy explanation of some hermeneutic point, it was a pleasure to listen to him. Sometimes I would deliberately let go my attention, facilitate the process of getting lost, in order to better enjoy the music of his words. At his best he was a one man orchestra.

It made no difference, when he was in the groove, what he chose to talk about—food, costume, ritual, pyramids, Trismegistus or Eleusinian mysteries. Any theme served as a means to exploit his virtuosity. In love with all that is subtle and intricate, he was always lucid and convincing. He had a feminine flair for preciosities, could always produce the exact timbre, shade, nuance, odor, taste. He had the suavity, velleity and mellifluousness of an enchanter. And he could put into his voice a resonance comparable in effect to the sound of a gong reverberating in the deathlike silence of a vast desert. If he spoke of Odilon Redon, for example, his language reeked of fragrant colors, of exquisite and mysterious harmonies, of alchemical vapors and imaginings, of pensive broodings and spiritual distillations too impalpable to be fixed in words but which words could evoke or suggest when marshaled in sensorial patterns. There was something of the harmonium in the use he made of his voice. It was suggestive of some intermediate region, the confluence, say, of divine and mundane streams where form and spirit interpenetrated, and which could only be conveyed musically. The gestures accompanying this music were limited and stereotyped, mostly facial movements—sinister, vulgarly accurate, diabolical when restricted to the mouth and lips, poignant, pathetic, harrowing, when concentrated in the eyes. Shudderingly effective when he moved his whole scalp. The rest of him, his body, one might say, was usually immobile, except for a slight tapping or drumming with the fingers now and then. Even his intelligence seemed to be centered in the sound box, the harmonium which was situated neither in the larynx nor in the chest but in a middle region which corresponded to the locus empyrean whence he drew his imagery.

Staring at him abstractly in one of those fugitive moments when I caught myself wandering among the reeds and bulrushes of my own vagaries, I would find myself studying him as if through a reflector, his image changing, shifting like swift-moving cloud formations: now the sorrowful sage, now the sybil, now the grand cosmocrator, now the alchemist, now the stargazer, now the mage. Sometimes he looked Egyptian, sometimes Mongolian, sometimes Iroquois or Mohican, sometimes Chaldean, sometimes Etruscan. Often very definite figures out of the past leaped to mind, figures he either seemed to incarnate momentarily or figures he had affinities with. To wit: Montezuma, Herod, Nebuchadnezzar, Ptolemy, Balthasar, Justinian, Solon. Revelatory names, in a way. However conglomerate, in essence they served to coalesce certain elements of his nature which ordinarily defied association. He was an alloy, and a very strange one at that. Not bronze, not brass, not electrum. Rather some nameless colloidal sort of alloy such as we associate with the body when it becomes a prey to some rare disease.

There was one image he bore deep within him, one he had created in youth and which he was never to shake off: "Gloomy Gus." The day he showed me a photograph of himself at the age of fifteen or sixteen I was profoundly disturbed. It was almost an exact replica of my boyhood friend, Gus Schmelzer, whom I used to tease and plague beyond endurance because of his somber, morose, eternally somber and morose mien. Even at that age— perhaps earlier, who knows?—there were engraved in Moricand's psyche all the modalities which such terms as lunar, saturnian and sepulchral evoke. One could already sense the mummy which the flesh would become. One could see the bird of ill omen perched on his left shoulder. One could feel the moonlight altering his blood, sensitizing his retina, dyeing his skin with the pallor of the prisoner, the drug addict, the dweller on forbidden planets. Knowing him, one might even visualize those delicate antennae of which he was altogether too proud and on which he placed a reliance which overtaxed his intuitive muscles, so to speak. I might go further— why not?—and say that, looking deep into his sorrowful eyes, somber, simian eyes, I could see skull within skull, an endless, cavernous Golgotha illumined by the dry, cold, murderous light of a universe beyond the imaginative bounds of even the hardiest scientific dreamer.

In the art of resuscitation he was a master. Touching anything that smacked of death, he came alive. Everything filtered through to him from the tomb in which it was buried. He had only to wave his wand to create the semblance of life. But, as with all sorcery, even the most poetic, the end was always dust and ashes. For Moricand the past was rarely a living past; it was a morgue which at best could be made to resemble a museum. Even his description of the living was but a cataloguing of museum pieces. There was no distinction in his enthusiasms between that which is and that which was. Time was his medium. A deathless medium which had no relation to life.

It is said that Capricorns get on well together, presumably because they have so much in common. It is my own belief that there are more divergences among these earth-bound creatures, that they have more difficulty understanding one another, than is the case with other types. Mutual understanding between Capricorns is more a surface agreement, a truce, so to speak, than anything else. At home in the depths or on the heights, seldom inhabiting any region for long, they have more kinship with the roc and the leviathan than with one another. What they do understand, perhaps, is that their differences are altitudinal, due primarily to shifts of position. Capable of running the whole gamut, it is easy for them to identify as you or me. This is their bond and explains their ability to forgive but never to forget. They forget nothing, ever. Their memory is phantasmagorical. They remember not only their personal, human tribulations, but their prehuman and subhuman ones as well. They can slither back into the protoplasmic slime with the ease of eels slipping through mud. They also carry remembrances of higher spheres, of seraphic states, as if they had known long periods of liberation from earthly thralls, as if the very language of the seraphim were familiar to them. Indeed, one might almost say of them that it is earthly existence to which they, the earth-bound, are of all types least suited. To them the earth is not only a prison, a purgatory, a place of expiation but it is also a cocoon from which they will eventually escape equipped with indestructible wings. Hence their mediumship, their ability and desire to practice acceptance, their extraordinary readiness for conversion. They enter the world like visitors destined for another planet, another sphere. Their attitude is one of having a last look around, of perpetually bidding good-bye to all that is terrestrial. They imbibe the very essence of the earth, and in doing so prepare the new body, the new form, in which they will take leave of earth forever. They die innumerable deaths whereas others die but once. Hence their immunity to life *or* death. Their true locus is the heart of mystery. There all is clear to them. There they live apart, spin their dreams, and are "at home."

He was hardly with us more than a week when he called me to his cell one day for a "consultation." It was about the uses of codeine. Beginning with a long preamble about his sufferings and privations since the year one, he ended with a brief account of the nightmare he had lived through during his recent sojourn in Switzerland. Though he was a Swiss citizen, Switzerland was not his country, not his climate, not his bowl of soup. After all the humiliations he had suffered during the war (the second one) came even worse ones which the unfeeling Swiss had imposed. All this by way of leading up to the seven-year itch. He paused to roll up his trousers. I was horrified. His legs were nothing but a mass of sores. There was no need to dwell further on the subject.

Now if he could only get a little codeine, he explained, it would help to calm his nerves, allow him to get some sleep at least, even though it could not cure the itch. Wouldn't I try to get some for him, perhaps tomorrow when I went to town? I said I would.

I had never used codeine or any drug that puts one to sleep or wakes one up. I had no idea that codeine could only be had by doctor's prescription. It was the druggist who informed me of this. Not wishing to disappoint Moricand, I called on two doctors I knew to ask if they would furnish me with the necessary prescription. They refused.

When I informed Moricand of the situation he was almost beside himself. He acted as if there were a conspiracy on the part of American physicians to keep him in misery. "How absurd!" he cried. "Even in Switzerland it's sold openly. I would have more chance, I suppose, if I asked for cocaine or opium."

Another day or two passed, during which time he got no sleep at all. Then another consultation. This time to inform me that he had thought of a way out. Very simple, too. He would write to his druggist in Switzerland and ask him to mail him the codeine in very small particles. I explained to him that such importation would be illegal, no matter how small the quantity. I explained further that he would be incriminating me too should he do such a thing.

"What a country! What a country!" he exclaimed, raising his hands heavenward.

"Why don't you try the baths again?" I suggested. He promised he would. He said it as if I had requested him to swallow a dose of castor oil.

As I was about to leave he showed me a letter which he had just received from his landlady. It was about the bill he owed and my failure to keep my promise. I had completely forgotten about her and her bloody bill.

We never had any money in the bank, but I did have a few bills in my pocket. I fished them out. "Maybe this will quiet her for a while," I said, laying them on his table.

About a week later he called me to his room again. He was

holding an envelope in his hand which he had just opened. He
wanted me to look at the contents. It was a letter from his Swiss
druggist to say that he was happy to be of service. I looked up and
saw the tiny pellets which he was holding in the palm of his hand.

"You see," he said, "there is always a way."

I was furious but tongue-tied. I could not deny that, were the
situation reversed, I would probably have done the same. He was
desperate, that was obvious. Besides, the baths had been no help.
They had aggravated his condition, if I was to believe him. At any
rate, he was through with the baths: they were poison to his
system.

Now that he had what he needed he took to roaming the forest
regularly. Good, thought I, he needs the exercise. But he overdid
it; the excessive walking made his blood boil. From another
standpoint these excursions did him good. The forest bequeathed
something which his Swiss spirit demanded. He always returned
from his walks elated and physically exhausted. "Tonight," he
would say, "I should be able to sleep without taking any pills."

He deceived himself. The itching grew worse. He continued to
scratch himself furiously, even in deep slumber. The itch had
traveled too. Now it had attacked his arms. Soon it would devastate
his whole body, all but his genitals.

There were remissions, of course. If guests arrived, particularly
French-speaking guests, his morale improved overnight. Or if he
received a letter from a dear friend who was still doing a stretch in
prison because of his activities during the Occupation. Sometimes
an exceptionally good dinner was sufficient to change his mood for
a day or two. The itching never ceased, apparently, but the
scratching might be halted for a while.

As the days passed, he became more and more aware that I was
a person upon whom it gave people pleasure to shower gifts. With
the mail there came packages containing all manner of things.
What astounded Moricand was that they were usually the very
things we were in need of. If we ran out of wine a friend was sure
to turn up with an armful of excellent bottles; if I needed wood, a
neighbor would appear with the gift of a load of wood, enough to
last several months. Books and magazines, of course, poured in
steadily. Now and then I would receive postage stamps, whole
sheets of them. Only money failed to pour in. That always came in
a trickle, a trickle which often dried up altogether.

It was with a falcon's eye that Moricand eyed this steady influx
of gifts. As for the steady flow of visitors, even the bores, the time
wasters, he observed, were instrumental in lightening our burdens.
"It's altogether natural," he would say. "It's there in your horo-

scope. Even when Jupiter deserts you at times you are never left unprotected. Besides, with *you* misfortune only works to your ultimate advantage. You can't possibly lose!''

I never dreamed of responding to such remarks by pointing out the struggles and the sacrifices I had made throughout my life. But to myself I would say: "It's one thing for 'it' to be in your horoscope; it's another to make it manifest.''

One thing seemed to escape his notice entirely—the favors, the services which my friends were constantly rendering him. He had not the slightest notion how much everyone was concerned for his welfare. He behaved as if it were all a matter of course, now that he was in the land of plenty. Americans were like that, naturally kind and generous, don't you know. They had no grave problems to worry about. They were born lucky, the gods looked after them. A shade of contempt always crept into his voice when he referred to the benevolence of the American. He lumped us with the huge cauliflowers, carrots, squash and other monstrous-looking vegetables and fruits we produce in inexhaustible quantity.

I had asked only one little favor of Moricand when I invited him to stay with us for the rest of his days. That was to teach my daughter French, if possible. I had asked it more to relieve him of an undue sense of gratitude than for any deep concern about the child's acquisition of French. All she ever learned during his stay with us was *Oui* and *Non,* and *Bon jour, Monsieur Moricand!* He seemed to have no use for children; they annoyed him, unless they were extremely well behaved. As with most people who stress behavior, being well behaved meant keeping out of sight and reach. He was utterly at a loss to understand my preoccupation with the child, the daily walks we took, the efforts I made to amuse, entertain and instruct her, the patience with which I listened to her idiotic questions, her excessive demands. He had no idea, naturally, of the joy she gave me. It was obvious, but perhaps he did not wish to recognize it, that she was my only joy. Val always came first. It irritated everyone, not only Moricand. And particularly my wife. The opinion roundabout was that I was an aging dolt who was spoiling his only child. Outwardly it did indeed seem so. The reality which underlay the situation, or the relationship, I hesitated to reveal even to my intimate friends. It was ironic, to be sure, that the very ones who levelled these reproaches were guilty of doing the same silly things, of showing the same exaggerated affection, for their pets. As for Val, she was my own flesh and blood, the apple of my eye; my only regret was that I could not give her more time and attention.

It was about this time that the little mothers all became inter-

ested in the dance. Some went in for singing too. Very fine.
Commendable, as we say. But what about the children? Were they
also taught to sing and dance? Not a bit. That would come later,
when they were old enough to be sent to the ballet class or
whatever the fad might be which the little mothers deemed indispensable in the cultural advancement of their progeny. The mothers were too busy at the moment cultivating their own latent
talents.

There came a day when I taught Val her first song. We were
marching home through the woods; I had hoisted her on my
shoulders to save her weary little legs. Suddenly she asked me to
sing. "What would you like?" I said, and then I gave her that
feeble joke of Abraham Lincoln about knowing only two songs:
one was "Yankee Doodle," the other wasn't.

"Sing it!" she begged.

I did, and with a vengeance. She joined in. By the time we
arrived home she knew the verse by heart. I was supremely
delighted. We had to sing it over and over, naturally. It was Yankee
Doodle this and Yankee Doodle that. Yankee Doodle dandy and
the Devil take the hindmost!

Moricand took not the slightest interest in such diversions.
"Poor Miller!" he probably said to himself, meaning what a
ridiculous figure I could cut.

Poor Val! How it cut me when, endeavoring to have a few words
with him, she would get for rebuff: "I speak no English."

At table she annoyed him incessantly with her silly chatter,
which I found delicious, and her poor table manners.

"She ought to be disciplined," he would say. "It's not good for
a child to receive so much attention."

My wife, being of the same mind, would chime in like a clock.
She would bemoan the fact that I frustrated all her efforts in this
direction, would make it appear that I took a diabolical pleasure in
seeing the child misbehave. She could not admit, naturally, that
her own spirit was of cast iron, that discipline was her only
recourse.

"He believes in *freedom*," she would say, making the idea of
freedom sound like utter rubbish.

To which Moricand would rejoin: "Yes, the American child is a
little barbarian. In Europe the child knows its place. Here the child
rules."

All too true, alas! And yet. . . . What he forgot to add is what
every intelligent European knows, what he himself knew only too
well and had admitted many times, namely, that in Europe, especially *his* Europe, the child becomes an adult long before his time,

that he is disciplined to death, that he is given an education which is not only "barbarous" but cruel, crazy, stultifying, that stern, disciplinary measures *may* make well-behaved children but seldom emancipated adults. He forgot, moreover, to say what his own childhood had been like, to explain what discipline, good manners, refinement, education had done for him.

To exculpate himself in *my* eyes he would wind up by explaining to my wife that I was a born anarchist, that my sense of freedom was a peculiarly personal one, that the very idea of discipline was abhorrent to my nature. I was a rebel and an outlaw, a spiritual freak, so to say. My function in life was to create disturbance. Adding very soberly that there was need for such as me. Then, as if carried away, he would proceed to rectify the picture. It was also a fact, he had to admit, that I was too good, too kind, too gentle, too patient, too indulgent, too forbearing, too forgiving. As if this balanced the violence, the ruthlessness, the recklessness, the treachery of my essential being. At this point he might even say that I *was* capable of understanding discipline, since, as he put it, my ability to write was based on the strictest kind of self-discipline.

"*C'est un être bien compliqué,*" he would conclude. "Fortunately, I understand him. I know him inside out." With this he would press his thumb against the table top, as if squashing a louse. That was *me* under his thumb, the anomaly which he had studied, analyzed, dissected, and could interpret when occasion demanded.

Often an evening that began suspiciously would end in an involved discussion of our domestic problems, something which I abhorred but which wives seem to enjoy, particularly when they have a sympathetic listener. Since I had long resigned myself to the futility of arriving at any understanding with my wife through discussion—I might as well have talked to a stone wall—I limited my participation to rectifying falsehoods and distortions of fact. For the most part I presented an adamant silence. Quite aware that there are always two sides to the picture, poor Moricand would struggle to shift the discussion to more fundamental grounds.

"One gets nowhere with a type like Miller," he would say to my wife. "He does not think in the way you and I do. He thinks in circular fashion. He has no logic, no sense of measure, he is contemptuous of reason and common sense."

He would then proceed to describe to her *her* virtues and defects, in order to demonstrate why we could never see eye to eye, she and I. "But I understand you both. I can act as arbiter. I know how to put the puzzle together."

As a matter of fact, he was quite correct in this. He proved to be a most excellent referee. In his presence, what might have ended in explosions ended only in tears or mute perplexity. Often, when I prayed that he would grow weary and take leave of us for the night, I could sense my wife doing the very opposite. Her only chance of talking with me, or at me, was in his presence. Alone we were either at one another's throats or giving each other the silence. Moricand often succeeded in lifting these furious and prolonged arguments, which had become routine, to another level; he helped us, momentarily at least, to isolate our thoughts, survey them dispassionately, examine them from other angles, free them of their obsessive nature. It was on such occasions that he made good use of his astrological wisdom, for nothing can be more cool and objective, more soothing and staying to the victim of emotion, than the astrological picture of his plight.

Not every evening was spent in argument and discussion, to be sure. The best evenings were those in which we gave him free rein. After all, the monologue was his forte. If by chance we touched on the subject of painting—he had begun life as a painter—we were sure to be richly rewarded for hearing him out. Many of the now celebrated figures in French art he had known intimately. Some he had befriended in his days of opulence. His anecdotes concerning what I choose to call the golden period—the two or three decades leading up to the appearance of *les Fauves*—were delicious in the sense that a rich meal is delicious. They were always spiced with uncanny observations that did not lack a certain diabolical charm. For me this period was fraught with vital interest. I had always felt that I was born twenty or thirty years too late, always regretted that I had not first visited Europe (and remained there) as a young man. Seen it *before* the First World War, I mean. What would I not give to have been the comrade or bosom friend of such figures as Apollinaire, Douanier Rousseau, George Moore, Max Jacob, Vlaminck, Utrillo, Derain, Cendrars, Gauguin, Modigliani, Cingria, Picabia, Maurice Magre, Léon Daudet, and such like. How much greater would have been the thrill to cycle along the Seine, cross and recross her bridges, race through towns like Bougival, Châtou, Argenteuil, Marly-le-roi, Puteaux, Rambouillet, Issy-les-Moulineaux and similar environs circa 1910 rather than the year 1932 or 1933! What a difference it would have made to see Paris from the top of a horse-drawn omnibus at the age of twenty-one! Or to view the *grands boulevards* as a *flâneur* in the period made famous by the Impressionists!

Moricand could summon all the splendor and misery of this epoch at will. He could induce that *"nostalgie de Paris"* which Carco is so adept at, which Aragon, Léon-Paul Fargue, Daudet,

Duhamel and so many French writers have given us time and again. It needed only the mention of a street name, a crazy monument, a restaurant or cabaret which exists no more, to start the wheels turning. His evocations were even more piquant to me because he had seen it all through the eyes of a snob. However much he had particiapted, he had never suffered as did the men he spoke of. His sufferings were to come only when those who had not been killed in the war or committed suicide or gone insane had become famous. Did he ever imagine in his days of opulence, I wonder, that the time would come when he would be obliged to beg his poor friend Max Jacob for a few sous—Max who had renounced the world and was living like an ascetic? A terrible thing to come down in the world when your old friends are rising on the horizon like stars, when the world itself, once a playground, has become a shabby carnival, a cemetery of dreams and illusions.

How he loathed the Republic and all it represented! Whenever he made mention of the French Revolution it was as if he were face to face with evil itself. Like Nostradamus, he dated the deterioration, the blight, the downfall from the day *le peuple—la canaille,* in other words—took over. It is strange, now that I come to think of it, that he never once spoke of Gilles de Rais. Any more than he ever spoke of Ramakrishna, Milarepa, or St. Francis. Napoleon, yes. Bismarck, yes. Voltaire, yes. Villon, yes. And Pythagoras, of course. The whole Alexandrian world was as familiar and vivid to him as if he had known it in a previous incarnation. The Manichean world of thought was also a reality to him. Of Zoroastrian teachings he dwelt by predilection on that aspect which proclaims "the reality of evil." Possibly he also believed that Ormuzd would eventually prevail over Ahriman, but if so it was an eventuality only realizable in a distant future, a future so distant as to render all speculation about it, or even hope in it, futile. No, the reality of evil was undoubtedly the strongest conviction he held. He was so aware of it, indeed, that he could enjoy nothing to the full; actively or passively he was always exorcising the evil spirits which pervade every phase, rung and sphere of life.

One evening, when we had touched on things close to his heart, he asked me suddenly if I had lost all interest in astrology. "You never mention it any more," he said.

"True," I replied. "I don't see what it would serve me to pursue it further. I was never interested in it the way you are. For me it was just another language to learn, another keyboard to manipulate. It's only the poetic aspect of anything which really interests me. In the ultimate there is only one language—the language of truth. It matters little how we arrive at it."

I forget what his reply to this was precisely, only that it conveyed a veiled reproach for my continued interest in Oriental thought. I was too absorbed in abstract speculations, he hinted. Too Germanic, possibly. The astrologic approach was a corrective I stood in need of. It would help to integrate, orient, and organize much in me that was *flou* and chaotic. There was always a danger, with a type like me, of becoming either a saint or a fanatic.

"Not a lunatic, eh?"

"Jamais!"

"But something of a fool! Is that it?"

His answer was—Yes and No. I had a strong religious strain, a metaphysical bent. There was more than a touch of the Crusader in me. I was both humble and arrogant, a penitent and an Inquisitioner. And so on.

· "And you think a deeper knowledge of astrology would help overcome these tendencies?"

"I would not put it exactly like that," he said. "I would say simply that it would help you to see more clearly . . . see into the nature of your problems."

"But I have no problems," I replied. "Unless they are cosmological ones. I am at peace with myself—and with the world. It's true, I don't get along with my wife. But neither did Socrates, for that matter. Or. . . ."

He stopped me.

"All right," I said, "tell me this—what has astrology done for *you?* Has it enabled you to correct your defects? Has it helped you to adjust to the world? Has it given you peace and joy? Why do you scratch yourself like a madman?"

The look he gave me was enough to tell me that I had hit below the belt.

"I'm sorry," I said, "but you know that I'm often rude and direct for a good reason. I don't mean to belittle you or make fun of you. But here's what I would like to know. Answer me straight! What is the most important—peace and joy or wisdom? If to know less would make you a happier man, which would you choose?"

I might have known his answer. It was that we have no choice in such matters.

I violently disagreed. "Perhaps," said I, "I am still very much of an American. That is to say, naive, optimistic, gullible. Perhaps all I gained from the fruitful years I spent in France was a strengthening and deepening of my own inner spirit. In the eyes of a European, what am I but an American to the core, an American who exposes his Americanism like a sore. Like it or not, I am a product of this land of plenty, a believer in superabundance, a believer in miracles. Any deprivation I suffered was my own doing. I blame nobody but myself for my woes and afflictions, for my shortcomings, for my transgressions. What you believe I might have learned through a deeper knowledge of astrology I learned through experience of life. I made all the mistakes that it is possible for a man to make—and I paid the penalty. I am that much richer, that much wiser, that much happier, if I may say so, than if I had found through study or through discipline how to avoid the snares and pitfalls in my path. . . . Astrology deals in potentialities, does it not? I am not interested in the potential man. I am interested in what a man actualizes—or realizes—of his potential being. And what is the potential man, after all? Is he not the sum of all that is human? *Divine,* in other words? You think I am searching for God. I am not. God is. The world is. Man is. We are. The full reality, that's God—and man, and the world, and all that is, including the unnameable. I'm for reality. More and more reality. I'm a fanatic about it, if you like. And what is astrology? What has it to do with reality? Something, to be sure. So has astronomy, so has biology, so has mathematics, so has music, so has literature; and so have the cows in the field and the flowers and the weeds, and the manure that brings them back to life. In some moods some things seem more important than others. Some things have value, others don't, we say. *Everything* is important and of value. Look at it that way and I'll accept your astrology. . . ."

"You're in one of your moods again," he said, shrugging his shoulders.

"I know it," I replied. "Just be patient with me. You'll have your turn. . . . Every so often I revolt, even against what I believe in with all my heart. I have to attack everything, myself included. Why? To simplify things. We know too much—and too little. It's the intellect which gets us into trouble. Not our intelligence. *That* we can never have enough of. But I get weary of listening to specialists, weary of listening to the man with one string to his fiddle. I don't deny the validity of astrology. What I object to is becoming enslaved to any one point of view. Of course there are affinities, analogies, correspondences, a heavenly rhythm and an earthly rhythm . . . *as above, so below.* It would all be crazy if it weren't so. But knowing it, accepting it, why not forget it? I mean, make it a living part of one's life, something absorbed, assimilated and distributed through every pore of one's being, and thus forgot-ten, altered, utilized in the spirit and the service of life. I abhor people who have to filter everything through the one language they know, whether it be astrology, religion, yoga, politics, economics or what. The one thing about this universe of ours which intrigues me, which makes me realize that it *is* divine and beyond all knowing, is that it lends itself so easily to any and all interpretations. Everything we formulate about it is correct and incorrect at the same time. It includes our truths and our errors. And, whatever we think about the universe in no way alters it. . . .

"Let me get back to where I started. We all have different lives to lead. We all want to make conditions as smooth and harmonious for ourselves as possible. We all want to extract the full measure of life. Must we go to books and teachers, to science, religion, philosophy, must we know so much—and so little!—to take the path? Can we not become fully awake and aware without the torture we put ourselves through?"

"Life is nothing but a Calvary," he said. "Not even a knowledge of astrology can alter that stern fact."

"What about the exceptions? Surely. . . ."

"There are no exceptions," he replied. "Everyone, even the most enlightened, has his private griefs and torments. Life is perpetual struggle, and struggle entails sorrow and suffering. And suffering gives us strength and character."

"For what? To what end?"

"The better to endure life's burdens."

"What a woeful picture! It's like training for a contest in which one knows in advance he will be defeated."

"There is such a thing as renunciation," he said.

"But is it a solution?"

"For some Yes, for others No. Sometimes one has no choice."

"In your honest opinion, do we ever really have what is called choice?"

He thought a moment before answering.

"Yes, I believe we do have a measure of choice, but much less than people think. Within the limits of our destiny we are free to choose. It is here precisely that astrology is of great importance: when you realize the conditions under which you have come into the world, which astrology makes clear, you do not choose the unchooseable."

"The lives of great men," said I, "would seem to tell us the opposite."

"As you say, *so it would seem*. But if one examines their horoscopes one is impressed by the fact that they could scarcely have chosen other than they did. What one chooses or wills is always in accordance with one's character. Faced with the same dilemma, a Napoleon would act one way, and a St. Paul another."

"Yes, yes, I know all that," I interrupted. "And I also know, or believe, that St. Francis would have been St. Francis, St. Paul St.

Paul, and Napoleon Napoleon, even if they had had a profound knowledge of astrology. To understand one's problems, to be able to look into them more deeply, to eliminate the unnecessary ones, none of that really interests me any longer. Life as a burden, life as a battleground, life as a problem—these are all partial ways of looking at life. Two lines of poetry often tell us more, give us more, than the weightiest tome by an erudite. To make anything truly significant one has to poetize it. The only way I get astrology, or anything else, for that matter, is as poetry, as music. If the astrological view brings out new notes, new harmonies, new vibrations, it has served its purpose—for me. Knowledge weighs one down; wisdom saddens one. The love of truth has nothing to do with knowledge or wisdom: it's beyond their domains. Whatever certitude one possesses is beyond the realm of proof.

"The saying goes, 'It takes all kinds to make a world.' Precisely. The same does not hold for views or opinions. Put all the pictures together, all the views, all the philosophies, and you do not get a totality. The sum of all these angles of visions do not and never will make truth. The sum of all knowledge is greater confusion. The intellect runs away with itself. Mind is not intellect. The intellect is a product of the ego, and the ego can never be stilled, never be satisfied. When do we begin to know that we know? When we have ceased to believe that we can ever know. Truth comes with surrender. And it's wordless. The brain is not the mind; it is a tyrant which seeks to dominate the mind.

"What has all this to do with astrology? Nothing perhaps, and yet everything. To you I am an illustration of a certain kind of Capricorn; to an analyst I'm something else; to a Marxist another kind of specimen, and so on. What's all that to *me?* What does it concern me how your photographic apparatus registers? To see a person whole and for what he is one has to use another kind of camera; one has to have an eye that is even more objective than the camera's lens. One has to see through the various facets whose brilliant reflections blind us to the real nature of an individual. The more we learn the less we know; the more equipment we have the less we are able to see. It's only when we stop trying to see, stop trying to know, that we really see and know. What sees and knows has no need of spectacles and theories. All our striving and struggling is in the nature of confession. It is a way of reminding ourselves that we are weak, ignorant, blind, helpless. Whereas we are *not.* We are as little or as much as we permit ourselves to think we are.

"Sometimes I think that astrology must have had its inception at a moment in man's evolution when he lost faith in himself. Or, to put it another way, when he lost his wholeness. When he wanted to know instead of to be. Schizophrenia began far back, not yesterday or the day before. And when man split he split into myriad fragments. But even today, as fragmented as he is, he can be made whole again. The only difference between the Adamic man and the man of today is that the one was born to Paradise and the other has to create it. And that brings me back to the question of choice. A man can only prove that he is free by electing to be so. And he can only do so when he realizes that he himself made himself unfree. And that to me means that he must wrest from God the powers he has given God. The more of God he recognizes in himself the freer he becomes. And the freer he becomes the fewer decisions he has to make, the less choice is presented to him. Freedom is a misnomer. Certitude is more like it. Unerringness. Because truthfully there is always only one way to act in any situation, not two, nor three. Freedom implies choice and choice exists only to the extent that we are aware of our ineptitude. The adept takes no thought, one might say. He is one with thought, one with the path.

"It seems as if I were straying far afield. I'm not, really. I'm merely talking another language. I'm saying that peace and joy is within everyone's province. I'm saying that our essential being is godlike. I'm saying that there are no limitations, either to thought or action. I'm saying that we're one, not many. I'm saying that we are there, that we never could be anywhere else except through negation. I'm saying that to see differences is to make differences. A Capricorn is a Capricorn only to another astrologer. Astrology makes use of a few planets, of the sun and the moon, but what of the millions of other planets, other universes, all the stars, the comets, the meteors, the asteroids? Does distance count, or size, or radiance? Is not all one, interactive, interpenetrating? Who dares to say where influences begin and leave off? Who dares to say what is important and what is not? Who owns this universe? Who regulates it? Whose spirit informs it? If we need help, guidance, directions, why not go straight to the source? And what do we want help, guidance and direction for? To make things more comfortable for ourselves, to be more efficient, to better achieve our ends? Why is everything so complicated, so difficult, so obscure, so unsatisfactory? Because we have made ourselves the center of the universe, because we want everything to work out as we wish it. What we need to discover is what *it* wishes, call *it* life, mind, God, whatever you please. If that is the purpose of astrology, I am all for it.

"There's something else I would like to say, to finish with the subject once and for all. It's about our everyday problems, principally the problem of getting along with one another, which seems to be the main problem. What I say is, if we are going to meet one another with a view or an awareness of our diversity and divergences we will never acquire enough knowledge to deal with one another smoothly and effectively. To get anywhere with another individual one has to cut through to the rock-bottom man, to that common human substratum which exists in all of us. This is not a difficult procedure and certainly doesn't demand of one that he be a psychologist or a mind reader. One doesn't have to know a thing about astrological types, the complexity of their reactions to this or that. There is one simple, direct way to deal with all types, and that is truthfully and honestly. We spend our lives trying to avoid the injuries and humiliations which our neighbors may inflict upon us. A waste of time. If we abandoned fear and prejudice, we could meet the murderer as easily as the saint. I get fed up with astrological parlance when I observe people studying their charts to find a way out of illness, poverty, vice, or whatever it may be. To me it seems like a sorry attempt to exploit the stars. We talk about fate as if it were something visited upon us; we forget that we create our fate every day we live. And by fate I mean the woes that beset us, which are merely the effects of causes which are not nearly as mysterious as we pretend. Most of the ills we suffer from are directly traceable to our own behavior. Man is not suffering from the ravages wrought by earthquakes and volcanoes, by tornadoes and tidal waves; he is suffering from his own misdeeds, his own foolishness, his own ignorance and disregard of natural laws. Man can eliminate war, can eliminate disease, can eliminate old age and probably death too. He need not live in poverty, vice, ignorance, in rivalry and competition. All these conditions are within his province, within his power, to alter. But he can never alter them as long as he is concerned solely with his own individual fate. Imagine a physician refusing his services because of danger of infection or contamination! We are all members of the one body, as the Bible says. And we are all at war with one another. Our own physical body possesses a wisdom which we who inhabit the body lack. We give it orders which make no sense. There is no mystery about disease, nor crime, nor war, nor the thousand and one things which plague us. Live simply and wisely. Forget, forgive, renounce, abdicate. Do I need to study my horoscope to understand the wisdom of such simple behavior? Do I have to live with yesterday in order to enjoy tomorrow? Can I not scrap the past instantly, begin at once to live the good life—if I really mean to? *Peace and joy.* . . . I say it's ours for the asking. Day by day, that's good enough for me. Not even that, in fact. Just today! *Le bel aujourd'hui!* Wasn't that the title of one of Cendrars' books? Give me a better one, if you can. . . ."

Naturally, I did not deliver this harangue all in one breath, nor exactly in these words. Perhaps much of it I merely imagine that I said. No matter. I say it now as of then. It was all there in my mind, not once, but repeatedly. Take it for what it's worth.

With the coming of the first good rain he began to grow despondent. It's true that his cell was tiny, that water leaked through the roof and the windows, that the sow bugs and other bugs took over, that they often dropped on his bed when he was asleep, that to keep warm he had to use an ill-smelling oil stove which consumed what little oxygen remained after he had sealed up all the cracks and crevices, stuffed the space beneath the door with sacking, shut all the windows tight, and so on. It's true that it was a winter in which we got more than our usual share of rain, a winter in which the storms broke with fury and lasted for days on end. And he, poor devil, was cooped up all day, restless, ill at ease, either too hot or too cold, scratching, scratching, and utterly incapable of warding off the hundred and one abominations which materialized out of the ether, for how else explain the presence of all these creeping, crawling, ugly things when all had been shut tight, sealed and fumigated?

I shall never forget his look of utter bewilderment and distress when he called me to his room one late afternoon to inspect the lamps. "Look," he said, striking a match and applying the flame to the wick. "Look, it goes out every time."

Now Aladdin lamps are quixotic and temperamental, as country people know. They have to be kept in perfect condition to function properly. Just to trim the wick neatly is in itself a delicate operation. Of course I had explained things to him a number of times, but every time I visited him I noticed that the lamps were dim or smoking. I knew too that he was too annoyed with them to bother keeping them in condition.

Striking a match and holding it against the wick, I was just about to say, "You see, it's simple . . . nothing to it"—when, to my surprise, the wick refused to ignite. I lit another and another, and still the wick refused to take fire. It was only when I reached for a candle and saw how it spluttered that I realized what was wrong.

I opened the door to let in some air and then tried the lamp again. It worked. "Air, my friend. You need air!" He looked at me in amazement. To get air he would have to keep a window open. And that would let the wind and rain in. *"C'est emmerdant!"* he exclaimed. It was indeed. It was worse than that. I had visions of finding him in bed one fine morning—suffocated.

Eventually he devised his own method of getting just enough air. By means of a string and a series of hooks inserted at intervals into the upper half of the Dutch door he could obtain as little or as much air as he chose. It was not necessary to open a window or remove the sacking beneath the door or dig out the putty with which he had sealed the various cracks and crevices in the walls. As for the bloody lamps, he decided that he would use candles instead. The candles gave his cell a mortuary look which suited his morbid state of mind.

Meanwhile the itch continued to plague him. Every time he came down for meals he rolled up his sleeves or the legs of his trousers to show us the ravages it had made. His flesh was by now a mass of running sores. Had I been in his boots I would have put a bullet through my brain.

Obviously something had to be done or we would all go crazy. We had tried all the old-fashioned remedies—to no avail. In desperation I begged a friend who lived some few hundred miles away to make a special trip. He was a capable all-round physician, a surgeon and a psychiatrist to boot. He also knew some French. In fact, he was an altogether unusual fellow, and generous and frank. I knew that he would give me good advice if he could not cope with the case.

Well, he came. He examined Moricand from head to toe and inside out. That done, he engaged him in talk. He paid no further heed to the running sores, made no further mention of the subject. He talked about all manner of things but not about the itch. It was as if he had completely forgotten what he had been summoned for. Now and then Moricand attempted to remind him of the object of his visit but my friend always succeeded in diverting his attention to some other subject. Finally he made ready to leave, after writing out a prescription which he left under Moricand's nose.

I escorted him to the car, eager to know what he really thought.

"There's nothing to do," he said. "When he stops thinking about it the itch will disappear."

"And in the meantime. . . ?"

"Let him take the pills."

"Will they really help?"

"That depends on *him*. There's nothing in them to hurt him, or to do him any good. Unless he believes so."

There was a heavy pause.

Suddenly he said: "Do you want my honest advice?"

"I certainly do," said I.

"Then get him off your hands!"

"What do you mean?"

"Just that. You might as well have a leper living with you."

I must have looked sorely puzzled.

"It's simple," he said. "He doesn't want to get well. What he wants is sympathy, attention. He's not a man, he's a child. A spoiled child."

Another pause.

"And don't worry if he threatens to do himself in. He'll probably pull that on you when everything else fails. He won't kill himself. He loves himself too much."

"I see," said I. "So that's how it stands. . . . But what in hell will I tell him?"

"That I leave to you, old pal." He started up the motor.

"O.K." I said. "Maybe I'll take the pills myself. Anyway, a thousand thanks!"

Moricand was lying in wait for me. He had been studying the prescription but could make nothing of it, the handwriting was too abominable.

In a few words I explained that in my friend's opinion his ailment was psychological.

"Any fool knows that!" he blurted out and in the next breath— "Is he really a doctor?"

"A quite famous one," I answered.

"Strange," said Moricand. "He talked like an imbecile."

"OH?"

"Asking me if I still masturbated."

"*Et puis. . .?*

"If I liked women as much as men. If I had ever taken drugs. If I believed in emanations. If, if, if. . . . *C'est un fou!*"

For a minute or two he was speechless with rage. Then, in a tone of utter misery, he muttered as if to himself: *"Mon Dieu, mon Dieu, qu'est-ce que je peux faire? Comme je suis seul, tout seul!"*

"Come, come," I murmured, "calm youself! There are worse things than the itch."

"Like what?" he demanded. He said it with such swiftness that I was taken aback.

"Like what?" he repeated. *"Psychological . . . pouah!* He must take me for an idiot. What a country this is! No humanity. No understanding. No intelligence. Ah, if only I could die . . . die tonight!"

I said not a word.

"May you never suffer, *mon cher Miller,* as I am suffering! The war was nothing compared to this."

Suddenly his glance fell on the prescription. He picked it up, clenched it in his fist, then threw it on the floor.

"*Pills!* He gives *me,* Moricand, pills! Bah!" He spat on the floor. "He's a quack, your friend. A charlatan. An impostor."

Thus ended the first attempt to pull him out of his misery.

A week passed and then who should turn up but my old friend Gilbert. Ah, I thought, at last someone who speaks French, someone who loves French literature. What a treat for Moricand!

Over a bottle of wine I had no difficulty in getting them to talk to one another. It was only a matter of a few minutes before they were discussing Baudelaire, Villon, Voltaire, Gide, Cocteau, *les ballets russes, Ubu Roi,* and so forth. When I saw that they were hitting it off nicely I discreetly withdrew, hoping that Gilbert who had also suffered the afflictions of Job, would raise the other's morale. Or at least get him drunk.

An hour or so later, as I was sauntering down the road with the dog, Gilbert drove up.

"What, going so soon?" I said. It was unlike Gilbert to leave before the last bottle had been emptied.

"I've had a bellyfull," he replied. "What a prick!"

"Who, Moricand?"

"Exactly."

"What happened?"

By way of answer he gave me a look of sheer disgust.

"Do you know what I'd do with him, *amigo?*" he said vengefully.

"No, what?"

"Push him over the cliff."

"That's easier said than done."

"Try it! It's the best solution." With that he stepped on the gas.

Gilbert's words gave me a shock. It was altogether unlike him to talk that way about another person. He was such a kind, gentle, considerate soul, had been through such hell himself. Obviously it hadn't taken long for him to see through Moricand.

Meanwhile my good friend Lilik, who had rented a shack a few miles down the road, was doing his utmost to make Moricand more at home. Moricand liked Lilik and had implicit faith in him. He could hardly feel otherwise, since Lilik did nothing but render him services. Lilik would sit with him by the hour, listening to his tales of woe.

From Lilik I gleaned that Moricand thought I was not paying him enough attention. "You never inquire about his work," he said.

"His work? What do you mean? What is he working at?"

"I believe he's writing his memoirs."

"That's interesting," I said. "I must have a look some time."

"By the way," said Lilik, "have you ever seen his drawings?"

"What drawings?"

"My God, haven't you seen them yet? He's got a whole stack of them in his portfolio. Erotic drawings. Lucky for you," he chuckled, "that the customs men didn't discover them."

"Are they any good?"

"Yes and no. They're certainly not for children to look at."

A few days after this conversation took place, an old friend turned up. Leon Shamroy. As usual, he was loaded with gifts. Mostly things to eat and drink.

This time Moricand opened his falcon eyes even wider.

"It's staggering," he murmured. He drew me to one side. "A millionaire, I suppose?"

"No, just the head camera man for the Fox Films. The man who wins all the Oscars."

"I only wish you could understand his talk," I added. "There's no one in all America who can say the things he says and get away with it."

Just then Leon broke in. "What's all the whispering about?" he demanded. "Who is this guy—one of your Montparnasse friends? Doesn't he talk English? What's he doing here? Sponging on you, I'll bet. Give him a drink! He looks bored—or sad.

"Here, let him try one of these," said Leon, fishing a handful of cigars out of his breast pocket. "They only cost a dollar apiece. Maybe he'll get a kick out of them."

He nodded to Moricand to indicate that the cigars were for him. With that he threw away the half-finished Havana he had allowed to go out and lit a fresh one. The cigars were almost a foot long and thick as seven-year-old rattlers. They had a beautiful aroma too. Cheap at twice the price, thought I to myself.

"Tell him I don't talk French," said Leon, slightly annoyed because Moricand had expressed his thanks in long-winded French. As he spoke he undid a package out of which spilled some luscious-looking cheeses, some salami and some *lachs*. Over his shoulder: "Tell him we like to eat and drink. We'll chew the rag later. Hey, where's that wine I brought? No, wait a minute. I've got a bottle of Haig and Haig in the car. Let's give him that. The poor bugger, I'll bet he's never had a tumbler of whisky in his life. . . . Listen, what's the matter with him? Doesn't he ever crack a smile?"

He went on sputtering like that, opening more parcels, cutting himself a hunk of corn bread, buttering it with delicious sweet butter, spearing an olive, tasting an anchovy, then a sour pickle, a little of this, a little of that, at the same time unearthing a box of sweets for Val, together with a beautiful dress, a string of beads and . . . *"Here,* this is for *you,* you bastard!" and he flung me a tin of expensive cigarettes. "I've got more for you up in the car. By the way, I forgot to ask you—how are things going with you? Haven't made your pile yet, have you? You and Bufano! A couple of orphans. Lucky you have a friend like me . . . someone who *works* for a living, what?"

Meanwhile Lilik had gone to the car and brought things down. We opened the Haig and Haig, then a beautiful brand of Bordeaux for Moricand (and for ourselves), looked appraisingly at the Pernod and the Chartreuse which he had also thought to bring. The air was already thick with smoke, the floor littered with paper and string.

"Is that shower of yours still working," asked Leon, unbuttoning his silk shirt. "I've got to take one soon. Haven't had any sleep for thirty-six hours. Christ, am I glad to get away for a few hours! By the way, can you bunk me for the night? Maybe two nights? I want to talk to you. We've got to make some real dough for you soon. You don't want to be a beggar all your life, do you? Don't answer! I know what you're going to say. . . . By the way, where are your water colors? Drag 'em out! You know me. I may buy a half dozen before I leave. If they're any good, I mean."

Suddenly he noticed Moricand was pulling on a cheroot.

"What's the matter with that guy?" he shouted. "What's he got that stink weed in his mouth for? Didn't we just give him some good cigars?"

Moricand explained blushingly that he was reserving the cigars for later. They were too good to smoke immediately. He wanted to fondle them a while before lighting up.

"Fuck that nonsense!" cried Leon. "Tell him he's in America now. We don't worry about tomorrow, do we? Tell him when he finishes those I'll send him a box from L.A." He turned his head away, lowered his voice a trifle, "What's griping him anyway? Has he been starved to death over there? Anyway, the hell with him! Look, I want to tell you a little joke I heard the other night. Translate it for him, will you? I want to see if he'll laugh."

My wife is making a vain attempt to set the table. Leon has already embarked on his little joke, a filthy one, and Lilik is farting like a stallion. In the middle of his tale Leon pauses to cut himself another hunk of bread, pour a drink, take off his shoes and socks, spear an olive, and so on. Moricand watches him goggle-eyed. A new specimen of humanity for him. *Le vrai type américain, quoi!*

I have a suspicion he's really enjoying himself. Sampling the Bordeaux, he smacks his lips. The *lachs* intrigues him. As for the corn bread, he's never seen or tasted it before. Famous! *Ausgezeichnet!*

Lilik's laughing so hard the tears are rolling down his cheeks. It's a good joke, and a filthy one, but difficult to translate.

"What's the trouble?" says Leon. "Don't they use that kind of language where he comes from?"

He observes Moricand diving into the viands, sipping his wine, trying to puff away at the huge Havana.

"O.K. Forget the joke! He's filling his belly, that's good enough. Listen, what did you say he was again?"

"Among other things an astrologer," I said.

"He doesn't know his ass from a hole in the ground. *Astrology!* Who wants to listen to that shit? Tell him to get wise to himself. . . . Hey, wait a minute, I'll give him my birth date. Let's see what he makes of it."

I give the dope to Moricand. He says he's not ready yet. Wants to observe Leon a little longer, if we don't mind.

"What did he say?"

"He says he wants to enjoy his food first. But he knows that you're an exceptional type." I added this to relieve the tension.

"He said a mouthful there. You're damned right I'm an exceptional type. Anyone else in my place would go crazy. Tell him for me that I've got his number, will you?" Then, turning directly to Moricand, he says: "How's the wine . . . the *vin rouge?* Good stuff, what?"

"Epatant!" says Moricand, unaware of all the innuendoes that had passed under his nose.

"You bet your ass it's good," says Leon. *"I* bought it. I know good stuff when I see it."

He watches Moricand as if his nibs were a trained otter, then turns to me. "Does he do anything else beside read the stars?" Giving me a reproachful look, he adds: "I'll bet he likes nothing better than to sit on his fat fanny all day. Why don't you put him to work? Get him to dig a garden, plant vegetables, hoe the weeds. That's what he needs. I know these bastards. They're all alike."

My wife was getting uncomfortable. She didn't want Moricand's feelings to be hurt.

"He's got something in his room you'll enjoy seeing," she said to Leon.

"Yeah," said Lilik, "right up your street, Leon."

"What are you trying to pull on me? What's the big secret? Out with it!"

We explained. Leon seemed strangely disinterested.

"Hollywood's full of that crap," he said. "What do you want me to do—*masturbate?*"

The afternoon wore on. Moricand retired to his cell. Leon took us up to inspect his new car, which could do ninety per in nothing flat. Suddenly he remembered that he had some toys for Val in the back of the car. "Where's Bufano these days?" says he, fishing around in the trunk.

"Gone to India, I think."

"To see Nehru, I bet!" He chuckled. "How that guy gets around without a cent in his pockets beats me. By the way, what are *you* doing for money these days?"

With this he dives into his pants pocket, hauls out a wad of greenbacks fastened with a clip, and begins peeling off a few.

"Here, take this," he says, shoving the greenbacks in my fist. "I'll probably owe you money before I leave."

"Have you anything good to read?" he asks suddenly. "Like that Giono book you lent me, remember? What about that guy Cendrars you're always pissing in the pants about? Has any of his stuff been translated yet?" He threw another half-finished Havana away, crushed it under his heel, and lit a fresh one. "I suppose you think I never look at a book. You're wrong. I read plenty. . . . Some day you're going to write a script for me—and earn some real dough. By the way"—he jerked his thumb in the direction of Moricand's studio—"is that guy taking you for a lot of dough? You're a chump. How did you ever fall into the trap?"

I told him it was a long story . . . some other time.

"What about those drawings of his? Should I have a look? He wants to sell them, I suppose? I wouldn't mind taking some—if it would help *you* out. . . . Wait a minute, I want to take a crap first."

When he returned he had a fresh cigar in his mouth. He was looking roseate.

"There's nothing like a good crap," he said, beaming. "Now let's visit that sad-looking bimbo. And fetch Lilik, will you? I want his opinion before I let myself in for anything."

As we entered Moricand's cell Leon sniffed the air. "For Christ's sake, make him open a window!" he exclaimed.

"Can't, Leon. He's afraid of draughts."

"Just like him, for crying out loud. O.K. Tell him to trot his dirty pictures out—and make it snappy, eh? I'll puke up if we have to stay here more than ten minutes."

Moricand proceeded to get out his handsome leather portfolio.

He placed it circumspectly before him, then calmly lit a *gauloise bleue*.

"Ask him to put it out," begged Leon. He drew a pack of Chesterfields from his pocket and offered Moricand one. Moricand politely refused, saying he couldn't stand American cigarettes.

"He's nuts!" said Leon. *"Here!"* and he proffered Moricand a big cigar.

Moricand declined the offer. "I like these better," he said, brandishing his foul French cigarette.

"If that's how it is, fuck it!" said Leon. "Tell him to get going. We can't waste the whole afternoon in this tomb."

But Moricand wasn't to be hurried. He had his own peculiar way of presenting his work. He allowed no one to touch the drawings. He held them in front of him, turning them slowly, page by page, as if they were ancient papyri to be handled with a shovel only. Now and then he drew a silk handkerchief from his breast pocket to remove the perspiration from his hands.

It was my first view of his work. I must confess the drawings left a bad taste in my mouth. They were perverse, sadistic, sacrilegious. Children being raped by lubricious monsters, virgins practicing all manner of illicit intercourse, nuns defiling themselves with sacred objects . . . flagellations, medieval tortures, dismemberments, coprophagic orgies, and so forth. All done with a delicate, sensitive hand, which only magnified the disgusting element of the subject matter.

For once Leon was nonplused. He turned to Lilik inquiringly. Asked to see some of them a second time.

"The bugger knows how to draw, doesn't he?" he remarked.

Lilik hereupon pointed out a few he thought were exceptionally well executed.

"I'll take them," said Leon. "How much?"

Moricand named a price. A stiff one, even for an American client.

"Tell him to wrap them up," said Leon. "They're not worth it, but I'll take them. I know someone would give his right arm to own one."

He fished out his wad, counted the bills rapidly, and shoved them back into his pocket.

"Can't spare the cash," he said. "Tell him I'll send him a check when I get home . . . *if he'll trust me."*

At this point Moricand seemed to undergo a change of heart. Said he didn't want to sell them singly. All or nothing. He named a price for the lot. A whopping price.

"He's mad," shrieked Leon. "Let him stick 'em up his ass!"

I explained to Moricand that Leon would have to think it over.

"Okay," said Moricand, giving me a wry, knowing smile. I knew that in *his* mind the bird was in the bag. A handful of trumps, that's what he was holding. "Okay," he repeated as we took leave of him.

As we sauntered down the steps Leon blurted out: "If the bastard had any brains he'd offer to let me take the portfolio and show them around. I could probably get twice what he's asking. They might get soiled, of course. What a finicky prick!" He gave me a sharp nudge. "That'd be something, wouldn't it, *to dirty that smut!*"

At the foot of the steps he paused a moment and caught me by the arm.

"You know what's the matter with him? He's *sick.*" He touched his cranium with his forefinger.

"When you get rid of him," he added, "you'd better disinfect the place."

Some few nights later, at the dinner table, we at last drifted into the subject of the war. Moricand was in excellent form and only too eager to relate his experiences. Why we had never touched on all this before I don't know. To be sure, in his letters from Switzerland he had given me an outline of all that had taken place since we parted that night in June of 1939. But I had forgotten most of it. I knew that he had joined the Foreign Legion, for the second time, joined it not out of patriotism but to survive. How else was he to obtain food and shelter? He lasted only a few months in the Legion, of course, being altogether unfit for the rigors of that life. Discharged, he had returned to his garret in the Hotel Modial, more desperate, naturally, than ever before. He was in Paris when the Germans marched in. The presence of the Germans didn't bother him as much as the absence of food. At the last ditch he ran into an old friend, a man who held an important post at Radio-Paris. The friend took him on. It meant money, food, cigarettes. An odious job, but. . . . At any rate, the friend was now in prison. A collaborator, evidently.

He rehearsed the whole period again, this evening, and in great detail. As though he felt compelled to get it off his chest. From time to time I lost the thread. Never interested in politics, in feuds, in intrigues and rivalries, I became utterly confused just at the crucial period when, by command of the Germans, he intimated that he had been forced to go to Germany. (They had even picked out a wife for him to marry.) Suddenly the whole picture got out of whack. I lost him in a vacant lot with a Gestapo agent holding a revolver against his spine. It was all an absurd and horrendous nightmare anyway. Whether he had been in the service of the Germans or not—he never defined his position clearly—was all one to me. I wouldn't have minded if he had quietly informed me that he had turned traitor. What I *was* curious about was—how did he manage to get out of the mess? How did it happen that he came off with a whole skin?

Of a sudden I realize that he's telling me of his escape. We're no longer in Germany, but in France . . . or is it Belgium or Luxembourg? He's headed for the Swiss border. Bogged down by two heavy valises which he's been dragging for days and weeks. One day he's between the French Army and the German Army, the next day between the American Army and the German Army. Sometimes its neutral terrain he's traversing, sometimes it's no mans land. Wherever he goes it's the same story: no food, no shelter, no aid. He has to get ill to obtain a little nourishment, a place to flop, and so forth. Finally he really is ill. With a valise in each hand he marches on from place to place, shaking with fever, parched with thirst, dizzy, dopey, desperate. Above the cannonade he can hear his empty guts rattling. The bullets whizz overhead, the stinking dead lie in heaps everywhere, the hospitals are overcrowded, the fruit trees bare, the houses demolished, the roads filled with homeless, sick, crippled, wounded, forlorn, abandoned souls. Every man for himself! War! War! And there he is floundering around in the midst of it: a Swiss neutral with a passport and an empty belly. Now and then an American soldier flings him a cigarette. But no Yardley's talc. No toilet paper. No perfumed soap. And with it all he's got the itch. Not only the itch, but lice. Not only lice, but scurvy.

The armies, all sixty-nine of them, are battling it out around him. They don't seem to care at all for his safety. But the war is definitely coming to an end. It's all over but the mopping up. Nobody knows why he's fighting, nor for whom. The Germans are licked but they won't surrender. Idiots. Bloody idiots. In fact, everybody's licked except the Americans. They, the goofy Americans, are romping through in grand style, their kits crammed with tasty snacks, their pockets loaded with cigarettes, chewing gum, flasks, crap-shooting dice and what not. The highest paid warriors that ever donned uniform. Money to burn and nothing to spend it on. Just praying to get to Paris, praying for a chance to rape the lascivious French girls—or old hags, if there are no girls left. And as they romp along they burn their garbage—while starving civilians watch in horror and stupefaction. *Orders*. Keep moving! Keep liquidating! On, on . . . on to Paris! On to Berlin! On to Moscow!

Swipe what you can, guzzle what you can, rape what you can.
And if you can't, shit on it! But don't beef! Keep going, keep
moving, keep advancing! The end is near. Victory is in sight. Up
with the flag! Hourrah! Hourrah! And fuck the generals, fuck the
admirals! Fuck your way through! Now or never!

What a grand time! What a lousy mess! What horripilating
insanity!

("I am that General So-and-So who is responsible for the death
of so many of your beloved!")

Like a ghost our dear Moricand, by now witless and shitless, is
running the gauntlet, moving like a frantic rat between the opposing armies, skirting them, flanking them, outwitting them, running
head on into them; in his fright speaking good English now and
then, or German, or just plain horseshit, anything to disengage
himself, anything to wiggle free, but always clinging to his saddle-
bags which now weigh a ton, always headed for the Swiss border,
despite detours, loops, hairpin turns, double-eagles, sometimes
crawling on all fours, sometimes walking erect, sometimes smothered under a load of manure, sometimes doing the St. Vitus dance.
Always going forward, unless pushed backward. Finally reaching
the border, only to find that it is blocked. Retracing his steps. Back
to the starting point. Double fire. Diarrhea. Fever and more fever.
Cross-examinations. Vaccinations. Evacuations. New armies to
contend with. New battle fronts. New bulges. New victories. New
retreats. And more dead and wounded, naturally. More vultures.
More unfragrant breezes.

Yet always and anon he manages to hold on to his Swiss
passport, his two valises, his slender sanity, his desperate hope of
freedom.

"And what was in those valises that made them so precious?"

"Everything I cherish," he answered.

"Like what?"

"My books, my diaries, my writings, my. . . ."

I looked at him flabbergasted.

"No, Christ! You don't mean to say. . . ."

"Yes," he said, "just books, papers, horoscopes, excerpts from
Plotinus, Iamblichus, Claude Saint-Martin. . . ."

I couldn't help it, I began to laugh. I laughed and laughed and
laughed. I thought I'd never stop laughing.

He was offended. I apologized.

"You lugged all that crap around like an elephant," I exclaimed,
"at the risk of losing your own hide?"

"A man doesn't throw away everything that is precious to him—
just like that!"

"I would!" I exclaimed.

"But my whole life was bound up in those encumbrances."

"You should have thrown your life away too!"

"Not Moricand!" he replied, and his eyes flashed fire.

Suddenly I no longer felt sorry for him, not for anything that had ever happened to him.

For days those two valises weighed me down. They weighed as heavily on my mind and spirit as they had on Moricand's when he was crawling like a bedbug over that crazy quilt called Europe. I dreamed about them too. Sometimes he appeared in a dream, Moricand, looking like Emil Jannings, the Jannings of *The Last Laugh,* the Grand Hotel porter Jannings, who has been sacked, who has lost his standing, who furtively smuggles his uniform out each night after he has been demoted to attendant in the toilet and washroom. In my dreams I was forever shadowing poor Conrad, always within shouting distance of him yet never able to make him hear me, what with the cannonades, the blitz bombs, the machine-gun fire, the screams of the wounded, the shrieks of the dying. Everywhere war and desolation. Here a shell crater filled with arms and legs; here a warrior still warm, his buttons ripped off, his proud genitals missing; here a freshly bleached skull crawling with bright red worms; a child impaled on a fence post; a gun carriage reeking with blood and vomit; trees standing upside down, dangling with human limbs, an arm to which a hand is still attached, the remains of a hand buried in a glove. Or animals in stampede, their eyes blazing with insanity, their legs a blur, their hides aflame, their bowels hanging out, tripping them, and behind them thousands more, millions of them, all singed, scorched, racked, torn, battered, bleeding, vomiting, racing like mad, racing ahead of the dead, racing for the Jordan, shorn of all medals, passports, halters, bits, bridles, feathers, fur, bills and hollyhocks. And Conrad Moriturus ever ahead, fleeing, his feet shod in patent leather boots, his hair neatly pomaded, his nails manicured, his linen starched, his mustache waxed, his trousers pressed. Galloping on like the Flying Dutchman, his valises swinging like ballast, his cold breath congealing behind him like frozen vapor. *To the border! To the border!*

And that was Europe! A Europe I never saw, a Europe I never tasted. Ah, Iamblichus, Porphyry, Erasmus, Duns Scotus, where are we? What elixir are we drinking? What wisdom are we sucking? Define the alphabet, O wise ones! Measure the itch! Flog insanity to death, if you can! Are those stars looking down upon us, or are they burnt holes in a filament of sick flesh?

And where is General Doppelgänger now, and General Eisenhower, and General Pussyfoot Cornelius Triphammer? Where the enemy? Where is Jack and where is Jill? How I would like to put a message through—to the Divine Creator! But I can't remember the name. I'm so utterly harmless, so innocent. Just a neutral. Nothing to declare but two valises. Yes, a citizen. A quiet sort of madman, nothing more. I ask for no decorations, no monuments in my name. Just see that the bags get through. I'll follow afterwards. I'll be there, even if I'm only a trunk. Moriturus, that's my name. Swiss, yes. A *légionnaire*. *Un mutilé de la guerre*. Call me anything you like. *Iamblichus,* if you wish. Or just—"The Itch"!

Taking advantage of the rainy season, we decided to break ground for a vegetable patch. We chose a spot that had never been dug up before. I began with a pick and my wife continued with the spade. I suppose Moricand felt slightly conscience-stricken to see a woman doing such work. To our surprise, he offered to do some spading himself. After a half-hour he was all in. It made him feel good just the same. In fact, he felt so good that after lunch he asked if we would put on some phonograph records—he was dying to listen to a little music. As he listened he hummed and whistled. He asked if we had any of Grieg's music, *Peer Gynt* particularly. Said he used to play the piano long ago. Played by ear. Then he added that he thought Grieg was a very great composer; he liked him best of all. That knocked me for a loop.

My wife had put on a Viennese waltz. Now he really became animated. All of a sudden he went up to my wife and asked her if she would dance with him. I nearly fell off the chair. Moricand dancing! It seemed incredible. Preposterous. But he did, and with heart and soul. He whirled and whirled around until he got dizzy.

"You dance beautifully," said my wife, as he took a seat, panting and perspiring.

"You're still a young man," I threw in.

"I haven't done this since the year 1920 something," he said almost blushingly. He slapped his thigh. "It's an old carcass but it still has a bit of life."

"Would you like to hear Harry Lauder?" I asked.

For a moment he was perplexed. Lauder, Lauder. . . ? Then he got it.

"Certainly," he said. Obviously he was in a mood to hear anything.

I put on "Roamin' in the Gloamin'." To my amazement he even tried to sing. I thought perhaps he had had a little too much wine at lunch, but no, it wasn't the wine or the food this time, he was just happy for once.

The horrible thing is that it was almost more pitiful to see him happy than sad.

In the midst of these pleasantries Jean Wharton walked in. She was living just above us now in a house which she had recently had built. She had met Moricand once or twice before, but merely to exchange greetings. This day, being in extraordinary good humor, he mustered enough English to carry on a little conversation with her. When she left he remarked that she was a very interesting woman, rather attractive too. He added that she had a magnetic personality, that she radiated health and joy. He thought it might be well to cultivate her acquaintance, she made him feel good.

He felt so good, indeed, that he brought his memoirs down for me to read.

All in all, it was a remarkable day for Moricand. The best day of all, however, was the day Jaime de Angulo came down from his mountain top to pay us a visit. He came expressly to meet Moricand. We had, of course, informed Moricand of Jaime's existence, but we had never made a point of bringing the two together. To tell the truth, I didn't think they would get along very well together, since they seemed to have so little in common. Besides, I was never certain how Jaime would behave after he had a few drinks under his belt. The occasions when he did visit us and leave without making a scene, without cursing, reviling and insulting everyone, were few and far between.

It was shortly after lunch that Jaime rode up, hitched his horse to the oak tree, gave it a punch in the ribs, and descended the steps. It was a bright, sunny day, rather warm for a day in February. As usual, Jaime wore a bright headband around his forehead—his dirty snotrag, probably. Brown as a walnut, gaunt, slightly bowlegged, he was still handsome, still very much the Spaniard—and still utterly unpredictable. With a feather in his headband, a little grease paint, a different costume, he might have passed for a Chippewa or a Shawnee Indian. He was definitely the outlaw.

As they greeted one another I could not help but remark the contrast they presented, these two figures (born only five days apart) who had passed their youth in a sedate, aristocratic quarter of Paris. Two "Little Lord Fauntleroys" who had seen the seamy side of life, whose days were now numbered, and who would never meet again. The one neat, orderly, immaculate, fussy, cautious, a man of the city, a recluse, a stargazer; the other the exact opposite.

The one a pedestrian, the other a cavalier. The one an aesthete, the other a wild duck.

I was wrong in thinking they had so little in common. They had much in common. Aside from a common culture, a common language, a common background, a common love of books, libraries, research, a common gift of speech, a common addiction—the one to drugs, the other to alcohol—they had an even greater tie: their obsession with evil. Jaime was one of the very few men I ever met of whom I could say that he had a streak of the Devil in him. As for Moricand, he had always been a diabolist. The only difference in their attitude toward the Devil was that Moricand feared him and Jaime cultivated him. At least, it always seemed thus to me. Both were confirmed atheists and thoroughly anti-Christian. Moricand leaned toward the antique pagan world, Jaime toward the primitive. Both were what we would call men of culture, men of learning, men of elegance. Jaime, playing the savage or the sot, was still a man of exquisite taste; no matter how much he spat on all that was "refined," he never truly outgrew the Little Lord Fauntleroy he had been as a boy. It was only through dire necessity that Moricand had renounced *la vie mondaine;* at heart he remained the dandy, the fop, the snob.

When I brought out the bottle and the glasses—the bottle only half-full, by the way—I anticipated trouble. It did not seem possible that these two individuals, having traveled such divergent paths, could get along together for long.

I was wrong about everything this day. They not only got along, they scarcely touched the wine. They were intoxicated with something stronger than wine—the past.

The mention of the Avenue Henri-Martin—they had discovered in the space of a few minutes that they had been raised in the very same block!—started the ball rolling. Dwelling on his boyhood, Jaime at once began to mimic his parents, impersonate his schoolmates, re-enact his deviltries, switching from French to Spanish and back again, acting now as a sissy, now as a coy young female, now as an irate Spanish grandee, now as a petulant, doting mother.

Moricand was in stitches. Never did I believe that he could laugh so hard or so long. He was no longer the melancholy grampus, nor even the wise old owl, but a normal, natural human being who was enjoying himself.

Not to intrude on this festival of reminiscence, I threw myself on the bed in the middle of the room and pretended to take a nap.

But my ears were wide open.

In the space of a few short hours it seemed to me that Jaime succeeded in rehearsing the whole of his tumultuous life. And what a life it was! From Passy to the Wild West—in one jump. From being the son of a Spanish grandee, raised in the lap of luxury, to becoming a cowboy, a doctor of medicine, an anthropologist, a master of linguistics, and finally a cattle rancher on the crest of the Santa Lucia range here in Big Sur. A lone wolf, divorced from all he held dear, waging a perpetual feud with his neighbor Boronda, another Spaniard, poring over his books, his dictionaries (Chinese, Sanskrit, Hebrew, Arabic, Persian, to mention but a few), raising a little fruit and vegetables, killing deer in season and out, forever exercising his horses, getting drunk, quarreling with everyone, even his bosom pals, driving visitors away with the lash, studying in the dead of night, coming back to his book on language, *the* book on language, he hoped it would be!—and finishing it just before his death. . . . Between times twice married, three children, one of them his beloved son, crushed to death beneath him in a mysterious automobile accident, a tragedy which had a lasting effect upon him.

Odd to listen to it all from the bed. Strange to hear the so-called shaman talking to the sage, the anthropologist to the astrologer, the scholar to the scholar, the linguist to the bookworm, the horseman to the boulevardier, the adventurer to the hermit, the barbarian to the dandy, the lover of languages to the lover of words, the scientist to the occulist, the desperado to the ex-*Légionnaire,* the fiery Spaniard to the stolid Swiss, the uncouth native to the well-dressed gentleman, the anarchist to the civilized European, the rebel to the well-behaved citizen, the man of the open spaces to the man of the garret, the drunkard to the dope fiend. . . .

Every quarter hour the *pendule* gave out its melodious chimes.

Finally I hear them speaking soberly, earnestly, as if it were a matter of grave concern. It is about language. Moricand says but little now. He is all ears. With all his knowledge, I suspect that he never dreamed that on this North American continent there once were spoken so many varieties of tongues, languages, not dialects merely, languages great and small, obscure and rudimentary, some extremely complicated, baroque, one might say, in form and structure. How could he know—few Americans know—that side by side there existed tribes whose languages were as far apart as is Bantu from Sanskrit, or Finnish from Phoenician, or Basque from German. The idea had never entered his head, cosmopolite that he was, that in a remote corner of the globe known as Big Sur a man named Jaime de Angulo, a renegade and a reprobate, was spending his days and nights comparing, classifying, analyzing, dissecting roots, declensions, prefixes and suffixes, etymologies, homologies, affinities and anomalies of tongues and dialects borrowed from all continents, all times, all races and conditions of man. Never had he thought it possible to combine in one person, as did this Angulo, the savage, the scholar, the man of the world, the recluse, the idealist and the very son of Lucifer. Well might he say, as he did later: *"C'est un être formidable. C'est un homme, celui-là!"*

Yes, he was indeed that, *a man,* dear Jaime de Angulo! A beloved, hated, detested, endearing, charming, cantankerous, pesky, devil-worshiping son-of-a-bitch of a man with a proud heart and a defiant soul, filled with tenderness and compassion for all humanity, yet cruel, vicious, mean and ornery. His own worst enemy. A man doomed to end his days in horrible agony—mutilated, emasculated, humiliated to the very core of his being. Yet even unto the end preserving his reason, his lucidity, his devil-may-care spirit, his defiance of God and man—and his great impersonal ego.

Would they ever have become bosom friends? I doubt it. Fortunate it was that Moricand never carried out his resolution to walk to the top of the mountain and offer a hand in friendship. Despite all they had in common they were worlds apart. Not even the Devil himself could have united them in friendship and brotherhood.

Reviewing their encounter that afternoon in my mind's eye, I see them as two egomaniacs hypnotized for a few brief hours by the mingling of worlds which overshadowed their personalities, their interests, their philosophies of life.

There are conjunctions in the human sphere which are just as fleeting and mysterious as stellar ones, conjunctions which seem like violation of natural law. For me who observed the event, it was like witnessing the marriage of fire and water.

Now that they have both passed beyond, one may be pardoned for wondering if they will ever meet again, and in what realm. They had so much to undo, so much to discover, so much to live out! Such lonely souls, full of pride, full of knowledge, full of the world and its evils! Not a grain of faith in either of them. Hugging the world and reviling it; clinging to life and desecrating it; fleeing society and never coming face to face with God; playing the mage and the shaman, but never acquiring wisdom of life or the wisdom of love. In what realm, I ask myself, will they meet again? And will they recognize one another?

One bright day as I was passing Moricand's cell—I had just dumped some garbage over the cliff—I found him leaning over the lower half of the Dutch door as if in contemplation. I was in an excellent mood because, as always when dumping the garbage, I had been rewarded by a breath-taking view of the coast. This particular morning everything was bright and still; the sky, the water, the mountains stared back at me as if reflected in a mirror. If the earth weren't curved I could have gazed right into China, the atmosphere was that clean and clear.

"Il fait beau aujourd'hui," said I, depositing the garbage can to light a cigarette.

"Oui, il fait beau," said he. "Come in a minute, won't you?"

I stepped in and took a seat beside his writing table. What now? I wondered. Another consultation?

He lit a cigarette slowly, as if debating how to begin. Had I been given ten thousand guesses, I could never have guessed what he was about to say. However, I was, as I say, in a most excellent mood; it mattered little to me what was disturbing him. My own mind was free, clear, empty.

"Mon cher Miller," he began in an even, steady tone, "what you are doing to me no man has a right to do to another."

I looked at him uncomprehendingly. "What I am doing to *you. . . ?"*

"Yes," he said. "You don't realize perhaps what you've done."

I made no reply. I was too curious to know what would follow to feel even the least indignation.

"You invited me to come here, to make this my home for the rest of my days. . . . You said I did not need to work, that I could do anything I pleased. And you demanded nothing in return. One can't do that to a fellow-man. It's unjust. It puts me in an unbearable position." It was undermining, he wanted to say.

He paused a moment. I was too flabbergasted to make reply immediately.

"Besides," he continued, "this is no place for me. I am a man of the city; I miss the pavement under my feet. If there were only a café I could walk to, or a library, or a cinema. I'm a prisoner here." He looked around him. "This is where I spend my days— and nights. Alone. No one to talk to. Not even you. You're too busy most of the time. Moreover, I feel that you're uninterested in what I am doing. . . . What am I to do, sit here until I die? You know I am not a man to complain. I keep to myself as much as I can; I occupy myself with my work, I take a walk now and then, I read . . . and I scratch myself continually. How long can I put up with it? Some days I feel as if I will go mad. I don't belong. . . ."

"I think I understand you," said I. "It's too bad it worked out this way. I meant only to do you a good turn."

"Oui, je le sais, mon vieux! It's all my fault. Nevertheless. . . ."

"What would you have me do? Send you back to Paris? That's impossible—at least right now."

"I know that," he said.

What he didn't know was that I was still struggling to pay back what I had borrowed to bring him to America.

"I was just wondering," he said, drumming his fingers on the table top, "how a city like San Francisco might be."

"Very good for a while," I said, "but how manage it? There's nothing you could work at, and I certainly couldn't support you there."

"Of course not," he said, "I wouldn't think of it. My God, you've done plenty already. More than enough. I shall never be able to repay you."

"Let's not go into *that!* The point is that you're unhappy here. Nobody is to blame. How could either of us have foreseen such an issue? I'm glad you spoke your mind. Perhaps if we put our heads together we can find a solution. It's true that I haven't given you or your work much attention, but you see what my life is like. You know how little time I have for my own work. You know, I too would like to walk the streets of Paris once in a while, feel the pavement under my feet, as you say. I too would like to be able to go to a café when I feel like it and meet a few congenial spirits. Of course, I'm in a different position from you. I'm not miserable here. Never. No matter what happens. If I had plenty of money I would get up and travel, I would invite my old friends to come and stay with me. . . . "I'd do all sorts of things I don't even dream of now. But one thing is certain in my mind—that this is a paradise. If anything goes wrong, I most certainly will not attribute it to the place. . . . It's a beautiful day today, no? It will be beautiful tomorrow when it pours. It's beautiful too when the fog settles down over everything and blacks us out. It was beautiful to *you* when you first saw it. It will be beautiful when you have gone. . . . Do you know what's wrong? (I tapped my skull.) *This up here!* A day like today I realize what I've told you a hundred different times—that there's nothing wrong with the world. What's wrong is our way of looking at it."

He gave me a wan smile, as if to say, "Just like Miller to go off on such a tangent. I say I'm suffering and he says everything is perfect."

"I know what you're thinking," I said. "Believe me, I feel for you. But you must try to do something for yourself. I did the best I could; if I made a mistake, then you must help me. Legally I'm responsible for you; morally you are responsible only to yourself. Nobody can help you but yourself. You think that I am indifferent to your suffering. You think I treat the itch too lightly. I don't. All I say is, find out what itches you. You can scratch and scratch, but unless you discover what's itching you you will never get relief."

"C'est assez vrai," he said. "I've reached bottom."

He hung his head a few moments, then looked up. An idea had flashed through his mind.

"Yes," he said, "I am that desperate that I am willing to try anything."

I was wondering what exactly that might mean when he promptly added: "This woman, Madame Wharton, what do you think of her?"

I smiled. It was a rather big question.

"I mean, does she really have healing powers?"

"Yes, she does," said I.

"Do you think she could help *me?"*

"That depends," I replied. "Depends greatly on you, on whether you want to be helped or not. You could cure yourself, I believe, if you had enough faith in yourself."

He ignored this last. Began pumping me about her views, her methods of operation, her background, and so on.

"I could tell you a great deal about her," I said. "I could talk to you all day, in fact. But what would it matter? If you wish to put yourself in someone else's hands, you must surrender completely. What she believes in is one thing; what she can do for you is another. If I were in your boots, if I were as desperate as you pretend to be, I wouldn't care how the trick was accomplished. All I would care about would be to get well."

He swallowed this as best he could, remarking that Moricand was not Miller and vice versa. He added that he believed her to be highly intelligent, though he confessed he could not always follow her thoughts. There was something of the mystic or the occult about her, he suspected.

"You're wrong there," I said. "She has no use for mysticism *or* occultism. If she believes in magic, it's everyday magic . . . such as Jesus practiced."

"I hope she doesn't want to convert me first," he sighed. "I have no patience with that humbug, you know."

"Maybe that's what you need," I said laughingly.

"Non! Seriously," he said, "do you think I could put myself in her hands? My God, even if it's Christianity she's going to spout, I'm willing to listen. I'll try *anything.* Anything to get rid of this horrible, horrible itch. I'll *pray,* if she wants me to."

"I don't think she'll ask you to do anything you don't want to do, my dear Moricand. She's not the sort to force her opinions on you. But I do think this. . . . If you listen to her seriously, if you believe that she can do something for you, you may find that you will think and act in different fashion than you now believe possible. Anyway, don't think one way and act another—not with *her!* She'll see through you immediately. And, after all, you wouldn't be fooling *her,* only yourself."

"Then she does have definite views . . . *religious* views, I mean?"

"Of course! That is, if you want to put it that way."

"What do you mean by that?" He looked slightly alarmed.

"I mean, old chap, that she has no religious views whatever. She's religious through and through. She acts out her views or beliefs. She doesn't think *about,* she thinks. She thinks things through—and acts them out. What she thinks about life, God, and all that, is very simple, so simple that you may not understand it at first. She's not a thinker, in *your* sense of the word. To her, Mind is all. What one thinks, one is. If there's something wrong with you, it's because your thinking is wrong. Does that make sense?"

"C'est bien simple," he said, nodding his head dolorously. (Too simple! is what he meant.) Obviously he would have been more excited had I made it sound intricate, abstruse, difficult to follow. Anything simple and direct was suspect to him. Besides, in his mind healing powers were magical powers, powers acquired through study, discipline, training, powers based on mastery over secret processes. Furthest from his mind was the thought that anyone could enter into direct communication with the source of all power.

"There's a force in her," he said, "a vitality which is physical and which I know can be communicated. She may not know from where it derives, but she possesses it and radiates it. Some times ignorant people have these powers."

"She's not ignorant, I can tell you that!" I said. "And if it *is* a physical force you feel in her presence you will never capture it for yourself, unless. . . ."

"Unless what?" he exclaimed eagerly.

"I won't say now. I think we've talked enough about her. After all, no matter what I tell you, the result depends on *you,* not her. Nobody has ever been cured of anything who did not want to be cured. The converse is just as true, only it's more difficult to swallow. It's always easier to take a negative view than a positive one. Anyway, whether the itch stops or not, it will be an interesting experiment for you. But think about it before you ask her aid. And you must ask her yourself, *compris?"*

"Don't worry," he replied. "I'll ask her. I'll ask her today, if I see her. I don't care what she orders me to do. I'll get down on my knees and pray, if that's what she wants. Anything! I'm at my wit's end."

"Good!" said I. *"On verra."*

It was too wonderful a morning to surrender myself to the machine. I took myself to the forest, alone, and when I had come to the usual halting place beside the pool, I sat down on a log, put my head in my hands and began to laugh. I laughed at myself, then at him, then at fate, then at the wild waves going up and down, because my head was full of nothing but wild waves going up and down. All in all, it was a lucky break. Fortunately, we were not married to one another; there were no children, no complications. Even if he wanted to return to Paris, I believed I could manage it somehow. That is, with a little cooperation on his part.

But what a lesson he had given me! Never, never again, would I make the mistake of trying to solve someone's problems for him. How deceptive to think that by means of a little self-sacrifice one can help another overcome his difficulties! How egotistical! And how right he was to say that I had undermined him! Right and yet wrong! Because, making a reproach like that, he should have followed it up with—"I'm leaving. Leaving tomorrow. And this time I won't even take a toothbrush with me. I'll strike out on my own, come what may. The worst that can happen to me is to be deported. Even if they ship me back to Hell it's better than being a burden to someone. At least, I'll be able to scratch myself in peace!"

As this point I thought of a strange thing—that I too was suffering from the itch, only it was an itch one couldn't get at, an itch that didn't manifest itself bodily. But it was there just the same . . . there where every itch begins and ends. The unfortunate part about my ailment was that nobody ever caught me scratching. Yet I was at it night and day, feverishly, frantically, without let. Like Paul, I was constantly saying to myself: "Who shall deliver me from the body of this death?" What irony that people should be writing me from all over the world, thanking me for the encouragement and inspiration my work had given them. No doubt they looked upon me as an emancipated being. Yet every day of my life I was fighting a corpse, a ghost, a cancer that had taken possession of my mind and that ravaged me more than any bodily affliction possibly could. Every day I had to meet and battle anew with the person I had chosen as a mate, chosen as one who would appreciate "the good life" and share it with me. And from the very beginning it had been nothing but hell—hell and torment. To make it worse, the neighbors regarded her as a model creature—so spry, so lively, so generous, so warm. Such a good little mother, such an excellent housewife, such a perfect hostess! It's not easy to live with a man thirty years older, a writer to boot, and especially a writer like Henry Miller. Everyone knew that. Everyone could see that she was doing her utmost. She had courage, that girl!

And hadn't I made a failure of it before? Several times, in fact? Could any woman on earth possibly get along with a man like me? That's how most of our arguments ended, on that note. What to answer? There was no answer. Convicted, sentenced, condemned to rehearse the situation over and over, until one or the other should fall apart, dissolve like a rotting corpse.

Not a day of peace, not a day of happiness, unless on my own. The moment she opened her mouth—*war!*

It sounds so simple: break it up! get a divorce! separate! But what about the child? Where would I stand, in court, claiming the right to keep my daughter? *"You?* A man with *your* reputation?" I could just see the judge foaming at the mouth.

Even to do away with myself would not remedy matters. We had to go on. We had to fight it out. No, that's not the word. Iron things out. (With what? A flatiron?) *Compromise!* That's better. It's not either! Then surrender! Admit you're licked. Let her walk over you. Pretend you don't feel, don't hear, don't see. Pretend you're dead.

Or—get yourself to believe that all is good, all is God, that there is nothing but good, nothing but God who is all goodness, all light, all love. *Get yourself to believe.* . . . Impossible! One has to just believe. *Punkt!* Nor is that enough. You have to *know.* More than that. . . . You have to *know* that you know.

And what if, despite everything, you find her standing before you, mocking, jeering, deriding, denigrating, sneering, lying, falsifying, distorting, belittling, calling black white, smiling disdainfully, hissing like a snake, nagging, backbiting, shooting out quills like a porcupine. . . ? What then?

Why, you say it's good, it's God manifesting, it's love appearing—only in reverse.

And then?

You look *through* the negative . . . until you see the positive.

Try it sometime—as a morning exercise. Preferably after standing on your head for five minutes. If it doesn't work, get down on your knees and pray.

It *will* work, it's got to work!

That's where you're wrong. If you think it's got to, it won't.

But it must, eventually. Otherwise you'll scratch yourself to death.

What is it my friend Alan Watts says? "When it is clear beyond all doubt that the itch cannot be scratched, it stops itching by itself."

On the way home I stopped at the edge of the clearing, where the huge abandoned horse trough stood, to see if the pots and pans were in order. Tomorrow, the weather permitting, little Val would fix me another make-believe breakfast. And I would probably give her a few make-believe suggestions for improving the bacon and eggs, or the oatmeal, or whatever she might decide to serve me.

Make believe. . . . Make believe you're happy. Make believe you're free. Make believe you're God. Make believe it's all Mind.

I thought of Moricand. "I'll get down on my knees and pray, if that's what she wants." How idiotic! He might equally well have said: "I'll dance, I'll sing, I'll whistle, I'll stand on my head . . . if that's what she wants." *She* wants. As if she wanted anything but his welfare.

I got to thinking of the Zen masters, one old dog in particular. The one who said, "It's your mind that's troubling you, is it? Well then, bring it out, put it down here, let's have a look at it!" Or words to that effect.

I wondered how long the poor devil would continue scratching himself if every time he dug his nails into his flesh one of those gay old dogs would appear out of the ether and give him thirty-nine blows with a stout cudgel.

And yet you know that when you get home she'll be facing you and you'll lose your temper!

Scratch that!

She need only say: "I thought you were in your studio working."

And you'll say: "Must I work all the time? Can't I take a walk once in a while?"

And like that, the fur will fly, and you won't be able to see through the negative. . . . You'll see red, then black, then green, then purple.

Such a beautiful day! Did *you* make it? Did *she* make it?

Fuck who made it! Let's go down and see what she wants to fight about. God made it, that's who.

So I go down, bristling like a porcupine.

Fortunately, Jean Wharton's there. Moricand's already been to see her. And she's given her consent.

How different the atmosphere is when Jean's around! As if the sun were pouring through all the windows with intensified light and warmth and love. At once I feel normal. Like my real self. One couldn't possibly bicker and wrangle with a person like Jean Wharton. At least, *I* couldn't. I take a look at my wife. Does she look any different? To be honest, she does. For one thing, there's no fight in her now. She too looks normal. Like any other human being, I'd say.

I won't go so far as to say that I can see God in her. No.

Anyway, there's a lull.

"So you're going to take him on?" I say.

"Yes," says Jean, "he seems to be desperately in earnest. Of course, it won't be easy."

I was going to say, "What language will you talk?" but the question answered itself. God's language, of course!

With anyone else it was bound to work. With Moricand. . . ?

God can talk to a stone wall and make it respond. But the human mind can be thicker, harder to penetrate, than even a wall of steel. What is it the Hindus say? "If God wished to hide, He would choose man to hide in."

That evening, as I was going up the garden steps to have a last look around, I met Jean sailing through the gate. She had a lantern in one hand and what seemed like a book in the other. She seemed to be floating through the air. Her feet were on the ground all right, but her body had no weight. She looked more beautiful, more radiant, than I had ever seen her before. Truly an emissary of light and love, of peace and serenity. In the few years since I first met her, at the Big Sur Post Office, she had gone through a definite transformation. Whatever she believed in, whatever it was that she was practicing, it had altered her physically as well as mentally and spiritually. Had I been Moricand, at that moment, I would have been made whole instantly.

But it didn't work out that way. It didn't work at all, as a matter of fact. A fiasco from start to finish.

It was the next morning that I got a full report from Moricand. He was not only incensed, he was outraged. "Such nonsense!" he cried. "Am I a child, a fool, an idiot, that I should be treated thus?"

I let him rave. After he had calmed down I got the details, at least the important one to his way of thinking. The fly in the ointment, what was it but *Science and Health!* He had done his best, he said, to follow Jean Wharton's talk—apparently he had understood almost nothing. The talk was difficult enough to swallow but then, in taking leave, she had thrust this Mary Baker Eddy book under his nose, urging him to read a few passages and dwell on them. She had indicated the passages she thought best to concentrate on. To Moricand, of course, the *Key to the Scriptures* had about as much value as a child's primer. Less, indeed. He had spent his whole life denying, ridiculing, suppressing this kind of "nonsense." What he had expected of Jean Wharton was a laying on of hands, a magical rapport which would aid him in exorcising the demon that made him scratch night and day. The last thing on earth he wanted was a spiritual interpretation of the art of healing. Or shall I say what is nearer the truth—that he did not want to be told he could heal himself, that indeed he *must* heal himself!

When I met Jean, a little later, and related what he had told me, she explained that she had left the book with him, not with any intention of converting him to Christian Science, but simply to make him forget himself for a while. She had understood him, his French, clearly enough and she had been prepared to wrestle with him anew the next night and for as many nights as might be necessary. She confessed that perhaps it had been a mistake to give him Mary Baker Eddy to read. However, as she well said, had he been sincere, had he been willing to surrender just the least bit, he would not have been so outraged by the book. A man who is desperate can find comfort in anything, sometimes even in that which goes against the grain.

The discussion about the book incited me to have a look at it myself. I had read quite a little about Mary Baker Eddy but I had never, strangely enough, gone to the book itself. I discovered immediately that I was in for a pleasant surprise. Mary Baker Eddy became very real to me. My critical opinion of her fell away. I saw her as the great soul she was, human, yes, human to the core, but filled with a great light, transformed by a revelation such as might occur to any of us were we big enough and open enough to receive it.

As for Moricand, it was as if we had removed the last stepping stone from under his feet. He was depressed as never before. Absolutely despondent, wretched, miserable. Every night he wailed like a banshee. Instead of an *apéritif* before dinner he would treat us to an exhibition of his sores. "It's inhuman," he would say. "You've got to *do* something!" Then, with a sigh, "If only I could take a warm bath!"

We had no bath tub. We had no miracle drugs. We had nothing but words, empty words. At any rate, by now he was just a flaming wretch who had delivered himself to the mercy of the Devil.

Only one evening before the final breakdown stands out clearly. I remember it well because earlier that evening, while we were still eating, he had expressed his irritation with Val, who was sitting beside him, in a way I can never forget. Bored with the conversation, she had begun to play with the knives and forks, rattle the dishes, anything to gain attention. Suddenly, in a playful way, she had snatched the piece of bread lying beside him. Furious, he snatched it from her fist and placed it on the other side of his plate. It was not the gesture of annoyance so much as the look in his eyes which startled me. It was a look full of hatred, the look of a man so beside himself that he might even commit murder. I never forgot it and I never forgave it.

It was a hour or two later, after the child had been put to bed, that he launched into a lengthy tale which I shall recapitulate briefly. What provoked it I no longer remember. But it was about a child, a girl of eight or nine. The telling of it seemed to take up the entire evening.

As often happened, when beginning a yarn, he shrouded the opening in irrelevant wrappings. It was not until (following him down the *grands boulevards*) he made mention of the Passage Jouffroy that I was aware that he was spinning a tale. The Passage Jouffroy happens to be one of those arcades which are freighted with souvenirs for me. Many things had happened to me, in years gone by, while strolling through that well-known landmark. I mean inner happenings, events one never thinks to write about because too fleeting, too impalpable, too close to the source.

And now here is Moricand suddenly shocking me into awareness of the fact that he is following on the heels of a woman and her daughter. They have just turned into the Passage Jouffroy, window shopping, seemingly. *When* he began following them, *why, how long,* has lost importance. It's the sudden inner excitement which his looks and gestures betray that takes hold of me, rivets my attention.

I thought at first it was the mother he was interested in. He had described her swiftly, deftly, much as a painter would. Described her as only Moricand could describe a woman of that type. In a few words he had stripped her of her nondescript garb, her pseudomaternal air, her pretense of strolling the boulevards with her innocent little lamb. He had recognized her for what she was the moment she had turned into the Passage Jouffroy, that moment when she had hesitated just the fraction of a second, as if she were about to look back, but didn't. He knew then that *she* knew he was following.

It was almost painful to hear him rhapsodize about the little girl. What was it about her that so excited him? *The look of the perverted angel!*

His words were so graphic, so diabolically searching, that despite myself, I was ready to believe that the child was steeped in vice. *Or else so innocent that. . . .*

The thought of what was passing through his mind made me shudder.

What followed was mere routine. *He* took a stand before a window display of manikins dressed in latest sports models while a few feet away the woman and child dallied to gaze upon a virginal figure garbed in a beautiful Communion dress. Observing that the child was rapt in wonder, he threw the woman a quick glance and nodded meaningfully toward her charge. The woman responded with the barest perceptible sway of her head, lowered her eyes a moment, then, looking straight at him, through him, grasped the child's hand and led her away. He permitted them to get a respectable distance ahead, then followed in their wake. Near the exit the woman stopped a moment to buy some sweets. She made no further sign, except to turn her bowed head in the direction of his feet; she then resumed what was to all appearances an innocent promenade. Once or twice the little girl made as if to turn around, as would any child whose attention had been caught by the flutter of pigeon wings or the gleam of glass beads.

There was no increase in their pace. The mother and daughter sauntered along as if taking the air, enjoying the sights. Leisurely they turned down one street and up another. Gradually they approached the neighborhood of the Folies-Bergère. Finally they came to a hotel, a hotel with a rather flamboyant name. (I mention it because I recognized the name; I had spent a week in this hotel once, in bed most of the time. During that week, flat on my back, I had read Céline's *Voyage au bout de la nuit*.)

Even as they entered the woman made no visible effort to see if he were following. She had no need to look: it had all been worked out telepathically in the Passage Jouffroy.

He waited outside a few moments to collect himself, then, though his guts were still quivering, he walked calmly up to the desk and booked a room. As he filled out the *fiche* the woman laid her key down a moment to stuff something in her purse. He didn't even have to turn his head to catch the number. He gave the *garçon* a liberal tip and, since he had no bags, told him it was unnecessary to show him the way. By the time he reached the top of the first flight of stairs his heart was in his mouth. He bounded up the next flight, turned quickly down the passage towards the room he was looking for, and came face to face with the woman. Though there was not a soul about, neither paused an instant. They brushed by each other like two strangers, she as if going to the lavatory, he as if to his room. Only the look in her eyes, the drooping, sidewise glance, conveyed the message he knew was forthcoming: *"Elle est là!"* He walked swiftly to the door, removed the key which had been left outside, and pushed his way in.

Here he paused in his narration. His eyes were positively dancing. I knew he was waiting for me to say "Then what?" I struggled with myself not to reveal my true feelings. The words he was waiting for got stuck in my throat. All I could think of was the little girl sitting on the edge of the bed, half-undressed probably, and nibbling at a piece of pastry. *"Reste-là, p'tite, je reviens toute de suite,"* the woman had probably said as she closed the door behind her.

Finally, after what seemed like an eternity, I heard myself saying to him: *"Eh bien,* what then?"

"What then?" he exclaimed, his eyes aflame with a ghoulish glee. *"Je l'ai eue,* that's what!"

As he uttered these words I felt my hair stand on end. It was no longer Moricand I was facing but Satan himself.

The rains continued to descend, the leaks grew worse, the walls got wetter and wetter, the sow bugs increased and multiplied. The horizon was now completely shut out; the wind had become a howling fury. Back of the two studios stood three tall eucalyptus trees; under the lash of the gale they seemed to bend in two. In Moricand's shattered state they were three demons with a thousand arms beating a terrifying tattoo upon his brainpan. Wherever he looked, indeed, there was nothing but a wall of water, a forest of swaying, swirling, twisting tree trunks. And with it, what disturbed him more than anything, the whine and moan of the wind, the whistling, crackling, hissing sound which never abated. To anyone in his right senses it was grand, magnificent, absolutely intoxicating. One felt deliciously helpless, insignificant, even less than a rubber doll. To venture outdoors at the height of it was to be slapped down. There was something insane about it. All you could do was to wait it out. It must die of its own fury.

But Moricand could not wait it out. He was at the breaking point. He came down one afternoon—it was already dark—saying that he couldn't stand it another minute. "It's a howling inferno!" he cried. "Nowhere in the world can it possibly rain like this. *C'est fou!"*

At dinner, rehearsing his miseries, he suddenly burst into tears. He begged me—supplicated, rather—to do something to relieve him of his torment. He pleaded and entreated as if I were made of stone. It was sheer torture to listen to the man.

"What *can* I do? said I. "What is it you think I *should* do?"

"Take me to Monterey. Put me in a hospital. I *must* get out of this place."

"Very well," I said. "I'll do that. I'll move you just as soon as we can get off this hill."

What did that mean? he wanted to know. A feeble look of terror spread over his countenance.

I explained that not only was my car not working but that the road leading to the highway was blocked with boulders; the storm would have to abate before we could even think about moving.

This only increased his desperation. *"Think, think!"* he begged. "There must be some way to get out of here. Do you want me to go stark mad?"

The only thing left to do was to walk down the road to the highway next morning and leave a note in the mailbox for the mail man to deliver to Lilik. The mail was still getting through. All day long and into the night the highway crew kept clearing the road of debris. I knew that Lilik would get to us if it were humanly possible. As for the boulders that blocked the foot of the road, I would just pray that some Titan would push them aside.

So I got down, dispatched the message, making it life and death, and told Moricand to be in readiness. I had told Lilik to come the next morning, at six o'clock, or perhaps I said five-thirty. I figured that by that time the storm would have moderated and some of the boulders been cleared away.

That night, his last night, Moricand refused to go back to his cell. He decided to sit up all night in the armchair. We kept him at table as long as we could, plied him with drink, regaled him as best we could, and finally, towards morning, bade him good night. There was just the one room, and our bed was in the middle of it. We climbed in and tried to go to sleep. A tiny lamp flickered on the table beside him as he sat in the big armchair, bundled up in overcoat and muffler, his hat pulled down over his eyes. The fire went out, and though not a window was open, the room soon grew damp and chill. The wind was still whistling around the corners of the house, but it seemed to me that the rain was letting up.

Naturally, I couldn't sleep. I lay there as quiet as I could and listened to him mumbling to himself. Every now and then he groaned and broke out with a *"Mon Dieu, mon Dieu!* when will it end?"* Or—*"Quel supplice!"*

About 5:00 A.M. I climbed out of bed, lit the Aladdin lamps, put some coffee on the stove, and dressed. It was still dark, but the storm had broken. There was just a normal high wind which was sweeping away the rain.

When I asked him how he felt, he groaned. Never had he known such a night. He was finished. He hoped he would have the strength to last till we reached the hospital.

As we were swallowing the hot coffee, he got a whiff of the bacon and eggs. That gave him a momentary lift. *"J'adore ça,"* he said, rubbing his hands. Then a sudden panic seized him. "How do we know he will come, Lilik?"

"He'll come, never fear," I said. "He would wade through Hell to rescue you."

"Qui, c'est un chic type. Un vrai ami."

By this time my wife had dressed, set the table, lit the stove, served the bacon and eggs.

"Everything will be fine," she said. "You'll see, Lilik will be here in a few minutes." She spoke to him as if he were a child. (Don't worry, dear, mamma's here, nothing can happen to you.)

Seized with a sense of the dramatic, I suddenly decided to light the lantern and go to the top of the road above us to signal Lilik. As I climbed the hill I heard his car snorting down below, probably at the bend near the Roosevelt's. I waved the lantern to and fro and, now thoroughly elated, gave a great shout. He must have seen the light, for immediately there came the honk-honk of his horn, and in a few moments the car came into sight, puffing and snorting like a wounded dragon.

"Christ!" I shouted, "What luck! You made it! *Grand!*" I gave him a warm hug.

"I had a bad time of it down below," he said. "I don't know how I ever cleared those rocks away. Luckily, I brought a crowbar with me. . . . How's Moricand? Is he awake yet?"

"Is he awake? Man, he's never been to sleep. Come on down and have a cup of coffee. Have you had breakfast?"

He hadn't. Not even a cup of coffee.

We walked in, and there was Moricand licking his chops. He seemed quite revived. As he greeted Lilik, tears came to his eyes. *"C'est la fin,"* he said. "But how good of you to come! You're a saint."

When it came time to go Moricand rose to his feet, tottered, staggered to the bed and collapsed.

"What's up?" cried Lilik. "You're not going to give out now, are you?"

Moricand looked up woefully. "I can't walk," he said. "Look!" And he pointed to the swelling between his legs.

"What's that?" we cried in unison.

"My testicles!" he exclaimed. "They've swollen up on me."

They had indeed. They were like two rocks.

"We'll carry you to the car," said Lilik.

"I'm too heavy," said Moricand.

"Nonsense!" said Lilik.

Moricand put his arms around our shoulders, and Lilik and I joined hands under his legs. He weighed a ton. Slowly, gently, we hoisted him up the garden steps and into the car. He groaned like a bull in agony.

"Easy, easy now. It will pass. Just hold your breath, grit your teeth. *Du courage, mon vieux!*"

As we cautiously picked our way down the winding hill, observing the havoc the storm had wrought, Moricand's eyes opened wider and wider. Finally we came to the last stretch, a rather steep descent. Huge boulders towered above menacingly. When we reached the highway I saw what Lilik had done. It didn't seem possible for human hands to have accomplished such a task.

Dawn had come, the rain had stopped altogether, and we were on our way. Every few yards we had to stop and clear the road of debris. This continued until we reached the sign which said: "Watch for falling rocks. Dangerous curves and falling rocks for the next 46 miles." But that was all behind us now.

My thoughts reverted to Moricand's promenade between the battlefronts. The two valises. And Iamblichus! By comparison, all that seemed unreal, a nightmare that he had dreamed up.

"How do your balls feel now?" I asked.

He felt them. Somewhat better, he thought.

"Good," said Lilik. "It's just nervousness."

I restrained a laugh. "Nervousness!" What a word to describe Moricand's anguish!

When we got to Monterey we stopped to fetch him a cup of coffee. The sun was out strong, the roof-tops glistened; life was pursuing its normal course again. Only a few more miles, we told him, and you'll be there. Meaning at the County Hospital in Salinas.

He felt his testicles again. The swelling had almost disappeared.

"What did we tell you!"

"*Quais!*" said Moricand. "*Mais, c'est drôle.* How do you explain it?"

"Nervousness," said Lilik.

"*Angoisse!*" said I.

We rolled up in front of the hospital. It didn't look as bad as I had imagined it would. From the outside, in fact, it seemed rather cheerful. Just the same, I was glad it wasn't my turn.

We went inside. It was still rather early. The usual routine: questions, explanations, papers to fill out. Then wait. No matter if you're dying, they always ask you to wait.

We waited a while, then inquired when the doctor would show

up. I had thought we would get Moricand a bed immediately, then see the doctor. No, first you see the doctor, then a bed—if there is one vacant!

We decided to have a second breakfast. There was a glassed-in dining room which was connected with the hospital, or so it seemed to me. We had bacon and eggs again. And more coffee. The coffee was vile and weak, but Moricand said it tasted good. He lit a *gauloise bleue*—and smiled. He was probably thinking of the comfortable bed, the attention he would receive, the luxury of relaxing in the midst of ministering angels.

Finally it came time to visit the clinic. It was like all such places, cold, bare, glittering with instruments, smelling of disinfectants. You bring your poor, frail body and you hand it over to be inspected. You are one thing and your body is another. Lucky you if you get it back again.

He's standing there nude, naked as a herring. The doctor is tapping at him, just like a woodpecker. We've explained that it's the itch he's suffering from. No matter. Must see if there's anything else first—phthisis, gallstones, asthma, tonsillitis, cirrhosis of the liver, miner's elbow, dandruff. . . . The doctor's not a bad chap. Affable, courteous, willing to chatter. Speaks French too. Rather pleased on the whole to see a specimen like Moricand for a change.

Moricand too seems rather pleased. At last some real attention. Something indefinable about his expression gives me the impression that he hopes the doctor will find something seriously wrong with him, something more than the itch.

Without a stitch he looks lamentable. Like a broken-down nag. It's not merely that he's potbellied, full of sores and scabs, but that his skin has an unhealthy look, is spotted like tobacco leaf, has no oil, no elasticity, no glow. He looks like one of those derelicts one sees in the washroom of a Mills hotel, like a bum that has just crawled out of a flophouse on the Bowery. His flesh seems never to have been in contact with air and sun; it looks half-smoked.

The physical examination over, and nothing seriously wrong except that he's run-down, anemic, bilious, weak heart, erratic pulse, high blood pressure, spavined and double-jointed, it's now time to investigate the itch.

It's the doctor's opinion that he's suffering from an allergy, perhaps several allergies. Allergies are his specialty. Hence his certitude.

No one demurs, not even Moricand. He's heard of allergies but never attached any importance to them. Neither have I. Neither has Lilik. However, today it's allergies. Tomorrow it will be something else. Allergies then. Go to it!

While assorting and arranging his test tubes, syringes, needles, razor blades and what not, in preparation for the tests, the doctor plies Moricand with questions.

"You've had the drug habit, haven't you?"

Moricand nods.

"I can tell," says the doctor, pointing to Moricand's legs, arms, thighs, where traces of the needle still showed.

"What did you use?"

"Everything," said Moricand. "But that was some years ago."

"Opium too?"

At this Moricand seemed somewhat surprised. "How did you know?" he asked.

"I've treated thousands of cases," said the doctor. He fiddled with something behind Moricand's back. As he wheeled around, he said swiftly: "How did you break it, tell me that!"

"By my own will," said Moricand.

"What's that?" said the doctor. "Say it again!"

Moricand repeated: "By my own will. It was not easy. It almost killed me."

"If that's true," said the doctor, taking his hand, "you're the first man I've known to accomplish it."

Moricand blushed as a man might who was being given a medal for a deed of valor he had never performed.

Meanwhile the doctor had begun the game of ticktacktoe on Moricand's back. He started up near the left shoulder, worked clear across to the right shoulder, then down and across. Each time he finished a game he waited a few minutes. The first game was all in blue ink, the second in pink, the third in green, and so on through the spectrum. Nobody was winning. Since Moricand's back was only human size, and since it was completely covered with welts from neck to waist, there was nothing to do but call it a draw for the day. There were still thirty or forty more tests that could be given. One of them had to turn out positive. At least, that was how the doctor regarded it.

"And now what about a bed?" said Moricand, slipping into his shirt and trousers.

"A *bed?*" said the doctor, looking at him in astonishment.

"Yes," said Moricand. "A place to rest . . . to recuperate."

The doctor laughed as if it were a good joke.

"We don't have beds enough for our serious cases," he said. "There's nothing very wrong with you. Come back day after tomorrow and I'll give you some more tests." He wrote out a prescription for a sedative. "You'll be all right in no time."

I explained that we lived in Big Sur, that it wasn't easy to make frequent trips to Salinas.

"Why don't you put him up in town for a while?" said the doctor. "In a week or so I'll know what's what. There's nothing to worry about. He's been through much worse, I can tell you that. . . . Just a bit dilapidated. Hypersensitive."

Outside we decided to look for a bar. We all needed a drink bad.

"How does your back feel?" said Lilik, raising his hands as if to give him a clap.

Moricand winced. "It feels like a hot grill," he said.

We found a dingy bar and, while putting away a few drinks, discussed the opium habit. An illuminating subject, if one penetrates deeply enough.

In Monterey I engaged a room for him at the Hotel Serra. A room with a private bath. In comparison with the cell he had been living in this was luxury. We tested the bed to see if it was soft and springy enough, switched the lights on and off to see if they were good enough to read and write by, showed him how to manipulate the window blinds, assured him that he would get fresh towels and soap every day, and so on. He was already unpacking the small valise he had brought along. Already the dresser was arranged as he invariably arranged things wherever he might find himself. As he was getting out his manuscripts, his writing tablet, his ink and ruler, I suddenly realized that the table beside the bed would be too small to work on. We called the manager to find if he couldn't apply a bigger one. In a jiffy the bellhop arrived with a table just the right size.

Moricand seemed really overcome with joy. He looked around as if he were in Heaven. The bathroom especially put him in ecstasy. We had explained that he could take a bath as often as he wished—no extra charge, as in France. (This was the good side of America again. "A wonderful country!")

It only remained now to hand him some money and arrange with someone who had a car to drive him back and forth to the hospital. I didn't know, as I said *au revoir,* that it would be the last time I would see him.

He had grown ten years younger in the space of a few minutes. As we shook hands, as I promised to look him up in a few days, he said: "I think I'll go down in a little while to have a *porto.*"

Walking down the street, Lilik and I, we ran into the painter, Ellwood Graham. After a few words we learned that he was making trips to the County Hospital every day. It would be a pleasure he informed us, to drive Moricand back and forth.

We ducked back to the hotel immediately only to find that Moricand had already left, presumably to have his *porto*. We left a note explaining that he would have the use of a car and a private chauffeur.

The feeling of relief I experienced on arriving home was beyond words. It was high time we were rid of him, for my wife was already pregnant several months. Yet she had borne up under the ordeal better than I.

A few days passed but I simply could not bring myself to go to Monterey and look him up. Instead I wrote him a note, making some excuse or other. He wrote back immediately to say that he was feeling better, that the doctor hadn't discovered yet what was wrong with him, but that he was enjoying his most comfortable quarters. A postscript reminded me that the rent would be due in a few days, also that he would need some fresh linen soon.

We exchanged notes for about two weeks or so, during which time I did go to town but without looking him up. Then one day I received word that he had made up his mind to go to San Francisco; he thought he could find something to do there, and, if not, he would make efforts to return to Paris. He added that it was obvious I didn't wish to see him any more.

On receipt of this message I immediately packed the remainder of his belongings, had someone deliver them to him at the hotel, and sent him enough money to last him a couple of weeks at least. That he was putting this much distance between us gave me a still greater feeling of relief. And the fact that he had at last found enough gumption to do something on his own.

I then fumigated his cell, as Leon had recommended.

In writing him I had given him elaborate explanations and instructions. I told him where to look for modest French restaurants, bars, and so forth. I even went to the extent of telling him that if he could not make himself understood he was to write the address down and show it to the cab-driver, the policeman, or whoever it might be. I told him where to find the library, the avant-garde cinemas, the museums and art galleries.

I soon learned that he had found a suitable hotel, but at a much higher rate than I had named; he had also discovered a little bar where he could get his meals and where there were a few congenial French people. His money was going fast, he explained, because wherever he wanted to go he had to take a cab; he wouldn't trust himself to take streetcars and buses, his English was too poor.

To all this I gave a patient ear, thinking that he would soon adjust himself and settle down to a less expensive routine. The business about the cabs nettled me. Paris was a far bigger city than San Francisco and I had managed to find my way about in it with less money in my jeans and less knowledge of French than he had of English. But then I had no one to fall back on. *Ça fait une différence!*

He had, of course, reported to the Swiss Consul and had quickly learned that there was no question of finding employment, not with a visitor's visa. He could, to be sure, take steps to become an American citizen, but he was not interested in becoming an American citizen.

What *was* he going to do, I wondered? Would he request the Swiss Consul to ship him back to Paris?

Perhaps he had asked the Swiss Consul to ship him home and perhaps they had told him that was *my* responsibility. At any rate, the impression I got was that he was simply drifting with the tide. As long as I could keep him in food, cigarettes, taxi fares, a comfortable room and bath, he was not going to get panicky. San Francisco suited him far better than Big Sur, even though he found it somewhat "provincial." At least there was solid pavement under his feet.

It was after he had been there over a month that the effort to maintain him in his own style became a strain. I had the feeling that the arrangement could continue indefinitely, so far as *he* was concerned. Finally I suggested that if he were seriously of a mind to return to Europe I would see what I could do to get him a passage back. Instead of being elated he replied in gloomy vein that if it came to a pinch, why yes, he would go back. As if he were doing me a great favor to even consider the thought!

It so happened that shortly after this exchange of views my good friend, Raoul Bertrand, came to visit us. He had met Moricand at our home several times and knew what I was up against. When I explained how matters now stood he volunteered to see if he could not secure passage for Moricand on a French freighter plying from San Francisco. A free passage, moreover.

I immediately apprised Moricand of the good news and drew an alluring picture of a long sea voyage through the Panama Canal, with stopovers in Mexico and Central America. I made it sound so enchanting that I began to wish I could change places with him.

What his reply was precisely, I no longer recall, only that he gave a grudging acquiescence. Meanwhile Bertrand had set to work. In less than a week he had found a freighter which offered Moricand passage. It would leave in thirty-six hours—just time enough to send Moricand a wire. In order to circumvent any misinterpretation of the message on the part of the telegraph company, I wrote the message out in English: a fifty-word telegram giving full details.

To my utter astonishment, I got a reply by mail after the boat had sailed, saying that his Highness was not to be rushed that way, that he should have had a few days' warning at least, that it was most inconsiderate of me to send him a message of such importance in a language, he didn't understand, and so on and so forth. Extremely hoity-toity, to put it mildly. Besides, as he went on to explain in a postscript, he was not at all certain that he would relish a long sea voyage; he was not a good sailor, he would be bored to death, etc., etc. At the very end—would I please send him some more money!

I was thoroughly incensed. And I let him know it in no uncertain terms. Then I wrote a profuse letter of apology to Raoul Bertrand. Here he was, a French consul, not Swiss, putting himself to all this trouble, and that louse, Moricand, hadn't even the decency to be grateful for his efforts.

Bertrand, however, understood better than I the manner of man we were dealing with. He was not at all perturbed or dismayed. "We'll try again," he said. "You've got to get him off your hands!" He added: "Perhaps next time we'll get him a plane passage. He can hardly refuse that."

And by God, in about ten days he did come up with a plane passage. This time we gave Moricand ample notice.

Once again he agreed, grumblingly, to be sure. Like a rat that had been cornered. But when the time came to depart he was not on hand. He had changed his mind again. What excuse he gave I no longer remember.

By this time a number of my intimate friends had got wind of "the Moricand affair," as they called it. Everywhere I went people would ask—"What's happened to your friend? Did you get rid of him yet? Has he committed suicide?" A few had the courage to let me know in plain language that I was nothing but an idiot. "Cut him loose, Henry, or you'll never get him off your hands! He'll bleed you dry." That was the general tenor of the advice I received.

One day Varda came to see me. He was now living in Sausalito on a ferry boat which he had converted into a houseboat, dance palace and studio. He was all agog about the Moricand business, having received all the juicy details from a dozen different sources. His attitude was one of high amusement and genuine concern. How could he get in touch with Moricand? He referred to him as some sort of parasitic monster for whom saints and simpletons were easy prey.

Regarding me as an utterly helpless victim, he then proposed a typical Varda solution. He said he knew a wealthy woman in San Francisco, a Hungarian or Austrian countess, still attractive though aging, who loved to "collect" bizarre figures such as Moricand. Astrology, occultism—that was just her meat. She had a huge mansion, money to burn, and thought nothing of having a guest remain a year or two. If Moricand were as good a talker as I said he was, he would be an attraction for her salon. Celebrities from all over the world converged there, he said. It would be a real haven for a man like Moricand.

"I'll tell you what I'll do," he went on. "As soon as I get back to Sausalito I'll ask her to arrange a soiree. I'll see that Moricand is invited. The man has only to open his mouth and she'll be hooked."

"Are you sure she won't expect something more of him?" said I. "An aging countess, and still attractive, as you say, may make demands Moricand is no longer able to satisfy."

"Don't worry about *that!*" he cried, giving me a knowing look. "She has only to wave her hand and she can have the pick of San Francisco's finest young blades. Besides, she has a pair of the most lecherous-looking lap dogs you ever laid eyes on. No, if she takes him, she'll use him for her salon."

I regarded Varda's proposal as a huge joke. Thought no more of it, indeed. Meantime another letter arrived from Moricand, a letter full of recriminations. Why was I in such haste to pack him off? What had he ever done to deserve such treatment? Was it his fault that he had fallen ill *chez moi?* He reminded me caustically that I was still responsible for his welfare, that I had signed papers to that effect, and that he had these papers in his possession. He even insinuated that if I didn't toe the mark he would inform the proper authorities of the scandal my books had created in France. (As if they didn't know!) He might even tell them worse things about me . . . that I was an anarchist, a traitor, a renegade, and what all.

I was ready to hit the ceiling. "That bastard!" I said. "He's actually beginning to threaten me."

Meanwhile Bertrand was making efforts to get him a second plane passage. And Lilik was getting ready to go to Berkeley on a business errand. He too was going to do something about this damned Moricand business. At least he would see him and try to talk some sense into him.

Then came a letter from Varda. He had arranged a soiree *chez* the Countess, had primed her for the jewel she was to get, found her sympathetic to the idea, and. . . . To make it short, Moricand had come, had taken one look at the Countess, and then had avoided her like sin for the rest of the evening. He had remained silent and glum the whole evening, except to unleash a cutting remark now and then about the vanity and stupidity of wealthy émigrées who exploited their salons to rustle up fresh bait to whet their jaded appetites.

"The bastard!" I said to myself. "Couldn't even take on a millionairess to help a fellow out!"

On the heels of this incident Bertrand came up with another plane passage, this one a good week off. Once again I informed his Highness that a silver bird of the air was at his disposal. Would he be so gracious as to give it a trial?

This time the response was clear and definite. All mystery was ripped away.

I give the gist of his letter. . . . Yes, he would consent to accept the passage which had been proffered him, but on one condition, that I first put to his account in a Paris bank the equivalent of a thousand dollars. It should be easy to understand the reason for such a request. He had left Europe as a pauper and he had no intention of returning as one. It was I who had induced him to come to America, and I had promised to take care of him. It was not his wish to return to Paris, but mine. I wanted to get rid of him, renounce my sacred obligation. As for the money I had spent thus far—he referred to it as if it were a bagatelle—he begged to remind me that he had left with me as a gift an heirloom, his one and only material possession, which was priceless. (He meant the *pendule,* of course.)

I was outraged. I wrote back at once that if he didn't take the plane this time, if he didn't get the hell out of the country and leave me in peace, I would cut him off. I said I didn't give a shit what became of him. He could jump off the Golden Gate Bridge, for all I cared. In a postscript I informed him that Lilik would be there to see him in a day or two, *with the pendule,* which he could shove up his ass, or pawn and live on the proceeds for the rest of his days.

Now the letters came thick and fast. He was in a panic. Cut him off? Leave him destitute? Alone in a foreign land? A man who was ill, who was getting old, who had no right to seek employment? No, I would never do that! Not the Miller he had known of old, the Miller with a great, compassionate heart who gave to one and all, who had taken pity on him, a miserable wretch, and sworn to provide for him as long as he lived!

"Yes," I wrote back, "it is the same Miller. He is fed up. He is disgusted. He wants nothing more to do with you." I called him a worm, a leech, a dirty blackmailer.

He turned to my wife. Long, whining letters, full of self-pity. Surely *she* understood his plight! The good Miller had taken leave of his senses, he had made himself into stone. *Le pauvre,* he would regret it some day. And so on and so on.

I urged my wife to ignore his pleas. I doubt that she heeded me. She felt sorry for him. It was her belief that he would come to his senses at the last minute, take the plane, forget his foolish demand. "Foolish!" she called it.

I thought of Ramakrishna's words regarding the "bound" souls. "Those who are thus caught in the net of the world are the *Baddha,* or bound souls. No one can awaken them. They do not come to their senses, even after receiving blow upon blow of misery, sorrow and indescribable suffering."

I thought of many, many things during the hectic days which followed. Particularly of the beggar's life I had led, first at home, then abroad. I thought of the cold refusals I had received at the hands of intimate friends, of so-called "buddies," in fact. I thought of the meals which were dished up to me, when I hung on like a shipwrecked sailor. And the sermons that accompanied them. I thought of the times I had stood in front of restaurant windows, watching people eat—people who didn't need food, who had already eaten too much—and how I vainly hoped they would recognize the look in my eye, invite me in, beg me to share their repast, or offer me the remnants. I thought of the handouts I had received, the dimes that were flung at me in passing, or perhaps a handful of pennies, and how like a whipped cur, I had taken what was offered while cursing the bastards under my breath. No matter how many refusals I received, and they were countless, no matter how many insults and humiliations were flung at me, a crust of bread was always a crust of bread—and if I didn't always thank the giver graciously or humbly, I did thank my lucky star. I may have thought once upon a time that something more than a crust of bread was my due, that the most worthless wretch, at least in a civilized country, was entitled to a meal when he needed it. But it wasn't long before I learned to take a larger view of things. I not only learned how to say "Thank you, sir!" but how to stand on my hind legs and beg for it. It didn't embitter me hopelessly. In fact, I found it rather comical after a while. It's an experience we all need now and then, especially those of us who were born with silver spoons in our mouths.

But that bastard, Moricand! To twist things the way he did! To make it appear, if only to himself, that in promising to take care of him I was obligated to keep him in a hotel, dole out cash for drink, theatre, taxis. And, if that proved irksome, why just deposit a thousand dollars to his account in Paris. Because he, Moricand, refused to be a pauper again!

I'm on the corner of Broadway and 42nd Street again. A chilly night, and the rain beating in my face. Scanning the throng once again for a friendly face, for a fleeting look that will assure me I won't get a rebuff, won't get a gob of spit instead of a handout. Here's a likely one! "Hey, mister, *please,* can you spare enough for a cup of coffee?" He gives it without stopping, without even looking me in the face. A dime! A lovely, shining little offering. A whole dime! How ducky it would be if one could only catch a generous soul like that on the wing, grab his coattail, pull him gently around, and say with utter conviction and the innocence of a dove: *"Mister,* what can I do with this? I haven't eaten since yesterday morning. I'm cold and wet through. My wife's home waiting for me. She's hungry too. And ill. Couldn't you give me a dollar, or maybe two dollars? *Mister,* we need it bad, terribly bad."

No, it's not in the book, that kind of talk. One has to be grateful even for a Canadian dime—or a stale crust of bread. Grateful that when it comes *your* time to be hooked, you can say—and mean it with all your heart!—"Here, take this! Do what you like with it!" And so saying, empty your pockets. So saying, *you* walk home in the rain, *you* go without a meal!

Have I ever done it? Of course I have. Many's the time. And it felt marvelous to do it. Almost too marvelous. It's easy to empty your pockets when you see your other self standing there like a dog, begging, whimpering, cringing. It's easy to go without a meal when you know you can have one for the asking. Or that tomorrow's another day. Nothing to it. It's you, Prince Bountiful, as gets the better of the deal. No wonder we hang our heads in shame when we perform a simple act of charity.

I wonder sometimes why rich guys never understand this business, why they never take the opportunity to give themselves a cheap puffing up? Think of Henry Miller, the uncrowned emperor of California, coming out of the bank each morning with a pocket filled with quarters, handing them out like King Solomon to the poor blokes lined up the sidewalk, each and every one mumbling humbly, "Thank you, sir!" and raising his hat respectfully. What better tonic could you give yourself, if you had a soul as mean as that, before tackling the day's work?

As for that phony bastard, Moricand, in his palmy days he had been quite a giver too, from all I have heard. Nor had he ever refused to share what he had when he had little or nothing. But he had never gone out into the street and begged for it! When he begged it was on good stationery, in elegant script—grammar, syntax, punctuation always perfect. Never had he sat down to pen a begging letter in trousers that had holes in the seat, or even patches. The room may have been ice cold, his belly may have been empty, the butt in his mouth may have been rescued from the waste basket, but. . . . I think it's clear what I'm getting at.

Anyway, he didn't take the second plane either. And when he wrote, saying that he was putting a curse on me, I didn't doubt for a minute that he meant just what he said. To avoid a repetition, I promptly informed his Satanic majesty that any subsequent letters from him would be left unopened. And with that off my chest, I consigned him to his fate. Never again would he see my handwriting, nor the color of my money.

This didn't stop the flow of letters, to be sure. Letters continued to arrive, *toujours plus espaceés,* but they were never opened. They are now in the library at U.C.L.A. Still sealed.

I recall of a sudden the way he worded his break with Cendrars, his old friend of the Foreign Legion days. It was one of those evenings when he had been reviewing the good old days, the wonderful friends he had made—Cendrars, Cocteau, Radiguet, Kisling, Modigliani, Max Jacob, *et alii*—and how one by one they had disappeared, or else deserted him. All but Max. Max had been faithful to the end. But Cendrars, whom he spoke of so warmly, whom he still admired with all his heart—why had Cendrars also deserted him? Here is the way he put it:

"One day—you know how he is!—he got angry with me. And that was the end. I could never reach him again. I tried, but it was useless. The door was shut."

I never revealed to him what Cendrars had said to me one day, in the year 1938, when I made the horrible mistake of telling him that I had become acquainted with his old friend Moricand.

"Moricand?" he said. *"Ce n'est pas un ami. C'est un cadavre vivant."* And the door went shut with a bang.

Well, the *pendule.* I had given it to Lilik to deliver to Moricand. And Lilik had taken it into his head to find out just how valuable the damned thing was. So, before delivering it, he takes it to the very watchmaker whose address Moricand had given me in the event that it should need repair. Its value? According to this bid, who knew something about timepieces, one would be lucky to get fifty dollars for it. An antique dealer might offer a little more. Not much more, however.

"That's ridiculous," I said, when he recounted the incident.

"That's what I thought," said Lilik. "So I took it to an antique dealer, and then to a hock shop. Same story. No market for such junk. They all admired it, of course. Wonderful mechanism. But who wants it?"

"I thought you'd like to know," he added, "since the bugger always made such a fuss about it."

He then went on to tell me of his telephone conversation with Moricand. (Seems the latter was too wrought up to receive him.) It was a conversation that lasted almost a half hour. With Moricand doing all the talking.

"Too bad you weren't there," said Lilik. "He was in top form. I never knew anyone could be so furious, so venomous, and talk so brilliantly at the same time. The things he said about you . . . Jesus, it would burn you up! And the names he called you! You know, after the first few minutes I began to enjoy it. Now and then I helped him along, just to see how far he *would* go. Anyway, be on your guard! He's going to do everything in his power to make trouble for you. I really think he's out of his mind. *Cuckoo.* Absolutely. . . . The last thing I remember him saying was that I would read about you in the French papers. He was formulating a *plaidoyer.* Said he would give them, your admirers, the lowdown on their beloved Henry Miller, author of the *Tropics,* sage of the mountain top . . . *'Quel farceur!'* That was his parting shot."

"Didn't he say—*'Je l'aurai'?"*

"Yeah, that's right. He did too."

"I thought as much. *Le couillon!'"*

The first intimation I had of Moricand's maneuvers was a letter from the Swiss Consulate in San Francisco. It was a polite, formal letter, informing me of Moricand's visit to their office, his desperate plight, and ended with a desire to have my view of the matter. I replied at some length, offering to send copies of Moricand's letters, and repeating what I had told Moricand, that I was through and that nothing would make me change my mind. To this I received a reply reminding me that, no matter what had taken place, I was, from an official standpoint, Moricand's sponsor. Would I mind sending the letters I had spoken of?

I sent photostat copies of the letters. Then I waited for the next move.

I could well imagine what must have ensued at this point. One couldn't repudiate what was written in one's own hand.

The next letter was to the effect that Moricand's was indeed a knotty case, that the poor fellow was obviously not all there. It went on to say that the Consulate would be only too glad to ship him back home had they funds for such a purpose. (They never do, of course.) Perhaps if he, the Vice-Consul, were to come down and talk it over with me, some suitable compromise might be arranged. Meanwhile they would look after Moricand as best they could.

Well, he came, and we had a long talk. Fortunately, my wife was there to corroborate my statements. Finally, after a snack, he brought forth a camera and took some snapshots of us and the surroundings. The place enchanted him. He asked if he could come again, as a friend.

"And that idiot couldn't stand it here!" he said, shaking his head. "Why, it's a Paradise."

"Paradise lost!" I countered.

"What will you do with him?" I ventured to ask, as he was leaving. He shrugged his shoulders.

"What *can* one do?" he said, "with a creature like that?"

Thanking me warmly for all I had done in behalf of a compatriot, expressing his regret for any annoyance he had caused me, he then said: "You must be a man of great patience."

I never had another word from him. Nor did I ever learn what happened to Moricand—until I received a copy of *Le Goéland,* the issue for July-August-September, 1954, announcing the news of his death. It was from the editor of *Le Goéland,* Théophile Briant— Moricand's last and only friend—that I recently received a few facts relating to the interval between our leave-taking in Monterey, hardly three months after his arrival in Big Sur, and his pitiful end.

It was in March 1948 when we parted. How he lasted until the fall of 1949, when he was deported by the immigration authorities, remains a mystery. Not even Briant could tell me much about this period. It was a black one, *évidemment.* Toward the end of September he appeared at Briant's home in Brittany, where he had been offered refuge. Here he lasted only six weeks. As Briant tactfully put it in his letter, "I perceived all too quickly that a life in common could not be prolonged indefinitely." Thus, the 17th of November his faithful friend drove him to Paris—and installed him in the same old Hotel Modial. Here, though he held out for some time, things went rapidly from bad to worse. Finally, in utter despair, fate decreed that he should accept the last humiliation, that is, apply for admission to a Swiss retreat for the aged on the Avenue de St. Mandé, Paris. It was an institution founded by his own parents. Here he chose a small cell giving on the courtyard, where from his window he could see the plaque commemorating the inauguration of the establishment by his mother and his brother, Dr. Ivan Moricand.

"Tous ses amis," writes Briant, *"sauf moi, l'avaient aban-*

donné. Ses nombreux manuscrits étaient refoulés chez les édi-
teurs. Et bien entendu, des drames épais surgirent bientôt entre
lui et les directrices de l'Asile. Je m'efforcai de le calmer, lui
représentant que cette cellule, qu'il avait d'ailleurs merveilleuse-
ment aménagée, constituait son ultime havre de grâce."

The end came quite suddenly. According to Briant's obituary article in *Le Goéland,* on the morning of the day he died Moricand received a visit from a dear friend, a woman. This was towards noon. As they parted he informed her quite simply that she would never see him again. As he seemed to be in good health and good spirits, and since nothing in their conversation had warranted such a remark, she dismissed it as a *boutade.* That very afternoon, towards four o'clock, he had a heart attack. He went to the kitchen for aid, but despite his grave condition no one saw any reason for alarm. A doctor was called but he was busy. He would come later, when he was free. When he did arrive it was too late. There was nothing to do but rush poor Moricand, already breathing his last, to the hospital. He was unconscious when they delivered him to the Hospital St. Antoine. At ten-thirty that evening he died without regaining consciousness. August 31st, 1954.

In his last moments, writes Briant, he was *"seul comme un rat,* *nu comme le dernier des clochards."*

The
Smile at the Foot
of the Ladder

Nothing could diminish the lustre of that extraordinary smile which was engraved on Auguste's sad countenance. In the ring this smile took on a quality of its own, detached, magnified, expressing the ineffable.

At the foot of a ladder reaching to the moon, Auguste would sit in contemplation, his smile fixed, his thoughts far away. This simulation of ecstasy, which he had brought to perfection, always impressed the audience as the summation of the incongruous. The great favorite had many tricks up his sleeve but this one was inimitable. Never had a buffoon thought to depict the miracle of ascension.

Night in and night out he would sit thus, waiting to be nubbed by the white horse whose mane fell to the ground in rivulets of gold. The touch of the mare's warm muzzle on his neck was like the departing kiss of a loved one; it awakened him gently, as gently as the dew enlivening each blade of grass.

Within the radius of the spotlight lay the world in which he was born anew each evening. It comprised only those objects, creatures and beings which move in the circle of enchantment. A table, a chair, a rug; a horse, a bell, a paper hoop; the eternal ladder, the moon nailed to the roof, the bladder of a goat. With these Auguste and his companions managed each night to reproduce the drama of initiation and martyrdom.

Bathed in concentric circles of shadow, there rose tier upon tier of faces, broken here and there by empty spaces which the spotlight licked with the avidity of a tongue in search of a missing tooth. The musicians, swimming in dust and magnesium rays, clung to their instruments as if hallucinated, their bodies swaying like reeds in the flickering play of light and shadow. The contortionist always moved to the muffled roll of the drum, the bareback rider was always introduced with a fanfare of trumpets. As for Auguste, sometimes it was the thin squeak of a violin, sometimes the mocking notes of the clarinet, which followed him about as he capered through his antics. But when the moment came to enter the trance, the musicians, suddenly inspired, would pursue Auguste from one spiral of bliss to the next, like chargers nailed to the platform of a carousel which has run wild.

Each evening, as he applied the *maquillage*, Auguste would hold a debate with himself. The seals, no matter what they were obliged to do, always remained seals. The horse remained a horse, the table a table. Whereas Auguste, while remaining a man, had to become something more: he had to assume the powers of a very special being with a very special gift. He had to make people laugh. It was not difficult to make people weep, nor even to make them laugh; he had found this out long ago, before he had ever dreamed of joining the circus. Auguste, however, had greater aspirations—he wanted to endow his spectators with a joy which would prove imperishable. It was this obsession which had originally prompted him to sit at the foot of the ladder and feign ecstasy. It was by sheer accident that he had fallen into the semblance of a trance—he had forgotten what it was he was supposed to do next. When he came to, somewhat bewildered and extremely apprehensive, he found himself being applauded wildly. The following evening he repeated the experiment, deliberately this time, praying that the senseless, raucous laughter which he so easily evoked would give way to that joy supreme which he longed to communicate. But each night, despite his almost devout efforts, the same delirious applause awaited him.

The more successful it was, this little skit at the foot of the ladder, the more wistful Auguste became. Each night the laughter become more jarring to his ears. Finally it became unbearable. One night the laughter suddenly changed to jeers and cat-calls, followed by hats, refuse and more solid objects too. Auguste had failed to "come back." For thirty minutes the audience had waited; then it had grown uneasy, then suspicious, with the tension finally snapping in an explosive outburst of derision. When Auguste came to in his dressing room he was astounded to find a physician bending over him. His face and head were a mass of cuts and bruises. The blood had coagulated over the paint, distorting his image beyond recognition. He looked like something which had been abandoned on the butcher's block.

His contract abruptly terminated, Auguste fled from the world he knew. Having no desire to resume his life as a clown, he took to wandering. He drifted unknown, unrecognized, among the millions whom he had taught to laugh. There was no resentment in his heart, only a deep sadness. It was a constant fight to keep back the tears. At first he accepted this new condition of the heart. It was nothing more, he told himself, than a malaise created by the sudden interruption of a lifelong routine. But when months had gone by he gradually came to realize that he was mourning the loss of something which had been taken from him—not the power to make people laugh, ah no! that he no longer cared about—something else, something deeper than that, something which was uniquely his own. Then one day it dawned on him that it was long, long ago since he had known the state of bliss. He trembled so upon discovering this that he could not wait to get to his room. Instead of rushing to his hotel, however, he hailed a taxi and ordered the driver to take him to the outskirts of the town. But where to exactly? the driver wanted to know. "Wherever there are trees," said Auguste impatiently. "But make haste, I beg—it's urgent."

Outside a coal yard they came upon a lone tree. Auguste ordered the driver to stop. "Is this the place?" asked the driver innocently.

"Yes, leave me in peace," responded Auguste.

For an endless time, it seemed, Auguste struggled to recreate a semblance of the mood which usually served as a prelude to the nightly performance at the foot of the ladder. Unfortunately the light was harsh: a scorching sun seared his eyeballs. "I shall just sit here," he thought to himself, "until night falls. When the moon comes out everything will fall into place." In a few moments he dozed off. It was a heavy sleep in which he dreamed that he was back again in the ring. Everything was as it had always been, except that it was no longer a circus in which things were going on. The roof had disappeared, the walls had fallen away. Above him was the real moon high in the heavens, a moon that seemed to race through stationary clouds. Instead of the usual circular tiers of benches there rose at a gentle incline, and straight to the sky, literally walls of people. Not a laugh could be heard, not a murmur. They hung there, these vast multitudes of spectres, suspended in fathomless space, each and every one of them crucified. Paralyzed with fear, Auguste forgot what it was he was supposed to do. After an intolerable period of suspense, during which it seemed to him that he was more cruelly deserted and abandoned than the Saviour himself had ever been, Auguste made a frantic dash to escape the arena. But in whichever direction he ran the exits were blocked. In desperation he took to the ladder, started climbing feverishly, and climbed and climbed until his breath gave out. After due pause he ventured to open his eyes wide and look about him. First he looked downward. The foot of the ladder was almost invisible, so far below lay the earth. Then he looked upward; rung after rung stretched above him, endlessly, piercing the clouds, piercing the very blue in which the stars were cushioned. Straight to the moon rose the ladder. It was a moon which lay beyond the stars, a moon infinitely remote, glued like a frozen disk to the vault above. Auguste began to weep and then to sob. Like an echo, faint, restrained at first, but gradually swelling into an oceanic wail, there came to his ears the groans and sobs of the countless multitude which walled him about. "Horrible," muttered Auguste. "It is like birth and death at once. I am a prisoner in Purgatory." With this he swooned, falling backwards into nothingness. He regained consciousness just as he realized that the earth was pressing forward to receive him. That, he knew, would be the end of Auguste, the real end, the death of deaths. And then, like a knife gleam, there came a flash of memory. Not another second was left him; a half second, perhaps, and he would be no more. What was it that had stirred in the depths of his being, flashed like a blade, only to precede him into oblivion? He thought with such rapidity that in the fleeting fraction of a second which was left him he was able to summon up the whole pageant of his life. But the most important moment in his life, the jewel about which all the meaningful events of the past clustered, he could not revive. It was revelation itself which was foundering with him. For he knew now that at some moment in time all had been made clear to him. And now that he was about to die, this, the supreme gift, was being snatched from him. Like a miser, with a cunning and an ingenuity beyond all reckoning, Auguste succeeded in doing the impossible: seizing this last fraction of a second which had been allotted him, he began dividing it into infinitesimal moments of duration. Nothing he had experienced during the forty years of his life, not all the moments of joy put together, could begin to compare with the sensual delight he now experienced in husbanding these splintered fragments of an exploded fraction of a second. But when he had chopped this last moment of time into infinitesimal bits, so that it spread about him like a vast web of duration, he made the alarming discovery that he had lost the power to remember. He had blanked himself out.

The following day, emotionally exhausted by the ravages of this dream, Auguste decided to remain in his room. It was only towards evening that he bestirred himself. He had spent the whole day in bed, listlessly toying with the throngs of memory which for some inexplicable reason had descended upon him like a plague of locusts. Finally, weary of being buffeted about in this vast cauldron of reminiscence, he dressed himself and sauntered out to lose himself in the crowd. It was with some difficulty that he managed to recall the name of the town through whose streets he was strolling.

At the outskirts of the town he came upon a group of circus folk, one of those fugitive bands of players who live on wheels. Auguste's heart began to beat wildly. Impulsively he rushed to one of the *roulottes*—they had been drawn up in the form of a circle— and timidly mounted the little steps which had been dropped from the rear of the vehicle. He was about to knock when the neighing of a horse close beside him arrested him. The next instant the muzzle of the horse was grazing his back. A deep joy pervaded Auguste's whole being. Putting his arms about the animal's neck, he spoke in gentle, soothing words, as if greeting a long lost friend.

The door behind him opened suddenly and a woman's voice smothered an exclamation of surprise. Startled almost out of his wits, he mumbled: "It's only me, Auguste."

"Auguste?" she repeated after him. "Don't know him."

"Excuse me," he mumbled apologetically, "I must be going."

He had gone only a few steps when he heard the woman shouting: "Hey there, Auguste, come back here! What are you running away for?"

He stopped dead, turned around, hesitated a moment, then broke into a broad grin. The woman flew towards him, arms outstretched. A mild panic seized Auguste. For a brief moment he had a notion to turn and flee. But it was too late. The woman's arms were now about him, clasping him tight.

"Auguste, Auguste!" she exclaimed over and over. "To think I didn't recognize you!"

At this Auguste paled. It was the first time in all his wandering that any one had caught up with him. The woman was still holding him like a vise. Now she was kissing him, first on one cheek, then the other, then the brow, then the lips. Auguste was quaking.

"Could I have a lump of sugar?" he begged, as soon as he could disengage himself.

"Sugar?"

"Yes, for the horse," said Auguste.

While the woman rummaged about inside the van Auguste made himself comfortable on the little steps. With soft, tremulous muzzle the horse was licking the back of his neck. It was just at this moment, strange coincidence, that the moon shook itself clear of the distant tree tops. A wonderful calm fell upon Auguste. For just a few seconds—it could have been hardly more than that—he enjoyed a sort of twilight sleep. Then the woman came bouncing out, her loose skirt brushing his shoulder as she leapt to the ground.

"We all thought you were dead," were her first words, as she seated herself on the grass by his feet. "The whole world has been looking for you," she added rapidly, passing him one lump of sugar after another.

Auguste listened mutely as the woman rattled on. The sense of her words came to him slowly, very slowly, as if traveling to his ears from some far distance. What enthralled him was the delicious sensation which spread through his body whenever the warm wet muzzle of the horse licked the palm of his hand. He was reliving intensely that intermediate stage which he used to experience nightly at the foot of the ladder, the period between the falling away of bliss and the wild burst of applause which always came to his ears like the roll of distant thunder.

Auguste never even thought of returning to the hotel to gather his few belongings. He spread a blanket on the ground beside a fire and, locked within the magic circle of wheels and wagons, he lay awake following the lurid course of the moon. When he at last closed his eyes it was with the decision to follow the troupe. He knew that he could trust them to keep his identity secret.

To help set up the tent, to roll the big rugs out, to move the props about, to water the horses and groom them, to do the thousand and one chores which were required of him, all this was sheer joy to Auguste. He lost himself with abandon in the pursuance of the menial tasks which filled his days. Now and then he indulged himself in the luxury of observing the performance as a spectator. It was with new eyes he noted the skill and the fortitude of his companions in travel. The miming of the clowns particularly intrigued him; it was a dumb show whose language was more eloquent to him now than when he was one of them. He had a sense of freedom which he had forfeited as a performer. O, but it was good to throw off one's role, to immerse oneself in the humdrum of life, to become as dust and yet . . . well, to know that one was still part of it all, still useful, perhaps even more useful thus. What egotism it was to imagine that because he could make men laugh and cry he was rendering them a great boon! He no longer received applause, nor gales of laughter, nor adulation. He was receiving something far better, far more sustaining—*smiles*. Smiles of gratitude? No. Smiles of recognition. He was accepted again as a human being, accepted for himself, for whatever it was that distinguished him from, and at the same time united him with, his fellow man. It was like receiving small change which, when one is in need, regenerates the heart's flow in a way that bank notes never do.

With these warm smiles which he garnered like ripe grain each day Auguste expanded, blossomed anew. Endowed with a feeling of inexhaustible bounty, he was always eager to do more than was demanded of him. Nothing one could ask of him was too much— that was how he felt. There was a little phrase he mumbled to himself continually as he went about his tasks: "*à votre service.*" With the animals he would raise his voice, there being no need to withhold such simple words from them. "*A votre service,*" he would say to the mare, as he slipped the feed bag over her head. To the seals likewise, as he patted their gleaming backs. Sometimes, too, stumbling out of the big tent into the starlit night, he would look above as if trying to pierce the veil which protects our eyes from the glory of creation, and he would murmur softly and reverently: "*A votre service, Grand Seigneur!*"

Never had Auguste known such peace, such contentment, such deep, lasting joy. Pay days he would go to town with his meagre earnings and wander through the shops, searching for gifts to bring the children—and the animals too. For himself a bit of tobacco, nothing more.

Then one day Antoine, the clown, fell ill. Auguste was sitting in front of one of the *roulottes*, mending an old pair of trousers, when the news was brought him. He mumbled a few words of sympathy and continued with his mending. He realized immediately, of course, that this unexpected event involved him. He would be asked to substitute for Antoine, no doubt about it. Auguste endeavored to quell the excitement which was rapidly mounting in him. He tried to think quietly and soberly what answer he would give when the moment came.

He waited and waited for some one to return, but no one came. No one else could take Antoine's place, he was certain of that. What was holding them back then? Finally he got up and wandered about, just to let them know he was there, that they could put the question to him whenever they wished. Still no one made effort to engage him in conversation.

At last he decided to break the ice himself. Why not, after all? Why shouldn't he volunteer his services? He felt so fortified, so full of good will towards every one. To be a clown again, it was nothing, nothing at all. He could just as well be a table, a chair, a ladder, if need be. He wanted no special privileges; he was one of them, ready to share their sorrows and misfortunes.

"Look," he said to the boss whom he had finally collared, "I'm thoroughly prepared to take Antoine's place tonight. That is," and he hesitated a moment, "unless you have some one else in mind."

"No, Auguste, there is no one else, as you know. It's good of you to offer . . ."

"But what?" snapped Auguste. "Are you afraid perhaps that I can no longer perform?"

"No, not that, not that. No, it would be a privilege to have you . . ."

"But what then?" demanded Auguste, almost trembling with apprehension, for he realized now that it was delicacy and tact with which he had to deal.

"Well, it's like this," the boss began in his slow, lumbering way. "You see, we've been talking it over among ourselves. We know how things are with you. Now then, if you were to take Antoine's place . . . damn it, what am I saying? Come, don't stand there looking at me like that! Look, Auguste, what I'm trying to say is . . . well, just this . . . we don't want to open old wounds. You understand?"

Auguste felt the tears rushing to his eyes. He grasped the other's two big hands, held them gently in his own and, without opening his mouth, poured out his thanks.

"Do let me take over tonight," he begged. "I'm yours as long as it's necessary—for a week, a month, six months. It will give me pleasure, that's the truth. You won't say no, hein?"

Some hours later Auguste was seated before the mirror, studying his face. It had been his habit, before applying the paint each night, to sit and stare at himself for long intervals. It was his way of preparing himself for the performance. He would sit looking at his own sad face and then suddenly he would begin erasing this image and impose a new one, one which every one knew and which was accepted everywhere as Auguste. The real Auguste no one knew, not even his friends, for with fame he had become a solitary.

Seated thus, invaded by memories of thousands of other nights before the mirror, Auguste began to realize that this life apart, this life which he had jealously guarded as his own, this secret existence which supposedly preserved his identity, was not a life at all, was nothing in fact, not even a shadow life. He had only begun to live from the day he had taken up with the troupe, from the moment he had begun to serve in the capacity of the humblest. That secret life had vanished almost without his knowing it; he was a man again like other men, doing all the foolish, trifling, necessary things which others did—and he had been happy thus, his days had been full. Tonight he would appear not as Auguste, the world-celebrated clown, but as Antoine, whom nobody had heard of. Because he had neither name nor fame, Antoine was accepted each night as a matter of course. No wild applause followed his exit from the ring; people simply smiled indulgently, showing no more appreciation of his art than they did of the amazing stunts of the seals.

At this point a disturbing thought suddenly shattered his reverie. Heretofore it was that private, empty life which he had struggled to shield from the public eye. But what if this evening some one should recognize him, recognize the clown Auguste? That would indeed be a calamity! Never again would he have any peace; he would be pursued from town to town, pressed to explain his strange behavior, importuned to resume his proper place in the world of *vedettes*. In some vague way he sensed that they might even accuse him of murdering Auguste. Auguste had become an idol; he belonged to the world. No telling to what lengths they would go to harass him . . .

There was a knock at the door. Some one had popped in just to see if everything was going all right. After a few words Auguste inquired how Antoine was doing. "Improving, I hope?"

"No," said the other gravely, "he seems to be getting worse. No one knows just what's wrong with him. Perhaps you would say a word to him before you go on, yes?"

"Certainly," said Auguste, "I'll be with you in a few minutes," and he proceeded with his make-up.

Antoine was tossing about feverishly when Auguste entered. Bending over the sick man, Auguste took Antoine's moist hand in his. "Poor fellow," he murmured, "what can I do for you?"

Antoine stared up at him blankly for several long minutes. He was staring with the expression of one looking at himself in a mirror. Auguste slowly understood what was passing through Antoine's mind. "It's me, Auguste," he said softly.

"I know," said Antoine. "It's *you* . . . but it could also be *me*. Nobody will know the difference. And you are great and I have never been anybody."

"I was thinking that very thing myself just a few moments ago," said Auguste with a wistful smile. "It's droll, what! A little grease paint, a bladder, a funny costume—how little it takes to make oneself into a nobody! That's what we are—*nobodies*. And *everybody* at the same time. It's not us they applaud, it's themselves. My dear fellow, I must be going in a moment, but first let me tell you a little thing I learned recently. . . . To be yourself, just yourself, is a great thing. And how does one do it, how does one bring it about? Ah, that's the most difficult trick of all. It's difficult just because it involves no effort. You try neither to be one thing nor another, neither great nor small, neither clever nor maladroit . . . you follow me? You do whatever comes to hand. You do it with good grace, *bien entendu*. Because nothing is unimportant. Nothing. Instead of laughter and applause you receive smiles. Contented little smiles—that's all. But it's everything . . . more than one could ask for. You go about doing the dirty work, relieving people of their burdens. It makes them happy, but it makes *you* much happier, do you see? Of course you must do it inconspicuously, so to say. You must never let them know what pleasure it gives you. Once they catch on to you, once they learn your secret, you are lost to them. They will call you selfish, no matter how much you do for them. You can do everything for them—literally kill yourself in harness—so long as they do not suspect that they are enriching you, giving you a joy you could never give yourself. . . . Well, excuse me, Antoine, I didn't mean to make a long speech. Anyway, tonight it is you who are making me a gift. Tonight I can be myself in being you. That is even better than being yourself, *compris*?''

Here Auguste checked himself, for in giving expression to this last thought he had suddenly hit upon a genial idea. It was not one to be imparted to Antoine then and there, however. There was a certain risk involved, an element of danger possibly. But he wouldn't think of that. He must hurry now, work it out as quickly as possible . . . this very night perhaps.

"Look, Antoine," he said almost gruffly, making ready to leave, "I will go on tonight, and maybe tomorrow night too, but after that you had better be up and about. I'm not eager to become a clown again, you understand? I'll drop in on you in the morning. There's something more I want to tell you, something that will buck you up!" He paused a moment, cleared his throat. "You always wanted to be a big shot, didn't you? Just remember that! I'm nursing an idea: it's for you to take advantage of. So long now, sleep well!" He patted Antoine roughly, as if to push him into well-being. Moving towards the door he caught the faint suggestion of a smile stealing over Antoine's lips. He closed the door softly and tiptoed out into the darkness.

As he strode towards the big tent, humming to himself, the idea which had seized him a few moments ago began to formulate itself more distinctly. He could scarcely wait for his cue, so keen was he to bring his plan to fruition. "Tonight," he said to himself, as he stood champing at the bit, "I shall give a performance such as no one has ever seen. Just wait, my buckos, just wait till Auguste takes over.''

He whipped himself into such a frenzy of impatience that when he emerged into the spotlight, accompanied by a few thin squeaks from the violin, he was cavorting like a crazy goat. From the moment his feet touched the sawdust it was sheer improvisation. Not one of these wild, senseless capers had he ever thought of before, much less rehearsed. He had given himself a clean slate and on it he was writing Antoine's name in indelible letters. If only Antoine were there, could witness his own début as a world figure!

In the space of a few minutes Auguste was aware that he held the audience in the palm of his hand. And he had hardly unlimbered, so to speak. "Wait, wait, my lads!" he kept mumbling as he flung himself about, "this is nothing yet. Antoine is only just being born, he hasn't even begun to kick his legs."

The preliminary skit over, he immediately found himself surrounded by an excited group. Among them was the boss. "But you must be mad!" were the latter's first words. "Are you trying to ruin Antoine?"

"Have no fear," said Auguste, flushing with joy. "I am *making* Antoine. Be patient. I assure you all will end well."

"But it's too good already, that's what I'm growling about. After this performance Antoine will be finished."

There was no time for more words. The ring had to be cleared for the trapeze artists. As the troupe was a small one, every one had to pitch in.

When it came time for the clowns to appear again there was a prolonged burst of applause. Auguste had scarcely shown his head when the audience burst into cheers. "Antoine! Antoine!" they shouted, stamping their feet, whistling, clapping their hands with joy. "Give us Antoine!"

It was at this point in the evening's entertainment that Antoine usually gave a solo performance, a rather worn little act from which the last breath of invention had evaporated years ago. Observing this routine night after night, Auguste had often thought to himself just how he would alter each little turn, were he obliged to do it himself. He now found himself executing the gags which he had so often rehearsed, sometimes in his sleep. He felt very much like a master putting the finishing touches to a portrait which a negligent pupil had abandoned. Except for the subject, there would be nothing left of the original. One began by touching it up here and there, and one ended by creating something wholly new.

Auguste went to it like an inspired maniac. There was nothing to lose. On the contrary, there was everything to gain. Each new twist or wrinkle meant a fresh lease of life, *for Antoine*. As he proceeded to perfect the turn from one phase to the next, Auguste made mental notes to explain to Antoine exactly how to reproduce the effects he was achieving. He was hopping about like three different beings at once: Auguste the master, Auguste as Antoine, and Antoine as Auguste. And above and beyond these there hovered a fourth entity which would crystallize and become more manifest with time: Antoine as **Antoine**. A new-born Antoine, to be sure, an Antoine *in excelsis.* The more he thought of this Antoine (it was amazing how much speculation he could indulge in while holding forth) the more considerate he was of the limits and susceptibilities of the figure he was recreating. It was Antoine he kept thinking of, not Auguste. Auguste was dead. He had not the slightest desire to see him reincarnated as the world-renowned Antoine. His whole concern was to make Antoine so famous that there would nevermore be mention of Auguste.

Next morning the papers were full of Antoine's praises. Auguste had, of course, explained his project to the boss before retiring that night. It was agreed that every precaution would be taken to keep the plan a secret. Since none but the members of the troupe knew of Antoine's illness, and since Antoine himself was still in ignorance of the glorious future which had been prepared for him, the outlook seemed relatively cheerful.

Auguste, of course, could scarcely wait to pay the promised visit to Antoine. He had decided not to show him the newspapers immediately but to simply let him know what he hoped to accomplish during the few brief days in which Antoine would be incapacitated. He had to win Antoine over before revealing to him the full extent of his accomplishment, otherwise Antoine might be intimidated by a success which he had acquired ready-made. All this Auguste rehearsed step by step before heading for Antoine's quarters. Not once did it occur to him that what he was about to propose was beyond Antoine's power of acceptance.

He held himself back until almost noon, hoping that by that time Antoine would be in the proper mood to receive him. When he set forth he was jubilant. He was certain he could convince Antoine that the heritage he was leaving him was a legitimate one. "After all," he said to himself, "it's just a little push I'm giving him. Life is full of little dodges which we must avail ourselves of. No man gets there alone, unaided." With this off his chest, he almost began to trot. "I'm not cheating or robbing him," he continued. "He always wanted to be famous, now he *is* famous! or he *will* be a week from now. Antoine will be Antoine . . . only more so. That's all there is to it. All it needs sometimes is just a little accident, a trick of fortune, a push from the beyond, and there you are—out in the limelight and on all fours."

Here he recalled his own sudden rise to fame. What had he, Auguste, to do with it? What had been a mere accident was acclaimed overnight as a stroke of genius. How little the public understood! How little any one understood, where fate was concerned. To be a clown was to be fate's pawn. The life in the arena was a dumb show consisting of falls, slaps, kicks—an endless shuffling and booting about. And it was by means of this disgraceful rigolade that one found favor with the public. The beloved clown! It was his special privilege to reenact the errors, the follies, the stupidities, all the misunderstandings which plague human kind. To be ineptitude itself, that was something even the dullest oaf could grasp. Not to understand, when all is clear as daylight; not to catch on, though the trick he repeated a thousand times for you; to grope about like a blind man, when all signs point the right direction; to insist on opening the wrong door, though it is marked *Danger!*; to walk head on into the mirror, instead of going around it; to look through the wrong end of a rifle, a *loaded* rifle!—people never tired of these absurdities because for millennia humans have traversed all the wrong roads, because for millennia all their seeking and questioning have landed them in a *cul-de-sac*. The master of ineptitude has all time as his domain. He surrenders only in the face of eternity. . . .

It was in the midst of such strange preoccupations that he caught sight of Antoine's *roulotte*. It startled him somewhat, though he knew not why, to observe the boss coming towards him, obviously from Antoine's bedside. He was even more startled when the boss raised his hand, motioning him to stop where he was. The expression on the man's face awakened in Auguste a distinct feeling of alarm. He stood where he was, obediently, waiting for the other to open his mouth.

When within a few feet of Auguste, the man suddenly threw up both arms in a gesture of despair and resignation. Auguste had no need to hear a word, he knew then what to expect.

"But when did it happen?" asked Auguste, after they had walked a few yards.

"Only a few minutes ago. Like that, it happened. Right in my arms."

"I don't understand," mumbled Auguste. "What *was* it that could have killed him? He was not so ill as all that last night when I spoke to him."

"Exactly," said the other.

There was something about this "exactly" which made Auguste jump.

"You don't mean. . . ?" He broke off; it was too fantastic, he refused to harbor the thought. But the next instant he broke out with it just the same. "You don't mean," and here he faltered again, "you don't mean that he heard. . . ?"

"Precisely."

Again Auguste jumped.

"If I were asked my candid opinion," continued the boss in the same rasping tone, "I would say that he died of a broken heart."

With this they both halted abruptly.

"Look" said the boss, "it is not your fault. Don't take it too much to heart. I know, we all know, that you are innocent. In any case it's a fact that Antoine would never have made a great clown. Antoine had given up long ago." He mumbled something under his breath, then continued with a sigh: "The question is, how will we explain last night's performance? It will be hard to conceal the truth now, you agree, do you not? We never counted on his dying suddenly, did we?"

There was an interval of silence, then Auguste said quietly: "I think I would like to be alone for a while, do you mind?"

"Righto!" said the boss. "Think it out by yourself. There is still time . . ." He did not add for what.

Distraught, dejected, Auguste wandered off in the direction of the town. He walked for quite a long time with not a thought in his head, just a sort of dull, numb pain permeating his whole body. Finally he took a seat on the edge of a *terrasse* and ordered a drink. No, decidedly he had never reckoned with this eventuality. Another trick of fate. One thing was very clear—either he would have to become Auguste again or Antoine. He could no longer remain anonymous. He fell to thinking of Antoine, of the Antoine whom he had impersonated the night before. Would he be able to go through it again, this evening, with anything like the same verve and gusto? He forgot all about Antoine lying cold and dead in the wagon. Without realizing it, he had stepped into Antoine's shoes. He rehearsed the part with exactitude, analyzing it, picking it to pieces, patching it up, improving it here and there . . . he went on and on, from one turn to another, one audience to another, night after night, town after town. And then suddenly he came to. Suddenly he sat up in his seat, began talking to himself in earnest. "So you're going to become a clown again, is that it? Haven't had enough yet, eh? You killed off Auguste, you murdered Antoine . . . what next? Only two days ago you were a happy man, a free man. Now you're trapped, and a murderer to boot. And you suppose, do you, that with a guilty conscience you can make people laugh? Ah no, that's carrying it a little too far!" Auguste brought his fist down on the marble-topped table, as if to convince himself of the seriousness of his words. "A great performance last night. And why? Because no one suspected that the man who made it great was the famous Auguste. It was talent, genius, they were applauding. Not a soul could have known. Perfect. Full triumph. *And*— Q.E.D.*" Once again he pulled himself up, like a horse. "How's that—*Q.E.D.*? Ah, so that's it! That's why Auguste was so eager to substitute for Antoine. Auguste never cared a button whether Antoine would become great or not, did he? *Yes or No*? Auguste cared only to make certain that the reputation he had created really belonged to him. Auguste jumped to the bait like a fish. Bah!" He spat out a bit of saliva disgustedly.

His throat had become so parched from excitement that he clapped his hands and ordered another drink. "My God," he resumed, after he had wet his palate, "to think that a man can lay such traps for himself! Happy one day, miserable the next. What a fool! What a fool I am!" Here he reflected a moment very soberly. "Well, there's one thing I understand now—my happiness was real but unfounded. I have to recapture it, but honestly this time. I have to hold on to it with two hands, as though it were a precious jewel. I must learn to be happy as Auguste, as the clown that I am."

He took another sip of wine, then shook himself like a dog. "Maybe this is my last chance, I shall start from the bottom once more." With this he fell to speculating on a new name for himself. This game took him far afield. "Yes," he resumed, having forgotten already the name he had decided on, "I'll work out something new, something totally new. If it doesn't make me happy it will at least keep me on the alert. Perhaps South America. . . ."

The resolution to begin afresh was so strong that he almost galloped back to the fair grounds. He went at once in search of the boss.

"It's decided," he said breathlessly, "I'm leaving right now. I'm going away, far away, where nobody will possibly know me. I'm going to begin all over again."

"But why?" exclaimed the big one. "Why do you have to start afresh when you've already established a great reputation?"

"You won't understand but I'll tell you just the same. *Because I want to be happy this time.*"

"*Happy*? I don't understand. Why happy?"

"Because usually a clown is happy only when he is somebody else. I don't want to be anybody but myself."

"Don't understand a word of it. . . . Listen, Auguste . . ."

"Look," said Auguste, wringing his hands, "what makes people laugh and cry when they watch us?"

"My dear fellow, what has all that to do with it? Those are academic questions. Let's talk sense. Let's get down to reality."

"That's what I've just discovered," said Auguste gravely. "*Reality*! that's the very word for it. Now I know who I am, what I am, and what I must do. *That's reality*. What you call reality is sawdust; it crumbles away, slips through the fingers."

"My dear Auguste," the other began, as if pleading with a lost one, "you've been thinking too much. If I were you I'd go back to town and have a good snort. Don't try to make a decision now. Come . . ."

"No," said Auguste firmly, "I want no consolation, nor advice. My mind is made up." And he held out his hand in parting.

"As you like," said the big fellow, humping his shoulders. "So it's good-bye, is it?"

"Yes," said Auguste, "it's good-bye . . . forever."

Once again he started out into the world, into its very bowels this time. Approaching the town, it came over him that he had not more than a few sous in his pocket. In a few hours he would be hungry. Then it would grow cold and then, like the beasts in the field, he would fold up and lie waiting for the first rays of the sun.

Why he had chosen to walk through the town, pursuing every street to the end, he knew not. He might just as well have conserved his strength.

"And if I do get to South America one day. . . ?" (He had begun talking aloud to himself.) "It may take years. And what language will I speak? And why will they take me, a stranger and unknown? Who knows if they even have a circus in such places. If they do, they will have their own clowns and their own language."

Coming to a little park, he flung himself on a bench. "This has to be thought out more carefully," he cautioned himself. "One doesn't rush off to South America just like that. I'm not an albatross, by God! I'm Auguste, a man with tender feet and a stomach that needs to be filled." One by one he began to specify all the very human attributes which distinguished him, Auguste, from the birds of the air and the creatures of the deep. His ruminations finally tailed off in a prolonged consideration of those two qualities, or faculties, which most markedly separate the world of humans from the animal kingdom—laughter and tears. Queer, he thought to himself, that he who was at home in this realm should be speculating on the subject like a schoolboy.

"*But I'm not an albatross!*" This thought, certainly not a brilliant one, kept repeating itself as he revolved his dilemma backwards and forwards. If not original or brilliant, it was never-theless very comforting, very reassuring to Auguste, this idea that not by any possible stretch of the imagination could he regard himself as an albatross.

South America—what nonsense! The problem was not where to go or how to get there, the problem was. . . . He tried to put it to himself very very simply. Wasn't it just this, that perhaps he was all right just as he was—without diminishing or augmenting himself? The mistake he had made was to go beyond his proper bounds. He had not been content to make people laugh, he had tried to make them joyous. Joy is God-given. Had he not discovered this in abandoning himself—by doing whatever came to hand, as he once put it?

Auguste felt that he was getting somewhere. His real tragedy, he began to perceive, lay in the fact that he was unable to communicate his knowledge of the existence of another world, a world beyond ignorance and frailty, beyond laughter and tears. It was this barrier which kept him a clown, God's very own clown, for truly there was no one to whom he could make clear his dilemma.

And then and there it came to him—how simple it was!—that to be nobody or anybody or everybody did not prevent him from being himself. If he were really a clown, then he should be one through and through, from the time he got up in the morning until he closed his eyes. He should be a clown in season and out, for hire or for the sheer sake of being. So unalterably convinced was he of the wisdom of this that he hungered to begin at once—without make-up, without costume, without even the accompaniment of that squeaky old violin. He would be so absolutely himself that only the truth, which now burned in him like a fire, would be recognizable.

Once again he closed his eyes, to descend into darkness. He remained thus a long time, breathing quietly and peacefully on the bed of his own being. When he finally opened his eyes he beheld a world from which the veil had been removed. It was the world which had always existed in his heart, ever ready to manifest itself, but which only begins to beat the moment one beats in unison with it.

Auguste was so utterly moved that he could not believe his eyes. He rubbed the back of his hand across them, only to discover that they were still wet with the tears of joy which he had shed unknowingly. Bolt upright he sat, with eyes staring straight ahead, struggling to accustom sight to vision. From the depths of his being there issued an incessant murmur of thanks.

He rose from the bench just as the sun was suffusing the earth with a last flush of gold. Strength and longing surged through his veins. New-born, he took a few steps forward into the magical world of light. Instinctively, just as a bird takes wing, he threw out his arms in an all-encompassing embrace.

The earth was swooning now in that deep violet which ushers in the twilight. Auguste reeled in ecstasy. "At last, at last!" he shouted, or thought he shouted, for in reality his cry was but a faint reverberation of the immense joy which rocked him.

A man was coming towards him. A man in uniform and armed with a club. To Auguste he appeared as the angel of deliverance. Auguste was about to throw himself into the arms of his deliverer when a cloud of darkness felled him like a hammer blow. He crumpled at the officer's feet without a sound.

Two bystanders who had witnessed the scene came running up. They knelt down and turned Auguste over on his back. To their amazement he was smiling. It was a broad, seraphic smile from which the blood bubbled and trickled. The eyes were wide open, gazing with a candor unbelievable at the thin sliver of a moon which had just become visible in the heavens.

Open Sesame!

In every period of despair, such as the present, attention is focused upon the young, as if in them lay our last hope. To set about re-educating the world is, however, an almost hopeless task. To give it real meaning, the execution of such a program would entail the aid of exceptional minds, the very ones whose counsel the world has ever refused to follow. Every great sage has maintained that it is impossible to impart wisdom. And it is wisdom we need, not more knowledge or even "better" knowledge. We need wisdom of life, which is a kind of knowledge that only initiates have thus far been known to possess.

In the opening pages of *Walden,* Thoreau writes: "The greater part of what my neighbors call good I believe in my soul to be bad, and if I repent of anything, it is very likely to be my good behavior. What demon possessed me that I obeyed so well? You may say the wisest thing you can, old man,—you who have lived seventy years, not without honor of a kind,—I hear an irresistible voice which invites me away from all that. . . ."

Rimbaud, with all the fire and genius of youth, said: "Everything we are taught is false." Jesus set about to destroy the old way of life, reminding us that the only true guide is the Spirit within us. And does not the Zen master, in his endeavor to free the mind of its trammels, employ any and every means to shatter our way of thinking?

In the book called *Siddhartha,* Hermann Hesse makes it clear repeatedly that to cope with the world his enlightened one relied only upon three "noble and invincible arts"—how to think, how to wait, and how to fast." Is it necessary to remark how altogether lacking is modern man with respect to these? What is worse, he is not even aware of the lack.

What is the great problem? Is it to develop beings who will be different in spirit from those who begat them? If so, how does one go about undoing the damage of the centuries? Can we raise children who will undo the evil we have done? How do we bring about a "brave, new world"? By education, by moral and religious instruction, by eugenics, by revolution? Is it possible to bring about a new order of men, to make a new heaven and a new earth? Or is it an age-old delusion?

The great exemplars all led simple lives. Inspiring though they be, no one follows in their footsteps. Only a rare few have even attempted to do so. Yet now and then, even today, a unique individual does break away, breaks free of the treadmill, as it were, and demonstrates that it is possible, even in this sad world, to lead one's own life. We know very little about the secret springs which enable such individuals to lift themselves above the great mass of mankind. All we know is that each one found the way for himself, and of himself. We suspect that the chosen path was never an easy one, never one that the man of common sense would elect to follow. "The Way is not difficult; but you must avoid choosing." There lies the great difficulty.

The men I speak of—gods in the eyes of most men—were all revolutionaries in the deepest sense of the word. The great thing about them, that which they had in common, was the ability to revolutionize themselves. In the process society itself was leveled from top to bottom. What they urged upon us, what they demonstrated first in their own person, was to think afresh, to look upon the world with new eyes. They did not address themselves exclusively to youth, but to one and all, regardless of age, sex, condition, belief, pursuit or education. They spoke not of gradual amelioration, not of ten- or twenty-year programs, but of instantaneous conversion. They were possessed of certitude and authority, inner authority, and they worked miracles.

Men still continue to worship and adore these shining figures. And in doing so they reject them. As for the pillars of society who exploit their names, they have long inoculated us with the very opposite of all these superior beings represented. This strange and contradictory behavior, which seems ingrained in men, has led to an impasse which can only be described as a kind of "cosmic schizophrenia."

Meanwhile "the Way" is always open for any and every one to follow. But who dares any longer to point the way?

The very first line of the booklet called "Open Sesame—Books Are Keys," reads thus: "The masses of the world are mentally starved." One could put it much stronger. Not only are the masses mentally starved, they are emotionally and spiritually crippled.

And it has been thus from the dawn of history. Madame Scheu-Riesz, the author of the booklet and the initiator of the delightful series of little books for children called "United World Books," is enlisting the aid of eminent men in various walks of life to help put at the disposal of youth the world over the best that exists in world literature and at a price within reach. Indeed, she has already done much to make this wish a reality.

It would take a bold spirit to say that Helene Scheu-Riesz and those who have rallied to her support are laboring in vain. Who does not wish to see a united world, a world at peace, a world in which health, reason, justice, love and joy of life prevail? Even our "enemies" profess the same desire. We are all advocates of a better world, and we are all the devil's disciples. We want to change the other fellow, not ourselves; we want our children to be better than us, but do nothing to make ourselves more worthy of our children.

The moment we begin to make new plans for the young, to select their reading, for example, or their playmates, the moment we begin to reorganize life, to separate the wheat from the chaff, as it were, we are up against something more than a problem, we are up against a conundrum. To judge, to select, to discriminate, to rearrange, reapportion—can there be any end to it ever? Try to assume that you are invested with the wisdom, the mercy and the powers of the Creator. Now put the world in order! Is this not the surest way to send one to the madhouse?

America has given the world one writer, the only one I know of, who sang, in every line he wrote, of acceptance. (Let us not forget, either, that in his day he was regarded as an obscene writer, an immoral person!) This doctrine of acceptance, the most difficult yet simple of all the radical ideas man has proposed to himself, embodies the understanding that the world is made up of conflicting members in all stages of evolution and devolution, that good and evil co-exist even though the one be but the shadow of the other, and that the world, for all its ills and shortcomings, was made for our enjoyment. It does not convey the idea that life is to be enjoyed when or if we all reach the stage of perfection. The salient idea is that life may, can and should be enjoyed now, under whatever conditions. The thought is so beautifully expressed by Hermann Hesse in the book previously mentioned that I am impelled to quote.

"Listen, my friend! [Siddhartha speaking] I am a sinner and you are a sinner, but someday the sinner will be Brahma again, will someday attain Nirvana, will someday become a Buddha. Now this 'someday' is illusion; it is only a comparison. The sinner is not on the way to a Buddha-like state; he is not evolving, although our thinking cannot conceive things otherwise. No, the potential Buddha already exists in the sinner; his future is already there. The potential hidden Buddha must be recognized in him, in you, in everybody. The world, Govinda, is not imperfect or slowly evolving along a long path to perfection. No, it is perfect at every moment; every sin already carries grace within it, all small children are potential old men, all sucklings have death within them, all dying people—eternal life. It is not possible for one person to see how far another is on the way; the Buddha exists in the robber and dice player; the robber exists in the Brahmin. During deep meditation it is possible to dispel time, to see simultaneously all the past, present and future, and then everything is good, everything is perfect, everything is Brahman. Therefore, it seems to me that everything that exists is good, death as well as life, sin as well as holiness, wisdom as well as folly. Everything is necessary, everything needs only my agreement, my assent, my loving understanding; then all is well with me and nothing can harm me. I learned through my body and soul that it was necessary for me to sin, that I needed lust, that I had to strive for property and experience nausea and the depths of despair in order to learn not to resist them, in order to learn to love the world, and no longer compare it with some kind of desired imaginary world, some imaginary vision of perfection, but to leave it as it is, to love it and be glad to belong to it. . . ."

So, let us begin with "Ali Baba and the Forty Thieves"—the first title in the series of United World (Open Sesame) booklets. Why not? It is a wonderful tale, and as a child I enjoyed it hugely. As to whether it did me harm or good, I am unable to say. I do know that some of the books which I devoured avidly, and of which I am even more uncertain (as to harm or good), will never be included in this or any other series of books for children. There are certain books which no serious "educator" would offer to the young, yet these very books opened my eyes as no "good" book could ever have done. The good books, as they are called, were usually so dull that they were incapable of doing harm or good. The point I make, if it is not already clear, is that no one, certainly not the parent or instructor, can possibly foresee which book or books, which sentence, which thought, which phrase sometimes it may be that will open the doors of vision for the child. We are given so much learned, pompous talk about reading for instruction, reading for inspiration, reading for a purpose, and so on. What I have discovered for myself, and I do not think my experience is unique, is that the books I enjoyed most, no matter what their specific gravity, were the ones that did the most for me . . . encouraged, inspired, instructed, awakened . . . whatever you will. What we learn, of value, we get indirectly, largely unconsciously. It is too often stressed, in my opinion, that we learn through sorrow and suffering. I do not deny this to be true, but I hold that we also learn, and perhaps more lastingly, through moments of joy, of bliss, of ecstasy. Struggle has its importance, but we tend to overrate it. Harmony, serenity, bliss do not come from struggle but from surrender.

Let us not worry too much about what our children feed on. Let them feed, forage and fend for themselves as we do, sharing our problems, nurturing our dreams, inspiring our love. Let them remain what they are, a very real part of this "one world" to which we all belong whether we know it or not, admit it or not. We can spare them nothing we do not spare ourselves. If we wish to protect them, we must first learn how to protect ourselves. But do we want to protect ourselves? Do we know what "protection" really means? Or what it involves? If we did we would long since have dropped the word from our vocabulary.

I trust that Madame Scheu-Riesz will not think that I am against her program. What I am against, if anything, is the illusion that reading the right books will make for us the right citizens. It is our destiny to live with the wrong as well as the right kind of citizens, and to learn from them, the wrong-minded ones, as much or more as from the others. If we have not yet succeeded—after how many centuries?—in eliminating from life the elements which plague us, perhaps we need to question life more closely. Perhaps our refusal to face reality is the only ill we suffer from, and all the rest but illusion and delusion.

"The Way is not difficult; but you must avoid choosing!" Or, as another ancient one put it—"The Way is near, but men seek it afar. It is in easy things, but men seek it in difficult things."

Anderson the Storyteller

I must say, to begin with, that I hardly knew Sherwood Anderson the man, having met him only in the last year of his life and then only two or three times. I had always lived in the hope of meeting him one day because I was extremely curious to observe whether he could tell a story as well as he could write one. My admiration for his tales has always been and always will be unbounded. Only a couple of months before our accidental meeting, in the lobby of his hotel, I had made an impromptu speech about him before a group of Greek friends in Constitutional Square, Athens. I remember well how pleased he was when I requested him to affix his signature to a few of his volumes which I was sending to my Greek friends shortly after my return to America. I was even more pleased than he, because the volume which I prized most—*Many Marriages*—was being dispatched to one of the greatest storytellers I have ever met, George Katsimbalis of Amaroussion, whom I have written about in *The Colossus of Maroussi*.

The good fortune I have had to know a few remarkable storytellers is due, I suppose, to the fact that I am what is called "the perfect listener." The ones I admire most, not forgetting the great Katsimbalis, are Hans Reichel, the painter; Blaise Cendrars, a French author known only slightly to English and American readers, more's the pity; and Conrad Moricand of Paris, an astrologer and occultist. Had I become better acquainted with Anderson there is no telling where I might place him in the rank of fascinating raconteurs. But I have only the memory of several all too brief meetings, and these in the presence of other persons.

I suppose the remark he made upon the occasion of our very first meeting is one that all his friends are familiar with. I had the feeling that he must have said it over and over again. It was a sort of apology to the effect that he had really stolen his material from other men—not from other writers, to be sure, but from simple, unsuspecting people who had no realization of the artistic possibilities hidden in their crude, faltering tales, the tales he listened to so patiently and reverently. The way he put it rather surprised me, for I had always been of the opinion that the writer looked to life for his material and not to his own empty little head. But Anderson, stressing it the way he did, laughing a bit sheepishly as he spoke, was either suffering from a guilt which was absurd or else revealing his abnormal sense of honesty. Perhaps too, there was something artful about his naïveté, a desire possibly to disguise the amount of labor he put into the telling of his artless tales. All the superb writers of stories, those especially who have a weakness for simplicity, slave like convicts over their manuscripts. Integrity and respect for one's métier are not the only explanations of this passionate, self-imposed toil. Writers of this genre get their material directly from life. Being artists, they are not content with the imperfections of life, but seek to refine the crude ore to bare, abstract quintessentials. They strive to make life more lifelike, as it were. It is a dilemma which will never be straddled by craftsmanship. The better their stories become, the worse for art. Art and life are separate, and the only link between them is the artist himself who, as he reveals himself more and more, realizes that union between the two which is entirely a matter of creation. Entirely a question of daring, I might say, for what is creation but imagination made manifest? The scrupulousness and meticulousness of the simplifier is a sign of fear. The nature or content of the story is nothing; the approach, the handling of it is everything. Saroyan is today the most daring of all our storytellers, and yet I feel that he is timid. He is timid, I mean, judged by his own criteria. His evolution is not in the direction one would imagine. He took a big hurdle in the beginning, but he refuses to go on hurdling. He is running now, and his stride is pleasant and easy, but we had expected him to be a chamois and not a yearling.

Of the storytellers I have known, the best are those who tell them. In the case of those who do both I prefer the man, the natural storyteller, to the writer. In saying this I feel I am paying these men a greater tribute than if it were the other way round. A story, to achieve its full effect, must be told; there must be gestures, pauses, false starts, confusion, raveling and unraveling, entanglement and disentanglement. There ought to be a certain amount of self-consciousness and embarrassment followed by a complete forgetfulness of self, followed by ecstasy and abandon and delirium. A story should be written in the air, consigned to the four winds, forgotten the moment it is told. In itself it is nothing—

an act of creation of which there are millions taking place constantly. The only important thing about a story is that a man felt like telling it. To preserve it between cloth covers and study it as if it were a dead insect, to try and imitate it or rival it or surpass it, all this is lost motion and kills creation. The storyteller is an actor who enriches and enhances the sense of life. The writer of short stories is more often than not a pest. If he is not doing it to keep a wife and child from starvation, he is doing it because he was defeated in his original aims, whatever they may have been. The writers of short stories, as a rule, do not go about their work joyously, recklessly, defiantly; they go at it grumblingly, grudgingly, with the most silly, painstaking effort, one eye on the clock and the other on the imaginary and often invisible pay check. They give their life blood to make it easy for uncreative dolts to pass the time away. The reward, when or if it comes, only serves to embitter them. They do not have an audience—they have "customers" who desert them like rats the moment a more tempting piece of cheese is dangled before their eyes.

What impressed me about Anderson was his genius for seizing on the trivial and making it important and universal. A story like "The Triumph of the Egg" is a classic. (In one of his latest books, *Kit Brandon,* there is another magnificent achievement, a little story in itself about the man who became a horse, who got down on all fours and was a horse for ten or fifteen minutes—such a horse as was never seen on land or sea or in the sky or in the myth.) I was extremely happy to be able to tell Anderson how much I enjoyed the book *The Triumph of the Egg.* It fell into my hands at a time when, in complete despair over my inability to say what I wanted to say, I was about to give up. That book encouraged me. All Anderson's books did. (Up to *Dark Laughter,* when I practically ceased reading American authors.) He seemed to have the real, the authentic American voice. The style was as free and natural, I thought then, as the glass of ice water which stands on every table in every home and restaurant. Later I learned that it was not so free and natural, that it had been acquired through long apprenticeship.

In Anderson, when all is said and done, it is the strong human quality which draws one to him and leads one to prefer him sometimes to those who are undeniably superior to him as artists. This quality I felt immediately when I met him. Dos Passos, whom I had also just met for the first time, was with us. We repaired to a bar nearby, just the three of us. "Now talk!" I said to myself. "Prove to me that you are the born storyteller I have always believed you to be!" And he did. That quality which I adore so much, that mania for trivia (which Cendrars has to an even greater degree) came immediately to the fore. I clung to every word he dropped, as though they were little round nuggets of gold. His way of stringing the words together, of breaking off, of fumbling and faltering, of searching and stumbling, all this was exactly as I had experienced it in his writing.

This talk of his, so natural, so easy-flowing, so gentle and good-humored, welled out of a man who was in love with the world. There was no malice, no chagrin, no meanness or pettiness about his language. At the worst there was a quiet melancholy—never a feeling of disillusionment. He had an unbounded faith in the little man. I think myself he made too much of him, but that is rather in Anderson's favor. One can't make too much of the nonentities; they are the hope of the future.

Other writers whom I have met were very much like their books. Anderson was more than his books. He was all his stories plus the man who wrote them—plus the man who listened to them! You could tell from the way he told a story about some character he had met, some trivial incident which had stuck in his crop, that he had reverence for his material which was almost religious. He didn't try to dominate or control or direct his subject matter. He always let his man speak for himself. He had the patience not just of the artist but of the religious man: he knew that there was bright shining ore beneath the scabby crust. He knew that fundamentally everything is of equal value, that manure is just as vital and inspiring as stars and planets. He knew his own limitations too. He didn't write about the common man as though he were some rare bird just discovered by the sociologist or his caricature the social worker; he wrote about the common man because he was one himself, and because he could only write about men and women he knew and understood.

I was told by one of his friends that when Anderson arrived in Paris and saw for the first time the Louvre, the Seine, the Jardin des Tuileries, he broke down and wept. The story has an authentic ring. Anderson had the gift of surrender. He was humble and reverent. He could become ecstatic about a knife and fork. He also recognized and admitted his own weaknesses—could make fun of them when it suited him to do so. He didn't try to crowd his fellow artists off the map; all he asked was that they make a little space for him, permit him to be one of them, one of the least among them. Sterling qualities and so rare nowadays.

Stressing the storyteller, as I do, I want to make a distinction, a very vital one, between him and the professional storytellers with whom America is infested. The professional storyteller bores me to tears. His yarns are sterile, saddening and maddening. What one misses in them is creation. All that they seem to accomplish, all indeed that they aim to accomplish obviously, is to postpone that moment which the American dreads most, the moment when he will be alone with himself and know that he is empty.

The other kind of storyteller, such as Anderson, is never trying to stave off a vacuum. If he tells a story it is to create a mood, an atmosphere, in which all may participate. He isn't seeking to hold the floor or put himself in the spotlight. He isn't worried about awkward silences or whether the evening will be a success or not. It's an exchange, a communion through words, by means of which the unique experiences of the others present may be melted into the common fund of human experience and make of a simple gathering a feast of real brotherliness. I liked the very way in which Anderson sat down to the table on the several occasions we were together. He plunked himself down to stay, secure in the knowledge that if nobody else had anything to contribute he did, because he never came without his instrument. I mean that instrument which he had made of himself. He brought himself along, that's how I want to put it. And he gave himself! What a relief to encounter such a man! Naturally his stories were good. They were like ripe fruit dropping from an overladen tree. You wouldn't want a man like that to argue with you, as Americans seem determined to do whenever they come together. You wanted to listen, to dream, to wander off in your own mind, just as he wandered off in his. You felt that you had his silent consent to do as you pleased. He wasn't fastening you down with a beady eye or expecting you to smile at the right moment or applaud him when he got through. He didn't pretend to be the Almighty telling the story of Creation. He was just an interpreter, a mouthpiece, an actor doing his part. You felt easy and rested when he had finished his story. You knew that another was coming if you'd just give him time to finish his drink or wipe his mouth. He made you feel that there was all the time in the world, that there was nothing better to do than just what you were doing. Part of him wasn't off somewhere trying to catch a train or organize a strike. He was all there and giving of himself in his easy, steady way ("easy does it!"), giving what was ripe and ready to fall to the ground, not straining, not pumping it up, not wondering if it were just the right quality or not.

And that's how I like to think of him now that he's gone. I like to think of him as a quiet, easy spirit seated at a round table under a shady tree holding converse with other departed spirits. Probably talking about celestial trivia, the stuff that wings are made of, or some such thing. Drinking celestial ambrosia and comparing it with the earthly imitations. Feeling the ethereal grass or stroking the astral cows. "A beautiful place!" I can hear him saying. "Rather like I imagined it would be. Not so different from down below either." Yes, I can follow him as he strolls leisurely about looking for a bridge perhaps where there might be a contented fisherman, wondering to himself what the man's story might be. Thanking his stars, no doubt, that here at least he will not be expected to put it down on paper. An eternity in which to wander about, touching things, smelling things, and swapping stories with old and new comers.

Most people think of Heaven as a boring place, but that's because they are themselves bores. I'm sure Anderson isn't finding it boring. Heaven was just made for him. And when we get there some day and meet again, what heavenly stories he'll have to beguile us with!

I don't feel the least bad about his passing. I envy him. I know he's at peace there, as he was here.

The Immorality of Morality

What is moral and what is immoral? Nobody will ever answer the question satisfactorily. Not because morals are constantly changing but because the principle behind it is a factitious one. Morality is for slaves, for men without spirit. And when I say spirit, I mean the Holy Spirit.

What had Jesus, in whose name so many crimes are committed, to do with morals? The word seems never to have crossed his lips. Elie Faure refers to him as "the great immoralist." At any rate, we know this for certain, that Jesus strove to give us a way of life, not a moral code.

It goes without saying that those who strive to maintain the *status quo* are the most immoral of all. To them the great sin is to question the prevailing order. Yet every great thinker, every great artist, every great religious teacher did just that.

The subject becomes more complicated when it is admitted that these rebels or iconoclasts found a way to live in the world without being part of it. "To render unto Caesar what is Caesar's. . . ." Ambivalence? Contradictoriness? Hypocrisy? Not at all. Still less, defeatism. No, the great triumph of these original souls lay in their discovery of a solution beyond the opposites. By not resisting evil, which Jesus meant absolutely and which no one seems willing to accept, these few shining examples of light and truth evaded the pitfalls which beset the ordinary believer.

Everyone wants a better world, everyone wants to be other than he is, everyone disclaims responsibility for the evils which beset us. Everyone believes in a Paradise or a Heaven, whether here and now or in the hereafter. No one seems able to support the idea that this may be the one and only world for us. Yet, unless one does accept this unpalatable fact, there can never be a Paradise— either in the beyond or here and now.

If there ever was a period when man did not possess a soul, certainly in gaining one—or even formulating the idea of one—the whole aspect of creation has changed. As a soulful being, man is no longer a "creature" but a partner in creation—*divine* creation, for there is but one kind of creation. Realizing the significance of his own nature, man has altered the nature of prayer. No man of spirit endeavors to placate or propitiate the Creator. Fully conscious, erect, face to face with his Maker, man can but sing His praises. The only form of prayer worthy of man is a prayer of thanksgiving.

But do we remember this in our trials and tribulations? No. What we all unreasonably demand is that life be given on *our* terms. We forget the extent to which, through inertia, through silence, through abject submission, we have contributed to our own defeat. We forget that we have seldom collaborated with the Creator, which is our one and only task. Ever straying from the Source, we naïvely wonder why we find ourselves howling in the wilderness.

Every day the choice is presented to us, in a thousand different ways, to live up to the spirit which is in us or to deny it. Whenever we talk about right and wrong we are turning the light of scrutiny upon our neighbors instead of upon ourselves. We judge in order not to be judged. We uphold the law, because it is easier than to defy it.

We are all lawbreakers, all criminals, all murderers, at heart. It is not our business to get after the murderers, but to get after the murderer which exists in each and every one of us. And I mean by murder the supreme kind which consists in murdering the spirit.

There is one thing I believe to be implicit in the story of martyrdom which Jesus enacted. It is this, that we do not need to repeat the sacrifice which he made. By assuming the burden of guilt and sin for mankind Jesus meant, in my opinion, to awaken us to the real meaning of life. What is the purpose and meaning of life? To enjoy it to the utmost. We can do so only by making ourselves one with life. "The life more abundant" means simply and unequivocally "life everlasting," nothing but life.

I have an old friend whom many would characterize as an unconscionable rogue. A rogue he is, but a delicious one. A rogue who is closer to being on the path than any righteous man I have ever met. He does nothing for the world, and very little for himself. He simply enjoys life, taking it as he finds it. Naturally he works as little as possible; naturally he takes no concern for the morrow. Without making a fetish of it, he takes inordinately good care of himself, being moderate in all things and showing discrimination with respect to everything that demands his time or attention. He is a connoisseur of food and wine who is never in danger of becoming a glutton or a drunkard. He loves women and knows how to make them happy. Though married, he does not deprive himself of extramarital relationships. He causes no one suffering and, if you asked him about it point-blank, he would probably answer that he never suffered in his life. He never thinks about suffering, either his own or other people's. He exists as if the world were perfect and made expressly for his own delectation. If there be a war, and if he is obliged to fight, he will fight—no matter on which side. He doesn't worry about whether he will be killed or not, but only about doing as little killing as possible. When he's radiantly happy, and he's almost always happy, he sometimes loves himself so much, is so delighted with his own happiness, so to speak, that he will kiss himself—on the hand or arm, whichever is most convenient. I believe he would kiss his own ass, if he could, in certain moments of exaltation.

Now why would one want to call such a lovable fellow a rogue? Obviously because he isn't playing the game as we expect it to be played. Obviously because he is enjoying life so thoroughly. Obviously because he doesn't worry about *our* misfortunes. Obviously because he doesn't care who rules the world. And most of all because he knows on which side his bread is buttered.

Those who don't think of him as a rogue call him childlike. This is meant to be even more condemnatory. That one can freely consort with publicans, sinners, harlots, drunkards and criminals is understandable to certain minds only if the person in question be regarded as a nitwit. My friend often refers to himself as a "half-wit." He does so smilingly, much as a Dostoevskian character would if he had a bit of the saint in him. Indeed, by poking fun at himself, minimizing himself, refusing to uphold or defend himself, my friend has a way of disconcerting the other fellow which is not only laughable but genuinely salutary. If he were pressed, for example, to say whether he believed in Christ or not, he is more than apt to answer: "I don't give a shit about Christ. What did he ever do for me?" He would answer that way out of annoyance, because he finds it stupid that people should ask one another such questions. But he is indubitably closer to Christ than to Satan. He is more like Christ, I wish to add, when he does those things which seem to be contrary to the way of Christ. Which is saying a great deal. Yet how can I better drive the point home? Jesus was never harsh with sinners, as we all know. He was harsh with moralists and hypocrites, with those who observed the letter of the law rather than the spirit of the law. Jesus had no social status whatever; he was fluid and flexible, until he had to do with those who were intolerant.

My friend knows very well when he is "sacrificing to the elementals," as he loves to put it. He doesn't use the word *sin*. When he gives in to the demands of the flesh he does it with the ease of a man relaxing after a hard day's work. He doesn't want to put too big a strain on himself, that is all. I'm not a hero, he means to say, or a saint, or a martyr. *I'm just me*. With such an attitude it follows that he seldom suffers from hang-overs and never from guilt complexes. He's always ready for the next issue, whether it be a feast or a spot of dirty work.

Sometimes I wonder if he'll ever die, he's so bright and fresh and new all the time. Never seems to be soiled, never gets used up. What health and vitality, what joy, radiates from his countenance! It's almost shameful to look that way in a world such as ours. And when he kisses himself all over, because the meal was good and he enjoyed it so much, he seems to be thanking the Creator in dog-like fashion. But if it be dog-like, his behavior, it is without a doubt meritorious. Would that we were all more dog-like!

If he lives on another twenty or thirty years—why not forty or fifty years?—he will have all the attributes which the Orientals find in their "gay old dogs." Which means that he will be as wise as the serpent and as gentle as the dove. He will not be hungering for immortality because he will have enjoyed everything life offers *in the flesh*. He will not have to prove anything by dying any more than he had to prove anything in living. Asked which is best for man, this way or that, he will be able to answer: "Any old way!" Or else: *"The way you are."*

This is what I mean by morality versus immorality. Be moral and you get yourself crucified; be immoral and you ruin yourself. "There was only one Christian and He died on the cross." There is more truth in this saying of Nietzsche's than is generally suspected. Jesus did not die on the cross in order that we should follow his example. He died on the cross in order that we might have life everlasting. He did not need to die on the cross; he might have given battle to the world and triumphed over it. He might have become the Emperor of the World instead of its scapegoat. He said: "I have *overcome* the world!" That was a far greater triumph. He overcame the world so thoroughly that it has never been able to get rid of him. The world is permeated with his spirit. It seeks in vain for a solution of its ills other than the way he pointed out. If it denies him, it is none the less subject to him. "I am the light of the world," he proclaimed, and that light still shines. "The Kingdom of Heaven is within you," he announced, restoring to every man his divinity and supremacy. When he healed a man or woman, when he cast out the devil, he would say: "Go and sin no more!" He never defined sin, he never fought against it. He annihilated it by not recognizing it. That is morality and immorality.

When I was quite young I read Lecky's *History of European Morals* from cover to cover, hoping to get to the bottom of this subject. I discovered only what one would discover if he looked at anything through a kaleidoscope. After Lecky I read the theologians, and after the theologians the mystics, and after the mystics I read the Cabalists. And so on. All I seem to have discovered, of importance, is that with every expansion of consciousness a radical change in morals ensues. Or, to put it more accurately, every innovator, every individual with a fresh vision or a larger vision of life, automatically destroys the existent moral code—in favor of spirit. But his disciples soon establish a new moral code, one just as rigid as the preceding one, forgetting that the spirit will again break the vessel which contains it.

We know all too little about the great precursors—Manu, Prometheus, Zoroaster, Hammurabi and such like. But what little we do know of them permits us to believe that the great truths they handed down were simple in essence. From the earliest times man seems to have been endowed with a conscience. When we penetrate the wisdom of the truth-sayers we discover that conscience was not meant to be a burden, that it was to be used instinctively and intuitively. It is only in periods of decadence that truth becomes complicated and conscience a heavy sack of guilt.

The neurotic character of our age is not only a sign of our guiltiness, it is also an indication of hopefulness. Instead of openly expressing their rebellion against the stupid and abominable scheme of things, men are expressing it through illness and maladaptation. The sick ones in our midst, and their number is increasing by leaps and bounds, are the criminals who have yet to be found out. They are undermining the social fabric even more than the industrialists and the militarists, even more than the priests and the scientists. Unable to buck the existent code, they render themselves inoperative—by becoming mental and moral cripples. They fail to realize, most of them, that it is precisely because of their spiritual nature that they have unwittingly outlawed themselves. They are symptomatic, in a negative way.

It sounds like defeatism to say to the young of our day: "Do not rebel! Do not make victims of yourselves!" What I mean, in saying this, is that one should not fight a losing battle. The system is destroying itself; the dead are burying the dead. Why expend one's energy fighting something which is already tottering? Neither would I urge one to run away from the danger zone. The danger is everywhere: there are no safe and secure places in which to start a new life. Stay where you are and make what life you can among the impending ruins. Do not put one thing above another in importance. Do only what has to be done—immediately. Whether the wave is ascending or descending, the ocean is always there. You are a fish in the ocean of time, you are a constant in an ocean of change, you are nothing and everything at one and the same time. Was the dinner good? Was the grass green? Did the water slake your thirst? Are the stars still in the heavens? Does the sun still shine? Can you talk, walk, sing, play? Are you still breathing?

With every breath we draw we are utilizing forces that are absolutely mysterious as well as all powerful. We are swimming in a sea of forces which demand only to be utilized and enjoyed. The problems which beset us are human problems, problems largely of our own making. The great problems remain untouched: we have not the vision as yet to recognize them. But in accepting our everyday problems, accepting them gladly and unreservedly, we may make ourselves fit to cope with the greater ones to come. The mathematician is not appalled by the problems which face him in his work, neither is the surgeon, nor anyone who engages seriously in whatever pursuit. Why then should man, as a species, be terrified of the problems which beset him? Why should he deny the monster which he has created with his own hands? If he has spawned a monster, let him devour his own monster!

The great sacrifice which we must all make, each and every one of us, is to burn away the dross. In other words, consign to the living flame that which is dead. If we put off the task, if we refuse to face the issue, the day will come when "the quick and the dead" are judged. There *is* a day of judgment, make no mistake about it. Life is continually weighing us in the balance. The Day of Judgment is not an invention of the religious-minded but a psychic or spiritual phenomenon obedient to the moving calendar of our own conscience. It is always Hades or Easter on the day of reckoning. It has been so since the beginning. And it promises to be so eternally.

This is the cross which man carries and on which he can burn with the flame of eternal life or be pilloried like a thief. There is no escape. As it says in the Avestas: "Evil exists not, only the past. The past is past; the present is a moment; the future is all."

Bonnie and Clyde:
A Toccata for Half-Wits

I had intended to sit down and let loose a stream of vitriol the morning after I saw the film, which is now three weeks ago, alas, and in the meantime I have cooled off somewhat. Nevertheless I am still furious, more toward the public which acclaims it *and enjoys it* than toward the producer and director, though I hold them fully responsible for this monstrous piece of entertainment.

I had never thought of seeing the film, after learning of the subject matter, until some of my good friends whose opinion I value urged me not to miss it. And so, taking three friends with me, I finally went to see it. In the first ten minutes I was ready to walk out. I was thoroughly bored, not to say disgusted by the sheer idiocy of the film. I waited for the supposed hilarity, for the sensational riot of fun. Only once during the entire showing did I crack a smile: I never once laughed, nor did I hear any hearty laughter from the audience, only an occasional titter.

I thought I was prepared for all the killing that goes on, having been told that it was all "innocent," "accidental," and so on, and that Bonnie and Clyde were a jolly, lovable pair who never intended to commit all the crimes which they did. But from the first murder till the last, try as I might, I got no fun out of it, only more and more disgust. I might say parenthetically that, like most American movie goers and TV victims, I have absorbed extraordinary doses of murder, rape, torture, and brutality unimaginable in my time. I remember once, when my son was about eight or nine, asking him why he always turned on these gruesome films and his reply was: "But little boys like murder once in a while!" I should add right here that I am not against, or rather I can understand, killing in self-defense or in a moment of blind passion; if I were a judge I would find it difficult to condemn such an act, since in this respect we are all potential killers. But wanton, senseless killing, cold-blooded murder, is another matter. Certainly murderers as a whole are sick people and should be treated as such rather than as criminals.

But what is worse than cold-blooded murder, in my opinion, is the presentation of murder as a form of entertainment. In such instances I feel compelled to look upon the viewers as even more sick than the killers they are watching. As regards the men who make money from such productions, I consider them not only as sick but as evil-minded individuals. They *know* what they are doing, they are not unintelligent. Yet they seem to lack all sense of guilt. They not only seek profit for their labors but fame and glory.

Curiously enough, the one film in this category which is an exception is Chaplin's *Monsieur Verdoux*. It was taken out of circulation before it had run very long, not so much because of the subject matter but because at the time it came out Chaplin was not in good odor in this country. This film, contrary to *Bonnie & Clyde*, was not only one of the funniest pictures I have ever seen but it also pointed a moral. Now would be an opportune moment to revive it. Now the moral of the tale is more likely to be appreciated, if not by the censors, then by the general public. For now we are in the midst of a senseless war[1] when once again all values have been upset, and right and wrong are more than ever confounded. Compared to what the military are doing, and what they are prepared to do in the face of so-called necessity, the murders perpetuated by a Bluebeard seem like child's play. Moreover, Chaplin's Bluebeard, alias Monsieur Verdoux, is not a psychopath but an intelligent human being much like you or I.

Today it is virtually taken for granted that ours is a sick society. Not only do statistics prove it but our leaders themselves proclaim it from the rooftops. Though I have been against our way of life ever since I was a young man, I have now covered a span of life sufficient to make vivid comparison between this period and the one I knew when I was a young man. With my own eyes I have witnessed what Whitman wrote of a hundred years ago, namely, the steady deterioration of the individual, the ever increasing corruption from the lowest to the highest levels of society, the increased resort to violence, frequently just for kicks, and the growing frenzy of senseless activity which can only be likened to some form of insanity. Whitman was not a Communist any more than Thoreau, Emerson, or other outspoken American writers. They were more American, indeed, than those who maligned and vilified them. They were seers, and like the prophets of old, they

[1] Vietnam War. This piece written at that time.

exposed the weaknesses of our people and the seeds of decay. As Georges Duhamel put it in one of his books: "America is like a fruit that rots before it has ripened."

What was not so marked in Whitman's time, it seems to me, is the frightening proportion of morons, imbeciles, psychopaths, and schizophrenics in our population. The number of mentally sick and criminal-minded in our midst today is absolutely alarming. We find them in all classes of society, and not just among the poor and down-trodden. We find them among our Congressmen as well as among our teachers, preachers, and do-gooders, especially among our do-gooders. Gradually we are discovering that what makes for success does not make for a healthy society. The Hippies may be goofy, unsocial, even drug addicts, but they have the good sense to reject current values, to remain apart, to make merry while Rome burns. Maybe they are not as crazy as we would like to believe. Maybe there is an element of a new sanity in their weird behavior. Maybe by refusing to be the Gadarene swine which most of us are they are injecting an element of hope and courage into our confused, frustrated, and desperate society.

And what has all this to do with *Bonnie and Clyde?* Everything. Bonnie and Clyde are morons, and so is C.W., whom I confess I feel more sympathetic toward than the others in the film. Bonnie and Clyde are sick, sick to the core. They smell bad. There is an aura of perversion about them, as well as stupid viciousness. In the case of the real Bonnie and Clyde I am given to understand that Clyde was a homosexual and Bonnie a sort of swinger who "did her thing," as they say, with no matter whom. She was supposed to be doing it with their companion, C.W. But in the film version Clyde is made out to be impotent and Bonnie some sort of half-witted sex maniac who stays slap happy no matter what gives.

One of the first things which turned me off, in the film, was the kind of half-witted way in which the two get together. There is Clyde, with a hebephrenic grin half sex half idiot, and Bonnie, all sex and no brains—like two lollypops saying Hello. The dialogue is nil, as it remains throughout the film. Then comes the scene in the car, with Bonnie devouring Clyde, hungry bitch that she is, and Clyde reacting like a castrated knight of the Round Table. Immediately one senses that something is rotten in Denmark. Immediately one senses that violence is the thing, not love, not sex. The impotent man with the gat gets his kick with the kill, not with his penis. Sick, sick.

And then the humor, such as it is. Somehow, though I have met the hillbillies, the tar heels, and the crackers, though I've travelled the backward regions of the South, I can't dig what passes for humor between Clyde and his brother, or between Clyde, Bonnie, and any of the other morons. It simply ain't real. No more than the shootings between the killers and the police. All this is fake realism, phony sociological hogwash. Don't insult the Oakies or the Arkies—they're far better than that, far more intelligent, far more sensitive, far more humorous.

And then there's the Grant Wood scene with the mother. The one touch of reality and gravity, but marred by the too obvious Grant Wood simulacrum. Even, toward the end, when the pair wish for a better life, for a way out, for what one might call "a decent way of life," it doesn't ring true. Two such half-wits haven't got it in them to know what a better way of life might be. What could a guy like Clyde do, for example? He has no brains, no feelings, no nothing. As for Bonnie, the only thing I could expect her to do is to make a first rate whore, a real whore—*but can she?* She's too fucked up to make anything or to be anything. She was a lost soul from the start. She was headed nowhere and she got nowhere. Frankly, though it goes against my principles to say it, the best moment in the film for me was when the two are finally riddled with bullets in the car. It seemed like a just and merciful end to their cavortings. They lie there like so much human garbage. They served no purpose in life, they had no possible future, and, one surmises, even in Hell they will be misfits.

CADENZA

The other day I saw a new film advertised; the caption read "Even more violent than *Bonnie & Clyde*." I also read in the papers of a young couple trying to imitate Bonnie and Clyde; unfortunately I don't remember how many they had killed before being apprehended. There will certainly be more imitators as time goes on and the film penetrates the hinterland.

What is sorely needed now as an antidote is a rash of erotic, pornographic, or obscene films, the more censorable the better. If the Hippies are on the love kick, what their elders need is the sex kick. Now and then, to be sure, we get such films from Sweden, Denmark, and other small countries whose inhabitants are well fed, immune to shock treatment, ultra normal, and in general bored to death. But what we need are American films of this variety. What we usually get from Hollywood are teasers; we never go the whole hog, as we are now doing in literature.

Anyway, what a relief it would be to see some real warm-hearted fucking on the screen. Relaxing, to say the least. I mean honest to God intercourse, not spiced with perversion, brutality, and dementia praecox. If any condiments were needed, why not a bit of froth and foam from Billy Graham, or an ecumenical epiphany from the Pope, or a Molotov cocktail à la Phyllis Diller? In other words reality instead of realism, instinct versus abstraction. How really strange, when you think of it, that you can sell people violence and perversity but not healthy, joyous sexual intercourse! If it is permissible in gangster and spy films, for example, to show victims being kicked in the face or in the balls, to show young punks slashing one another with knives or setting someone aflame with gasoline, or a sniper picking an innocent driver off with a shot gun, why is it not permissible to show the sexual organs engaged in friendly combat?

I say nothing of documentary films in which we see the enemy being routed out of caves with flame throwers, or smoked out with phosphorus, or burned to a crisp with Napalm, or torn to shreds with fragmentation or guava bombs, et cetera et cetera. Such films aren't offered to the public for entertainment but for instruction. They want us to know that "war is hell," but that war is necessary every ten or twenty years, otherwise civilization condones mass slaughter, destruction of the soil and all means of subsistence, condones destruction of churches, libraries, museums, hospitals. . . . What does it not condone in the holy name of civilization? Peace, how wonderful! But peace, oddly enough, is always something that has to be fought for. Peace comes only as the kiss of death.

Just as the movie makers seem to feel that no one will go to the movies if there is not sensationalism and violence, so governments, the big ones, at least, seem to think that people will get too comfortable, too peaceful, too smug and content, if there are no wars.

And does all this have anything to do with *Bonnie & Clyde?* Yes, in the sense that a people which finds senseless murder funny and entertaining can hardly be shocked when they find themselves in the midst of war. How noticeable it is, when listening to the news reports which are largely filled with murder, rape, and arson, if not corruption, mendacity, and treachery in high places, how monstrous and obscene it is to watch commercials about bad breath, headaches, and other disorders following upon the assassination of an important figure or the destruction of a whole village by earthquake or volcano. The cosmetic, the depilatory, the silky toilet paper get almost equal space and attention as the horripilating disasters. Or take the news commentator himself and his manner of reporting the varied happenings of the day. Does he ever break down with grief, does he ever become paralyzed by the horror and gravity of his reports? He goes from horrendous, nauseating, shocking incidents to the trivia of everyday life with scarcely a change of intonation in his voice. He avoids comment of his own, even though the news is shattering. He likens himself as much as possible to a machine, a tape recorder, a tickertape. Even the reporters at the front try as much as possible to keep their *sang-froid*. We want facts, not emotions, sensation but no hang-overs.

And despite all the cold-blooded accounting and recounting, the facts are often lies. It depends on who is reporting, on who is putting up the dough, on who is trying to save face, or whose pocket is being hurt. We can't depend on governments for the truth nor upon reporters whose hands are tied and mouths gagged. We can't even depend on our own intelligence and acumen, for we are all brain-washed and walking in our sleep.

As the Zulus say—"The time of the hyena is upon us." The Brazilians put it another way: "When shit acquires value the poor are born without ass-holes." And if I may add my own little bit, I would say: "What we thrive on is hatred and violence; if we were a peaceable people we would have peace tomorrow."

And so, to be downright honest, we must conclude (editorially speaking) that the real monsters are not Bonnie and Clyde but we, the public at large. We sit back in our comfortable seats, our bread baskets stuffed with rich food, and we say—"Sock it to us, we'll take anything you've got." We pay without slightest complaint to be shocked, nauseated, terrified, and brain-washed. And on the day of atonement, when the awards are handed out, the men who served these ugly dishes are given the Oscar. What could be fairer? So, Mr. Beatty, Miss Dunaway, Mr. Penn, Mr. Newman and Mr. Benton, Mr. Warner Bros., if I appear to have been a little harsh, a little too broad and sweeping in my criticism of your creation, please know that in the last analysis your *Bonnie & Clyde* is but a tiny symbol of all that ails us, and that in my heart of hearts I don't think you are really any worse than many other members of your clan. In fact, I am almost certain that, given a bit of pot or a dose of L.S.D., you may come up one day with something really funny, really entertaining, if not instructive or therapeutic.

"Why Don't You Try to Write?"

. . . **I**nstead of rushing out of the house immediately after dinner that evening, as I usually did, I lay on the couch in the dark and fell into a deep reverie. *"Why don't you try to write?"* That was the phrase which had stuck in my crop all day, which repeated itself insistently, even as I was saying thank you to my friend MacGregor for the ten-spot which I had wrung from him after the most humiliating wheedling and cajoling.

In the darkness I began to work my way back to the hub. I began to think of those most happy days of childhood, the long summer days when my mother took me by the hand, led me over the fields to see my little friends, Joey and Tony. As a child it was impossible to penetrate the secret of that joy which comes from a sense of superiority. That extra sense, which enables one to participate and at the same time to observe one's participation, appeared to me to be the normal endowment of every one. That I enjoyed everything more than other boys my age I was unaware of. The discrepancy between myself and others only dawned on me as I grew older.

To write, I meditated, must be an act devoid of will. The word, like the deep ocean current, has to float to the surface of its own impulse. A child has no need to write, he is innocent. A man writes to throw off the poison which he has accumulated because of his false way of life. He is trying to recapture his innocence, yet all he succeeds in doing (by writing) is to inoculate the world with the virus of his disillusionment. No man would set a word down on paper if he had the courage to live out what he believed in. His inspiration is deflected at the source. If it is a world of truth, beauty and magic that he desires to create, why does he put millions of words between himself and the reality of that world? Why does he defer action—unless it be that, like other men, what he really desires is power, fame, success. "Books are human actions in death," said Balzac. Yet, having perceived the truth, he deliberately surrendered the angel to the demon which possessed him.

A writer woos his public just as ignominiously as a politician or any other mountebank; he loves to finger the great pulse, to prescribe like a physician, to win a place for himself, to be recognized as a force, to receive the full cup of adulation, even if it be deferred a thousand years. He doesn't want a new world which might be established immediately, because he knows it would never suit him. He wants an impossible world in which he is the uncrowned puppet ruler dominated by forces utterly beyond his control. He is content to rule insidiously—in the fictive world of symbols—because the very thought of contact with rude and brutal realities frightens him. True, he has a greater grasp of reality than other men, but he makes no effort to impose that higher reality on the world by force of example. He is satisfied just to preach, to drag along in the wake of disasters and catastrophes, a death-croaking prophet always without honor, always stoned, always shunned by those who, however, unsuited for their tasks, are ready and willing to assume responsibility for the affairs of the world. The truly great writer does not want to write: he wants the world to be a place in which he can live the life of the imagination. The first quivering word he puts to paper is the word of the wounded angel: pain. The process of putting down words is equivalent to giving oneself a narcotic. Observing the growth of a book under his hands, the author swells with delusions of grandeur. "I too am a conqueror—perhaps the greatest conqueror of all! My day is coming. I will enslave the world—by the magic of words. . . ." Et cetera ad nauseam.

The little phrase—*Why don't you try to write?*—involved me, as it had from the very beginning, in a hopeless bog of confusion. I wanted to enchant but not to enslave; I wanted a greater, richer life, but not at the expense of others; I wanted to free the imagination of all men at once because without the support of the whole world, without a world imaginatively unified, the freedom of the imagination becomes a vice. I had no respect for writing *per se* any more than I had for God *per se*. Nobody, no principle, no idea has validity in itself. What is valid is only that much—of anything, God included—which is realized by all men in common. People are always worried about the fate of the genius. I never worried about the genius: genius takes care of the genius in a man. My concern was always for the nobody, the man who is lost in the shuffle, the man who is so common, so ordinary, that his presence is not even noticed. One genius does not inspire another. All geniuses are leeches, so to speak. They feed from the same source—the blood of life. The most important thing for the genius is to make himself useless, to be absorbed in the common stream, to become a fish again and not a freak of nature. The only benefit, I reflected, which the act of writing could offer me was to remove the differences which separated me from my fellow-man. I definitely did not want to become the artist, in the sense of becoming something strange, something apart and out of the current of life.

The best thing about writing is not the actual labor of putting word against word, brick upon brick, but the preliminaries, the spade work, which is done in silence, under any circumstances, in dream as well as in the waking state. In short, the period of gestation. No man ever puts down what he intended to say: the original creation, which is taking place all the time, whether one writes or doesn't write, belongs to the primal flux: it has no dimensions, no form, no time element. In this preliminary state, which is creation and not birth, what disappears suffers no destruction; something which was already there, something imperishable, like memory, or matter, or God, is summoned and in it one flings himself like a twig into a torrent. Words, sentences, ideas, no matter how subtle or ingenious, the maddest flights of poetry, the most profound dreams, the most hallucinating visions, are but crude hieroglyphs chiseled in pain and sorrow to commemorate an event which is untransmissible. In an intelligently ordered world there would be no need to make the unreasonable attempt of putting such miraculous happenings down. Indeed, it would make no sense, for if men only stopped to realize it, who would be content with the counterfeit when the real is at everyone's beck and call? Who would want to switch in and listen to Beethoven, for example, when he might himself experience the ecstatic harmonies which Beethoven so desperately strove to register? A great work of art, if it accomplishes anything, serves to remind us, or let us say to set us dreaming, of all that is fluid and intangible. Which is to say, *the universe*. It cannot be understood; it can only be accepted or rejected. If accepted we are revitalized; if rejected we are diminished. Whatever it purports to be it is not: it is always something more for which the last word will never be said. It is all that we put into it out of hunger for that which we deny every day of our lives. If we accepted *ourselves* as completely, the work of art, in fact *the whole world of art,* would die of malnutrition. Every man Jack of us moves without feet at least a few hours a day, when his eyes are closed and his body prone. The art of dreaming when wide awake will be in the power of every man one day. Long before that books will cease to exist, for when men are wide awake *and* dreaming their powers of communication (with one another and with the spirit that moves all men) will be so enhanced as to make writing seem like the harsh and raucous squawks of an idiot.

I think and know all this, lying in the dark memory of a summer's day, without having mastered, or even half-heartedly attempted to master, the art of the crude hieroglyph. Before ever I begin I am disgusted with the efforts of the acknowledged masters. Without the ability or the knowledge to make so much as a portal in the façade of the grand edifice, I criticize and lament the architecture itself. If I were only a tiny brick in the vast cathedral of this antiquated façade I would be infinitely happier; I would have life, the life of the whole structure, even as an infinitesimal part of it. But I am outside, a barbarian who cannot make even a crude sketch, let alone a plan, of the edifice he dreams of inhabiting. I dream a new blazingly magnificent world which collapses as soon as the light is turned on. A world that vanishes but does not die, for I have only to become still again and stare wide-eyed into the darkness and it reappears. . . . There is then a world in me which is utterly unlike any world I know of. I do not think it is my exclusive property—it is only the angle of my vision which is exclusive in that it is unique. If I talk the language of my unique vision nobody understands; the most colossal edifice may be reared and yet remain invisible. The thought of that haunts me. What good will it do to make an invisible temple?

It was in Ulric's studio not so many months ago that I had finished my first book—the book about the twelve messengers. I used to work in his brother's room where some short time previously a magazine editor, after reading a few pages of an unfinished story, informed me cold-bloodedly that I hadn't an ounce of talent, that I didn't know the first thing about writing—in short that I was a complete flop and the best thing to do, my lad, is to forget it, try to make an honest living. Another nincompoop who had written a highly successful book about Jesus-the-carpenter had told me the same thing. And if rejection slips mean anything there was simple corroboration to support the criticism of these discerning minds. "Who *are* these shits?" I used to say to Ulric. "Where do they get off to tell me these things? What have they done, except to prove that they know how to make money?"

Well, I was talking about Joey and Tony, my little friends. I was lying in the dark, a little twig floating in the Japanese current. I was getting back to simple abracadabra, the straw that makes bricks, the crude sketch, the temple which must take on flesh and blood and make itself manifest to all the world. I got up and put on a soft light. I felt calm and lucid, like a lotus opening up. No violent pacing back and forth, no tearing the hair out by the roots. I sank slowly into a chair by the table and with a pencil I began to write. I described in simple words how it felt to take my mother's hand and walk across the sun-lit fields, how it felt to see Joey and Tony rushing towards me with arms open, their faces beaming with joy, I put one brick upon another like an honest brick-layer. Something of a vertical nature was happening—not blades of grass shooting up but something structural, something planned. I didn't strain myself to finish it; I stopped when I had said all I could. I read it over quietly, what I had written. I was so moved that the tears came to my eyes. It wasn't something to show an editor: it was something to put away in a drawer, to keep as a reminder of natural processes, as a promise of fulfillment.

Every day we slaughter our finest impulses. That is why we get a heart-ache when we read those lines written by the hand of a master and recognize them as our own, as the tender shoots which we stifled because we lacked the faith to believe in our own powers, our own criterion of truth and beauty. Every man, when he gets quiet, when he becomes desperately honest with himself, is capa-ble of uttering profound truths. We all derive from the same source. There is no mystery about the origin of things. We are all part of creation, all kings, all poets, all musicians; we have only to open up, only to discover what is already there.

What happened to me in writing about Joey and Tony was tantamount to revelation. It was revealed to me that I could say what I wanted to say—if I thought of nothing else, if I concentrated upon that exclusively—*and* if I were willing to bear the conse-quences which a pure act always involves.

Creation

The world would only begin to get something of value from me the moment I stopped being a serious member of society and became—*myself*. The State, the nation, the united nations of the world, were nothing but one great aggregation of individuals who repeated the mistakes of their forefathers. They were caught in the wheel from birth and they kept at it till death—and this treadmill they tried to dignify by calling it "life." If you asked anyone to explain or define life, what was the be-all and the end-all, you got a blank look for answer. Life was something which philosophers dealt with in books that no one read. Those in the thick of life, "the plugs in harness," had no time for such idle questions. *"You've got to eat, haven't you?"* This query, which was supposed to be a stop-gap, and which had already been answered, if not in the absolute negative at least in a disturbingly relative negative by those who knew, was a clue to all the other questions which followed in a veritable Euclidian suite. From the little reading I had done I had observed that the men who were most *in* life, who were molding life, who were life itself, ate little, slept little, owned little or nothing. They had no illusions about duty, or the perpetuation of their kith and kin, or the preservation of the State. They were interested in truth and in truth alone. They recognized only one kind of activity—*creation*. Nobody could command their services because they had of their own pledged themselves to give all. They gave gratuitously, because that is the only way to give. This was the way of life which appealed to me: it made sound sense. It *was* life—not the simulacrum which those about me worshipped.

I had understood all this—with my mind at the very brink of manhood. But there was a great comedy of life to be gone through before this vision of reality could become the motivating force.

The tremendous hunger for life which others sensed in me acted like a magnet; it attracted those who needed my particular kind of hunger. The hunger was magnified a thousand times. It was as if those who clung to me (like iron filings) became sensitized and attracted others in turn. Sensation ripens into experience and experience engenders experience.

What I secretly longed for was to disentangle myself of all those lives which had woven themselves into the pattern of my own life and were making my destiny a part of theirs. To shake myself free of these accumulating experiences which were mine only by force of inertia required a violent effort. Now and then I lunged and tore at the net, but only to become more enmeshed. My liberation seemed to involve pain and suffering to those near and dear to me. Every move I made for my own private good brought about reproach and condemnation. I was a traitor a thousand times over. I had lost even the right to become ill—because "they" needed me. I wasn't *allowed* to remain inactive. Had I died I think they would have galvanized my corpse into a semblance of life.

"I stood before a mirror and said fearfully: 'I want to see how I look in the mirror with my eyes closed.' "

These words of Richter's, when I first came upon them, made an indescribable commotion in me. As did the following, which seems almost like a corollary of the above—from Novalis:

"The seat of the soul is where inner world and outer world touch each other. For nobody knows himself, if he is only himself and not also another one at the same time."

"To take possession of one's transcendental I, to be the I of one's I, at the same time," as Novalis expressed it again.

There is a time when ideas tyrannize over one, when one is just a hapless victim of another's thoughts. This "possession" by another seems to occur in periods of depersonalization, when the warring selves come unglued, as it were. Normally one is impervious to ideas; they come and go, are accepted or rejected, put on like shirts, taken off like dirty socks. But in those periods which we call crises, when the mind sunders and splinters like a diamond under the blows of a sledge-hammer, these innocent ideas of a dreamer take hold, lodge in the crevices of the brain, and by some subtle process of infiltration bring about a definite, irrevocable alteration of the personality. Outwardly no great change takes place; the individual affected does not suddenly behave differently; on the contrary, he may behave in more "normal" fashion than before. This seeming normality assumes more and more the quality of a protective device. From surface deception he passes to inner deception. With each new crisis, however, he becomes more strongly aware of a change which is no change, but rather an intensification of something hidden deep within. Now when he closes his eyes he can really look at himself. He no longer sees a mask. He sees without seeing, to be exact. Vision without sight, a fluid grasp of intangibles: the merging of sight and sound: the heart of the web. Here stream the distant personalities which evade the crude contact of the senses; here the overtones of recognition discreetly lap against one another in bright, vibrant harmonies. There is no language employed, no outlines delineated.

When a ship founders it settles slowly; the spars, the masts, the rigging float away. On the ocean floor of death the bleeding hull bedecks itself with jewels; remorselessly the anatomic life begins. What was ship becomes the nameless indestructible.

Like ships, men founder time and again. Only memory saves them from complete dispersion. Poets drop their stitches in the loom, straws for drowning men to grasp as they sink into extinction. Ghosts climb back on watery stairs, make imaginary ascents, vertiginous drops, memorize numbers, dates, events, in passing from gas to liquid and back again. There is no brain capable of registering the changing changes. Nothing happens in the brain, except the gradual rust and detrition of the cells. But in the mind, worlds unclassified, undenominated, unassimilated, form, break, unite, dissolve and harmonize ceaselessly. In the mind-world ideas are the indestructible elements which form the jeweled constellations of the interior life. We move within their orbits, freely if we follow their intricate patterns, enslaved or possessed if we try to subjugate them. Everything external is but a reflection projected by the mind machine.

Creation is the eternal play which takes place at the borderline; it is spontaneous and compulsive, obedient to law. One removes from the mirror and the curtain rises. *Séance permanente*. Only madmen are excluded. Only those who "have lost their mind," as we say. For these never cease to dream that they are dreaming. They stood before the mirror with eyes open and fell sound asleep; they sealed their shadow in the tomb of memory. In them the stars collapse to form what Hugo called "a blinding menagerie of suns which, through love, make themselves the poodles and the Newfoundlands of immensity."

The creative life! Ascension. Passing beyond oneself. Rocketing out into the blue, grasping at flying ladders, mounting, soaring, lifting the world up by the scalp, rousing the angels from their ethereal lairs, drowning in stellar depths, clinging to the tails of comets. Nietzsche had written of it ecstatically—and then swooned forward into the mirror to die in root and flower. "Stairs and contradictory stairs,'' he wrote, and then suddenly there was no longer any bottom; the mind, like a splintered diamond, was pulverized by the hammer-blows of truth.

There was a time when I acted as my father's keeper. I was left alone for long hours, cooped up in the little booth which we used as an office. While he was drinking with his cronies I was feeding from the bottle of creative life. My companions were the free spirits, the overlords of the soul. The young man sitting there in the mingy yellow light became completely unhinged; he lived in the crevices of great thoughts, crouched like a hermit in the barren folds of a lofty mountain range. From truth he passed to imagination and from imagination to invention. At this last portal, through which there is no return, fear beset him. To venture farther was to wander alone, to rely wholly upon oneself.

The purpose of discipline is to promote freedom. But freedom leads to infinity and infinity is terrifying. Then arose the comforting thought of stopping at the brink, of setting down in words the mysteries of impulsion, compulsion, propulsion, of bathing the senses in human odors. To become utterly human, the compassionate fiend incarnate, the locksmith of the great door leading beyond and away and forever isolate. . . .

Men founder like ships. Children also. There are children who settle to the bottom at the age of nine, carrying with them the secret of their betrayal. There are perfidious monsters who look at you with the bland, innocent eyes of youth; their crimes are unregistered, because we have no names for them.

Why do lovely faces haunt us so? Do extraordinary flowers have evil roots?

Studying her morsel by morsel, feet, hands, hair, lips, ears, breasts, traveling from navel to mouth and from mouth to eyes, the woman I fell upon, clawed, bit, suffocated with kisses, the woman who had been Mara and was now Mona, who had been and would be other names, other persons, other assemblages of appendages, was no more accessible, penetrable, than a cool statue in a forgotten garden of a lost continent. At nine or earlier, with a revolver that was never intended to go off, she might have pressed a swooning trigger and fallen like a dead swan from the heights of her dream. It might well have been that way, for in the flesh she was dispersed, in the mind she was as dust blown hither and thither. In her heart a bell tolled, but what it signified no one knew. Her image corresponded to nothing that I had formed in my heart. She had intruded it, slipped it like thinnest gauze between the crevices of the brain in a moment of lesion. And when the wound closed the imprint had remained, like a frail leaf traced upon a stone.

Haunting nights when, filled with creation, I saw nothing but her eyes and in those eyes, rising like bubbling pools of lava, phantoms came to the surface, faded, vanished, reappeared, bringing dread, apprehension, fear, mystery. A being constantly pursued, a hidden flower whose scent the blood-hounds never picked up. Behind the phantoms, peering through the jungle brush, stood a shrinking child who seemed to offer herself lasciviously. Then the swan dive, slow, as in motion pictures, and snow-flakes falling with the falling body, and then phantoms and more phantoms, the eyes becoming eyes again, burning like lignite, then glowing like embers, then soft like flowers; then nose, mouth, cheeks, ears looming out of chaos, heavy as the moon, a mask unrolling, flesh taking form, face, feature.

Night after night, from words to dreams, to flesh, to phantoms. Possession and depossession. The flowers of the moon, the broad-backed palms of jungle growth, the baying of blood-hounds, the frail white body of a child, the lava bubbles, the rallentando of the snow-flakes, the floorless bottom where smoke blooms into flesh. And what is flesh but moon? and what is moon but night? Night is longing, longing, longing, beyond all endurance.

"Think of *us!*" she said that night when she turned and flew up the steps rapidly. And it was as if I could think of nothing else. We two and the stairs ascending infinitely. Then "contradictory stairs": the stairs in my father's office, the stairs leading to crime, to madness, to the portals of invention. How *could* I think of anything else?

Creation. To create the legend in which I could fit the key which would open her soul.

A woman trying to deliver her secret. A desperate woman, seeking through love to unite herself with herself. Before the immensity of mystery one stands like a centipede that feels the ground slipping beneath its feet. Every door that opens leads to a greater void. One must swim like a star in the trackless ocean of time. One must have the patience of radium buried beneath a Himalayan peak.

It is about twenty years now since I began the study of the photogenic soul; in that time I have conducted hundreds of experiments. The result is that I know a little more—about myself. I think it must be very much the same with the political leader or the military genius. One discovers nothing about the secrets of the universe; at the best one learns something about the nature of destiny.

In the beginning one wants to approach every problem directly. The more direct and insistent the approach, the more quickly and surely one succeeds in getting caught in the web. No one is more helpless than the heroic individual. And no one can produce more tragedy and confusion than such a type. Flashing his sword above the Gordian knot, he promises speedy deliverance. A delusion which ends in an ocean of blood.

The creative artist has something in common with the hero. Though functioning on another plane, he too believes that he has solutions to offer. He gives his life to accomplish imaginary triumphs. At the conclusion of every grand experiment, whether by statesman, warrior, poet or philosopher, the problems of life present the same enigmatic complexion. The happiest peoples, it is said, are those which have no history. Those which have a history, those which have made history, seem only to have emphasized through their accomplishments the eternality of struggle. These disappear too, eventually, just as those who made no effort, who were content merely to live and to enjoy.

The creative individual (in wrestling with his medium) is supposed to experience a joy which balances, if it does not outweigh, the pain and anguish which accompany the struggle to express himself. He lives in his work, we say. But this unique kind of life varies extremely with the individual. It is only in the measure that he is aware of more life, the life abundant, that he may be said to live in his work. If there is no realization, there is no purpose or advantage in substituting the imaginative life for the purely adventurous one of reality. Everyone who lifts himself above the activities of the daily round does so not only in the hope of enlarging his field of experience, or even of enriching it, but of quickening it. Only in this sense does struggle have any meaning. Accept this view, and the distinction between failure and success is nil. And this is what every great artist comes to learn en route—that the process in which he is involved has to do with another dimension of life, that by identifying himself with this process he *augments* life. In this view of things he is permanently removed—and protected—from that insidious death which seems to triumph all about him. He divines that the great secret will never be apprehended but incorporated in his very substance. He has to make himself a part of the mystery, live *in* it as well as with it. Acceptance is the solution: it is an art, not an egotistical performance on the part of the intellect. Through art then, one finally establishes contact with reality: that is the great discovery. Here all is play and invention; there is no solid foothold from which to launch the projectiles which will pierce the miasma of folly, ignorance and greed. The world has *not* to be put in order: the world *is* order incarnate. It is for us to put ourselves in unison with this order, to know what is the world order in contradistinction to the wishful-thinking orders which we seek to impose on one another. The power which we long to possess, in order to establish the good, the true and the beautiful, would prove to be, if we could have it, but the means of destroying one another. It is fortunate that we are powerless. We have first to acquire vision, then discipline and forbearance. Until we have the humility to acknowledge the existence of a vision beyond our own, until we have faith and trust in superior powers, the blind must lead the blind. The men who believe that work and brains will accomplish everything must ever be deceived by the quixotic and unforeseen turn of events. They are the ones who are perpetually disappointed; no longer able to blame the gods, or God, they turn on their fellow-men and vent their impotent rage by crying "Treason! Stupidity!" and other hollow terms.

The great joy of the artist is to become aware of a higher order of things, to recognize by the compulsive and spontaneous manipulation of his own impulses the resemblance between human creation and what is called "divine" creation. In works of fantasy the existence of law manifesting itself through order is even more apparent than in other works of art. Nothing is less mad, less chaotic, than a work of fantasy. Such a creation, which is nothing less than pure invention, pervades all levels, creating, like water, its own level. The endless interpretations which are offered up contribute nothing, except to heighten the significance of what is seemingly unintelligible. This unintelligibility somehow makes profound sense. Everyone is affected, including those who pretend not to be affected. Something is present, in works of fantasy, which can only be likened to an elixir. This mysterious element, often referred to as "pure nonsense," brings with it the flavor and the aroma of that larger and utterly impenetrable world in which we and all the heavenly bodies have their being. The term nonsense is one of the most baffling words in our vocabulary. It has a negative quality only, like death. Nobody can explain nonsense: it can only be demonstrated. To add, moreover, that sense and nonsense are interchangeable is only to labor the point. Nonsense belongs to other worlds, other dimensions, and the gesture with which we dismiss it, testifies to its disturbing nature. Whatever we cannot include within our narrow framework of comprehension we reject. Thus profundity and nonsense may be seen to have certain unsuspected affinities.

Why did I not launch into sheer nonsense immediately? Because, like others, I was afraid of it. And deeper than that was the fact that, far from situating myself in a beyond, I was caught in the very heart of the web. I had survived my own destructive school of Dadaism: I had progressed, if that is the word, from scholar to critic to pole-axer. My literary experiments lay in ruins, like the cities of old which were sacked by the vandals. I wanted to build, but the materials were unreliable and the plans had not even become blueprints. If the substance of art is the human soul, then I must confess that with dead souls I could visualize nothing germinating under my hand.

To be caught in a glut of dramatic episodes, to be ceaselessly participating, means among other things that one is unaware of the outlines of that bigger drama of which human activity is but a small part. The act of writing puts a stop to one kind of activity in order to release another. When a monk, prayerfully meditating, walks slowly and silently down the hall of a temple, and thus walking sets in motion one prayerwheel after another, he gives a living illustration of the act of sitting down to write. The mind of the writer, no longer preoccupied with observing and knowing, wanders meditatively amidst a world of forms which are set spinning by a mere brush of his wings. No tyrant, this, wreaking his will upon the subjugated minions of his ill-gotten kingdom. An explorer, rather, calling to life the slumbering entities of his dream. The act of dreaming, like a draught of fresh air in an abandoned house, situates the furniture of the mind in a new ambiance. The chairs and tables collaborate; an effluvia is given off, a game is begun.

To ask the purpose of this game, how it is related to life, is idle. As well ask the Creator why volcanoes? why hurricanes? since obviously they contribute nothing but disaster. But, since disasters are disastrous only for those who are engulfed in them, whereas they can be illuminating for those who survive and study them, so it is in the creative world. The dreamer who returns from his voyage, if he is not shipwrecked en route, may and usually does convert the collapse of his tenuous fabric into other stuff. For a child the pricking of a bubble may offer nothing but astonishment and delight. The student of illusions and mirages may react differently. A scientist may bring to a bubble the emotional wealth of a world of thought. The same phenomenon which causes the child to scream with delight may give birth, in the mind of an earnest experimenter, to a dazzling vision of truth. In the artist these contrasting reactions seem to combine or merge, producing that ultimate one, the great catalyzer called *realization*. Seeing, knowing, discovering, enjoying—these faculties or powers are pale and lifeless without realization. The artist's game is to move over into reality. It is to see beyond the mere "disaster" which the picture of a lost battlefield renders to the naked eye. For, since the beginning of time the picture which the world has presented to the naked human eye can hardly seem anything but a hideous battle ground of lost causes. It has been so and will be so until man ceases to regard himself as the mere seat of conflict. Until he takes up the task of becoming the "I of his I."

Childhood in Brooklyn

Early Remembrances:

Born with a silver spoon in my mouth. Got everything I craved, except a real pony. Writing Santa to send me a drum *and* a magic lantern. Returning work socks and mitten to teacher in kindergarten—to give to the poor in the class. When my mother sees me returning from kindergarten X'mas Eve and no gifts she asks what happened. I say "Nothing, I just returned them to the teacher. I know Santa is going to bring me better things." With this she slaps me hard, grabs the lobe of one ear and drags me one long block to the school, to apologize to the teacher for my rudeness.

I couldn't understand what I had done wrong. . . . This was my first big misunderstanding. It registered deeply (I never forgot nor forgave) and left in my childish mind the feeling that my mother was stupid and cruel.

In later years I only slightly modified this view of my mother. She always pretended to be proud of me but she neither understood nor loved me.

More about Mother. . . .

Next to kindergarten episode, around same period, is when she shows me a wart on her finger which is annoying her and I say— "Why don't you cut it off?" And she does, gets blood poisoning, and a few days later, when I am sitting in my little chair by the fire, she comes over to me, scowling and threatening (her finger now heavily bandaged) and slaps me some more saying—"You were the one who told me to cut the wart off!"

As she lies abed, only a few days away from death, I bring my friend Vincent to see her. He is handsome, well-mannered, and an air pilot. My mother's eyes glow when she sees him. It is obvious that she has immediately taken him to heart. Suddenly she raises herself from the pillow—I am standing by the side of the bed—and exclaims: "If only I had had a son like you, Vincent," looking me in the eye while speaking. (And I was fresh from Europe where I was idolized as a great American writer. All this meant nothing to her. She never forgave me for becoming a writer instead of a tailor!)

The culminating and rather gruesome final episode takes place in a funeral parlor where she is laid out in state for her friends and relatives to say farewell to her. She is there about a week before being buried. I visit the place now and then—not everyday. Each time I come and bend over the coffin, one of her eyes opens, as if to stare at me. It seems to me she is reproving me even in death. It gives me shivers. I always notify the director of the funeral parlor who always closes the eye without saying a word.

(more or less upon actual return from
France penniless as when I left.)

Early Days

Rereading a book I read long long ago *(Heart of a Boy)* I was impressed by certain resemblances between the life of Italian boys and the ones I knew in dear old Brooklyn. For one thing we both understood what Carlyle referred to in one of his books—*Heroes and Hero Worship*. We admired the boys who inspired our admiration unashamedly. We also were hard on weaklings and dummies. Now and then we acknowledged that so-and-so was a real saint. He was apt to be six or eight years older than us, poor, hauling coal and wood for a living (this early in life), but with a golden heart. Johnny Paul, an Italian teenager, was in my humble opinion a saint; though I wasn't yet quite aware of what saints were supposed to be like. (I was brought up in a Presbyterian Church, not a Catholic one. We didn't talk of saints and Virgin Mary's there.)

We tried to win the favor of our heroes. Were they to give us a smile or a pat on the back, we were in Seventh Heaven.

In my particular neighborhood, we kids never used the word "prostitute," nor did we ever hear it. Whores was our word and one of our little girl friends was known as the whore of the neighborhood. Jenny was her name and she was a charming, gentle creature who may have shaped my image of "whore' very early in life. When I first got to Paris I made friends with the whores very readily, one of the first short stories I wrote there was about "Mlle. Claude." Somehow they were always aware that I regarded them differently than most men.

To get back to Jenny. We used to pretend to fuck her in someone's cellar—"a penny a crack." Actually all we did was to touch genitals. But we got almost as great a thrill from doing that as we did out of "a good fuck" later on.

The word I always use about my early days (from five to ten) is *golden*. In my memory this period stands out (even today) above all the others. Perhaps because everything was "new" to me. And I was a fast learner. Not only did I learn in the street but at home, seated at one end of my grandfather's bench. (He was a coat maker and worked for my father, who was a Fifth Avenue tailor.) I would sit at his bench reading one of my books. Sometimes I read to him aloud. Sometimes he handed me a couple of pieces of cloth, a needle and thread, and told me to make something to please my father when he would come home. (Even at that early date there was a conspiracy afoot to make me a tailor too.)

Sometimes I brought Stanley (my first friend) to the room that grandfather worked in. We would play with my toys while my grandfather sang "Shoo-fly, don't bother me. . . ."—his favorite ditty.

In that same room, on a rainy day, I recall singing songs in a hearty, lusty voice. And my aunt, working in the kitchen nearby, would come out and clap her hands, kiss me, beg me to sing some more.

Years later, many years later, with Val or Tony on my back, I would trudge through the forest teaching them songs like "Yankee Doodle Dandy" and the like. They loved these jaunts through the forest.

One of the outstanding things about this period, which is so vivid in my memory, is that already we were incipient psychologists. We (Stanley and I) had every boy in the neighborhood sized up. The heroes, like Eddie Carney and Lester Reardon, stood apart. When Lester Reardon walked down North First Street—just one block—I stood in awe, watching him. If he had been the Pope, I could not have paid more reverence. Then there were the potential criminals, like Alfie Letcha and Johnny Goeller. As a matter of fact, they both ended up in Sing Sing.

Sing Sing! A notorious prison on the Hudson. One day, again many years later, the ex-warden of Sing Sing comes to visit me at my office in the Western Union Telegraph Co., where I was then employment manager. He came, representing some Catholic organization which tried to rehabilitate ex-convicts. I told him immediately that I was forbidden to hire ex-convicts. He disregarded my remark and began telling me he would pay with his life for any misdemeanor on the part of anyone he sent me. I was so taken by his earnestness that I hired three or four ex-convicts the next day. Not only did I find them efficient and reliable (which the young boys were not!) but, on leaving the service they would always come to thank me for what I had done and leave me some token gifts, such as a ring or a watch. Often they blessed me. . . .

Uncle Harry

In several of my books I have dwelled on ancestral stock, usually playing up the Germanic strain. At bottom, to be sure, I look upon the German blood as of fairly recent origin. We all know how Europe was ravished again and again by alien hordes. In a word the real German, real Frenchman, real Spaniard, etc., etc. is rare indeed. All Europeans are of mixed blood. Even America is nothing but a mixture of very different races—the only true American being the despised, the outcast Indian. To conclude this brief preamble, myself I disavow my supposed heritage, and trace it back to very early times. Thereby concluding, in my own mind, that I am a mixture of Mongol, Chinese, Tibetan, and Jewish bloods. . . . And now for the other side of the picture—the homespun dour East American, so to say.

Uncle Harry. With Uncle Harry a wholly new blood strain crept into the Miller-Nieting family. Harry was born Harry Smith of an up-N.Y. State old American family. But he first appeared on the scene at 662 Driggs Ave., under the name of Harry Brown. That was because he was courting Aunt Mary, my favorite aunt of the Nieting tribe. She was eighteen or twenty years old at the time and I just a tot of six or seven. Harry Brown came bouncing into our quiet family life, with buck teeth and a boozy breath. My grandfather, father of Aunt Mary, looked upon Harry Brown immediately as a no-good sort of bum. But my Aunt seemed stuck on him and so Harry lingered on and around.

Then one day it was discovered that he was masquerading under a false name, that his real name was Smith, not Brown. This caused quite a commotion for a while. If I remember rightly, it ended by Harry bringing his mother and his Aunt Joy down from Newburgh to show that he was of decent stock and not an ex-convict or something of the sort.

Grandma Smith, as we called his mother (why I don't know),

was a very personable woman. She was about 60 years old, same as Grandpa Nieting, and, oddly enough, those two very different creatures soon got to like one another very much. As a boy, I remember what a thrill it gave me to hear Grandma Smith address Grandpa as "my dear Mr. Nieting." Her voice was lovely, charming, soothing, so different from the voices of the Nieting family. We soon learned that *her* ancestors had come over on the Mayflower.

Naturally, Harry was quickly absolved of his pecadillos. But that was only his first mistake—Brown—Smith. Soon he was accused of rifling the petty cash in the office where he worked. And, after that came the discovery that he was a booze hound. (Had they looked a little deeper they would have uncovered that he was a cunt-chaser too.) With it all Harry was a good fellow, full of cheer, always alert and bright, always with another scheme up his sleeve—all these elements new and disturbing to the Miller-Nieting ménage.

When there was a family reunion, entailing endless cooking, decorations, speeches, and what not, I and my little cousins would be obliged to make frequent visits to the side door of the saloon across the street and bring back huge pitchers of foaming lager. One of Harry's most distinguished traits was his smile. In those days it was referred to as the smile that won't come off. One died with that sort of smile on one's lips.

Often, during a long day of festivities, the uncles would go out "for a walk," as they put it. Actually, it was to do a bit of private pub crawling. There were two famous saloons in our neighborhood. The one across the street from our house and the other at the corner of Grand St. It was this latter saloon, owned and run by the ward healer Pat McCarren, that our uncles loved to patronize. Pat McCarren was often there himself, spouting away, and always in a frock coat with a shamrock in the buttonhole. He wore a stovepipe hat which lent him a solemn air. He was indeed from "the ould country."

Anyway, whenever we kids were ordered to scout for our uncles and bring them home for dinner, we would always repair first to Pat McCarren's saloon. We would first kneel in the doorway and look under the swinging doors. Sure enough, there would be Harry at the bar with a tall glass of beer in his hand, a sailor straw hat cocked to one side, his moustache full of foam and delivering his opinions about this and that while the others tackled the free lunch. Smiling as usual, of course.

Harry was at his best at funerals. It was customary after the burial for the family and relations to go to the beer garden just opposite the cemetery gates—"Trommer's" it was called—and regale themselves with food and drink. During these feasts anecdotes were exchanged about the deceased. Always with a humorous or ridiculous touch. Harry was a master at this. It was right up his street. He could mock and mimic the deceased to a T.

When his own little son died, a boy just a year or two younger than myself, his mother—good old Aunt Mary—decided to hold funeral services at their own home. She invited the minister of their church to do the ritual. I was seated up front, I remember, and had a hard time keeping a straight face, because on solemn occasions I always had nervous fits of laughter. The minister was handing out the usual shit about how our little angel was now safely in Heaven. I was as red as a beet from restraining my laughter. Suddenly out of the corner of my eye I caught Uncle Harry tiptoeing into the kitchen. I knew what he went there for— to down a quick bottle of beer. Soon he returned and the minister droned on. Harry repeated the performance several times, until finally the minister realized something was amiss. He threw a disconcerted glance at my Aunt Mary who was already suspicious of her husband's behavior. Suddenly she followed Harry into the kitchen and soon I heard her grieved, upraised voice exclaiming: "Oh Harry, not now, not *here*. How could you? And Howard (the dead son) lying in the next room. And the minister delivering such a beautiful funeral oration. . . ." Etc., etc. After which Harry stole back to his seat with a grin from ear to ear. When the minister left he addressed the assembled relatives and neighbors now with a broad unashamed smile: "Friends," he began, "nobody could love little Howard more than I. The minister told you he was safely in Heaven. That got my goat. That's why I had to have a drink and another and another." His grin had broadened into an outrageous, sacrilegious smile. "You all know," he continued, "that I was never much for church. I never believed in Heaven or Hell nor angels and devils either. (By now Aunt Mary was sobbing hysterically.)

"Maybe what I did the minister calls a *sin*. I don't know much about sin either. I always do pretty much as I please, whether the minister likes it or not."

(By now the room was almost empty. And I can see my own mother with one hand over her mouth in hypocritical fashion as usual.)

In short, Harry never finished the speech. But I never forgot his words or his attitude. Even at that tender age I didn't have any use for fucking and fucked up ministers of the clergy.

Harry died a happy death—in the mud gutter during a prolonged spree. His straw hat was lying beside him. There was a broad smile on his face.